Handbook of
PULP AND PAPER
TECHNOLOGY

EDITED BY

KENNETH W. BRITT

Associate Director
Research Division
Scott Paper Company
Philadelphia, Pennsylvania

New York
REINHOLD PUBLISHING CORPORATION
Chapman & Hall, Ltd., London

Publisher's Foreword

This volume has been designed to replace the famous "Modern Pulp and Paper Making" originally compiled by George Witham, later revised by his son and still more recently again revised under the Editorship of the late John B. Calkin. The first edition, which appeared in 1921, was one of the very first books ever published by Reinhold. The work was undertaken largely because of the enthusiasm and guidance of Francis M. Turner, who was at that time an officer of the Chemical Catalog Company, predecessors of the Reinhold Publishing Corporation. To a far greater extent than is normally the case, Mr. Turner nursed the undertaking to completion, supplying much of the literary and organizational ability required for a successful book project. His contribution also extended to the second edition, which was published in the early 1940's.

The publishers now feel that this fine book has in many ways outlived its usefulness and that a more modern treatment of this tremendous field is necessary. They were fortunate in enlisting the abilities and enthusiasm of Kenneth Britt of the Scott Paper Company, and the present book was developed under his leadership.

Preface

The amount of material relating to the pulp and paper industry currently being published is enormous. For the year ending in August 1962, the *Abstract Bulletin of the Institute of Paper Chemistry* published 10,267 abstracts of books, periodical articles, patents and other publications. At the present time, abstracts are being made at the rate of about 1,000 per month.

In view of this flood of information, it is somewhat sobering to undertake a description of the pulp and paper industry within the covers of one volume. Obviously, the work cannot be comprehensive or highly detailed. It is hoped that the necessary selectivity has been exercised with some measure of wisdom.

The work has been undertaken with a firm belief that such a volume can serve a highly useful purpose. As the name "handbook" connotes, this volume is intended to be readily at hand to answer questions and to furnish topical reading. It is aimed at the desktop and the home study rather than merely the library shelf. Its purpose is to provide, in convenient form, the basic information upon which more detailed knowledge may be built.

The editor wishes to pay special tribute to the chapter authors whose generous effort has made this book possible. These men hold responsible and demanding positions, and it was no small task for them to assume the additional burden of writing a chapter for a book. It is such men, active in the field and close to the subject, who have much to contribute to an enterprise of this sort.

Finally, it is important to thank the many individuals, too numerous to mention, who gave advice and counsel, who read manuscripts and otherwise aided most effectively and generously in bringing the work to completion.

KENNETH BRITT

Philadelphia, Pennsylvania
January 1, 1964

Contents

CHAPTER I

Introduction

KENNETH W. BRITT

Scott Paper Company

The "Paper Dictionary" defines paper as being "all kinds of matted or felted sheets of fiber . . . . . . formed on a wire screen from water suspension." That these paper products are of enormous importance in modern life is obvious to everyone. No manufactured product is more constantly a part of human activity nor has such diversity of use. Paper is the basic means for the communication and dissemination of information. Paper records economic, political and social transactions. It carries the symbol of value in the form of money and certificates. It serves the needs of art, literature and science, as well as preserving the great legacy of human knowledge for the future. Also, paper provides the means for wrapping and packaging a vast array of other materials and products. The list of special uses for paper is interminable.

It is the purpose of this volume to describe the materials and processes that constitute the basis of the modern paper industry.

HISTORICAL BACKGROUND OF PAPER

The word "paper" is derived from the name of the reedy plant, papyrus, which grows abundantly along the Nile River in Egypt. In ancient times, the fibrous layers within the stem of this plant were removed, placed side by side, and crossed at right angles with another set of layers similarly arranged. The sheet so formed was dampened and pressed. Upon drying, the sugary sap of the plant served as an adhesive to cement the layers together. Note that complete defibering, which is an indispensable element in modern paper making, was not a part of making papyrus sheets. Papyrus was the most widely used of writing materials of ancient times. Many of these records still survive.

The material that we know as paper, however, originated in China about 100 A.D. by the discovery that a mat or layer of fibers could be formed by filtering a water suspension of the beaten and macerated fibers through a fine screen. The fibers first used were those composing the inner bark (bast) of certain plants such as bamboo and mulberry. The mat so formed, upon drying, became a strong, coherent sheet suitable for writing and the drawing of pictures. It is this property of natural cellulosic fibers, after being beaten in water, to bond or adhere to each other upon pressing and drying, that has furnished the basis for paper technology.

Paper making developed into a highly skilled art in China. Many beautiful examples of ancient Chinese illustration on paper are still in existence. Over a period of many centuries, the art of paper making spread westward to the Arabic countries and then to Europe. During this period, the use of cotton and linen rags supplanted the orig-

View of part of an 18th century paper mill from the Encyclopedia of D. & D'Alèmbert Diderot.

inal bast fibers of plants and became the principal raw material for paper. The history of paper making has been narrated in a book by Dard Hunter. (See Bibliography).

The first paper mill in America was established in 1690 on Wissahickon Creek near Philadelphia by one William Rittenhouse who had learned the art in Germany. The Rittenhouse mill used linen rags as the source of paper and is supposed to have turned out 100 pounds of paper per day. The present mill of the Scott Paper Company, a few miles from the site of the Rittenhouse mill, produces 100 pounds of paper in about six seconds.

MILESTONES IN THE DEVELOPMENT OF PAPER MAKING

A.D. 105. Traditional date of the invention of paper making by Ts' ai Lun, an official attached to the Imperial Court of China. The sources of fiber included mulberry and other bast fibers as well as fish nets, rags and hemp.

751. In its slow travel westward, the art of paper making reached Samarkand in Central Asia.

793. First paper made in Baghdad in the time of Harûn-Al-Raschid. This coincided with golden age of Arabic power and culture which brought paper making to the frontiers of Europe.

1390. By this date a number of paper mills existed in Europe, particularly in Spain, Italy, France and Germany.

1455. The Gutenberg Bible, which marked the beginning of book printing and the consequent increased demand for paper.

1495. First paper mill in England established in Hertfordshire by John Tate.

1680. Invention of the "hollander" beater

for maceration of paper stock in preparation for sheet making. Previously beating had been performed by "stamping mills."

1690. First paper mill in America established by William Rittenhouse near Germantown, Philadelphia, Penna.

1765. Publication of treatises by Jacob Christian Schäffer on the use of various plant materials for making paper.

1774. Discovery of chlorine by Karl Wilhelm Scheele (1742-86), a Swedish chemist. The bleaching ability of chlorine was quickly recognized and it was soon used for bleaching paper stock. Unfortunately, lack of chemical knowledge at the time resulted in producing inferior paper by this method which brought much discredit upon chlorine bleaching. Eventually, chlorine bleaching became a valuable part of paper making.

1798. The invention of the paper machine by Nicholas-Louis Robert in France. The French Government recognized Robert's work by the granting of a patent. However, the paper machine did not become a practical reality until the work of John Gamble and Bryan Donkin some years later in England.

1800. The discovery of vat sizing with rosin and alum by Moritz Friedrich Illig, in Germany. Previous to this time paper sheets were sized by the expensive and tedious process of impregnating the sheets with animal glue or vegetable gums. Illig published his discovery in 1807, but not until about 1830 did the method become widely used in paper making.

1801. Publication of book by Mathias Koops suggesting new materials that might be used for paper making. The work of Schäffer and Koops foreshadowed the development of practical methods for the manufacture of wood pulp and other vegetable pulps.

1807. Patent issued to Henry and Sealy Fourdrinier for an improved paper machine. Also active in this development were John Gamble, who was familiar with the work of Robert in France and brought the idea of a paper machine to England, and Bryan Donkin, an engineer, engaged by the Fourdriniers.

1809. Invention of the cylinder paper machine by an English paper maker, John Dickinson.

1817. First paper machine in America installed in the paper mill of Thomas Gilpin on the Brandywine near Wilmington, Delaware. This machine was the Dickinson cylinder type.

1827. First Fourdrinier type paper machine erected in America. The machine was built by Bryan Donkin in England and installed in a paper mill at Saugerties, N.Y.

1840. Groundwood pulp made in Germany by Friedrich Gottlob Keller. Process did not come into commercial use until about 1870.

1854. First manufacture of soda pulp from wood, by Watt and Burgess in England.

1867. Patent issued to Benjamin C. Tilghman of Philadelphia disclosing the basic principles of the sulfite pulping process.

1874. Sulfite pulp manufactured in Sweden by Carl Daniel Ekman and in Germany by Alexander Mistcherlich.

1875. By this time paper coated by machinery was being made for use in printing of halftones by the new photo engraving process.

1884. Invention of sulfate (kraft) pulp by Carl F. Dahl in Danzig, Germany.

1897. Paper machine speeds had reached 500 feet per minute by this time.

1909. First kraft pulp and paper made in the United States.

1920. Paper machines attain speeds of 1000 feet per minute.

Since 1920 there has been a rapid pace of technical progress in the paper industry. These advances are generally the result of team work by a number of people working together in large organizations. Hence, it is difficult to assign credit to individuals or to be exact about dates and places. Some of the more important developments in recent decades are listed on the following page.

(1) Multistage bleaching of kraft pulp, leading to availability of fully bleached kraft pulp.

(2) Use of chlorine dioxide for pulp bleaching permitting higher brightness with retention of strength.

(3) Coating of paper while passing through paper machine dryer section, greatly expanding use of coated paper for printing.

(4) Use of soluble bases for sulfite pulping permitting pulping of more species of wood by the sulfite process.

(5) Bleaching of high yield pulps, groundwood and semichemical, with peroxide and hydrosulfite.

(6) Wet strength paper: use of synthetic resins for economic production of wide variety of papers that are strong when wet.

(7) Multi-stage sulfite pulping permitting greater variety of pulp properties.

(8) Continuous cooking of kraft and semichemical pulps making possible reduction in capital and operating cost.

(9) High-yield pulping: combined chemical and mechanical action to produce pulp from wood in high yield, particularly advantageous with hardwoods.

(10) The use of synthetic fibers admixed with wool or in the form synthetic fabric as the sheet carrying and water removal felt of the paper machine press section.

BASIS OF THE MODERN PAPER INDUSTRY

The basis of the present mass production of paper lies in two developments that formed a part of the great surge of industrial development of the nineteenth century. These were, first, the invention of machinery for making an endless sheet of paper at a high rate of speed; and, second, the discovery of methods for converting wood into paper pulp.

Until well along in the nineteenth century, all paper was made by hand and the size of a single sheet was limited to the size of frame and screen that a man could dip into a vat of stock and lift out of the vat after it had become full of stock. In 1799, Louis Robert in France constructed a moving screen belt that would receive a continuous flow of stock from a vat and deliver a continuous sheet of wet paper to a pair of squeeze rolls. This idea was taken to England where an engineer by the name of Donkin, financed by the Fourdrinier brothers, London stationers, made the first successful paper machine. From this humble beginning, evolved the modern paper-making equipment described in Chapter 12 of this volume.

During the period that linen and cotton rags were the sole source of paper making fiber, the paper mills were often plagued by a shortage of raw material. At times, government subsidies and publicly and privately sponsored publicity campaigns were resorted to in order to obtain rags for vitally needed paper. This also stimulated a search for other sources of fiber. Numerous investigators worked with straw, wood and other plant materials attempting to make suitable paper pulp.

The period from about 1844 to 1884 witnessed the discovery of four processes for the manufacture of paper pulp from wood. Since that time, there has been a continuous development and evolution of these processes and of the equipment used for their commercial utilization. The first of these four, the soda process, has achieved only a limited volume of production. The other three, the sulfite process, described in Chapter 6, the kraft process (Chapter 7), and the mechanical or groundwood process (Chapter 9) have all achieved large scale use. In recent years, a number of processes using a combined chemical and mechanical action upon wood have attained important commercial success. These processes, referred to as "semichemical" are described in Chapter 8.

During the early years of the wood pulp industry, only the more suitable species, notably spruce and fir, were used to an important degree for pulp. As the demand for pulp has increased, a number of trends have been developed to meet that demand. There has been an ever wider use of wood species accompanied by modifications of pulping technique to accommodate those species more difficult to pulp; there has been large scale use of waste from other lumber operations, such as slabs from saw mills and waste from veneer plants; there has been emphasis in research and development to attain higher yields of pulp from a given quantity of wood.

We have used the paper machine as a symbol of the mechanization of the paper industry, but it is important to keep in mind that every step of production, from the felling of trees to the shipment of the finished product, has also seen a dramatic increase in mechanization and reduction in hand labor. Paper-making operations require the repeated movement of large amounts of material, and hence design and mechanization in materials handling has been and continues to be an important aspect of industry development. One result of extensive use of mechanized equipment in the paper industry is high capital investment per employee, recently estimated to be $22,600, or more than three times that of all manufacturing.*

The first phase of the mechanization of the paper industry occurred as part of the industrial revolution of the nineteenth century and was largely the replacement of hand labor with mechanical power. It has been estimated (*ibid.*) that by 1886 six men could produce the same quantity and quality of paper as would require 100 men in 1800. The trend toward greater use of power continues and, in addition, the use of automatic control is a significant modern trend. From 1947 to 1960 the average annual rate of increase in output per production worker man-hour was 3.7%, compared with 3.5% for all manufacturing (*ibid.*).

* U.S. Department of Labor Bulletin No. 1347 (1962).

THE PAPER INDUSTRY AS A SECTOR OF THE MODERN ECONOMY

In 1962 the total production of paper and paperboard in the United States was 37,580,000 tons. Because of an excess of imports over exports (largely newsprint from Canada) the consumption of all paper products is reported to be 42,260,000 or 453 pounds per capita.*

Paper products fall into two broad categories: paper, in the specific sense of the term, and paperboard. Paper is lighter, thinner and more flexible; paperboard is heavier and more rigid. Obviously, the line of demarcation between the two is somewhat indistinct. The U.S. production for 1959 is classified as follows:

Paper	16,305,000 tons
Paperboard	17,746,000 tons
Total	34,051,000 tons

The U.S. Census Bureau † divides the statistics of paper production into eight general groups of products as follows:

1959	*Tons*	*Per Cent of Total*
Newsprint	1,920,000	11.8
Book (incl. magazine)	4,525,000	27.7
Fine (writing)	1,706,000	10.4
Wrapping (incl. bags)	3,943,000	24.2
Tissue	237,000	1.5
Sanitary papers	1,846,000	11.3
Building papers	1,382,000	8.5
Other	746,000	4.6
Total	16,305,000	100

This great consumption of paper is brought about by its abundance and low cost and by the diversity of forms and properties in which paper can be made. Although paper-like materials have been known since ancient times, the factors that have given

* American Paper and Pulp Association
† A more detailed breakdown of production statistics by grades of paper will be found in "Current Industrial Reports, Pulp Paper and Board" published by the Industry Division, U.S. Bureau of the Census.

AMERICAN PAPER AND PULP ASSOCIATION
122 East 42nd Street
New York 17, N.Y.

INDUSTRY FACT SHEET

Sept. 3, 1963

	1961	1962[P]	1963			1963 YEAR TO DATE	
			MAY	JUNE	JULY[P]	Annual Rate	% From Comparable 1962 Period
PAPER AND PAPERBOARD – Thousands of Tons *Annual Rate*							
Production - Paper	15,742	16,459	18,048	16,860	15,360	16,922*	+ 3
- Paperboard	16,443	17,648	18,936	18,444	17,040	18,009*	+ 2
- Wet Machine Board	156#	133	150	143	120	132*	+ 1
- Construction Paper & Board	3,244	3,340	3,900	3,696	3,540	3,492*	+ 6
TOTAL	—	--	41,028	39,144	36,060	—	+ 3
TOTAL - SEASONALLY ADJUSTED	35,585	37,580	39,252	37,176	39,804	38,555*	--
Imports (including products)	5,779	5,871	6,096	5,796	--	5,340	- 7
Exports (including products)	1,216	1,191	1,500	1,404	--	1,262	+ 4
Apparent Consumption	40,148	42,260	45,624	43,536	40,380	42,741	+ 2
Production to Capacity %							
Paper (6.6 days per wk. basis)	89.5	89.8	95.2	92.8	82.7	91.4	--
Paperboard (6 days per wk. basis)	91	92	95	96	84	93	--
WOOD PULP – Thousands of Tons – *Annual Rate*							
Total - Production	26,523	27,831	30,936	28,764	27,696	29,076	+ 4
- Imports	2,468	2,789	2,664	3,072	--	2,732	- 2
- Exports	1,178	1,181	1,776	1,296	--	1,360	+ 19
- New Supply	27,813	29,439	31,824	30,540	--	30,678	+ 3
Market - Production	2,974	3,095	3,612	3,468	--	3,392	+ 5
- Imports	1,614	1,830	1,656	2,028	--	1,786	- 3
- New Supply	3,410	3,746	3,780	4,128	--	3,858	- 2
RAW MATERIALS CONSUMPTION – **PAPER & BOARD MILLS (000 Tons per year)**							
Wood Pulp ##	26,683	28,106	31,656	29,448	--	29,972	+ 5
Waste Paper	9,018	8,997	9,300	8,904	--	8,822	- 4
Other	894	937	1,476	1,224	--	1,252	+ 38
PULPWOOD CONSUMPTION							
Thousands of Cords - Annual Rate	42,191	44,071	48,072	46,320	42,660	45,516	+ 3
EMPLOYMENT (Thousands)							
Paper and Allied Products - Total	589.5	602.0	602.0	609.5	608.9	606*	+ 0.9
" " " " - Other Workers	120.0	124.4	126.5	127.8	129.0	127*	+ 2.9
" " " " - Prod. Workers	469.5	477.6	475.5	481.7	479.9	479*	+ 0.3
Pulp, Paper and Board Mills - Total	291.3	293.8	294.2	--	--	292.8	+ 0.7
" " " " " - Other Workers	55.9	57.1	57.5	--	--	57.6	+ 2.3
" " " " " - Prod. Workers	235.4	236.7	236.7	--	--	235.2	+ 0.3

AVERAGE HOURLY EARNINGS OF PROD. WORKERS—$							
Paper and Allied Products	2.34	2.41	2.47	2.47	2.50	2.46	+ 3.0
Pulp, Paper Mills	2.50	2.59	2.64	--	--	2.63	+ 2.9
Paperboard Mills	2.52	2.63	2.67	--	--	2.67	+ 3.7
CAPITAL EXPENDITURES	680	720	650 QI	750 QIIG	750 QIIIG	710 (Full yr. G)	+1
INDEX OUTPUT PER PRODUCTION WORKER MAN–HOUR							
Paper and Allied Products　(1957–59=100)	112	115	118	119	120	118	+ 3
Pulp, Paper and Board	111	116	120	--	--	120	+ 2
PAPER AND ALLIED PRODUCTS— Millions $ per yr.							
Sales (All Companies, Dept. of Commerce)	13,560	14,430	15,000	15,000	15,000	14,950	+ 4
Sales (Corporations Only, SEC-FTC)	12,525	13,698	14,124 - IV '62		13,312 - I '63	13,312	+ 2
Earnings "	583	628	644 - IV '62		492 - I '63	492	- 14
Depreciation " "	531	583	632 - IV '62		596 - I '63	596	+ 8
Net Worth " " (End of Pd.)	7,612	7,766	7,766 - IV '62		7,763 - I '63	7,763	+ 0.4
PRICE INDEXES (BLS 1957–59=100)							
Pulp, Paper and Allied Products	98.8	100.0	99.1	99.3	99.1	99.1	- 1
Pulp	95.0	93.2	91.3	91.3	91.7	90.7	- 4
Waste Paper	80.5	97.5	89.8	90.8	91.4	93.1	- 6
Paper	102.1	102.6	102.2	102.2	102.2	102.2	- 0.5
Paperboard	92.7	93.2	94.1	94.1	94.1	94.1	+ 2
Pulp, paper & products, (ex. bldg. paper & bd.)	98.7	100.2	99.2	99.5	99.2	99.2	- 1
Converted Paper and Board Products	99.5	101.0	99.9	100.0	99.8	99.8	- 2
Building Paper and Board	100.8	97.1	96.2	97.4	97.5	95.8	- 2

CAPACITY (Year-end; thousands of tons; annual rate)	1961	1962	1963	1964	1965	63/62	64/63	65/64
Paper (6.6 days per wk. basis)	18,134	18,767	19,399	19,545	19,694	+ 3.0	+ 1.1	+ 0.8
Paperboard (6.5 " " " ")	20,165	20,426	20,985	21,458	21,932	+ 2.7	+ 2.3	+ 2.3
Bldg. Paper & Bd. (6.1 " " " ")	4,287	4,259	4,310	4,321	4,323	+ 1.2	+ 0.3	0
Wet Mach. Bd. (5.8 " " " ")	214	213	220	230	230	+ 3.3	+ 4.5	0
TOTAL PAPER & BD. (6.5 " " " ")	42,800	43,665	44,854	45,554	46,179	+ 2.7	+ 1.6	+ 1.4
PULP	31,909	32,228	32,765	32,826	—	+ 1.7	+ 0.2	—

P = Preliminary.　　　　G = Government Estimate.　　　　(OVER)

*Seasonally Adjusted.　　#Originally reported total was 130 thousand tons.　　##Estimated by APPA.

				1963		1963 YEAR TO DATE	
REQUIREMENTS FACTORS* (INDEXES 1957-59 PRODUCTION=100)	1961	1962 P	MAY	JUNE R	JULY P	Annual Rate	% From Comparable 1962 Period
PAPER							
Total Paper Production (ex. newsprint & building paper)	111.9	117.6	124.1	119.2	122.0	121.2	+ 3.6
Total Paper Requirements 1)	112.1	116.6	120.6	120.9	122.1	119.3	+ 2.9
Total End-Use Index	112.8	117.8	122.3	122.6	123.8	121.0	+ 3.3
Prod. of nondurable goods (40%)	112.9	119.6	124.7	125.3	126.5	123.5	+ 4.1
Disposable Income (constant $) (15%)	109.0	113.8	117.6	118.0	118.1	116.8	+ 3.4
Total Printing & Publishing	111.5	114.6	118.4	118.6	120.0	114.8	0
Printing & Publishing - ex. News (45%)	114.0	117.6	121.7	121.5	123.3	120.2	+ 1.4
1) Includes trend factor of -0.4% per year.							
PAPERBOARD							
Total Paperboard Production	113.0	121.2	125.5	120.5	129.6	124.4	+ 2.3
Total Requirements 2)	112.2	120.8	127.1	128.5	129.0	125.9	+ 4.7
Total End-Use Index	110.9	118.8	124.4	125.7	126.2	123.2	+ 4.2
Prod. of Consumer Goods (58.2%)	112.7	119.7	124.1	125.6	126.0	123.7	+ 3.7
Prod. of Equipment (8.7%)	108.3	119.8	121.8	123.4	124.8	122.1	+ 4.1
Prod. of Materials (33.1%)	108.4	116.8	125.7	126.3	126.9	122.4	+ 5.2
2) Includes add'l growth factor of about 1/2% per yr.							
NEWSPRINT							
NEWSPRINT U.S. (Thousand Tons, Annual Rate)							
Consumption by Publishers - Total Industry	7,380	7,486	8,305	7,786	6,785	7,080	- 4
NEWSPAPERS							
Advertising Lineage (Millions of Lines, Annual Rate)	2,777	2,798	3,224	2,917	2,550	2,729	+ 1
Newspaper publishing & printing employment Total (000)	339.1	342.2	343.9	--	--	329.9	- 4
PRINTING AND FINE PAPERS							
MAGAZINES							
Advertising Pages (thousands) - Annual Rate	104.1	105.3	104.1	92.0	76.4	102.0	0
WHOLESALERS SALES (Million Dollars, Annual Rate)							
Total Paper & Paper Products - ex. Wallpaper	4,275	4,412	4,668	4,320	--	4,430*	- 2
Paper Only	3,540	3,675	3,948	3,672	--	3,668	0
EMPLOYMENT (Thousands)							
Printing, Publishing & Allied Industries - Total Workers	926.3	932.9	934.8	938.6	940.2	929*	0
" " " " " - Prod. "	595.7	596.7	591.0	592.0	591.7	589*	- 1
Periodical publishing & printing - Total "	71.0	68.7	67.4	--	--	68.4	- 2
Books - Total "	73.0	75.2	77.0	--	--	75.9	+ 2

Commercial printing	- Total	"	289.8	291.6	289.4	--	--	289.8	0
Bookbinding and related industries	- Total	"	47.1	48.0	49.4	--	--	48.5	+ 3
Other publishing & printing industries	- Total	"	106.3	107.7	107.8	--	--	107.8	+ 2

COARSE AND SPECIAL INDUSTRIAL PAPERS See (1) Production of nondurable goods, consumer goods, materials and total industrial production; (2) Wholesalers sales; and (3) Retail sales of nondurable goods.

TISSUE PAPERS

TOTAL SALES OF RETAIL STORES — Bill. $ per yr. Seas. Adj. **	218.8	235.0	243.0	245.8	248.6	244.1	+ 6
Durable Goods Stores - Seasonally Adjusted **	67.3	74.7	78.8	79.4	80.2	79.0	+ 7
Nondurable Goods Stores - Seasonally Adjusted **	151.5	160.3	164.2	166.4	168.5	165.1	+ 5
Grocery Stores	49.9	52.1	52.6	53.5	--	53.0	+ 3

GENERAL ECONOMIC DATA

Total Industrial Production (Index 1957-59 = 100)	109.8	118.2	124.4	125.6	126.5	122.8	+ 5
TOTAL CONSUMER CREDIT OUTSTANDING — Bill. $ (End of Per.)	57,678	63,458	64,165	64,892	--	64,892	+ 10

GROSS NATIONAL PRODUCT DATA - Annual Rate, Billions $			┌ 1962 ┐ QIV	┌ 1963 ┐ QI	QIIR		
Gross National Product or Expenditure	518.2R	554.9R	565.2	571.8	579.6	575.2	+ 5
Total Personal Consumption Expend.	336.8	355.4	362.9	367.4	370.4	368.9	+ 5
Durable Goods	43.6	48.2	50.5	50.6	51.0	50.8	+ 7
Nondurable Goods	155.1	161.4	163.6	165.3	165.9	165.6	+ 4
Services	138.0	145.7	148.9	151.4	153.5	152.5	+ 6
Total Gross Private Domestic Investment	69.0	78.8	78.8	77.8	80.7	79.3	+ 1
Total Fixed Investment	67.1	73.2	74.9	72.7	80.7	76.7	+ 8
New Construction	41.6	44.4	45.0	43.7	45.8	44.8	+ 4
Producers Durable Equipment	25.5	28.8	29.9	29.0	30.7	29.9	+ 6
Total Business Inventory Change	+ 1.9	+ 5.5	+ 4.0	+ 5.1	+ 3.6	4.4	--
Nonfarm Inventory Change	+ 1.5	+ 4.9	+ 3.2	+ 4.3	+ 3.6	4.0	--
Net Exports of Goods & Services	+ 4.4	+ 3.8	+ 3.3	+ 3.6	+ 4.8	4.2	--
Govt. Purchase of Goods & Services	107.9	117.0	120.2	123.0	123.8	123.4	+ 7

PERSONAL INCOME & SAVINGS - Annual Rate, Billions $							
Personal Income	417.4	442.1	444.9	453.9	459.9	456.9	+ 5
Disposable Personal Income	364.4	384.4	348.2	394.5	400.0	397.3	+ 17
Personal Savings	27.6	29.1	28.5	27.1	29.6	28.4	- 3

**Not directly applicable, but shown for completeness.   P - Preliminary.   R - Revised.
*Seasonally adjusted.

paper its position in the modern economy are of relatively recent origin. During most of its long existence, paper was a relatively scarce commodity. Only recently has it become the common product that it is today.

The tables on the preceding pages, compiled by the American Paper and Pulp Association give a comprehensive view of the economics of the paper industry of the United States. These fact sheets, issued monthly, give an up-to-the-minute review of the state of the industry.

The United States Bureau of the Census divides the manufacturing portion of the economy into twenty major groups. In terms of value added by manufacture (v.a.m.), paper and allied products ranks tenth among these groups as shown below:

Designation	V.A.M. 1958	$ Millions 1954
20 Food and kindred products	$ 16,574	$ 13,400
37 Transportation equipment	14,783	13,926
35 Machinery (except electrical)	14,568	12,339
28 Chemicals and allied products	12,422	7,596
33 Primary metal industries	11,264	9,747
36 Electrical machinery	9,192	7,403
27 Printing and publishing	7,818	6,265
39 Miscellaneous manufacturers	6,032	4,473
23 Apparel and related products	5,904	5,147
26 Paper and allied products	5,642	4,581
32 Stone, clay and glass products	5,435	3,822
22 Textile mill products	5,100	4,749
24 Lumber products (except furniture)	3,093	3,188
38 Instruments and related products	2,813	2,129
29 Petroleum and coal products	2,512	2,209
25 Furniture and fixtures	2,401	1,966
30 Rubber products	2,294	1,904
31 Leather and products	1,833	1,637
21 Tobacco manufacturers	1,415	988
Total	$140,318	$116,913

Value added by manufacture is only one of several measures of industry size. Others include manufacturers' sales, number employed, dollar assets and profits generated. The use of any of these measures would not greatly change the position of the paper industry in the economy. In the above table, the paper industry contributes about 4% of

value added by all manufacturing. Manufacturing represents about ⅓ of the nation's business. Other sectors of importance are agriculture, mining, construction, trade, finance, transportation, communications, services and government enterprise. In terms of national income, the paper and allied industries in recent years have contributed somewhat over 1%.

The point could be made that the true measure of the paper industry in today's economy is more properly the ubiquitous and versatile service rendered by its products rather than the cost in dollars of that service.

Rate of Growth

At the present time there is great interest in rate of growth as a measure of comparison among industries and among various segments of the economy. Despite its ancient origin, the paper industry deserves the title of a "growth industry," and it is in the forefront in that category even when compared with those industries of modern origin.

It is interesting to note in a recent report from the National Industrial Conference Board (see Bibliography) that paper and paperboard production is given an exceptionally favorable predicted growth position. By mathematical analysis of the growth rate of various products and industries over an extended period of time, the "critical year" for each industry is determined. The "critical year" is defined as the point of time on the industry growth curve separating the period of increasing increments to annual production from the period of declining increments. This analysis gives the paper industry a "critical year" farther in the future (2219 A.D.) than that of any other manufacturing industry included in the survey. Although the equations of growth represent a broad summary of the industry's experience, they do not of themselves afford an explanation for that growth experience. However, it is reasonable to suppose that the paper industry has found new impetus to growth at periodic intervals due to the penetration of its products into new areas of use.

There are many criteria by which growth of an industry may be measured. Production in total tons may fail to give a true picture because it does not reflect the balance between higher value refined products and low value bulk products. Sales volume in dollars may be misleading because it may be affected by fluctuations in prices of raw material and supplies of extraneous significance. It is suggested that "value added by manufacture" as reported by U.S. Bureau of the Census is free of these objections and one of the best measures of industry growth.

From 1899 to 1958 the value added by manufacture for all industries increased from $4,647 million to $140,318 million or 30 times; for the paper industry alone, v.a.m. increased from $90 million to $5,642 million or about 63 times during the same period. Thus, from 1899 to 1958 the rate of growth of the paper industry was more than twice that of the manufacturing segment of the economy as a whole.

For the period from 1923 to 1958, the following table compares the rate of growth of the paper industry with a number of other typical industry groups. Comparable data are not available for all industry groups nor for a longer period of time.

U.S. Census Bureau Classification Number	Industry Group	Number of Times Increase (v.a.m. factor) 1923-1958
38	Instruments and related products	11.5
36	Electrical machinery	11.4
28	Chemical and allied products	10.6
26	Paper and allied products	9.96
32	Stone, clay and glass products	5.6
29	Petroleum and coal products	5.2
27	Printing and publishing	5.1
30	Rubber products	4.98
25	Furniture and fixtures	4.7
23	Apparel and related products	3.4
31	Leather and products	2.3
24	Lumber products (except furniture)	2.2
22	Textile mill products	2.1

The v.a.m. factor is in terms of dollars and hence it is affected by inflation during the period shown. The actual tonnage increase in paper and paperboard production from 1923 to 1958 was about 4 times. However, inter-industry comparison would not be changed by inflation occurring during the comparison period.

We have seen that the paper industry shows a highly favorable growth record over an extended period in the past. Whether this rate of growth can be maintained over the coming years is a question of great significance. One of the important measures of the economic position of the paper industry is the consumption of paper and paperboard products in pounds per capita per year. This factor has the advantage of being available for every recent year and has the advantage over tonnage alone in making allowance for population growth.

The following table shows the trend in this factor since 1899, and gives the figure for each year since 1955.

	Pounds of paper consumed in U.S. per capita, per year
1899	57.9
1909	90.5
1919	119.1
1925	180.0
1929	220.3
1939	244
1946	319
1950	382
1955	420
1956	434
1957	412
1958	406
1959	436.5
1960	431.4
1961	437
1962	453

It appears that a leveling off trend has set in since 1955. However, it may well be that some factors other than the rate of consumption or use of paper products are affecting the pounds per capita figure. There is much interest in reducing the "basis weight" or weight per unit area of paper products. Both the raw materials and the finished products of the paper industry must be transported repeatedly and over long distances. It is economically of great importance to reduce the weight per unit area as much as possible and still meet the use requirement of the product. Advancing technology is showing the way toward making less fiber do an equivalent or better job to everyone's advantage. To the extent that this research is successful, the pounds per capita per year will be held down even though the use of paper and the service rendered continues to expand.

THE PAPER INDUSTRY AS A CONSUMER

The paper industry is an important consumer of materials and in that sense contributes greatly to the growth and prosperity of many other industries. The most important raw material is, of course, the pulp or fiber that is converted into paper. In fact, pulp manufacture is generally considered an integral part of the paper industry rather than a supplier. As will be described later, a considerable portion of the wood pulp that is manufactured goes into "dissolving pulp" rather than into paper manufacture. However, materials consumed by the paper industry are usually considered to be those chemicals that play a part in the pulping, bleaching, paper-making and converting operations.*

In the following table are given the estimated quantities of the important chemicals consumed in wood pulp manufacture for the year 1960.

	Estimated Consumption (tons)
Salt cake	925,000
Limestone	191,000
Lime	446,000
Sulfur	471,000
Soda ash	390,000
Ammonia	62,000
Magnesium hydroxide	47,000

*For a comprehensive treatment of this subject which has recently become available, see the Bibliography at the end of this chapter.

	Estimated Consumption (tons)
Chemicals used for Pulp Bleaching	
Chlorine	365,000
Caustic soda	190,000
Lime	148,000
Sodium hypochlorite	90,000
Calcium hypochlorite	51,000
Sulphuric acid	56,000
Sodium chlorate	34,000
Sodium chloride	83,000
Chemicals used for Paper Making	
China clay	479,000
Alum	422.000
Starch	321,000
Rosin size	150,000
Paraffin wax	63,000
Titanium dioxide	45,000
Wet-strength resins	21,200
Surface-active agents	17,500
Dyes	7,800
Foam killers	7,900
Slimicides	9,800
Chemicals for Converting	
China clay	459,000
Titanium dioxide	8,000
Calcium carbonate	10,000
Casein	9,300
Animal glue	17,000
Starch	10,300
Latex	11,000

For a number of these materials the paper industry consumes an important part of the total national production as shown below.

Material	Annual Consumption by Paper Industry (tons)	Total National Production (tons)	% used by Paper Industry
Salt cake	925,000	1,300,000	71
Soda ash	419,000	4,650,000	9
Caustic soda	322,000	4,850,000	6.6
Sulfur	477,000	5,500,000	8.7
Chlorine	369,000	4,500,000	8.2
Titanium dioxide	53,000	460,000	11.5

Although the major constituent of paper is cellulosic fiber, it is obvious that quite a number of other materials are also ingredients of many papers.

By taking the reported consumption of raw materials and comparing this with reported production of paper it is possible to establish a material balance or "yield." The figures are for the year 1959.

	Tons
Wood pulp consumption for paper	25,157,000 *
Waste paper	9,021,000 **
All other: rags, straw, bagasse, flax, etc.	968,000 **
Total fiber	35,146,000
Fillers	1,056,000 †
Sizing agents	264,000 †
Bonding agents: starches, resins, casein, glue, latex, etc.	406,000 †
Total nonfibrous	1,726,000
Grand total	36,872,000
Paper production	34,007,000
Apparent loss	2,865,000

Sources:
Pulp and Paper, Annual Review Number (July 11, 1960). From American Paper and Pulp Association.
** Current Industrial Report, Pulp Paper and Board. U.S. Department of Commerce, February 20, 1961.
† *Paper Trade J.*, 46 (January 11, 1961).

It is of considerable interest to note that these statistics indicate an apparent consumption of 36,872,000 tons of materials in order to make 34,007,000 tons of paper. We must hasten to add that these statistics are subject to some error in reporting and compilation and that some are estimates. It is well recognized, however, that the yield of saleable paper is certain to be considerably less than the amount of material going into the process. Wood pulp contains nonfibrous material in the form of water-solubles, pitch and nonfibrous cells that are largely washed out in the paper making process. With additives such as fillers, sizing agents and bonding agents, the retention on the paper machine is never 100% of the additive, and in some instances is less than 50% of the amount added.

WORLD-WIDE PAPER INDUSTRY

Although there are wide differences in the degree of development of the paper industry in various areas of the world, the industry is nevertheless truly world wide in scope. As the industrially underdeveloped countries of the world advance toward higher standards of living the demand for paper products will show a corresponding growth. The rate of consumption of paper products is a measure of educational and cultural activities as well as being an indication of standards of convenience and cleanliness.

In a recent article * it has been pointed out that the world-wide demand for paper and paperboard is expected to reach 147,-400,000 tons by 1975. This will require increased pulp production from the present 60,000,000 tons to 130,000,000 tons by 1975. Such an expansion of the industry is estimated to require new capital investment at a rate between 1 and 1½ billion dollars per year between now and 1975. Providing such quantities of capital, especially in the underdeveloped countries most in need of paper industry expansion, is no small problem.

Canada is second only to the United States in the production of pulp and paper. An abundance of wood species well suited to pulp manufacture, availability of water and water power, and ready access to large markets have combined to give Canada a strong position in the world paper industry. In particular, Canada is second only to Scandinavia in the export of wood pulp and is the world leader in the export of newsprint.

The statistics of the Canadian industry for 1960 and 1961 follow:

	1960	1961
Production, paper and paperboard, tons	8,612,267	8,668,983
Per capita consumption, paper and paperboard, lb	280	280
Newsprint production, tons	6,738,611	7,734,759
Exports of newsprint, U.S.A., tons	5,259,653	5,226,673
Exports of newsprint, Overseas, tons	986,072	988,867
Total wood pulp production, tons	11,182,907	11,570,522
Exports of wood pulp, tons	2,605,799	2,683,974

Over half of the total pulp production is groundwood, making Canada the world

* F. T. Peterson: "Pulping Around the World," from "Challenges of Forestry," State University College of Forestry, Syracuse University, 1961.

leader in this type of pulp. Canadian exports accounted for over 72% of the newsprint consumption in the U.S.A. in 1959.

The countries of Western Europe have shown a huge increase in the consumption of paper during the decade from 1950 to 1960. In the eight countries, United Kingdom, France, West Germany, Italy, Sweden, Netherlands, Belgium and Norway, the total paper and paperboard consumption for 1960 was reported as 18,849,836 tons or 160 pounds per capita, up more than 100% from 1950. Vigorous growth in production and use of paper products is the watchword in Western Europe today.

On the other side of the world, Japan has shown an increase in per capita consumption of paper and paperboard of nearly five-fold since 1950, reaching a total consumption of nearly 4,800,000 tons in 1960. Imports of paper into Japan account for relatively little of this consumption, hence this has been brought about by a parallel growth in domestic production.

The consumption of paper in pounds per capita for the years 1950, 1955, 1960 and 1962 for selected industrialized countries outside North America is given below.*

	1950	1955	1960	1962
Australia	96	141	176	181
France	74	94	127	141
Great Britain	102	187	236	233
Italy	26	35	63	87
Japan	22	53	103	126
Poland	22	52	47	51
Russia	N.A.	26	33	36
Sweden	122	200	265	282
West Germany	60	121	174	186

In the various Latin American countries the consumption of paper varies from less than 10 pounds per capita for the less industrialized countries to over 30 pounds per capita for those countries with greater industrial development.

In many African and Asian countries the consumption of paper is less than 5 pounds

*Source: "Pulp and Paper Annual Review," Nos. 1960, 1961, 1962.

per capita per year. However, almost without exception, there is evidence of rapid growth in the use of paper in the African and Asian countries with the prospect of continued expansion in the future both in domestic production of paper and of imports of pulp and paper products.

World-wide expansion of the paper industry is largely dependent upon the development of local sources of fiber. The original basis of the wood pulp industry was the mechanical or chemical defibering of a few coniferous wood species of the Northern Hemisphere. Even in those countries where wood pulping originated, it has long been necessary to utilize many wood species once considered unsuitable for pulp and to modify the pulping processes to produce acceptable pulp from these woods. In large areas of the world, there are no forest resources of any kind adequate to sustain a large pulp industry. In other areas, particularly in the tropics, the wood species are those not hitherto successfully used for pulp.

Thus we see a number of significant trends that in the course of time will have a profound effect upon the world industry. Among these are the utilization of non-wood fibers such as sugar cane bagasse, straw, esparto, reeds and other annual plants. In India and other Southeast Asia countries, the use of bamboo is of growing importance. The use of tropical or semi-tropical woods is attracting much attention. In Australia, New Zealand and Brazil, eucalyptus wood is used for pulp in significant amounts. Reforestation can be of great benefit to many underdeveloped countries. Also, these areas of the world will continue to offer substantial markets for Northern Hemisphere wood pulps to supplement and upgrade local fiber supplies.

In addition to developing methods for utilizing local sources of fiber, there is an evident trend toward high-yield pulping processes and continuous methods of digestion. It is also likely that there will be a rising demand for pulp imports from Northern Hemisphere countries with surplus wood pulp capacity over domestic needs. Increased recovery of waste paper should make a substantial contribution to satisfying future fiber requirements.

FIBERS USED FOR PAPER MAKING IN DIFFERENT COUNTRIES

I—Wood:

1. *Softwoods*—North America, Eastern and Western Europe, Japan, Eastern Russia, China, Vietnam, New Zealand, Brazil, Chile, Mexico, Turkey, Middle and South Africa.
2. *Temperate Zone Hardwoods*—North America, Eastern and Western Europe, Eastern Russia, China, Japan, Argentina.
3. *Tropical and Semitropical Hardwoods*
   a. Eucalyptus—Australia, Brazil, Argentina, Portugal, Israel, North and South Africa, Spain.
   b. Mixed—Brazil, Mexico, French Africa
   c. Low Density—Argentina, Brazil, India, South Africa

II—Other Than Wood:

1. *Straws*
   a. Wheat
   b. Rye
   c. Rice
   { North America, Mexico, Eastern and Western Europe, Egypt, Turkey, Taiwan, China, India, Pakistan, Indonesia, Thailand, Argentina, Brazil, Chile, South Africa, Egypt, Philippine Islands.

2. *Grasses*
   a. Bamboos—India, Taiwan, China, Indonesia, Brazil
   b. Sabai Grass—India, Pakistan
   c. Lemon Grass—Guatemala
   d. Parana Grass—Ecuador
   e. Capim—Brazil
   f. Esparto—England, Spain, France, North Africa

3. *Canes and Reeds*
   a. Sugar Cane Bagasse—United States, Mexico, Argentina, Brazil, Colombia, Peru, Venezuela, Hawaiian and Philippine Islands, India, Taiwan, China, South Africa.
   b. Corn Stalks—United States, Israel (formerly)
   c. Arundo donax—Italy
   d. Phragmitis communis—Egypt, Rumania, Russia

4. *Woody Stalks with Bast Fibers*
   a. Flax — United States, Canada
   b. Hemps, Jute — United States and others
   c. Mulberry — China, Vietnam
   d. Cotton & Soybean Stalks — United States
   e. Mitsumata, Kozo — Japan

5. *Leaf Fibers*
   a. Manila Hemp (old ropes) — United States
   b. Sisal, Henequen, Caroa (old ropes, etc.) — United States
   c. Palm — United States

6. *Seed Hair*
   Cotton, rags, linters — United States and others

RESEARCH IN THE PAPER INDUSTRY

In common with all industries in recent years, there has been a great increase in research and development in the paper industry since World War II. Practically all major companies have new or expanded research facilities.

The following table shows the expected research and development expenditures for various industrial groups for 1963.*

1963 INDUSTRY R&D EXPENDITURES (DOLLARS)

Primary metals	200 million
Machinery	900 million
Electrical equipment	2.2 billion
Chemicals	850 million
Paper and pulp	97 million
Rubber and allied products	113 million
Petroleum and Petro-chemical	350 million
Food and beverages	140 million
Fabricated metals	340 million
Autos and allied products	900 million
Aircraft and parts	3.3 billion

It is characteristic of an old established industry such as paper that research and development expenditures are much less than in those new industries whose very

* Karmatz, F. N., *Industrial Research,* **20** (January, 1963).

existence has come about through the application of scientific discoveries. There is ample evidence that there will be increasing application of scientific discoveries to paper making, a greater use of laboratory findings, and extension of pilot plant and experimental models for studying paper processes.

Research in pulp and paper is not limited to that conducted by paper companies. Suppliers of equipment and materials have long been active in bringing about innovations in paper-making practice. There is every indication that there will be continued expansion in research and development activity by suppliers. A number of government agencies are active in paper research including the Department of Agriculture through its forest service divisions and regional laboratories and the Bureau of Standards.

In the academic world, the industry supported Institute of Paper Chemistry carries out both an educational and a research program. A number of colleges and universities offer education and/or research in pulp and paper, often but not always connected with forestry departments.

BIBLIOGRAPHY

Historical:

Hunter, Dard, "Papermaking: The History and Technique of an Ancient Craft." Second Edition, New York, Alfred A. Knopf, 1957.

Clapperton, R. H., "The Invention and Development of the Endless Wire, or Fourdrinier Paper Machine," *The Paper Maker (U.S.)*, **23**, No. 1 (1954).

Voorn, H., "In Search of New Raw Materials," *The Paper Maker (U.S.)*, **21**, No. 2 (1952).

Renker, A., "Moritz Friedrich Illig, Inventor of Rosin Sizing," *The Paper Maker (U.S.)*, **30**, No. 2, 37 (1961).

Note: The three articles listed above are selected from many of historical interest appearing over the past twenty years in *The Paper Maker (U.S.)* published by Hercules Powder Company, Wilmington, Delaware.

Economic:

1958 Census of Manufactures, Bureau of the Census, Washington, D.C., U.S. Department of Commerce.

Monthly Statistical Summary, American Paper and Pulp Association, New York. (1962 is Vol. XL of this publication).

"World Review 1961," *Pulp and Paper* (July 24, 1961).

"Facts and Figures for the Chemical Process Industries," *Chem. Eng. News:* September 4, 1961.

United States Paper Industry, "A Capital and Income Survey—1939-1960," American Paper and Pulp Association, New York, 1961.

"The Market for Chemicals in the Paper and Pulp Industry," New York, Lockwood Trade Journal Co., Inc., 1960.

"1959-1960 Sales and Profits of 60 Paper and Allied Companies," *Paper Mill News*, **84**, No. 17, 56 (April 24, 1961).

Leontief, W. W., and Hoffenberg, M., "The Economic Effects of Disarmament," *Sci. Am.*, **204**, No. 4, 47 (April, 1961).

McLeod, N., "Paper Industry Economics." *Paper Trade J.*, 38 (June 5, 1961).

Slatin, B., "Paper Industry of Tomorrow." *Paper Trade J.* (June 19, 1961).

Slatin, B., "Economic Position of the Paper Industry." *Tappi*, **45**, No. 12, 10A (December, 1962).

J. Frank Gaston: "Growth Patterns in Industry: A Reexamination," New York, National Industrial Conference Board, 1961.

CHAPTER 2

Technology of Paper-making Materials

KENNETH W. BRITT

Scott Paper Company

Paper consists of a matted or felted sheet of fibers formed from water suspension and usually modified by additional materials. The fibrous raw materials or "pulp" is the most important raw material with which the paper industry is concerned. It has been stated that paper of some sort can be made from the fibers of any vascular plant found in nature. In a technical sense, this is probably true, but from an economic standpoint, the number of plant materials suitable for paper making is much more limited. A recent publication by Isenberg lists and describes the naturally occurring sources of paper-making fibers.[1]

In natural fibers, it is the substance *cellulose* that determines the character of the fiber and permits its use in paper making. Cellulose is a *carbohydrate*, meaning that it is composed of carbon, hydrogen and oxygen with the latter two elements in the same proportion as in water. The elemental composition of cellulose was early determined to be $C_6H_{10}O_5$, but it was also recognized that the molecular weight was much greater than the 162 represented by this formula. Hence, cellulose is a *polysaccharide*, indicating that it contains many recurring sugar units and is represented by the formula $(C_6H_{10}O_5)_n$ where n is indefinite, varying with different sources of cellulose, and with the treatment that it has received. The value of n is believed to be from 800-1500 for cellulose in the form of paper-making fibers.

Cellulose is the most abundant of the products of photosynthesis in the plant kingdom and is produced annually in enormous amounts by natural plant growth. It is, therefore, a replaceable natural resource and one in which the supply could be greatly augmented. It follows, also, that wasteful and irresponsible exploitation can greatly diminish the supply and actually create scarcity.

The determination of the molecular structure of cellulose is one of the classical achievements in chemical research. The structure of cellulose is shown below, the recurring unit of the molecular chain being two consecutive *glucose anhydride* units

Cellulose (β)

forming a cellobiose unit. A treatment of the chemistry of cellulose is beyond the scope of this volume. The reader interested in the subject is referred to standard texts dealing with cellulose chemistry.[2, 3]

Cellulose occurs in nature in relatively pure form as cotton seed hairs and is also obtained in quite pure form from flax and ramie by comparatively simple treatment of those plants. However, most cellulose occurs in nature intimately associated with other substances composing the plant structure, from which it can be separated only with considerable difficulty. Thus, to provide abundant supplies of comparatively pure cellulose fiber for paper making, as well as for other applications, it was necessary to develop chemical processes for removing the so-called "encrusting" materials.

Two significant results follow from this situation which have a bearing upon the methods of paper manufacture. First, in the conversion of plant material into paper pulp, there may be a removal or dissolution of from 20 to 70% of the plant substance. This not only represents an economic loss in the sense of growing, harvesting, transporting and treating large amounts of material that becomes waste of little or no value, but even represents a serious problem in disposal. The second result is that most paper products are not pure cellulose, but also contain more or less non-cellulosic material of the plant source. The amount and kind of these materials can markedly affect the paper-making qualities of the fiber, for better or for worse. With the current trend to higher-yield pulps, the effect upon paper properties of the non-cellulosic constituents is of even greater importance than formerly. To cite an example of the part they play in paper, consider newsprint, which is largely composed of mechanical wood pulp or groundwood. The groundwood process (see Chapter 9) represents a defibering of the wood without chemical separation or purification. The presence of noncellulosic material, especially *lignin,* accounts for the yellowing and general deterioration of newsprint with age. For temporary use this is of little importance, but for permanent papers these constituents must be removed or perhaps stabilized.

FIBER PROPERTIES

Cellulose has a number of properties which are essential to the function that it must perform in nature and which fit equally well the requirements of a fiber in paper making. Cellulose fiber has long been recognized as having *high tensile strength.* In making strength comparison, it is important to give consideration to methods of reporting. There are two methods by which the tensile strength of materials may be expressed: first, the force required to rupture the material per unit of cross-sectional area of the test specimen, (pounds per square inch (psi) or kg per sq mm); second, the force required to rupture the material per unit of linear mass (grams per denier). The first is really strength per unit volume and the second is strength per unit weight. The first is used extensively where the material is essentially homogeneous and non-porous and is available in forms of easily determined cross-sectional area; the second is more suitable for materials that are not homogeneous, that may be porous and which have cross sections difficult to measure accurately.

In Table 2.1, strength values of various filamentary materials are given, expressed both as strength per volume and strength per weight. It is obvious that cellulose fibers compare favorably in tensile strength with the strongest metal wire on a "strength per weight" basis, but fall much below it on a "strength per volume" basis.

It is well recognized that paper does not utilize the ultimate strength of all the fibers of which it is composed. At the same time, fiber strength is an important factor in sheet strength, and there is believed to be a direct relationship between the two where conditions are such that a high degree of sheet strength is obtained. It is important to remember that paper-making fibers differ widely in strength depending upon the natural source and upon the pulping and refining treatments the fibers have received. An average strength value as given in Table

2.1 is compiled from a wide range of individual strength values.

TABLE 2.1. STRENGTH OF VARIOUS FILAMENTARY MATERIALS *

Material	psi	Tensile Strength kg/ sq mm	mg/ mg/ 100 m	grams/ denier
Copper wire, maximum	65,000	45.5	68.5	0.76
Steel wire, maximum	460,000	322	525	5.83
Tungsten wire, maximum	590,000	413	277	3.08
Glass fiber	236,000	165	656	7.3
Nylon fiber, maximum	133,000	93.5	826	9.2
Rayon fiber, regular	45,000	32	216	2.4
Rayon fiber, high tenacity	95,000	66.5	450	5.0
Cotton fiber, average	75,000	53.6	351	3.9
Wood pulp fiber	80,300	56.2	370	4.1

* Data obtained from various published sources. Strength values for cotton and wood pulp fibers cover wide range. Averages only are given above. Value for wood pulp fiber represents average from various sources compiled by the author.

There is offered in Table 2.1 a new expression for the strength of paper-making fibers, namely milligrams per milligram per one hundred meters. Milligrams per 100 meters of fiber length is the "coarseness" or weight per unit length of the filament defined in TAPPI Method T234sm-60. The expression for tenacity of textile fibers, grams per denier, multiplied by 90, gives mg per mg per 100 meters.

Cellulose fiber is supple and yet resistant to plastic deformation. This combination of properties is brought about by the molecular structure of cellulose as well as the morphological structure of the fiber itself. The molecular structure is characterized by long chains of cellobiose units free of chemical cross links, but held together by secondary valence forces, with highly ordered crystalline regions interspersed with less well ordered amorphous regions. This structure gives cellulose fibers the ability to yield without breaking. On a somewhat larger scale the molecules form bundles or fibrils which are arranged in recognizable layers

within the cell wall and generally run in a spiral pattern with respect to the fiber axis. It follows from this fiber structure that when wet cellulose fibers are subjected to mechanical action there results a stepwise fraying or unraveling of the fiber rather than a shattering and reduction to fine particles. It is this characteristic upon which much of the paper-making art depends and which will be described more fully in Chapter 11. The reader interested in a study of fiber structure is also referred to a recent compilation of articles on this subject.[4]

Also as a result of its molecular structure, cellulose is both hydrophilic and water-insoluble. It is readily wetted by water—indeed it absorbs and is swollen by water—but remains insoluble even under severe chemical and mechanical conditions. Here again, since paper making takes place in an aqueous medium, the hydrophilic nature of the fiber plays an important part. (Substituting a synthetic, hydrophobic fiber in the paper system serves to emphasize this difference in fibers.) The cellulose-water relationship has been the subject of numerous investigations. Because of the special importance of this relationship in the beating and refining of fiber preparatory to sheet formation, this subject will be treated more fully in the chapter on stock preparation (Chapter 11).

Paper-making fibers generally comprise a great variety of *size and shape*. Not only is there a wide range in fiber dimensions among such different plant sources as coniferous wood, deciduous wood, cotton, flax, hemp and straw, but also the fibers of any one plant vary considerably in size and shape. In addition, the beating and refining of paper stock results in cutting and bruising of the fiber and in creation of short fragments or "fines." With rare exceptions, therefore, paper consists of fibrous particles of a wide range of dimensions. It is generally accepted that many paper products benefit from being composed of both long fibers and short fibers or fragments. The short, fine fibers tend to fill the spaces among the longer, coarser fibers. The resulting sheet shows a favorable combination of strength, contributed by the longer fibers, and a smooth, uniform surface brought about by the short and fine fiber.

In spite of this heterogeneity in fiber size, there are certain well-recognized limits that define the general range of paper-making fiber. Such fibers as cotton, flax and hemp are available in lengths up to several inches. However, in order to make paper of acceptably uniform formation, it is necessary to cut these fibers by refining to a length that does not exceed about ⅛ inch. Even coniferous wood pulp of average fiber length of 3 to 4 mm requires either refining or admixture with shorter fiber in order to achieve uniform formation. At the other end of the scale, if we attempt to make a sheet of all hardwood pulp having a fiber length from 1 to 1.5 mm, the resulting paper will be deficient in some or all of the durability factors, such as tensile strength, tearing strength and folding endurance.

It is fundamental in the paper-making process that the fibers of the head box stock be free and evenly dispersed. If the fibers flocculate into clumps or strings, the resulting uneven formation will be detrimental to the physical properties desired in most papers. The tendency of fibers to flocculate is increased by greater fiber length; hence, there is a maximum fiber length that will give acceptable formation. This maximum length varies considerably as the result of other factors. For example, at a given fiber length, fine fibers tend to flocculate more readily than do coarse fibers. Flocculation is also greatly influenced by the colloidal conditions of the fiber surface, which in turn are affected by adsorption of ions (charged particles) or hydrophilic colloids, from the surrounding liquid.

Fiber flexibility is recognized as being important in the ability of fibers to make intimate contact with neighboring fibers during sheet formation and, hence, is a determining factor in the area and strength of interfiber bonding. A fiber that is soft and flexible in the wet, swollen condition will promote interfiber bonding; one that is stiff will resist bonding. Considerable research on fiber flexibility is presently being carried out in various pulp and paper laboratories. Although progress has been made in measuring this property, we still lack generally accepted methods for its determination.

Inherent bonding ability is a property of pulp fibers of direct importance to paper making. It varies widely among various types of pulp. The maximum bonding ability among wood pulps is found in those from which most of the lignin has been removed but which still contain substantial amounts of hemicellulose. On the other hand, pulps in which hemicellulose and easily dissolved cellulose are removed by alkaline extraction (alpha pulps) have little interfiber bonding ability. Pulps containing substantial amounts of lignin, such as groundwood and semichemical pulps, have limited interfiber bonding capacity. Groundwood differs from other wood pulps in showing practically no increase in interfiber bonding with beating. The response of fiber to the beating action in the development of bonding is of great significance.

From the early days of paper making, pulps have been known to differ in their ability to *absorb modifying additives*. The sizing of paper stock with emulsified rosin and alum to produce a paper resistant to wetting was one of the original stock treatment methods. Pulps have been classified as being "easy to size" or "difficult to size." In course of time, many additives have come into use for the treatment of paper stocks. Dyes, synthetic resins, natural rosin emulsions, wax emulsions, starches, gums and latices are among the materials currently used as paper stock additives. That fibers differ in receptivity toward these agents is universally recognized. The specific properties of fiber that cause these differences are still obscure. The ability of fibers to absorb and hold additives through the paper-forming step is of great practical significance in paper manufacture. This subject will be treated more fully in Chapter 11.

MICROSCOPY OF PULP FIBER

Figure 2.1 shows a cross section of spruce wood at a magnification of about 110 times. The principal structural elements of the softwoods (coniferous woods) are the *tracheids* comprising normally over 90% of the wood volume. These elongated, longitudinal cells function both as conducting elements for the sap in the living tree and for the support and rigidity of the tree. Note in Figure 2.1 the distinction between the thin-walled *springwood* tracheids with large *lumens* (center cavities) and the thicker-walled *summerwood* tracheids with smaller lumens. This distinction creates the *annular ring* which is characteristic of tree growth. The wood shown in Figure 2.1 has a relatively small proportion of summerwood. Other

coniferous trees, particularly southern pines, commonly have larger amounts of summerwood, which is often comparable in volume to the springwood. Because of the thicker cell wall and narrow lumen, wood having a high content of summerwood is of high density.

Other features of wood structure visible in Figure 2.1 are *medullary rays* and *longitudinal resin ducts*. The rays are visible as irregularly spaced striations extending in a radial direction from the center of the tree outward. The rays are composed of small block-like cells commonly containing gums, resins, and water-soluble nutrients. Since the cell walls of the rays are cellulosic, they are chemically similar to, though not identical with, the cell walls of tracheids. Because of the small size and block-like shape of ray cells, they contribute little to the strength of paper and appear in the papermaking system as fines. The *resin ducts* appear in Figure 2.1 as cavities bordered

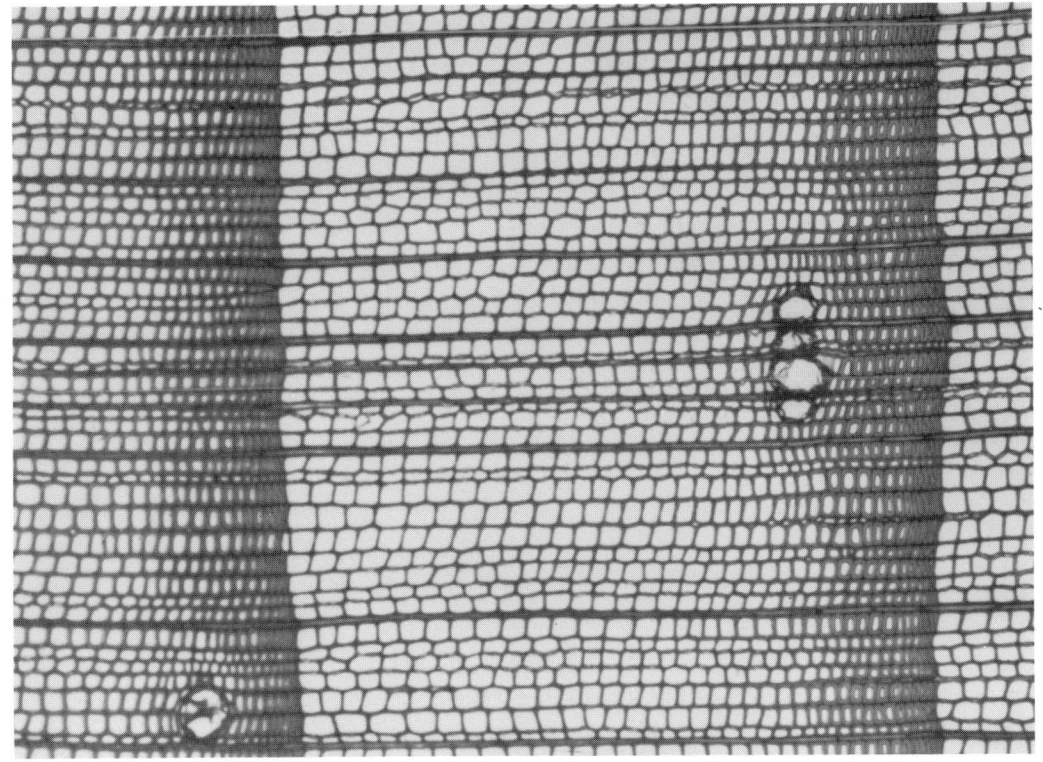

Fig. 2.1. Cross section of spruce wood. 75×.

by a layer of small cells. These ducts are the chief source of wood resin or "pitch"— a bane to papermakers as long as wood pulp has been used.

Figure 2.2 shows a *tangential* view of the same spruce wood. Figure 2.2 is taken at right angles to Figure 2.1 and looking toward the center of the tree. Visible in this picture are the end views of the medullary rays, section views of the *bordered pits* which connect adjacent tracheids, and transverse resin ducts.

Figure 2.3 shows a cross section of birch, a typical deciduous wood or "hardwood." In this type of wood, the function of transporting sap in the living tree is performed by *vessels*, shown in Figure 2.3 as oval-shaped cavities. The supporting elements are the *wood fibers* which differ from coniferous tracheids in being considerably shorter—generally about half as long—

more slender, with thicker walls, and smaller lumens. Medullary rays occur abundantly in hardwoods. In some species of oak over 30% of the wood volume consists of ray cells. Thus, a typical hardwood pulp consists of three rather distinct components, the wood fibers, vessel segments and ray cells.

In evolutionary terms, the conifers are the most primitive of pulpwood trees. Geological evidence traces the origin of conifers to the late Carboniferous Period or about 200,000,000 years ago. The conifers reached their maximum abundance during the Cretaceous Period about 100,000,000 years ago.

According to geological evidence, the hardwood trees, which belong to the group of flowering plants known as *angiosperms,* are of more recent origin. The earliest fossils of this group are dated in the Jurassic Period of the Mesozoic Era about 125,-

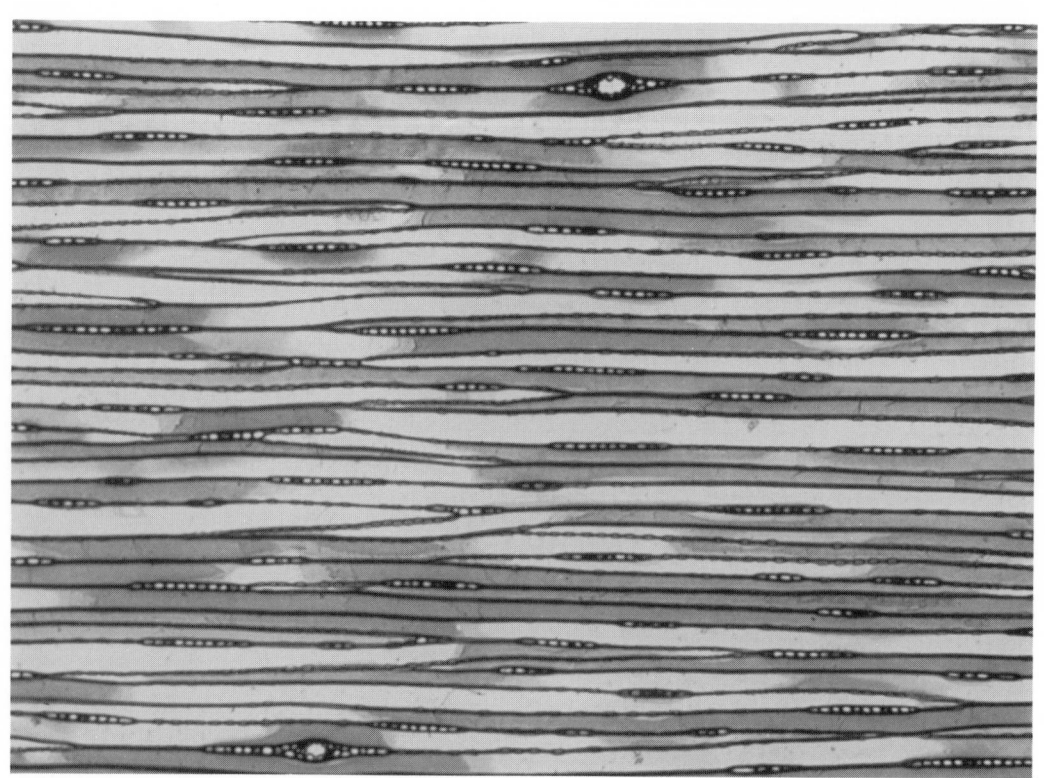

Fig. 2.2.   Tangential view of spruce wood. 75×.

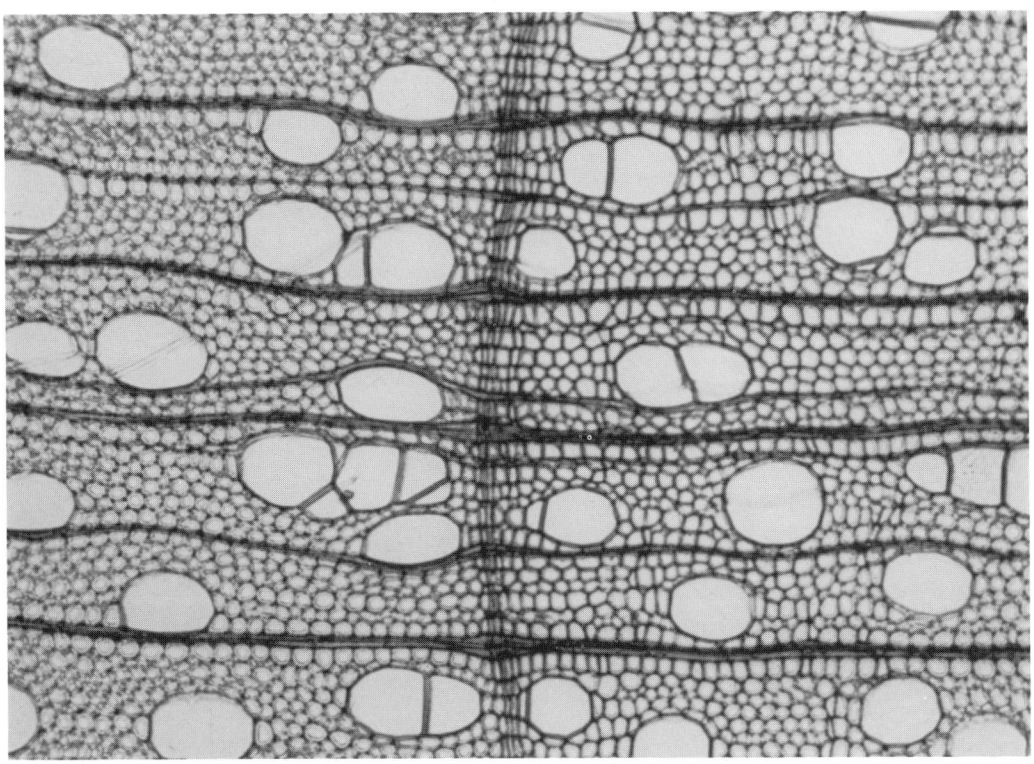

Fig. 2.3. Cross section of birch wood. 75×.

000,000 years ago. The *diffuse porous* hardwoods, such as aspen, cottonwood, beech, birch, maple and red gum, appear early in the history of the angiosperm group. The *ring porous* hardwoods, such as chestnut, oak, elm, black locust and ash, are of much more recent origin dating back only to the Miocene Epoch or about 30,000,000 years ago.

We have seen that the conversion of wood or any other vegetable material into paper-making pulp consists essentially of separating and freeing the individual fibers. At one extreme this may consist of the complete dissolving and removal of the *middle lamella,* which is the highly lignified layer between the cellulosic fibers. At the other extreme, pulp is made by subjecting the wood to a mechanical grinding action (groundwood pulp), which depends upon the greater ease of rupture of the middle lamella to produce defibering. Between these two ex-

tremes, pulping may be accomplished by softening the middle lamella by chemical action, thereby permitting defibering by less drastic mechanical action than in the groundwood process.

Figure 2.4 shows cross-section tracings of full chemical sulfite pulp fibers from western hemlock (*Tsuga heterophylla*). Note the pronounced tendency of the springwood fibers to collapse into flat ribbons. The thicker-walled summerwood fibers have less tendency to collapse, but, even so, very few retain the cross-sectional shape as they existed in the wood. Figure 2.6 shows fibers from the same pulp as in Figure 2.4 in the typical side view in the microscope. Flat, flexible, ribbon-like fibers are favorable to interfiber bonding and tend to give smooth dense sheets.

Figure 2.5 shows cross-section tracings of pulp fibers produced by a high-yield, neutral sulfite, chemi-mechanical process from

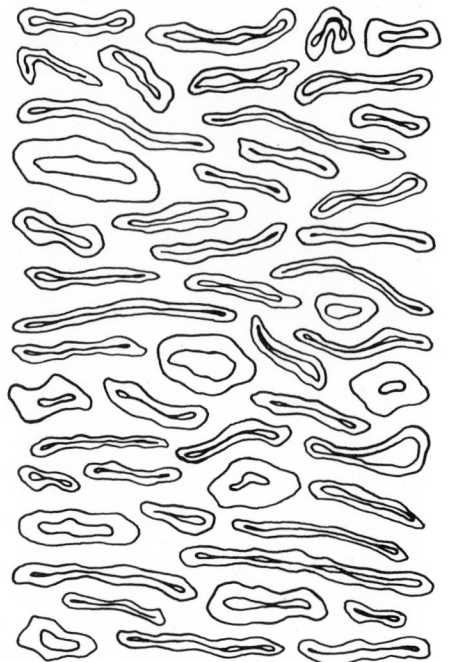

Fig. 2.4. Cross sections of western full chemical sulfite pulp. 400×.

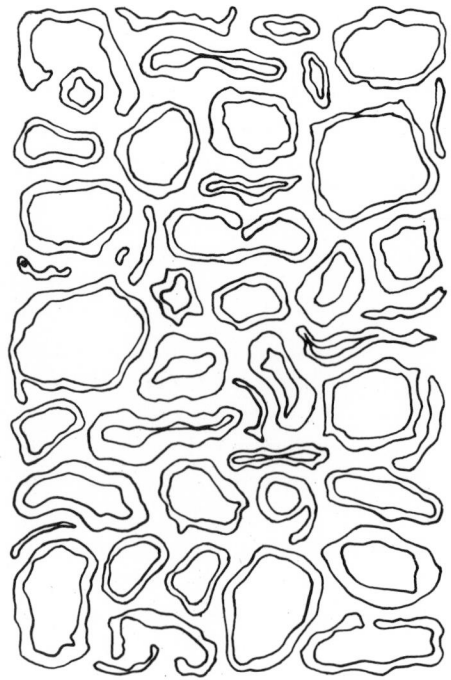

Fig. 2.5. Cross sections of balsam fir chemi-mechanical pulp. 400×.

eastern coniferous wood. Note, in contrast to Figure 2.4, that most of the fibers are not collapsed and also that some rupture of the cell wall can be observed. Such fibers tend to produce bulkier and less bonded sheets.

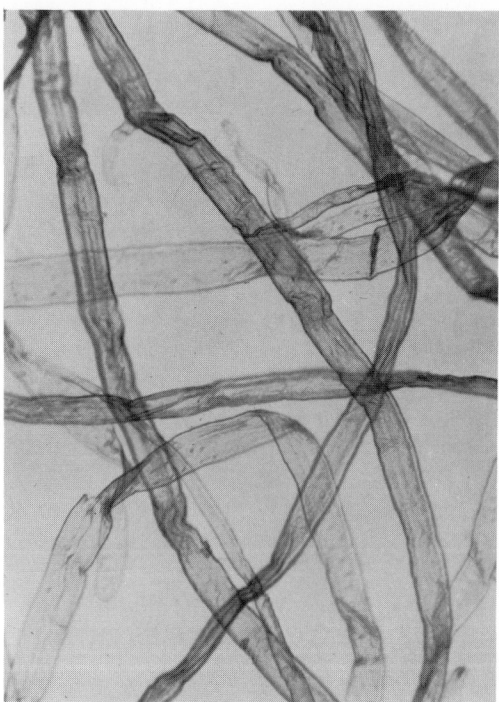

Fig. 2.6. Western hemlock full chemical sulfite pulp fibers. 100×.

Figure 2.7 shows cross-section tracings of fibers from pulp produced by the "cold soda" chemi-mechanical process in a yield of over 90% from hardwood. Note the absence of fiber collapse and the presence of fiber bundles, both being characteristic of high-yield pulps. In comparison with fibers in Figures 2.4 and 2.5, note the smaller diameter of the hardwood fibers, and also that there is less distinction between the springwood and summerwood fibers and that the thin-walled vessel segments of the hardwood appear only as fragments.

Figure 2.8 shows cross-section tracings of groundwood fibers from eastern coniferous wood. Frequent rupture of the cell walls, the occurrence of unseparated fiber bundles, and the resistance to collapse are evident. Such well-known characteristics of groundwood fibers as bulkiness, high surface area, roughness of surface, and springiness under compression (both wet and dry) are discernible from the appearance of these sections.

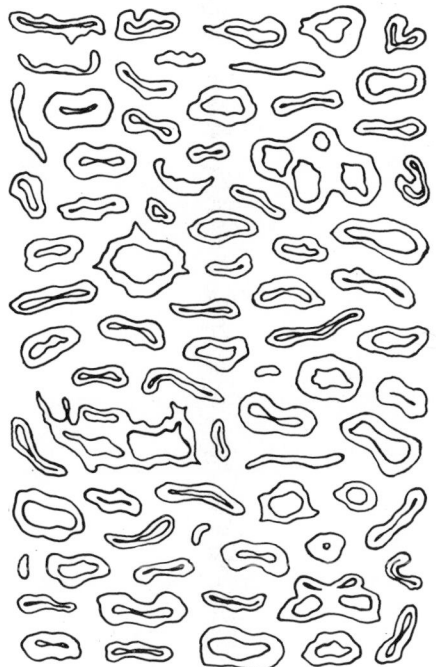

Fig. 2.7. Cross sections of cold soda chemi-mechanical pulp from hardwood. 400×.

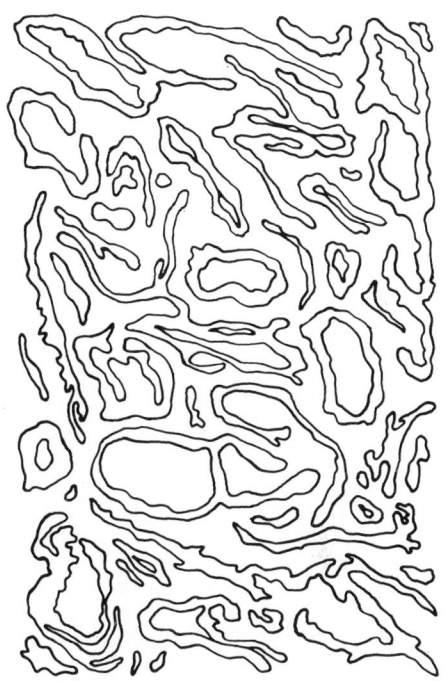

Fig. 2.8. Cross sections of ground wood pulp from soft wood. 400×.

After converting wood into pulp, an additional beating or refining action in water is necessary for most papers. Figure 2.9 shows the same pulp fiber as that in Figure 2.6 after a moderate amount of beating. The fibrillation visible in this view is characteristic of natural cellulosic fiber and is important in obtaining intimate contact and bond formation between adjacent fibers during sheet formation.

Having gone to great pains to separate individual fibers from wood and to disperse them freely in water suspension, the papermaker must now re-integrate these fibers into a coherent sheet as the final step in paper manufacture.

Figure 2.10 shows the surface of news-

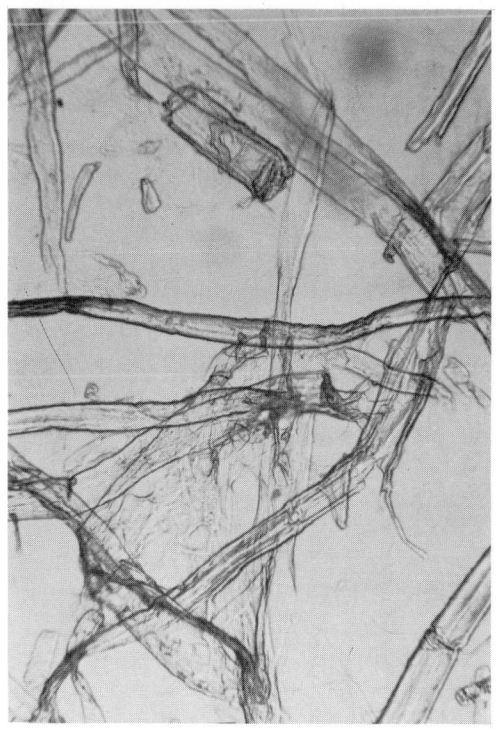

Fig. 2.9. Western hemlock full chemical sulfite fibers beaten to 336 freeness. 100×.

Fig. 2.10. Newsprint top side. 275×. (*Courtesy British Paper and Board Industry Research Association*)

print paper (275×) by the plastic replica and metal shadowing technique developed by H. W. Emerton, D. H. Page and J. Watts at the British Paper Board Industry Research Association laboratory.[5]

Figures 2.11 and 2.12 show similar views of machine-glazed kraft and cigarette paper respectively. The technique is briefly as follows: methyl methacrylate monomer is polymerized on the surface of the paper to be replicated by gentle application of heat. After stripping away the specimen, a positive replica is cast within the matrix so formed. This replica is made from polyvinyl alcohol, about 0.5 mm thick, and is readily separated mechanically from the methacrylate. For the shadowing, antimony has proved to be satisfactory. After shadowing the positive replica may be cut to suitable size and permanently mounted under a cover glass.

TESTING AND EVALUATION OF PULP

The test methods available for the evaluation of pulp are essentially empirical in nature. These methods depend upon exposure of pulp samples to carefully defined chemical or physical procedures leading to

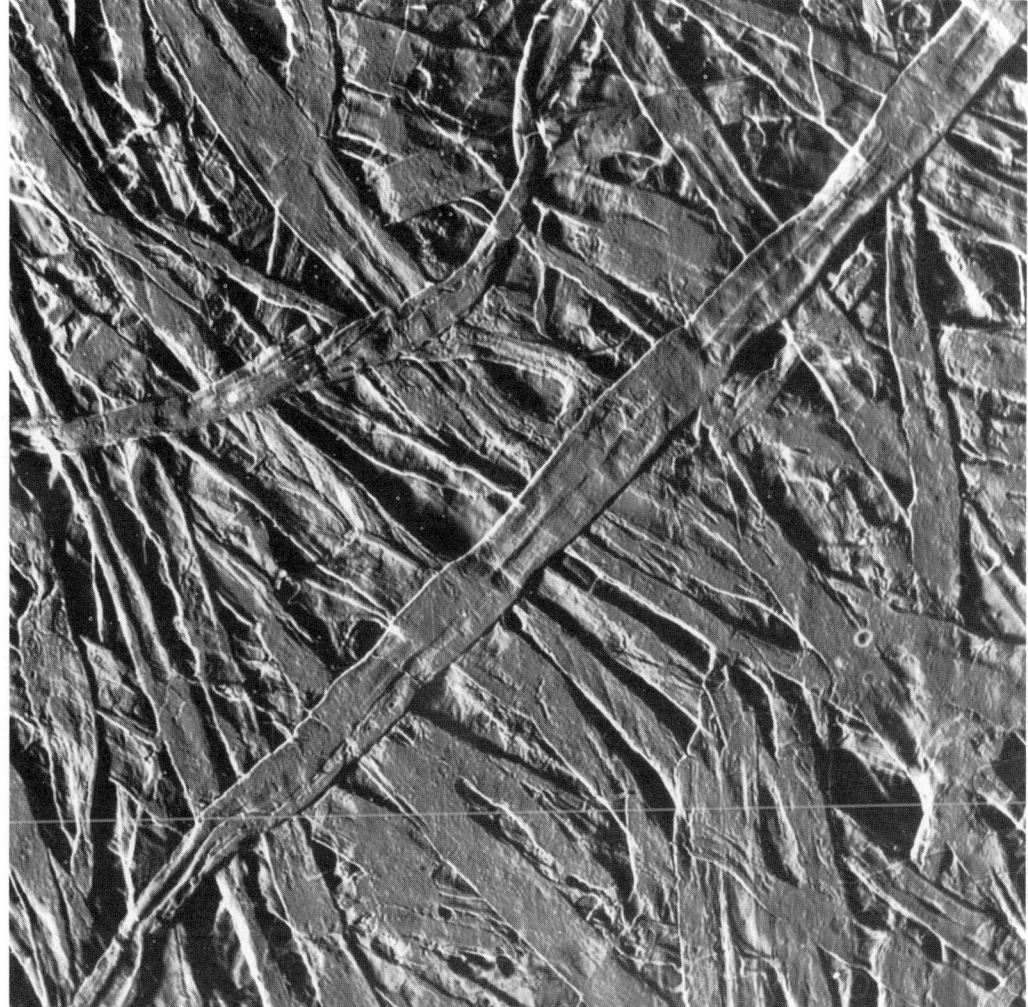

Fig. 2.11. Machine glazed kraft. 275×. (*Courtesy British Paper and Board Industry Research Association*)

measurable chemical or physical results. The reproducibility of the results depends upon how closely the test conditions are duplicated and does not give absolute predictions as to the behavior of the pulp in subsequent manufacturing operations.

At the same time, these tests are essential to pulp mill operations as an index of the uniformity of the output, as a guide to the effect of deliberate changes in raw material and process, and as a signal of any unforeseen swings in operating conditions. Likewise, to the pulp buyer or user they are an indispensable part of the pulp performance record.

The numerous laboratories of the pulp and paper industry throughout the world have devised a vast number of tests for application to pulp. Many of these have similar objectives; however, due to the empirical nature of the tests, they are not freely interchangeable. Other tests have been developed to serve the special needs of particular organizations and are not of universal interest. In this chapter the discussion will be limited to a few selected test methods that have received official sanction, which illustrate important principles in pulp quality and which are of essentially universal interest and significance.

Fig. 2.12. Cigarette paper. 275×. (*Courtesy British Paper and Board Industry Research Association*)

Chemical Testing of Pulp

In a chemical sense, pulps may vary in their *cellulose content* or *purity*, or, to put it in another way, in their content of *lignin* or other non-cellulosic material. Further, the cellulose content itself may vary in its proportion of highly resistant cellulose (usually referred to as *alpha* cellulose) to the less resistant or more easily dissolved cellulose.

Kappa Number of Pulp. The non-cellulosic ingredients (particularly lignin) react rapidly with acidified $KMnO_4$ whereas cellulose reacts slowly and with difficulty. This permits a rapid, empirical test method capable of classifying a wide range of pulps for relative purity with respect to cellulose. TAPPI Method T236m-60 describes the detailed procedure. According to this method, a weighed sample of pulp in the range of 3 to 4 grams is exposed to the action of 100 ml of $0.1N$ $KMnO_4$ (acidified) in a volume of 1,000 ml at 25°C for 10 minutes. The reaction is stopped by adding an excess of KI solution and the $KMnO_4$ consumed is determined from the results of back-titrating the liberated iodine with standard thiosulfate. The *Kappa Number* so obtained is the ml of $0.1N$ $KMnO_4$ consumed per gram of pulp.

This method is an improvement of the original Permanganate Number of Pulp (TAPPI Method T214m-50) usually referred to as "K Number." The improved method permits the use of the method on pulps of high yields of up to 70% of the wood. It is important to keep a clear distinction between Kappa Number and K Number. The following table gives data from various pulps expressed both ways.

	Kappa Number T236m-60	K Number T214m-50
Unbleached pulp, soft cook	19-21	10-12
Unbleached pulp, medium cook	35-40	18-21

The Kappa Number of pulp is useful in determining cooking degree, that is, whether the pulp has been cooked to a high degree of removal of non-cellulosic constituents of wood, or whether a considerable amount of lignin remains in the pulp. By the same token, for pulps that are to be bleached, it indicates the amount of chlorine that will be required.

The Chlorine Consumption of Pulp described in TAPPI Method T202m-45, like the Kappa Number, is related to the lignin content of the pulp. In this method, 2 grams of wet pulp are exposed to a measured quantity of chlorine gas (about 100 ml) for 15 minutes at 20°C in a gas absorption apparatus. The *Chlorine Number* represents the grams of chlorine absorbed by 100 grams of moisture-free pulp. The method is principally useful as a direct prediction of total chlorine required in the bleaching operation.

Cellulose Content of Pulp. The total cellulose content of pulp may be determined by the classical Cross and Bevan Method by means of successive extractions of a pulp sample of known weight with chlorine gas, sulfur dioxide solution, and sodium sulfite, followed by weighing the undissolved residue. This method, described in TAPPI T201m-54, is of minor interest in pulp man-

ufacture. Pulp testing is more concerned with the residual lignin as indicated by permanganate or chlorine numbers or resistant cellulose described below.

Resistant cellulose content of pulp is determined most simply by exposure of the pulp to concentrated sodium hydroxide. (See below.) The resistant fraction of cellulose is usually referred to as "alpha-cellulose" and pulps are said to have such and such alpha content, and those with a high percentage of resistant cellulose are called "alpha pulps." Strictly speaking, the term "alpha-cellulose" should be reserved for that determined by TAPPI Method T203.

TAPPI Method T235m-60 provides for the determination of solubility of pulp in sodium hydroxide of various concentrations at 20°C, using a pulp sample of 1.5 grams and an exposure time of 1 hour. After washing of the sample, the amount of dissolved cellulose in the filtrate is determined by oxidation with potassium bichromate in sulfuric acid, the amount of bichromate used being determined by back titration with KI and thiosulfate.

The drastic chemical and physical conditions incident to the cooking and bleaching of pulp are liable to bring about a *depolymerization* of the cellulose chains as well as oxidation of some of the hydroxyl groups of the cellulose molecules to aldehyde or carboxyl. An indication of the degree of polymerization of the cellulose in pulp may be obtained by measuring the viscosity of solution of cellulose of known concentration. The cellulose solvents useful for this purpose are cuprammonium (cf. TAPPI Method T206m-55) and cupriethylene diamine. The latter method has displaced the former for most purposes because of the greater stability of the solvent solution and because of its ability to dissolve cellulose more rapidly.

The standard viscosity of pulp as defined in T230m-50 is the viscosity in centipoises of a 1% solution of moisture-free pulp in a cupriethylene diamine solution 0.5 molar with respect to copper at 25°C in the absence of air. For details of preparation of reagents, solution of the sample, determination of viscosity and calculation of results the reader is referred to the official method above cited.

As pointed out above, the viscosity measurement is an indication of degradation or depolymerization of cellulose resulting from chemical or physical treatment to which the pulp has been subjected. For best results, the viscosity of paper grade pulps should not be below 80 centipoises. As this limit is passed, the first properties to show an adverse effect are tear, fold and zero span tensile. As the viscosity decreases still further, the tensile and burst properties suffer. Pulps below 10 centipoises viscosity are practically worthless for paper making.

TAPPI Data Sheet 113C (December 1950) * gives the relationship between cellulose viscosity, and the D.P. (degree of polymerization) in terms of average number of glucose anhydride ($C_6H_{10}O_5$) units in the cellulose chains of the sample. The following values for 1% cupriethylene diamine viscosity and D.P. are taken from Data Sheet 113C.

T230m-50 Viscosity (centipoises)	D.P.
11	500
15	600
21	700
30	800
40	900
60	1,000
80	1,100
120	1,200
290	1,500

It has been stated [6] that digestion should be stopped while the D.P. of cellulose is still over 1,500 units. By careful control of conditions, it is possible to produce bleached pulp with a D.P. of 1,300. Below D.P. 800, the strength properties of pulp decrease rapidly.

Another chemical reaction of a destruc-

* Available from Technical Association of the Pulp and Paper Industry, 360 Lexington Avenue, New York, New York.

tive nature toward cellulose is oxidation of hydroxyl groups, more or less independent of the depolymerization action. This type of degradation is indicated by the *copper number* which is the tendency of the pulp (or paper) to reduce an alkaline solution of copper. Highly lignified fibers (groundwood, high yield, raw cooked pulps) also contain reducing material which produce a high copper number. It is important that the investigator identify the proper cause for a high copper number in a sample of pulp or paper, i.e., whether it is due to oxidation of cellulose or to presence of noncellulose reducing material.

In TAPPI Method T215m-50, a 1.5-gram sample of pulp is exposed to an excess of copper sulfate made alkaline by a standard carbonate-bicarbonate solution at steam bath temperature for 3 hours. The reduced copper in the form of Cu_2O is adsorbed by the fiber. After removal of the above reagents by washing, the fiber containing the Cu_2O is contacted with molybdophosphoric acid. The reduced molybdenum corresponding to the amount of Cu_2O is filtered and titrated with standard permanganate.

The copper number is defined as the number of grams of metallic Cu in the Cu_2O reduced from copper sulfate by 100 grams of pulp fibers.

Physical Properties of Pulp

Fiber length is measured or indicated by two general methods: (1) by microscopic examination and direct measurement of a representative number of fibers and (2) by classification of a sample of pulp into fractions by screens of different fineness.

TAPPI Method T232m-58 describes a method fiber length determination in which a microscopic slide having a known weight of fibers is projected upon a grid pattern and the average fiber length is determined mathematically by counting intersections between fibers and the grid pattern. Numerous workers in paper research have devised other methods of arriving at average fiber length by microscopic examination. Two points should be made concerning the microscopic method. The test result is obviously dependent on the number of fibers counted and on whether the fibers selected for counting are representative of the sample of pulp. This requires considerable experience, dependability and objectivity on the part of the microscopist. The results may be used to obtain a *number* average in which the fiber length is reported as the total length of all fibers counted divided by the number of fibers. It is generally agreed that this puts too much emphasis upon the shorter fibers, and a *weighted* average in which each fiber counts toward the average in proportion to its length is preferred.

TAPPI Method T233m-53 describes a *fiber classifier* for the separation of a sample of pulp into fractions according to length. A dilute dispersion of fiber in water is caused to move with high velocity parallel to the face of the screen while a much slower rate of flow passes through the screen. In this way the fibers are presented lengthwise to the screen and only those short enough not to bridge the mesh pass through to the next chamber. Suitable screen meshes are as follows:

Medium and long fibered pulps—14, 28, 48
Short fibered pulps—20, 28, 48, 100.

The operation of the classifier requires a careful and well-trained technician, but does not require the judgment and objectivity required in microscopic determination of fiber length.

In the formation of a paper sheet, water is drained through the forming mat or sheet of fibers. The resistance of the fibers to the flow of water is a fundamental property of pulp or stock furnish. The classical method of determining this property in North America is the *Canadian Standard Freeness* Tester and Method described as Canadian Pulp and Paper Association Official Testing Method C.I. and TAPPI Standard Method T227m-58.

A suspension of 3 grams of thoroughly defibered pulp in 1,000 ml of water is placed in a bronze cylinder having a capacity slightly greater than 1,000 ml and provided with a tight fitting hinged lid with stopcock and a screen plate perforated with .020-inch holes spaced 625 per sq inch at the bottom. Mounted below the cylinder is a rate-measuring conical funnel provided with a bottom orifice 0.120 inch in diameter and with a side orifice tube of 0.50 inch diameter projecting into the funnel and at standard height above the bottom orifice.

As the cylinder containing the sample is opened, water flows through the screen plate into the funnel while a mat of fiber forms on the plate. The more rapid the flow of water, the greater is the proportion which emerges from the side orifice of the funnel. The number of milliliters emerging from the side orifice is the *freeness*.

Full chemical pulps from softwoods and in the unbeaten state have a high freeness of 700 ml or more. Hardwood and semi-chemical pulps are considerably lower in freeness. Groundwood pulps have the lowest freeness of all, being in the range of 50 to 200. Freeness is especially important as a measure of the *beating* or *refining* that a pulp has undergone. Full chemical pulps may be reduced in freeness from about 700 to around 500 with a moderate amount of beating. With continued beating in the laboratory a value as low as 200 may be reached. Values of freeness attained by laboratory beating of pulps cannot be directly compared with values obtained in a mill stock preparation system because the recirculation of fines in the latter results in considerably lower freeness values with roughly equivalent degrees of refining.

Despite its widespread use, serious objections have been raised to the validity of the freeness test for indicating stock strength and drainage properties. In particular, J. d'A. Clark [7] has pointed out that the freeness test is unduly influenced by the presence of fiber debris. For this reason, groundwood pulp gives a lower freeness than highly beaten full chemical pulp, but shows faster drainage on the paper machine. Also, the addition of "white water" to stock has an effect upon the freeness test out of proportion to its effect on other paper-making properties. For these reasons, Clark proposes, in place of the freeness test, that stock be evaluated by a combination of procedures as follows:

(1) Ratio of long fibers to fines as determined in a fiber classifier,

(2) Drainage time (or factor) in accordance with TAPPI Standard T221-m.

(3) Percentage of shrinkage of sheet during unrestrained drying,

(4) Burst factor of sheets (TAPPI Standard T220-m).

Testing of Pulp Handsheets

The most important question about pulp is: What kind of paper does it make? The best answer to that question that has become available so far is a miniature paper-making operation in which every step of the process is made as controlled and as reproducible as possible. The laboratory procedures leading to this answer consist of three general steps: (1) a beater or refiner capable of treating a small sample of pulp, e.g., from 60 grams up to 5 pounds, in a manner that is reproducible over a period of time, (2) an apparatus for forming, pressing and drying individual paper sheets, again under reproducible conditions, and (3) physical tests to be performed on the handsheets that give the required information concerning sheet properties. Pulp and paper laboratories all over the world have devised various methods for accomplishing these steps. There is no doubt that a variety of equipment and methods is in use for this purpose. The present discussion must be limited to the more common, widely accepted methods.

For the laboratory beating of pulp, TAPPI recognizes three types of equipment. The ball mill (T224m-45) uses porcelain-lined crocks 10.5 to 10.7 inches in diameter and 13.0 to 13.5 inches deep charged with 90 to 110 porcelain balls 1.25 inches in diameter. A sample of pulp previously disinte-

grated and having a consistency of 4.3% and a volume of 2.1 liters is charged into each crock. Thus, each charge is 90 grams air dry. The first crock is rotated at 60 rpm for 20 minutes or 1,200 revolutions. Subsequent charges are rotated for 3,600, 4,800 and 6,000 revolutions respectively.

At the completion of the beating period the contents of each crock are dumped into a bucket, the balls removed, the fiber diluted to 1% consistency and enough pulp withdrawn to prepare sets of test sheets.

The beater method (T200m-60) makes use of a miniature Hollander type beater in which the dimensions of the apparatus, the pressure between roll and bedplate, speed of the roll and method of grinding in the roll and bedplate are specified. The test sample consisting of 360 grams of moisture-free pulp is disintegrated in 10 liters of water and diluted in the beater to 23 liters or 1.57% consistency. After a few minutes circulation, the pressure is applied to the bedplate. A series of beating intervals is chosen which may extend from 5 to 90 minutes depending upon the type of pulp. Samples are withdrawn from the beater at the selected intervals for making handsheets as described below.

The Kollergang Method (T225m-60) utilizes a ring-shaped trough with sloping sides. In the valley so formed, three rollers revolve producing a rolling action upon the fibers of the pulp slurry. Dimension, pressure of rollers and speed are specified in the standard instrument. The charge consists of 75 grams of moisture-free pulp thoroughly disintegrated in 2,500 ml of water. The standard beating periods are 1, 2, 4, 8, 16, 32, 64, 128 revolutions per gram of pulp (rpg). At the end of each beating period, 250 ml of stock (7.5 grams dry weight) are withdrawn for preparation of handsheets. It is reported that beating in the average mill is about 2 to 4 rpg for book papers, 4 to 8 rpg for writings, 8 to 16 rpg for wrappings, about 32 for semi-glassine and over 64 for glassine.

The laboratory processing of pulp is one

aspect of wet mechanical processing of fiber that plays an essential role in paper making and which has occupied much attention from students of paper-making technology. More complete description of the theory of beating is found in Chapter 11. Laboratory beating for making test sheets is more concerned with reproducibility of results than with exhibiting the full range of mechanical action or with duplicating mill equipment. Its usefulness is primarily to show the relative rate of response of a pulp to the beating process, the maximum strength that is developed, and the relationships that prevail among such tests as tensile, tear, burst, density, etc. The laboratory processing of pulp is frequently used to evaluate chemical additives such as bonding and sizing agents, dyes and fillers.

Forming and Testing of Handsheets. Numerous types of handsheet-making apparatus have been devised. Many of these are performing useful service in the pulp and paper laboratories of the world. TAPPI Method T205m-58 describes the apparatus and procedure known as the British Standard. The mold forms a circular sheet 6½ inches in diameter using deckle box consisting of a cylinder 15.75 inches high. The height of the cylinder is such that the sheets are formed from stock of relatively low consistency. The sheets are formed on a 150 mesh wire mounted on a grid plate. The sheets are couched from the wire by means of paper blotters pressed under specified conditions with stainless steel plates in contact with the wet sheet on the opposite side from the couching blotter. In the pressing operation the sheet is transferred from the blotter to the plate. Sheets and plates are mounted in drying rings which prevent shrinkage of the sheets during the drying process. Drying is normally accomplished by means of a current of air of standard conditions of humidity and temperature. The physical testing of the sheets is described in T220m-60. Standard paper testing methods and instruments are used as described in Chapter 14.

RAG PAPER MAKING *

Ever since paper making was invented by the Chinese, before the dawn of the Christian era, rags have been used. Up until 1860, rag fibers (cotton and linen) were the sole sources of paper-making materials and all papers, even newsprint, were made from 100% rag.

It is indeed fortunate that about that time the various pulping processes were invented, since the paper industry was being kept from further growth due to shortages of fibrous raw materials. Even now, when the rag content portion of the industry is such a small percentage of the total, the industry is finding difficulty in procuring sufficient rags to meet its strict requirements.

That the rag content industry—or, as it is sometimes called, the cotton fiber paper industry—is still an important portion of the paper industry is evidenced by production figures, which indicate that for the past few years, production of rag content papers have averaged about 120,000 tons. This, of course, includes papers containing from 25 to 100% rag content.

The term "rag" has come to include such materials as cotton or linen threads, flax and hemp, raw cotton and other textile wastes, and cotton linters, as well as rags. Most of the rags used by the rag content industry are new cotton clippings which come from various textile mills and garment factories. They are generally collected by rag dealers who may take the entire waste collection of a great many factories. They then sort these materials into several standard grades which have been set up by waste dealers and approved by the mills. Some of the more important grades are:

> No. 1 unbleached muslins
> No. 1 white shirt cuttings
> No. 1 bleached underwear cuttings
> No. 1 bleached canton flannel cuttings
> No. 1 bleached shoe cuttings

(*Cont'd on page 34*)

* L. B. Tucker, Technical Director, Crane and Co.

No. 1 blue denims
No. 1 percales
No. 1 light prints
Sun tan khaki cuttings
Fancy shirt cuttings

In all, there are about 80 well-defined grades of rags which are regularly collected and sold to the mills. In sorting and packing them for the paper industry, a reliable rag dealer tries to eliminate such materials as rubber, metal, wool, and the various types of synthetic materials.

New rags are divided into two main classes: white or unbleached, and colored. Of course, the white or unbleached are more expensive, since colored rags are more difficult to process and cannot be used in all grades of paper. Generally speaking, a higher-grade paper can be produced from white or unbleached rags than from colored rags since the cooking and bleaching conditions are much less drastic. The price of rags is subject to wide fluctuations due to supply and demand and the cost of the better grades has varied from 10 to 22¢ per pound during the last ten years. Formerly, used or old rags were used to a considerable extent in the rag paper industry, but due to their dirtiness and low strength they are now mainly used in roofing felt mills.

One thing to keep in mind is that rag fiber and wood pulp and, therefore, the papers made from them, are not competitive in price. The cost of rag fiber ready for the beater is substantially higher than the cost of wood pulp. Besides this greater original cost, rag fibers need to be beaten longer and rag papers are produced at slower speeds, thus widening the gap between the two papers.

The following desirable qualities which rag papers should possess are as follows:

Maximum strength
Maximum durability
Maximum permanence
Fine formation, color, texture and feel
Excellent writing and erasure qualities.

Due to these outstanding characteristics, rag papers are used extensively for the following purposes:

(1) Banknote and security papers.

(2) Life insurance policies and legal documents where permanence is of prime importance.

(3) Technical papers, such as tracing paper, vellums, intermediate, blue print and other reproduction papers.

(4) High-grade bond letterheads for concerns where appearance is of great importance, such as banks, law firms, etc.

(5) For light-weight specialties such as cigarette, carbon and bible papers.

(6) High-grade stationery paper where beauty, softness and fine texture are demanded.

It should be mentioned that rag papers cover a considerable spread of products, from 100% rag to the so-called rag content papers which are made from various percentages of wood fiber and rag fiber, generally 25, 50 and 75% rag. The 100% rag papers should have the exceptional qualities listed above and as the rag content is reduced, the paper possesses these properties to a lesser degree.

The following set of specifications, tabulated from Federal Specifications UUP121j, indicates what can be expected from the various rag content papers.

Since the 100% rag paper is purchased for permanent records, the specifications are quite stringent.

The present raw material supply for the rag paper industry leaves much to be desired. Not only is there a shortage of the more desirable grades, but the rags of all grades are becoming more and more contaminated with foreign material. Rubber and wood have always been sources of trouble, and the amount of rubber used in cotton fabrics seems to be increasing in such materials as underwear cuttings, bandages, tire cords, and waterproof materials. The great increase in the use of synthetic materials is making textile wastes less and less desirable. Some of these synthetics like rayon are not

PAPER, BOND AND WRITING—SUBSTANCE 20

	Type I, 100% New Rag	Type II, 50% Rag	Type III, 25% Rag	Type IV, 100% Chemical Wood Pulp
Double folds, each direction				
Schopper	1000	150	100	65
M.I.T.	800	120	100	40
Alpha-cellulose, not less than	95%	—	—	—
Copper number, not to exceed	1.0	—	—	—
Acidity, pH value not less than	5.0	4.8	4.7	4.4
Sizing				
Rosin, not to exceed	1.2%	2.0%	2.0%	2.5%
Tub	High grade animal glue	Starch	Starch	Starch

definitely objectionable, except that rayon is a poor paper-making material. Other synthetics, such as fused cellulose acetate, nylon, etc., may actually form undesirable specks which result in large percentages of rejected paper.

When the rags are received at the paper mill in bales weighing 400 to 1200 pounds, they are taken to the sorting room. They may first be mechanically threshed to open up the rags and remove dirt. Then they are sorted by hand to remove such foreign matter as rubber, metal, rags containing various synthetic fibers and finishes, paper and so on. It is sometimes necessary to cut the rags in order to reduce them to proper size for handling and inspection. Great care must be used in the sorting room, since, if the various foreign materials are not eliminated, the paper produced will probably be unsatisfactory.

After sorting, the rags are placed on conveyors and carried to cutters which reduce them to smaller sizes. The cutters slit the rags lengthwise and then cut them into short lengths with an action similar to a lawn mower. Often the rags pass from one cutter to another until reduced to the proper size.

From the cutters, the rags are carried to dusters and then to magnetic rolls which remove such metallic items as nails, paper clips and bottle caps.

The rags are now ready for cooking. This process is less drastic than in pulping wood since the rags are 85 to 95% cellulose. Certain materials must be removed, such as the natural waxes in the fiber, fillers, oil and starches added at the textile factories and the grease and dirt accumulated during handling.

The cooking is done in large cylindrical drums called bleach boilers (although no bleaching is done in them). The conventional rotary boiler is 8 feet in diameter and 25 feet in length with a capacity of 5 tons of rags. The boilers are set in a horizontal position and are supported on each end by trunnions resting on bearings. The rags are fed into manholes and it is often necessary for a man to be in the boiler to pack and distribute them properly.

After the boiler is loaded, the cooking liquor is added. This is normally a weak alkaline solution made up of either lime, a mixture of lime and soda ash, or caustic soda. In some cases, wetting agents and detergents are used. A volume of approximately 3 pounds of cooking liquor to 1 pound of rags is used. After the manholes have been covered, steam is admitted through the trunnions and pressure increased to approximately 35 psi. During the cooking process, the boiler revolves slowly at a rate of one-third revolution per minute. The rags are cooked from 3 to 10 hours, depending on the grade. The steam and liquor is then blown off, no attempt being made to recover the cooking liquor due to its low chemical content. The rags are rinsed with clean water before emptying. The manhole covers are then removed and the rags which do not fall out into carts while the boiler is rotated are pulled out with potato hooks.

The recent tendency for paper mills installing new boilers is to change to spherical boilers. The advantages of this type are easier loading and unloading, greater capacity, and greater strength which allows the use of higher cooking pressures.

After cooking, the rags are washed in what are essentially Hollander beaters equipped with washing cylinders—octagonal drums which revolve on the surface of the stock in the washer. The faces of the drums are covered with fine-mesh wire or punched brass plates. Water passes through the mesh of the wire and as the drum revolves, the water is lifted up and discharged through the side of the drum to the sewer. A washing cylinder can remove water at a rate of 80 to 200 gallons per minute.

The rags are dumped into the washer as water is being added. The roll is lifted well away from the plate and as the stock circulates, water is added as rapidly as the washing cylinder will remove it. If an effort were made to break up the rags at this time, the dirt would be ground into them and the washing would be inefficient. The quality of water used is most important since it must be clean and free from iron and coloring material.

After one to two hours, when the rags are quite clean, the washerman starts lowering the roll so as to break the rags up into fibers. This is an important procedure since often the type of paper produced depends to a considerable extent on the fiber length of the half stock.

When the stock is of proper length and clean, the washing water is turned off and the stock is ready for bleaching. In the case of white or unbleached rags, the bleaching operation is simple, requiring the addition of as low as .05% chlorine in the form of calcium or sodium hypochlorite. The bleaching action, which is carried on at a pH of 8.0-9.0, is completed in 1 to 2 hours; the entire washing and bleaching process generally takes 4 to 8 hours. A normal washer will hold 1000 to 1500 pounds of rags at a consistency of 3 to 5%.

After bleaching, the stock is emptied into small basement rooms, called drainers, which have porous tile bottoms. The water gradually seeps away leaving the so-called half stock on the tile floor. Several washers are normally emptied to a drainer and after a period of several days, the stock is ready to be dug out and furnished to the beaters. Recently, several mills have eliminated the drainer and run the bleached half stock over a wet lap machine.

There are several chemical control tests which can be used to determine the kind of stock produced, such as alpha-cellulose, copper number, ash, and viscosity. The ash determination indicates the efficiency of the washing. Copper number is a test for determining how much the cellulose has been degraded. A high copper number indicates overbleaching. This type of stock should not be used in permanent record papers because this degradation will continue even in the finished sheet. Cuprammonium or cupriethylene diamine viscosity determinations are probably the most valuable test for indicating whether the stock has been injured during the cooking and bleaching process, and to what degree. The range of cuprammonium viscosities is very wide, varying from stock as low as 10 in the case of old or overbleached stock to a high of 300 for a lightly bleached stock made from new rags. By means of this test, changes in cooking and bleaching procedures can readily be followed.

Since a customer pays a premium price for rag papers, the preparation of rag stock should be carried out with great care. Cooking and bleaching chemicals should be kept to a minimum and carefully checked.

If a paper is to be made for maximum strength, durability and permanence, new white or unbleached rags should be used. From these rags, if properly processed, very high-grade half stock can be prepared. However, as the name half stock indicates, the fiber is only half way from rags to paper. The second part of the process must also be carefully carried out. The half stock should be carefully beaten to develop the desired strength. Sizing materials such as rosin and alum must be kept low, since excess rosin causes discoloration and excess alum causes low pH which leads to embrittlement of the paper and lack of permanence. The paper should be run on the machine at a speed at which a well formed sheet can be produced. The paper is then normally tubsized and redried.

PAPER STOCK *

Definitions

The term "waste paper" has gained general use over the years. Nevertheless, it has been frequently pointed out that its appropriateness is limited. To the manufacturer who uses paper or paperboard as raw material and has trim or spoiled material to dispose of, "waste" accurately describes the material. To the paper or board manufacturer that uses it in the production of new products, it is not waste but rather raw material. Therefore, the Paper Stock Institute of America has adopted certain terms and definitions. "Waste paper" is taken to mean the material as it is produced, but not necessarily in salable condition. The term "paper stock" has been adopted to apply to the products after it has been cleaned, sorted and baled ready for the market. The Waste Paper Utilization Council has adopted this nomenclature also.

Statistics

In 1960, the paper industry in the United States consumed 9,021,000 tons of all grades of paper stock as raw material. This amounted to 25.3% of total fibrous raw material. It was 23.1% of the total paper and paperboard consumed. For the most part, the volume of paper stock is determined by

* Ralph K. Kumler, Formerly Director, Waste Paper Utilization Council.

demand rather than by supply. In 1944, when a shortage of virgin pulp developed due to war conditions, 35.5% of all paper and board consumed was reclaimed as paper stock. Had this rate of collection prevailed in 1960, 13,800,000 tons would have been used, and there is little doubt that such a quantity could have been made available if there had been such a demand. In periods of tight demand, prices are usually high, permitting collectors to go further afield and gather from small sources that cannot be serviced economically in a depressed market. However, the development of new sources requires time and educational work. Sudden increases (or decreases) in paper stock requirements create problems for the dealers.

Grades and Sources

The Paper Stock Institute of America has defined 42 grades of paper stock with broad specifications for each. This is set forth in Bulletin PS-61, obtainable from the National Association of Secondary Materials Industries. Actually, there are more grades than this shipped commercially, as many mills request special packs. However, all these grades may be grouped into four main categories: high grades, old corrugated boxes, printed news and mixed paper. These are listed in order of price from the highest to the lowest. Each group comprises a number of grades. For instance, high grades include envelope cuttings, hard white shavings, soft white shavings, white and colored ledger, tabulating cards, book and magazine stock, unprinted news, and trim from practically all grades of paper or board except those containing the three lowest grades of paper stock. Corrugated waste is classified as to whether the corrugated portion consists of chemical kraft or semichemical pulp. Printed news is graded on the basis of cleanliness and the presence or absence of colored inks, such as those used to print comic sections. Mixed papers vary widely in composition and consist of mixtures of various kinds of paper and board that cannot be economically segregated into well defined grades.

High grades and corrugated come mainly from mercantile and industrial establishments. White paper wastes arise in envelop and printing plants, while tabulating cards are supplied by offices of the larger companies. Much magazine stock comes from newsstand returns, but some comes from homes. Corrugated waste is supplied by manufacturing plants and retail stores that purchase materials in corrugated containers. Printed news is derived partly from newsstand returns, but much also is supplied by homes through church, school and Boy Scout organizations, the Salvation Army and other charitable institutions. Mixed paper is largely derived from the contents of waste baskets in office buildings.

Preparation for Market

The procedure for getting waste paper from the generator to the consumer in acceptable form varies considerably according to the type of waste, quantity produced at a given point, and the business policy of the generator and the packer. The smaller industrial producers collect the waste in burlap bags or carts. It may or may not be segregated into grades. The packer hauls it in trucks to his warehouse sorting plant where the paper is gone over carefully, separated into grades and unwanted materials eliminated. He then bales the paper and ships it to his customers.

Some of the larger industrial plants have their own baling equipment. In such cases the paper may be graded, baled and shipped to the consumer directly, but usually through the agency of a broker.

Few waste paper generators have extensive storage capacity and the paper must be removed as it accumulates. The paper mills must have paper stock as needed. Shortages at some points and surpluses at others are relieved by considerable transferring of stock from one dealer to another. The industry acts as a kind of surge pool that absorbs waste as it is produced and,

yet, assures the consumer of a steady supply. Because of this service rendered by the Paper Stock Industry, sales made by the generator directly to the paper mill are rare, except where there is some ownership connection between the two.

Use of Paper Stock

Paper stock is delivered to the paper mill in bales weighing up to a ton each, although newspapers are sometimes shipped in small bundles. Procedures at the mills vary widely. Mills making high-grade products usually open the bales, spread the paper on a sorting belt and carefully remove any materials that would give trouble in the paper-making process. In other cases only a superficial inspection is made and some of the mills merely cut the bale ties and dump everything into the pulper. The bale ties are removed mechanically.

Deinking. Most paper stock is used without chemical treatment or any attempt to remove printing or writing ink that is present. About 5 to 6% of total waste paper consumed is deinked. The deinking process will be only summarized here as a detailed discussion on deinking is given in TAPPI Monograph #16, "The Deinking of Waste Paper." Figure 2.13 shows a flow diagram of the deinking process.

The bales are opened, inspected and fed into a pulper of one of various designs. Various deinking chemicals are added and the stock is heated to a temperature somewhere between 150° and 190°F. Agitation is continued, which serves to rub off ink and to separate the fibers. It is important that the agitation be not excessively violent so that pieces of cellophane or other film are not broken into fine pieces. If they are left as nearly intact as possible, they can later be removed by screening. The dwell time with chemicals present varies, but is usually about one hour.

The amount and type of chemicals used vary considerably from mill to mill. Caustic soda is by far the most generally used, but is sometimes supplemented with soda ash,

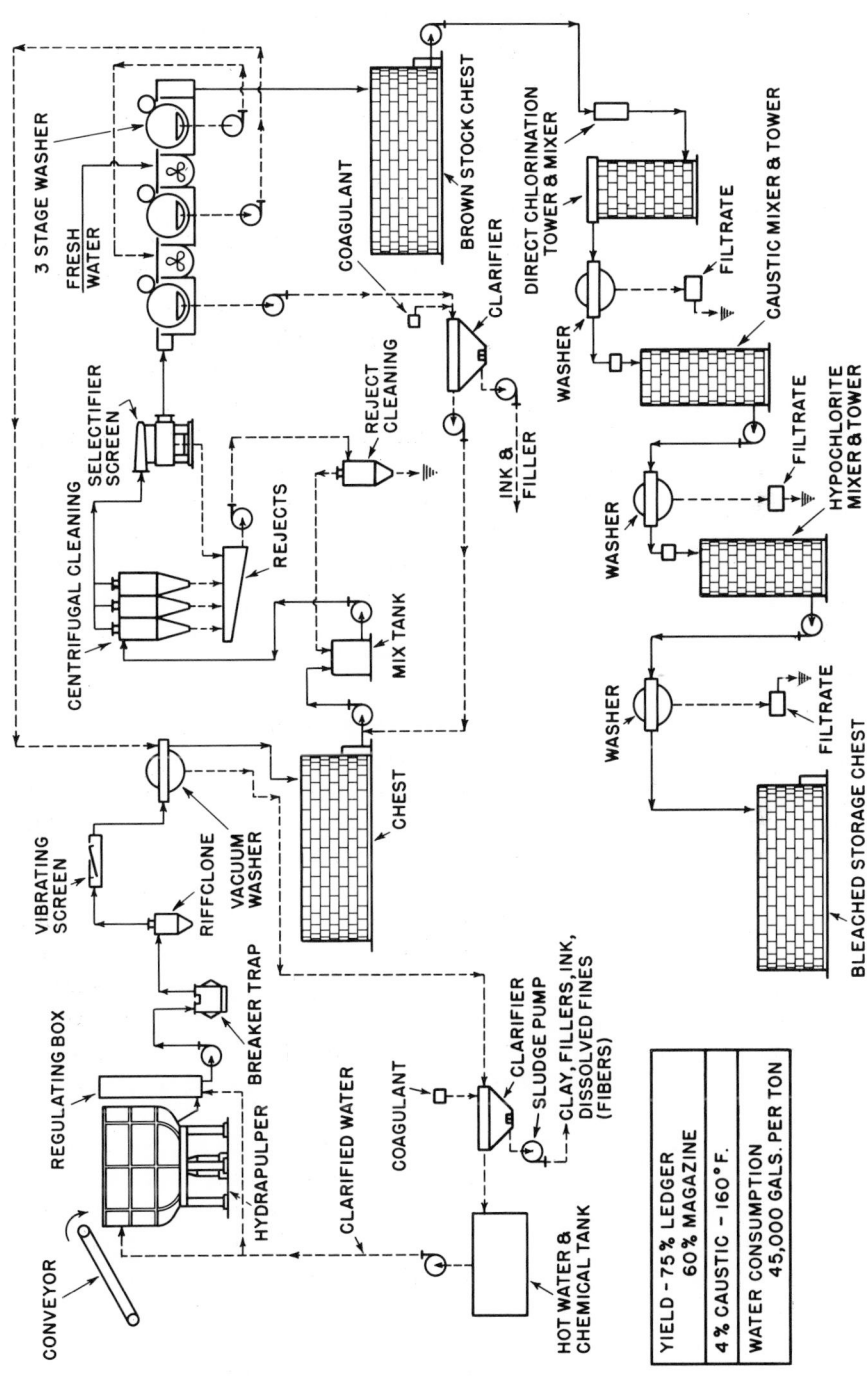

Fig. 2.13. Deinking modern ledger-kraft and sulfites–magazine–coated paper.

silicate of soda, sodium peroxide, one or another of the sodium phosphate compounds, or one of several surfactants. The choice of chemical formula depends on the type of stock being handled, the equipment employed, local water conditions and the thoroughness of ink removal required. Caustic soda can be used alone where inks containing drying oils predominate, as the alkali combines with the fatty acids in the oils to form soaps that assist in suspending the pigments.

The older processes included cooking in a stationary digester. The liquor was circulated, but not the paper. The belief was widely held that the ink should be loosened and freed from the paper before fiber separation was accomplished in order to facilitate removal of ink pigments. This thinking appears to have been largely abandoned because in most deinking plants cooking and pulping are carried out simultaneously. In a few cases, a considerable dwell time is allowed with chemicals present, while maintaining an elevated temperature before fiber separation is completed.

In most cases the first step following cooking is the removal of coarse foreign material, such as paper clips, staples and other metallic objects. It is important that this be done early in the process in order to protect from damage equipment that is used in subsequent stages. Some pulpers are provided with junk removers which are based on the tendency of metal pieces to settle into a trough from which they are removed at intervals by means of a conveyor.

Another device for the early removal of heavy foreign material is the riffler box. This consists of a trough fitted with dams or baffles. The cooked and defibered stock is caused to flow through the trough at low consistency and heavy material collects in the comparatively quiescent pools behind the dams. Periodical cleaning is, of course, necessary.

Some mill managers prefer coarse screens to rifflers or may use both. The screen plates are perforated with rather large holes, $\frac{1}{8}$

to $\frac{3}{16}$ inch, and are made to vibrate at high frequency and low amplitude. The acceptable stock passes through while pieces of plastic film, cloth, metal pieces and other foreign material are rejected, unless in finely divided condition. At this stage occasional pieces of wet-strength paper that failed to break up completely in the cooking are eliminated.

The next step is washing, usually carried out by means of cylindrical washers in series or by side hill washers. This removes the materials that were set free from the fibers by the cooking process, such as ink vehicles and pigments, as well as loading materials such as clay and other pigments. To remove fine dirt, washing is followed by treatment with one or more types of cleaning equipment: (1) flat screens, (2) rotary screens, (3) centrifugal screens, or (4) cyclone cleaners.

Bleaching

Usually, but not invariably, bleaching follows cooking and washing. In most cases this is accomplished by treating with 2 to 5% available chlorine as sodium or calcium hypochlorite. Temperature is maintained between 80° and 120°F. If not more than 10% groundwood and no unbleached kraft pulp is present, this gives a fairly bright pulp. When the hypochlorite is exhausted, or nearly so, the pulp is washed to remove bleach residues. Residual bleach may interfere with sizing and coloring in the subsequent paper making operation.

If considerable groundwood or unbleached kraft is present in the paper stock, bleaching is usually begun with elemental chlorine. A typical procedure includes the following steps: (1) chlorine treatment, (2) washing, (3) treatment with caustic soda, (4) washing, (5) treatment with calcium or sodium hypochlorite, (6) washing. If unbleached kraft is being processed, two chlorination stages may be used, each followed by washing and alkali extraction.

After bleaching, the stock goes through whatever refining is necessary before being delivered to the paper machine. In most cases, the deinked stock is blended with some virgin pulp.

Non-Deinking Use

By far the larger tonnage of paper stock is consumed with no attempt to remove ink or lighten the color. In 1958, paperboard mills used 76% of the total paper stock consumed in the United States. Some of this was in the form of unprinted waste which served as a direct substitute for pulp. The lower grades were largely used in the inner or back plies of cylinder board where color is of secondary importance.

However, cleanliness is an object in practically all grades. Purchasers of paper and board products have steadily become less tolerant of dirt specks. Consequently, cleaning is a most important step in the use of paper stock, whether or not it is deinked.

As in deinking, pulping is the first step in preparing paper stock in non-deinking mills. This is accomplished in one of the various types of pulpers which operate on the principle of violent agitation and shearing action within the mass of disintegrating paper. Hot water at temperatures ranging from 140° to 170°F. is generally employed, but in a few cases the process is carried out at room temperature. Pulping is sometimes completed in a machine called a "breaker trap." It consists of a cylinder with parallel bars imbedded in its surface revolving in a shell lined with a similar bar structure. The clearance between cylinder and shell is close, but there is no metal-to-metal contact. This completes fiber separation, but does not grind up pieces of plastic or cellophane film. Provision is made to remove metal before the stock reaches the working area.

Cleaning follows the pulping stage, and the arrangements for doing this vary considerably. Where paper stock is being processed, the first step is generally coarse screening as mentioned above. A riffler may also be used to remove sand, small metal pieces and other heavy dirt.

Before fine screening is carried out, it is common to refine the stock. Since it has already been processed to make the original paper or board, less refining is required than if virgin pulp were being used. However, additional refining provides means of controlling freeness and maintaining uniform characteristics of the pulp. Refining is done in jordans or equivalent equipment. (See Chapter 11.)

For removing fine dirt, various types of equipment are used, such as flat screens, rotary screens, centrifugal screens, and cyclone type, pressure-drop cleaners. Since the types of dirt found in paper stock is of such great variety, more types of cleaning equipment are required than when virgin pulp is being processed.

End Uses of Paper Stock

It is estimated that approximately half the paper and paperboard mills in the United States use some paper stock. In some products, such as chip board, it is the sole fibrous raw material and in folding boxboards it may constitute as much as 90% of the furnish. Some papers are made wholly of deinked stock. In other cases, paper stock is used in minor proportions with virgin pulp.

The U.S. Bureau of Census gives the following paper stock consumption figures of various paper and board products for 1958:

	Tons
Groundwood paper, uncoated	47,163
Paper, machine-coated	56,187
Book paper, uncoated	424,715
Fine paper	103,299
Special industrial paper	145,856
Container board	1,809,331
Special food board	168,221
Folding and other board	2,520,199
Nonbending, special paperboard, cardboard and wet machine board	1,970,115
Construction paper	780,378
Hardboard and insulating board	231,321

Paper stock was also used in newsprint, coarse paper and sanitary and other tissue, but figures were not given to avoid disclosure of confidential information. In 1954 the tissue mills consumed 252,234 tons.

A few comments can be made regarding the grades of paper stock used in manufacturing the above products. Book and fine papers take the bulk of deinked stock. Deinkers use mostly ledger (white or colored) tabulation card and magazine stocks. Folding boxboard mills consume large amounts of white unprinted high grades such as white envelope cuttings and hard and soft white shavings. Construction paper and container board mills use large amounts of old corrugated containers and corrugated clippings. Mixed paper finds large uses in roofing paper, chip boards and wet machine boards. News grades of paper stock are used widely in various types of cylinder boards.

Clause [8] has presented the advantages of using deinked paper pulp rather than virgin pulp.

(1) It is low in cost.

(2) It imparts a high degree of opacity.

(3) Little or no beating is required.

(4) Fibers are already blended to suit many furnishes.

(5) Brightness can be better controlled than with virgin pulp.

Other points which seem to be valid, but are debatable:

(6) Better bonding, less fuzz,

(7) Less moisture sensitivity,

(8) Less tendency of finished paper to curl.

Doane [9] comments further on the subject of the moisture sensitivity of paper made from deinked stock. Fibers that have been previously dried one or more times do not imbibe water as readily as fibers in slush pulp coming directly from the pulp mill. This explains superficially, at least, why more dimensionally stable paper can be made from paper stock than from slush pulp, whether or not it is deinked.

Prokupek [9] has studied the pros and cons of the use of high grade paper versus pulp in the manufacture of boxboard. Advantages of paper stock are:

(1) Lower fiber cost

(2) Lower cost for chemicals

(3) Less power consumption

(5) Improved formation.

Disadvantages are:

(1) Non-uniformity of color

(2) Non-uniformity of strength

(3) Troubles with contaminants

(4) Higher handling and storage costs.

McKee [9] has made laboratory studies on the effect of beating virgin kraft of 350 cc freeness (Canadian Standard) and repeatedly forming it into a sheet, drying and repulping it. Six repulping cycles were thus completed, each time refining the pulp to the original freeness. On testing the sheets from each cycle, decreases were noted in bursting, tensile and bonding strengths. Tearing strength increased but zero span tensile (individual fiber strength) was little changed. The bonded area remained almost constant, but the degree of swelling of the fibers fell markedly from the first to the last cycle. McKee concludes that the losses in tensile and bursting strength are due to weaker bonds, occasioned by less swelling of the fibers in water. This checks with the findings noted above in connection with the loss of sensitivity to water of fibers that have been repeatedly dried.

The Problems

The use of paper stock in the paper mill is not without its difficulties due mainly to the presence of foreign materials. Miscellaneous trash has always required operators to be on guard, and its presence depends on the source of the waste and the care with which it is prepared for market. Some packs are completely free of it.

In recent years converters of paper and paperboard have adopted the use of new materials combined with paper to enable their products to perform functions that paper or board alone would not serve. This has broadened the market for paper, but it has posed new problems for the user of paper stock. The most common items are asphalt, synthetic adhesives, metal foils, plastic and cellulose derivative films and certain printing inks.

Some objectionable materials can be sorted from waste paper, and packers generally try to remove them completely. However, some items are difficult to detect, especially by a person who has no advance notice of what to expect. The producer of waste paper, knowing the materials he is using, can segregate trouble-causing substances at the source. Much depends on good cooperation and communication among the papermaker, dealer, packer and producers in order that all may understand what is acceptable and what is not.

Adhesives. Adhesives made from water-soluble materials such as glue and starch products present no serious problems in paper stock use. In recent years, it has become more and more common to use adhesives made from synthetic resins. Most of these are insoluble in water, but some are dispersible in alkali. Those containing rubber, natural or synthetic are not dispersible in either water or alkali and have created the most serious problems for the paper stock user. It is reliably reported that two pounds of rubbery adhesive will destroy the value of 100 tons of paper stock, which is undoubtedly true where high-grade products are being manufactured. It is therefore imperative that such materials be eliminated at the source or that the paper stock dealers take care to ship the stock to a mill that can accept it.

Plastic Film. Plastic and cellulose-derivative films are generally shunned by papermakers. However, in certain cases the fibers can be reclaimed from papers or board laminated to plastic film. If the film is sufficiently tough, the fibers can be separated from it while the film remains essentially intact, and it may be later screened out. A brittle or fragile film breaks into small pieces that pass through screens that produce specks and spots in the finished product. Polyethylene film can be separated from fibers by mills that possess the proper equipment.

Foils. Nearly all foils combined with paper and board are of aluminum. Since it is soluble in caustic soda, limited amounts can be tolerated by deinking mills. Non-deinking mills find any foil difficult to remove completely.

Asphalt. With conventional stock preparation equipment asphalt present in paper stock appears as black specks in the finished paper which is ruinous to most paper or board products. Equipment has now been developed whereby stock is treated at high temperature under steam pressure. This disperses the asphalt so that it does not appear in the finished product other than to cause a darkening which is slight if the amount of asphalt is small. Many mills lack this equipment and to them asphalt is most objectionable.

Printing Inks. To mills that do not deink, the only requirement of the ink is that it must break up finely enough to produce no visible specks in the finished product. Some ink vehicles are film formers and remain in visible pieces. Examples are inks containing rubber or chlorinated rubber as the bonding agent for the pigments. For the deinking mill, the ink must be dispersible in alkali and subsequently washable.

Wet-Strength Papers. Papers that have been treated in the course of manufacture to render them strong after being wetted are sometimes found in paper stocks. The resins used to produce this effect are of two different types: amino-aldehyde resins and polyamide resins. Papers made with either type of resin can be reclaimed rather easily if their presence and the type of resin are known in advance. In the case of the aldehyde wet-strength resins, strong agitation at high temperature and low pH is required. Where polyamide resin has been used, high pH and moderately high temperatures give best results. In either case, the mill must be prepared to provide the proper conditions.

NATURAL PAPER-MAKING FIBERS OTHER THAN WOOD

It has been noted that cellulose fiber is a major constituent of the stems of all vascular plants. Hence, a vast number of plants represent potential sources of paper fiber, and many of these have been pulped experimentally. A rather substantial number of plant sources have even been used commercially, at least on a small scale, and at various times and places. In fact, the use of cereal straws for paper making antedates the use of wood pulp and is widely practiced today throughout the world, although on a relatively small scale of production. For reasons already cited, the development of the paper industry in many parts of the world appears to depend to a considerable degree upon the use of annual plants and of agricultural fibers.

Cellulose in nature (with the exception of cotton seed hairs) occurs intimately associated with other materials, particularly lignin, hemicellulose, pentosans and pectin. The non-woody plant stems differ from wood in containing less total cellulose, less alpha-cellulose, less lignin, more pentosans and hence, more hemicellulose. The composition of a number of grasses and dicotyledons have been reported [10] as ranging from about 47% to about 58% total cellulose and about 30% to about 38% alpha-cellulose. Lignin averages about 17% and pentosans range from about 18 to 30%. The chemical composition of these annual plants means this: pulps of a high degree of purity will be produced in relatively low yield, while pulps produced in high yield will contain high proportions of pentosan and hemicellulose and papers made therefrom will tend to be dense, stiff and of low tear.

The morphology of the cells of annual plants also differs considerably from wood. Whereas the nonfibrous cells in coniferous wood comprise a minor proportion of the wood substance, in annual plants nonfibrous parenchyma cells usually comprise a substantial proportion of the plant substance. Since hardwoods also contain a considerable quantity of nonfibrous cells, there is a closer resemblance between hardwood pulps and pulps from annual plants. Fibers from non-wood plants show a wide range in both length and diameter.

The preferred pulping reagents for nonwood plants are the alkalies: caustic soda, lime and soda ash, and kraft liquor (caustic soda and sodium sulfide). A characteristic of the pulping of annual plants compared with wood, is the milder treatment necessary to produce pulp. For example, straw may be pulped with milk of lime, $Ca(OH)_2$, in a spherical rotary digester with 25 pounds steam pressure and a total cooking time of 8 to 10 hours. The amount of lime used is about 10% as CaO based on dry weight of straw. The modern trend, however, is to use caustic soda or sodium sulfite.

Recently, there has been a trend toward continuous pulping of straws, reeds and grasses. Semicommercial equipment using the Pandia system of continuous cooking is described in a recent article.[11] Data obtained with the above equipment, using various materials, and illustrating rapid pulping, is shown in Table 2.2.

Cereal Straws

In the United States straw pulp is used mostly for corrugating board and hence is cooked to high yield, giving a dense, stiff, well-bonded sheet. It has been reported [12] that the total production of pulp from straws and grasses in the United States for 1959 was 600,000 tons, which represents a decline of about 30% since 1950. This decline in the production of straw pulp is attributed to its replacement by hardwood semichemical pulp for economic reasons.

The fibers of straw average 1.0 to 1.5 mm in length, which is about the same as hardwoods. It has been estimated [13] that sufficient rice straw is available in the United States to produce 1,680,000 tons of pulp or roughly 6% of the present total production of pulp. It has been found uneconomical to transport straw for pulping more than 30 to 35 miles and this factor, together with the problem of storage of a reasonable crop residue, has generally made straw uneconomical compared with wood pulp, even for those products in which the quality of straw pulp is satisfactory. Obviously, in

TABLE 2.2. CONDITIONS AND RESULTS FOR RAPID CONTINUOUS PULPING OF CERTAIN ANNUAL FIBROUS MATERIALS AND BAMBOO

		Pulping Conditions			Results	
Fibrous Material	Process	Na_2O [1] (per cent)	Time (minutes)	Pressure (psi)	Yield (per cent)	K No.
Wheat straw [2]	Soda	4.6	8	75	67	—
	Soda	10.0	8	80	50	—
Rice straw [2]	Soda	9.8	5.5	100	39	4.9
Bagasse [3]	Sulphate	12.0	10	130	52	7.5
Reeds [2]	Soda	13.8	20	130	48	15.0
Esparto	Soda	12.4	20	120	52	6.0
Napier grass [3]	Soda	15.0	30	150	44	15.0
Bamboo [4]	Sulphate	18.2	30	130	45	10.0
Cotton linters	Soda	5.6	18	100	75	2.7

[1] Chemical applied on dry, raw fiber basis.
[2] Uncleaned raw fiber used.
[3] Depithed or cleaned raw fiber used.
[4] *Bambusa arundinacea* from India.

those countries where wood supply is limited, straw pulp is, and will continue to be, of considerable importance.

Bagasse

The residue from the crushing of sugar cane contains about 65% fiber, 25% pith cells and 10% water-solubles and foreign material. An essential element in the conversion of bagasse to a satisfactory paper pulp is the mechanical removal of a substantial proportion of the pith (parenchyma) cells prior to the pulping operation.[14] Pulping may be carried out either with soda or with kraft cooking liquor and by batch or continuous digesting systems. Bagasse fiber averages 1.5 to 2.0 mm in length and the fibers are relatively fine as compared with wood pulp, i.e. they have a high ratio of length to diameter. As with other annual plants, bagasse contains a high proportion of hemicellulose and hence high-yield bagasse pulp produces dense, well-bonded sheets with low tearing strength. It has been estimated that 400,000 tons of bagasse pulp are produced by about 25 mills throughout the world.

Esparto

Esparto, *Stipa tenacissima* and *Lygeum spartum* is a desert plant growing wild in the Mediterranean area, especially in southern Spain and northern Africa. It is a perennial, rush-like plant attaining a height of 10 to 30 inches. Esparto has a higher content of total cellulose and of alpha-cellulose than most similar plants and has a greater uniformity of fiber size and shape. The use of esparto for paper-making pulp was introduced into Great Britain by Thomas Routledge in 1856. By 1862 the amount of esparto used was 9,534 tons, in 1890 190,000 tons, and in 1955 300,000 tons.[15]

The traditional method of pulping esparto uses cylindrical upright digesters with capacities of 2 to 5 tons of grass, with caustic soda as the cooking chemical in amounts of 12 to 17% of the grass, and a cooking time of 2 to 5 hours at a steam pressure of 30 to 60 psi. The pulp is readily bleached with single-stage hypochlorite. The modern trend in esparto cooking is the use of Kamyr or Pandia continuous digesters together with conventional three-stage bleaching.

Esparto has held its own against wood pulp competition because of possessing certain favorable qualities. Esparto stock is easy to form on the paper machine because of freer drainage and uniform fiber length as compared with rag or wood pulp. Esparto printing papers possess good resilience in contact with the printing plate, have good opacity and flatness and are relatively lint-free. Another important characteristic of papers made with esparto pulp is dimensional stability with respect to moisture changes.

Bamboo

Botanically, bamboo is classified as a grass even though it attains a considerable size and the stems or culms are hard and resistant to mechanical and chemical action. It was demonstrated many years ago by W. Raitt [16] that satisfactory pulp could be made from bamboo, using a two-stage kraft process. Commercial operation has been successfully conducted on a small scale based upon Raitt's pioneering efforts. The modern trend is the use of a single stage kraft process.

Because of the abundance of bamboo in Southeast Asia, where increased production of paper is greatly needed, much interest has been displayed in bamboo pulp development. The growing cycle of bamboo is favorable, permitting cutting in cycles of one to four years, and it probably represents the greatest production of cellulosic fiber from a given land area and in a given time of any of the paper-making plants. The principal problem is one of harvesting and transportation costs.[17] Another problem is that the high density of bamboo creates some difficulty in cooking liquor penetration. One of the biggest problems with bamboo pulping has been the preparation of the chips. Developments in chippers have helped solve this problem. The chipper being used in the newest mills is a horizontal feed chipper with crushing rolls situated on the feed conveyor.

The chemical composition of one species of bamboo, *Phyllostachys bambusoides*, has been reported as follows: [1]

	Per Cent
Total cellulose	58.1
Alpha-cellulose	34.8
Pentosans	28.5
Lignin	23.0

Bamboo fiber is considerably longer than most other perennial grasses and annual plants, often exceeding 3 mm in length, and therefore is comparable to coniferous wood pulp. The fibers are extraordinarily fine, showing a high length to width ratio. Consequently, a wide range of papers may be made from bamboo including those requiring high tearing strength. However, the bamboo fibers do not bond as well as softwood fibers, even after full processing, and papers made from 100% bamboo pulp tend to be low in bursting and tensile strengths.

Flax, Hemp, Jute

These plants are characterized by high proportion of long, flexible bast fibers which are readily separated and purified from other materials in the plant. In consequence, these fibers have long been used as textile and rope-making fiber. Most of this fiber reaching the paper industry in the past has been as secondary or waste fiber and has been highly prized because of the durability that can be imparted to paper by its use; for example, tags, abrasive papers, cover stock and other heavy-duty paper, as well as duplicating and manifold papers where extremely light weight must be combined with strength. Considerable quantities of flax are grown expressly for quality cigarette papers where a high degree of filler loading must be combined with tearing and tensile strength. The length of the flax fiber is favorable to this requirement.

SYNTHETIC FIBERS IN PAPER MAKING

The development and use of a great variety of man-made fibers has created a revolution in the textile industry in recent decades. It has been predicted that similar widespread use of synthetic fibers may eventually occur in the paper industry. Active interest in the use of synthetic fibers for paper making has been evident in recent years both on the part of fiber producers and by paper manufacturers.

The natural cellulosic fibers that constitute the greater proportion of paper-making raw material today are highly heterogeneous in size and shape. Hence, where uniformity in fiber dimensions is of importance, the choice among pulps from natural sources is considerably limited. The chemical composition offers even less choice, the fibers being basically cellulose with more or less of the natural "encrusting materials" present. These fibers present a problem in dimensional stability due to variation in moisture content with atmospheric conditions. Also, cellulosic fibers are not highly resistant to heat or to chemical action. In contrast, man-made fibers offer exactly controlled and uniform dimensions and relatively pure chemical composition. Thus, synthetic fibers offer such choices as chemical resistance, heat resistance, dielectric properties, dimensional stability, bacteriological resistance and many other properties not possible with cellulose. It is reasonable to expect that these advantages will result in the use of synthetic fibers in a number of paper products.

In considering synthetic fibers for paper making several factors come to mind. First is cost. The least expensive of the man-made fibers is regenerated cellulose (rayon) at approximately 30 cents per pound; from there the cost ranges to over $1 per pound for polyamides (nylon), polyesters ("Dacron," "Dynel"), acrylics ("Orlon," "Creslon," "Acrilan," etc.), and glass. Acetate rayon and polyethylene lie in the intermediate price range. In contrast, the cost of market wood pulp of paper-making grade ranges from about 4 cents to about 8 cents per pound. This difference in cost does not preclude the use of synthetics for paper, but it will certainly limit their use to special items in which the extra service rendered will justify the cost.

The second consideration is the problem of interfiber bonding upon which the strength of the finished sheet depends, as well as the "wet web strength" of the formed but undried sheet, and which greatly affects the operation of a paper machine. As pointed out previously, natural cellulose fibers have a "built in" ability to bond together, a property that synthetics normally do not have. Consequently, much research has been devoted to the problem of interfiber bonding of synthetics in the laboratories of the fiber producers and of certain paper manufacturers interested in this field. Their efforts have resulted in the publication of a number of methods to accomplish interfiber bonding with man-made fibers.

Bonding of Synthetic Fiber Papers

Interfiber bonding of synthetic fiber papers may be supplied by the addition of vinyl, polyamide, acrylic and similar latices. It has been found that the development of strength comparable to cellulose papers requires the addition of from 20 to 40% of the synthetic binder. Such quantities of binder are not satisfactorily retained by beater addition and hence an impregnation step after sheet formation is commonly required. The latex bonding method does not supply a desirable level of wet web strength for paper machine operation. Lack of wet web strength can be made up by incorporation of cellulose pulps in amounts of 25% or more. It comes about, therefore, that latex type bonding and the use of synthetic and cellulose blends often go together.

Certain types of man-made fibers have fibrillating properties similar to natural cellulose. Acrylic fibers having such properties are described in a recent article.[18] After development of this fibrillation by mechanical action, these fibers have sufficient coherence to satisfy the paper-making requirement of wet web strength. The final strength of the sheet is developed by exposure to sufficient temperature to produce a heat bonding between adjacent fiber surfaces. This method provides a 100% synthetic fiber paper.

The typical viscose rayon textile fiber, even though chemically similar to native cellulose, does not form interfiber bonds in the paper-making sense. However, by using special spinning conditions, rayon can be made self-bonding.[19] Such fibers develop a high degree of sheet strength with no bonding additives. The interfiber bonding developed by this special rayon is not due to fibrillation, as observed in natural cellulose, but rather to the nature of the fiber wall that permits intimate contact between adjacent fibers.

Another noteworthy contribution to the bonding of synthetic paper is reported in a recent article from the du Pont laboratories.[20] In order to improve upon the method of bonding with latex dispersions, polymers were formed having chemical structures similar to the fibers to be bonded. In physical form these polymers resembled well beaten wood pulp. When incorporated in the synthetic furnish these so-called "fibrids" are reported to contribute significantly to wet web strength and, when heat-cured, to produce sheets of a high order of strength. The amount of "fibrid" necessary for optimum strength development is in the order of 25 to 30% of the furnish. Calendering is carried out slightly above the fusing temperature of the fibrid, or about 400°F for those fibrids currently available.

Properties of Synthetic Fiber Papers

The fiber length of wood pulp is limited to that produced by nature. The longest wood pulp fibers are only about 3.5 mm, and much of the pulp manufactured today is less than 2 mm in fiber length. In contrast, man-made fibers are available in any length. For such properties as tensile strength, and especially tearing strength, longer fiber is advantageous. However, in a practical sense, the ability to obtain uniform sheet formation limits the fiber length of paper furnishes. As Hentschel has shown,[20] as the fiber length is increased, a point is soon reached where the strength properties fall off due to poor formation. Exactly where this limit is depends upon several factors: coarser fibers can be formed at greater length than fine fibers; keeping head box consistency low aids in forming sheets of long fibers; the presence of colloids, such as well beaten cellulose, aids in the formation of long-fibered stock. Under the most favorable conditions fiber length

of about ½ to ⅝ inch is probably the limit for reasonably good formation. Even this range is sufficient to produce papers of highly superior durability properties.

In speaking of fiber length, it is important to remember that long fibers were available for paper making long before man-made fibers came along. Flax and cotton were among the original paper-making materials, and other long natural fibers such as manila, jute and sisal are made into paper. The use of these fibers has persisted and in some areas expanded over the years largely because of the advantages of fiber length.

As noted above, an important property of certain of the man-made fibers is that of dimensional stability in an environment of changing humidity. One of the most characteristic properties of cellulosic fibers is the highly variable moisture regain, depending upon the water vapor content of the surrounding air. The dimensions of cellulosic fiber change with moisture content, and this may cause curling and warping of a paper or paperboard. Since many of the synthetic fibers have little or no moisture regain, papers made therefrom have excellent dimensional stability. Such fibers as "Dacron," polyethylene, "Dynel," glass, and nylon are examples of such fibers.

Cellulosic fibers are readily attacked and disintegrated by strong acids and are swollen by alkalies and by many salt solutions. For this reason cellulosic papers are not suitable for filtration of such chemical solutions. Many of the synthetic fibers are highly resistant to these chemical solutions and hence the field of industrial infiltration offers an attractive opportunity for such papers.

Synthetic fibers also offer advantages in papers of high dielectric or insulating properties, greater heat resistance, immunity to bacterial attack and possessing a high degree of absorbence toward resin-impregnating syrups.

It is too early to assess the final position that synthetic papers will eventually reach in the industry. There is no doubt that such papers can offer properties not attainable with cellulose fibers. It is equally true that, in comparison with wood pulp, the synthetics are much more expensive. The final verdict on whether synthetics will expand their application in the paper industry beyond a few small volume specialties will depend on actual experience in the market place.

There is a distinct similarity between synthetic fiber "papers" and the class of sheet materials known as "non-wovens." As a step in the manufacture of yarn, staple fibers are carded, that is, separated and combed, to form a uniform, light weight and fragile fibrous web. Subsequently this web is gathered together to form a strand or "sliver" which is drawn and spun into yarn. However, if several of the flat webs are laminated together, and the fibers bonded to give strength and coherence, a "non-woven" fabric results, which has properties resembling both paper and woven cloth.[20a] Machines have been developed which combine a mechanical combing and separating action upon the fibers with the action of a current of air to carry the fibers and aid in web formation. In this area, it is difficult to draw a clear distinction between what is paper and what is textile. Processes are now available to form sheets from the same fiber by both the dry forming process and the water forming or paper-making process. When textile fibers are formed into webs by either of these processes, the resulting products have properties that enable them to compete in some fields traditionally served by textiles. It is generally agreed that the term "paper" refers to a fibrous sheet formed from water suspension.

WATER

As a raw material for use in the manufacture of pulp and paper, water is second in importance only to the fiber itself. Thus it is natural that the pulp and paper industry should gravitate to areas where water supplies are abundant and of high quality. At the same time, these areas are usually remote from the population centers where lie the great markets for paper. This creates a counter-attraction and paper mills do exist in localities where water supplies are less abundant and where pollution is a serious problem.

Water technology is a highly complex study, and the interested reader is referred to the bibliography at the end of this chapter for more detailed information.[22-26]

There are two general sources of industrial water supplies: surface water from rivers, streams and lakes, and ground water from wells. Surface waters tend to have more turbidity in the form of suspended matter, more color from dissolved organic matter, and are subject to wider variation in quality due to floods and drouth; ground waters usually have more dissolved mineral matters (hardness) due to percolating through strata of rock. The most important constituents of natural waters are as follows.

Dissolved Mineral Salts. Calcium and magnesium occur as bicarbonates or sulphates to a greater or less degree in practically all natural waters and cause the property of water called "hardness." Soft water contains less than about 30 ppm (parts per million) of calcium and magnesium hardness, while very hard water may contain several hundred ppm. These calcium and magnesium salts may cause scale formation in mill equipment, require excessive use of alum in sizing, and increase the ash content of the paper. Boiler water containing calcium and magnesium must be treated to prevent scale formation. Sodium and potassium occur in small amounts in most rivers and streams, but are of little significance except where brackish water from the ocean or salt lakes seeps into underground water supplies or when sea water backs up tidal estuaries during periods of drouth. This brackish water causes severe corrosion in paper mill equipment, foaming in boilers and interference with the sizing of paper.

Iron and manganese often occur in water supplies, and iron may be added to the water after it enters the mill by corrosion of equipment. Even a few parts per million of these metals can seriously reduce the brightness of pulp and paper by being adsorbed by the fiber.

It is important for the paper technologist to remember that paper stock can be seriously affected by the constituents of water in two distinct ways. The natural cellulosic fibers have the property of ion exchange to a considerable degree and hence react readily with numerous ions, with resultant change in color and ability to adsorb treating materials such as dyes, sizes and resins. Secondly, a paper machine stock system is usually a complex mixture of colloidal materials derived both from the pulp furnish and from various added materials to produce desired effects in the paper—all in a state of somewhat unstable equilibrium. Ions derived from the water supply may upset this equilibrium, causing such troubles as pitch spots, off color shades, poor sizing, poor wet strength efficiency and many others.

Turbidity and Color. Turbidity is suspended matter and includes inorganic silt and organic debris. Color is due to dissolved material of much smaller particle origin. The amount of these contaminants that can be tolerated by a paper mill is largely dependent upon the grade of paper being made.

Dissolved Gases. The most common dissolved gases encountered in water supplies are oxygen and carbon dioxide, and these are chiefly of interest because of corrosion of equipment. Where corrosion is of critical importance, as in boiler water, these must be removed.

Table 2.3 shows some typical water analyses from various parts of the United States. It must be kept in mind that any given water source will vary in content of chemical materials from time to time due to variations in rainfall and to the flow of waste materials into the stream. However, the data of this table serve to illustrate how various water sources and various regions of the country compare with each other in a few selected properties.

Amount of Water Consumed by the Pulp and Paper Industry

There are numerous steps in the manufacture of pulp and paper which require immense quantities of water. Likewise, there are many opportunities for the re-use of water. Since there is wide variation in the abundance and cost of fresh water, and great differences in product requirements, there is wide range in quantity of water used by different mills. Amounts range from 10,000 gallons per ton for mills making single products such as groundwood pulp or paperboard to 100,000 gallons per ton for integrated mills making several grades of pulp and several grades of paper. A recently

TABLE 2.3. TYPICAL WATER ANALYSES

Water Source	Total Hardness (ppm)	Ca (ppm)	Mg (ppm)	Alkalinity as Cabonate (ppm)	Sulfate (ppm)	Turbidity Units
Penobscot River, Maine	20	16	4	16	5	
St. Lawrence River, New York	140	116	32	56	45	
Delaware River, New Jersey	82	50	32	32	50	15
Tennessee River, Alabama	90	70	20	57	23	
Wisconsin River, Wisconsin	50	36	14	36	17	12
Fox River, Wisconsin	169	95	52	144	20	
Columbia River, Washington	68	48	20	56	13	
Savannah River, Georgia	11	6	5	13	4	30
Well water, Florida	142	104	38	120	11	
Well water, California	134	52	82	136	4.4	

built kraft pulp mill has a water plant designed to supply 72,000 gallons of water per ton of pulp. An extensive survey of water consumption throughout the paper industry will be found in TAPPI Monograph No. 18.[22]

Data from a recent article based upon figures from the 1959 Census of Manufacturers (Table 2.4), shows the pulp and paper industry in third place among all industry groups in the United States in total intake of water of 1937 million gallons for the year.[23] When re-use of water is included, the paper industry leads all industry groups at 5989 million gallons or about 24% of all industrial water use. The discharge to surface waters is shown to be 1765 million gallons. By the nature of the paper industry, much of this discharged water

carries dissolved and suspended wastes. Therein lies one of the major problems confronting the industry.

Reduction in the pollution load of wastes discharged to streams has received concentrated attention from practically all pulp and paper companies in recent years. This effort has included cooperative research directed toward finding uses for waste products and toward methods for preventing detrimental effects of wastes upon natural waters. Substantial sums have been expended for waste disposal systems for reducing the pollution load. Governmental agencies have shown increasing concern over the stream pollution load from all sources.

That these efforts have brought substantial progress is evident. A recent article states that since 1943 the pollution load

TABLE 2.4 INDUSTRY MAY USE LARGE QUANTITIES
OF WATER, BUT WITHDRAW RELATIVELY LITTLE FROM THE ORIGINAL SOURCE [a]

(1 million gallons per year; slight discrepacies in total result from independent rounding of raw data)

| | Users | | Intake (I) | | | Re-Users | | Discharge (D) to | | | % |
| | | Re-users,[b] | | | | Use (U) includ-ing re-use | Actual Con-sump-tion (I − D) | Sur-face Waters | Ground Waters | Users Other | re-use $\left(\frac{U-I}{I}\right)$ |
Industry	Total Intake	%	Total	Fresh Water	Brackish Water						
Primary metal industries (steel, etc.)	3702	72	3284	2998	285	5255	142	3100	20	22	60
Chemicals, allied products	3240	74	2633	1768	864	4617	163	2345	17	109	75
Paper, allied products	1937	88	1884	1724	159	5989	110	1765	9	1	218
Petroleum, coal products	1319	88	1232	655	577	5692	114	1111	5	2	362
Food, allied products	624	70	518	458	60	1192	48	433	20	17	130
Transportation equipment	260	72	235	180	55	497	31	201	3	1	112
Stone, china, glass products	295	61	223	207	16	587	22	200	3	c	163
Machinery, less electrical	171	70	141	117	23	222	5	134	1	c	57
Lumber, wood products	140	74	110	88	23	154	10	95	1	3	40
Rubber, plastics products	127	78	97	93	4	306	8	87	2	1	216
Textile mill products	135	58	91	90	c	137	12	78	c	1	51
Electrical machinery	93	70	82	72	11	149	5	77	1	c	82
Fabricated metal products	44	59	30	29	1	56	2	27	c	c	87
Instruments, related products	23	74	20	20	c	58	1	19	c	c	190
Ordnance, misc. manu-facturing	26	78	18	17	c	49	2	15	1	c	172
Apparel, related products	10	68	9	9	c	10	0	8	c		11
Leather, leather products	12	50	7	7	c	9	0	7	1		29
Printing, publishing	13	66	5	5	5	39	1	5	c		680
Tobacco products	3	87	3	3		44	1	2	c		1367
Furniture, fixtures	3	79	2	2	c	3	0	2	c		50
Total	12,177		10,624	8542	2083	25,065	677	9711	84	157	
Corresponding %		72									136

[a] 1959 Census of Manufacturing Establishments. Steam electric generation excluded. Includes all major users among firms withdrawing 20 million gallons or more per year.
[b] Incomplete coverage among firms withdrawing 20 million gallons or more may affect this column slightly.
c Less than 500 million gallons.

from the pulp and paper industry has been reduced 50% in the face of a 100% increase in production.[24] A high order of ingenuity has been demonstrated in bringing about a substantially increased re-use of water within a cost structure compatible with the competitive position of the industry.

Water Treatment

The degree of treatment given the water supply of a pulp or paper mill depends upon the condition of the water as received and upon the quality requirements of the product. The treatment may vary all the way from simple screening to complete sterilization and demineralization. The modern trend is toward higher degrees of purification of the water supplies in the interests of better machine operation, higher quality products and cleaner piping.

Filtration. For the removal of suspended solids, water is passed through filter beds consisting of successive layers of sand, gravel or other granular material in which the layers are successfully coarser from inlet to discharge. The beds are kept in good operating condition by frequent back washing. The engineering of a water filtration system is quite precise and requires a high order of technical competence and extensive practical experience.

Coagulation. In order to obtain more rapid filtration and better clarification of water, it is customary to add aluminum sulphate to the water prior to filtration, thereby producing a flocculent precipitate which entraps finely divided particles. This floc is allowed to settle as sludge in a settling basin and the partially clarified supernatant water goes to the filters.

The coagulation is a series of colloidal chemical reactions. If there is not sufficient natural alkalinity present in the water to react with the alum, it must be supplemented by the addition of such alkaline compounds as hydrated lime, $Ca(OH)_2$, caustic soda, NaOH, or soda ash Na_2CO_3. The formation of floc from natural alka-

linity of water may be represented by the following equation:

$$3\,Ca(HCO_3)_2 + Al_2(SO_4)_3 \longrightarrow$$
$$2\,Al(OH)_3 + 3\,Ca{+}{+} + 3\,SO_4^{=} + 6\,CO_2$$

Under the proper condition of pH, temperature and agitation the aluminum hydroxide of the above equation forms highly reactive colloidal aggregates having the ability to attract and adsorb a great variety of particles present in water. Note that it does not remove the hardness (calcuim) present in the water. Also, although many bacteria and other living organisms are trapped and removed by the floc, this treatment is not sterilizing or bacteriocidal.

For water difficult to coagulate, there are several materials available which will accelerate floc formation and produce a more dense floc. Activated silica derived from sodium silicate and acid is an example of such a material. Various clays function in a similar manner.

Through engineering design there have been developed several types of equipment for controlled addition of chemicals, for mixing and flocculating, and for settling and clarification.

The newly constructed (1960) water treatment plant of the Continental Can board mill at Augusta, Georgia is described in a recent article by C. T. Wise.[21] The capital investment for raw water pumping facilities and for the water treatment plant was $1,-745,000 or about $77,000 per million gallons per day (mgd). The rated capacity of the treatment plant is 22,000,000 gallons per day. The mill has an integrated capacity of 350 tons per day of bleached kraft pulp and the same amount of paperboard. Thus, the water consumption is about 63,000 gallons per ton. Liquid alum is metered automatically on the basis of pH to the raw water, the normal amount being 8 to 10 parts per million (ppm). Hydrated lime is used as the alkaline coagulant and is fed by a gravimetric dry feeder. The chlorine dosage is normally 3 to 4 ppm.

After thorough mixing with the chemical

feed, the water flows to two 105-foot diameter concrete, up-flow, sludge contact-type clarifiers. The mixed water enters the center coagulation or flocculation zone, having slow recirculation type flow and a retention time of 25 minutes. The sedimentation compartment of the clarifier has a rise rate of about one gallon per minute (gpm) per square foot of area, and a detention time of about 2 hours and 15 minutes.

The filtration system consists of six twin filters, with each half unit 13 by 40 feet in area. At the design rate of 22 mgd the filtration rate is 2.5 gpm per square foot of bed. The filter media includes a 30-inch depth of silica sand with an effective size of 0.45 mm above a 12 inch deep bed of graded gravel supported on the under-drain system. The settled water going to the filter plant has a turbidity of about 5 ppm compared with about 30 ppm for the raw water. After filtration the turbidity is normally zero.

Sterilization and Slime Control

Natural waters invariably contain living organisms, which, in the presence of nutrient materials, will grow and multiply giving rise to a series of troubles to mill operation. In the presence of light, a green plant (algae) may form in the water system causing clogging of filters and other parts of the system. The most common control method for algae is the addition of copper sulfate at appropriate parts of the system or in storage ponds. A few parts per million of copper will destroy algae.

There are numerous other types of bacteria which may cause the formation of "slime" due to the gelatinous capsule with which many bacteria surround themselves, or which may discolor paper stock, or which may generate obnoxious odors. Many paper mill systems, due to low pH (acid) condition, are favorable to the growth of fungi. The filamentous nature of fungi leads to adherent growth "strings" on walls or equipment. These "strings" eventually break loose with deleterious effects on machine operation and product quality.

For all these reasons a sterile or nearly sterile system is highly desirable, but the very nature of the pulp and paper processes make this difficult to achieve. Because of the importance of eliminating bacterial growth, both in the water supply systems and in the paper system, the modern trend is to chlorinate the water supply to the point of sterilization as the first step in water treatment. This may require up to 5 or 6 ppm of chlorine and must be enough to ensure a positive residual of free chlorine. Water does not normally carry enough nutrient to permit extensive growth of slime. However, it may permit colonies to grow which can serve as seed for infection of the fiber systems where nutrient is abundant. A sterile water supply is an important first step in a clean mill system.

In an "open" mill system where fresh water is widely used, slime control might be accomplished by delivering to the mill fresh water carrying a fairly high chlorine residual. However, with the tighter closing of the machine system, with greater re-use of white water, the chlorination of fresh water can have but little effect in the stock system itself.

It is important for the paper technologist to remember that a stock system of either a pulp mill or of a paper mill is a fertile field for the growth of microorganisms. Nutrient is present in abundance. Many organisms have the ability to decompose cellulose fiber itself, while the other woody materials present in groundwood, unbleached and high-yield pulps, furnish food for a variety of organisms. Such additives as starch may also add to the food supply. The conditions are favorable for growth, if not actually ideal. For example, the temperature range is neither too high nor too low and the constant agitation spreads infection and distributes nutrient.

There are ready sources of infection of a mill system but much can be done to control them. As noted above, it is possible to eliminate the water supply as a source of infection. Also, pulp itself is sterile as it is discharged from the digester. Pulp infection comes from colonies of bacteria nesting in corners and crannies of the stock system. In spite of all precautions, some inoculation of the paper machine system will occur by air-borne particles.

In most paper machine systems, it is necessary to add bacteriocides at strategic points. Chlorine is the ideal bacteriocide for water, but is less so for stock systems. This is because chlorine can react with some of the fiber constituents, lignin in particular, as well as with other organic materials always present in a stock system. Hence the effect of chlorine is somewhat temporary, but still of great usefulness in control of stock systems.

Among other bacteriocides in common use in the paper industry today are the phenyl-mercuric salts, and other organo-mercurials and the sodium salts of phenols and various chlorinated phenols. The choice of bacteriocide for a given mill, the dosage and point of addition are all technical questions requiring knowledge of the conditions in the particular mill and extensive background in slime control.

Much can be accomplished in slime control by proper design of paper mill stock systems. The ideal system avoids stagnant pockets, using smooth, easily cleaned surfaces, keeping all parts readily accessible for periodic clean-ups.

Corrosion

The extensive exposure of equipment in the pulp and paper industry to water, and to water dispersions and solutions containing a variety of materials, creates corrosion conditions practically without parallel in all industry. Corrosion is the effect upon equipment of exposure to environmental conditions. Thus, environmental conditions may be aggressive or mild in producing corrosion and the material surface may be highly resistant or highly susceptible to corrosion. The technologist requires an understanding of the factors producing corrosion, of means of modifying the environment toward greater protection of the equipment surfaces, and by knowledge of materials of construction in order to make a proper selection for the great variety of services required in the pulp and paper industry.

In some areas of the industry, such as pulp digesters and bleach plant equipment, corrosion is of such paramount importance that exhaustive engineering studies and developments have been devoted to these areas.

We will mention here only those areas which are parts of the stock and water systems.

Role of pH. Acidity is invariably an important factor in metallic corrosion. In order to produce special properties in the finished paper, stock systems often operate on the acid side, pH 4 or even below. In the absence of protective films, iron, steel, zinc, aluminum and many other metals are corroded rapidly. Low pH also tends to accelerate the effect of other corrosive agents, such as chlorine, oxygen and salts, all of which are much more corrosive at low pH than under neutral or alkaline conditions. It has been reported that at the pH limits most common in the paper industry, pH 4.3 to pH 9.5, dissolved oxygen plays a more important role than does pH in the rate of corrosion.

Dissolved Gases. In addition to dissolved oxygen, other gases such as carbon dioxide, hydrogen sulfide and sulfur dioxide can have important effects in the corrosion of metals. Carbon dioxide dissolved in water forms the weakly dissociated acid, carbonic acid. The corrosion resulting from carbon dioxide is chiefly important in steam and condensate lines. The carbon dioxide is released in the boiler water by decomposition of carbonates. Hydrogen sulfide is usually encountered as the result of bacterial decomposition and may attack many metals with the formation of sulfides. The seriousness of sulfide corrosion is greatly affected by the mechanical and chemical conditions that determine whether the sulfide coating is adherent and therefore protective or whether it is removed with exposure of fresh surface. Sulfur dioxide is highly acidic when dissolved in water and is corrosive for that reason. The preparation and handling of sulfite cooking liquor requires equipment resistant to this acid. The atmosphere surrounding sulfite mills invariably carries some sulfur dioxide.

Dissolved Solids. It is recognized that higher concentrations of ionizable salts increase the rate of corrosion. This is especially true of mineral salts such as $NaCl$, Na_2SO_4, $CaCl_2$, $MgCl_2$ and similar salts. It is assumed that the greater conductivity of the water resulting from these dissolved salts accelerates the galvanic action between dissimilar metals and between anodic and cathodic areas of the same metal. Another effect of dissolved salts is upon the adherence of films of initial products of corrosion to the metal surface. Salts often make such films less adherent.

Flow rate and temperature both accelerate corrosion, as would be expected. High flow rates tend to remove products of corrosion with resultant exposure of fresh surface. The accelerating effect of higher temperature is similar to that of all chemical reactions.

When two dissimilar metals are in contact through an aqueous solution, corrosion is often accelerated in one of these metals. This is known as galvanic action, one of the metals becoming an anode, the other a cathode. The relationship of metals to each other in such couples is known as the electromotive series. At one end of the series are the metals that are most anodic, or most easily corroded, while at the other end are the metals that are most cathodic, most "noble," most resistant to corrosion. The order of all metals and alloys used for construction is not exact and metals and alloys may occupy different positions in the series depending upon environmental conditions or upon previous surface treatment.

The following listing gives an electromotive series of common metals and alloys arranged in the order found most common in the pulp and paper industry.[22]

Corroded End
(anodic, least noble)

Magnesium and alloys
Zinc
Aluminum 25
Cadmium
Aluminum 175 T
Steel or iron
Cast iron
Chromium iron (active)
Ni-resist
18-8 Cr-Ni-Fe (active)
18-8-3 Cr-Ni-Mo-Fe (active)
Hastelloy C
Lead-tin solders
Lead
Tin
Nickel (active)
Inconel (active)
"Hastelloy A"
"Hastelloy B"
Brasses
Copper
Bronzes
Copper-Nickel Alloys
Titanium
"Monel"
Silver Solder
Nickel (passive)
"Inconel"
Chromium iron (passive)
18-8 Gr-Ni-Fe (passive)
18-8-3 Cr-Ni-Mo-Fe (passive)
Silver
Graphite

Protected End
(cathodic or most noble)

The selection of materials of construction is a highly complex calculation of resistance of the metal, estimate of the environment, expected life and initial cost. The more resistant metals usually involve high initial cost while the cheaper metals may involve short life.

One of the new developments in paper mill construction is the use of nonmetallic materials of construction such as glass-fiber reinforced plastic piping and panels. It is to be expected that nonmetallic materials and the more resistant metals will make great strides in paper mill construction in the future.

Softening and Demineralization

The ultimate step in water purification is the removal of all dissolved inorganic material. The degree of water purification is often necessary for boiler water for the modern steam plant producing high pressure steam and at high evaporation rates.

The hardness of water is due to the presence of dissolved calcium and magnesium salts, or in effect, the presence of Ca^{++} and Mg^{++} ions. Associated with these ions are various anions such as bicarbonate, sulfate, chloride or nitrate. The hardness of water may be removed by precipitation of the calcium and magnesium salts as insoluble compounds which settle out as a sludge.

The common treatments for softening water by precipitation are by addition of lime and soda ash and by the addition of phosphate. Lime, $Ca(OH)_2$, reacts with any free carbon dioxide present to form insoluble $CaCO_3$; it reacts with bicarbonates, the Ca and Mg salts of which are appreciably soluble, to form carbonates which are insoluble; it reacts with magnesium compounds to form the insoluble magnesium hydroxide. The sodium carbonate (soda ash) is added to convert Ca and Mg sulfates, chlorides or nitrates to carbonates.

The lime-soda softening process may be used either as a hot or a cold treatment, the former results in more complete softening, the coagulation of the precipitate is more rapid, and deaeration of the water and removal of silica occurs at the same time. For these reasons it is widely used for boiler feed water. The cold lime-soda process is more suitable for process water where deaeration is less important and hot water feed is not desired. Coagulation basins and settling tanks have been especially designed for this process.

The second widely used system for water softening is the ion exchange or zeolite method. Various natural and synthetic materials have the capacity of absorbing ions from solution and later releasing these ions when exposed to a salt solution. Thus water containing Ca and Mg is softened by passing through a granular bed of cation exchange resin or mineral and is regenerated, after its capacity to absorb the hardness ions is exhausted, by exposure to a brine of sodium chloride which converts the ion exchange material back to its sodium form.

Synthetic ion-exchange resins are available which can exchange hydrogen ions for other cations; thus carbonates or bicarbonates are converted into carbonic acid which becomes free carbon dioxide, while sulfates and chlorides become sulfuric acid and hydrochloric acid.

Other synthetic ion-exchange resins have the ability to absorb anions. Thus by passing water from the hydrogen exchanger described above, through the anion exchanger, the effluent is freed from practically all soluble material and is equivalent to distilled water. The hydrogen exchange is regenerated with a strong acid, such as sulfuric acid, and the anion exchanger is regenerated with a strong base such as caustic soda.

It is obvious that complete demineralization of water is of importance only for highly critical uses such as boiler feed water or for make up of chemical solutions. For most uses in the pulp and paper industry for process water, that is water which comes into contact with fiber, no more than coagulation and filtration is required. In fact, as a mill system becomes more closed and the usage of fresh water per ton of product is reduced, the effect of dissolved materials present in the water becomes proportionately less. However, there may be instances where the level of hardness or other dissolved material is such that a mill may benefit in improved operations and in product quality by additional purification of water beyond coagulation with alum and filtration.

REFERENCES

1. Isenberg, I. H., "Papermaking Fibers," *Econ. Botany,* 10, No. 2, 176 (April-June, 1956).
2. Ott, E., Spurlin, H. M., and Graflin, M. W., "Cellulose and Cellulose Derivatives," 2nd Edition, Vol. 3, New York, Interscience Pub., 1954-1955.
3. Meyer, K. H., "Natural and Synthetic High Polymers: Cellulose and its Derivatives," 2nd Edition, p. 283, New York, Interscience Pub., 1950.
4. Balam, Francis., ed., "Fundamentals of Papermaking Fibers," Technical Section, British Paper and Board Makers Association, 1958.
5. Page, D. H., and Emerton, H. W., *Svensk Papperstid.,* 62, No. 9, 318 (1959).
6. Tomlinson, G. H. II, *Tappi,* 44, No. 1, 133A (January, 1961).
7. Clark, J. d'A., *Tappi,* 37, No. 3, 140A (March, 1954).
8. Clause, J. L., *Tappi,* 41, No. 9, 147A (September, 1958).
9. Proceedings First Waste Paper Symposium, Waste Paper Utilization Council, New York.
10. Nelson, G. H., *et al.,* "A Search for New Fiber Crops, Part III," *Tappi,* 44, No. 5, 319 (May, 1961).
11. McGovern, J. N., "Progress in Continuous Pulping of Straws, Reeds and Grasses." *World Paper Trade Review,* 153, No. 14, 1233 (April 7, 1960).
12. Ritchie, J. L., "Fiber Competition Seen," *Pulp & Paper,* 34, No. 10, 86 (September, 1960).
13. May, Isenberg and McLeod, *Paper Trade J.,* 142, No. 1, 36 (January 6, 1958).
14. Cusi, D. S., "New Bagasse Process." *Pulp and Paper International,* 1, No. 3, 42 March, 1959).
15. Watson, B. G., "The Search for Papermaking Fibers: Esparto," *Paper Maker,* (United States) 26, No. 1 (1957).
16. Raitt, W., "The Digestion of Grasses and Bamboo for Papermaking," London, 1931.
17. Adamson, G. A., "Bamboo, Long Known as Source of Paper Pulps, Awaits Developments in Handling and Chipping," *Pulp and Paper International,* 2, No. 5, 23 (May, 1960).
18. Arledter, H. F., *Tappi,* 42, No. 2, 177A (February, 1959).
19. Shearer, H. F., *Paper Trade J.,* 144, No. 45, 42 (November 7, 1960).
20. Hentschel, R. A. A., *Tappi,* 44, No. 1, 22 (January, 1961).
20a. Buresh, "Nonwoven Fabrics," New York, Reinhold Publishing Corp., 1962.
21. Wise, C. T., *Paper Trade J.,* 145, 20 (April 24, 1961).
22. "Water Technology," TAPPI Monograph No. 18, New York, 1957.
23. Clark, F. E., "Industrial Re-Use of Water," *Ind. Eng. Chem.,* 54, No. 2, 18 (January 26, 1962).
24. Cadigan, A. M., *Pulp and Paper,* 35, No. 17, 48 (August 21, 1961).
25. Camp, "Water and Its Impurities," New York, Reinhold Publishing Corp., 1963.
26. Nordell, E., "Water Treatment," New York, Reinhold Publishing Corp,, 1962.

CHAPTER 3

Forest Management in Modern Pulp and Paper Making

KARL A. SWENNING

Scott Paper Company *

The author of Chapter 1 has pointed out that the present mass production of paper is based on two developments, namely, the invention of machinery for making an endless sheet of paper at a high rate of speed and the discovery of methods of converting wood into paper pulp. It is this latter discovery that has been a major factor in creating the economic climate essential for the practical application of those disciplines which constitute forestry or, more specifically, the management of a forest.

Chapter 1 has also given data on the growth of the paper industry in the United States and thereby indicated the resulting increase in demand on the pulpwood resources of the nation. In order that this demand may be put in proper perspective and a yardstick provided by which that demand can be measured, reference is made to Table 3.1.

WHAT IS PULPWOOD?

At this point it becomes necessary to clarify what is meant by pulpwood and how it is measured. Pulpwood is wood that has been cut or prepared from trees primarily for processing into pulp for further manufacture into paper, paperboard or other products. The trees are felled in the woods

TABLE 3.1. U.S. PULPWOOD CONSUMPTION *
BY YEARS

	All Species	Softwood	Hardwood
1910	4,094,306	N.A.	N.A.
1920	6,114,072	"	"
1930	7,119,524	"	"
1935	7,628,274	"	"
1940	13,742,958	"	"
1945	16,911,861	"	"
1950	23,627,217	"	"
1952	26,461,000	22,661,000	3,800,000
1954	29,679,363	24,891,124	4,788,239
1955	33,356,476	27,728,005	5,628,471
1956	35,748,582	29,691,138	6,057,444
1957	35,529,916	29,450,996	6,078,920
1958	34,960,402	28,737,289	6,223,113
1959	39,084,097	30,947,399	8,136,698
1960	40,165,302	31,521,688	8,643,614
1961	42,191,483	33,094,861	9,096,622

N.A.—Not Available.

Source: Pulpwood Statistical Review Issued May 1958 and supplements of 1959 and 1960 by American Pulpwood Association.

* In cords (128 c.f.) of rough wood.

and are usually cut up there into suitable lengths for transportation to a pulp mill. Occasionally after the trees are felled and limbs removed, they are hauled in tree length to a loading yard where they are then cut into pulpwood lengths.[4]

The standard unit of measure is the cord, which is a stack of wood piled 4 feet

* Retired.

wide, 4 feet high and 8 feet long. These dimensions give a volume of 128 cubic feet, but this volume is not all solid wood because of the thickness of the bark and the irregular shapes of the logs. It is this variation in solid cubic volume which is bringing about a change to measurement of wood consumed on either a bone dry or a green weight basis. However, since historically the "cord" has been the unit of measure for statistical purposes, it is used in Table 3.1.

PULPWOOD CONSUMPTION

To provide the yardstick by which the consumption of approximately forty million cords in the U.S. in 1960 can be measured, let it be assumed that a pulp mill produces 500 tons of unbleached kraft pulp per day and that for each such ton, 1.80 cords of wood are required, giving a daily usage of 900 cords. Assuming further that the plant operates at this rate for 345 days in a calendar year using a total of 310,500 cords, a pile of wood four feet high and four feet wide reaching from Chicago to Omaha (approximately 470 miles) would be consumed.

Further reference to Table 3.1 will bring sharply into focus the very considerable increase in pulpwood used during the twenty years prior to 1960, but more particularly the dramatic increase in the last decade. Projections as to future demands are always open to question, but it has been estimated [10] that by 1975 consumption will be 72 million cords and by the year 2000, 100 million cords. A study made in 1954 by Stanford Research Institute projected pulpwood use in 1965 at 38,100,000 cords, which figure has already been surpassed. Their 1975 estimate of 47,500,000 cords seems low in the light of 1960 actual and 1961 estimated consumption.

Pulpwood is, however, but one of several drains on the forest resources of the nation; this means that plans of the forest manager must be keyed to over-all timber requirements. This statement requires explanation. Although the title of this chapter is "Forest Management in Modern Pulp and Paper Making," there is today but little forest management directed solely to the growing of trees exclusively for use in pulp manufacture, nor is it anticipated that such will be the situation in the foreseeable future. Later in this chapter the reasons for this will be discussed.

In 1952 domestic consumption of forest products was divided approximately as follows, expressed in the common denominator of millions of cubic feet: [10]

Sawlogs for lumber	6,419
Pulpwood	2,697
Veneer logs and bolts	451
Cooperage, piling, poles, posts, ties, etc.	699
Total	10,266

It is estimated [10] that domestic requirements in these categories will be increased as follows in terms of per cent of their 1952 usage:

Product	1975	2000
Sawlogs for lumber	21	33
Pulpwood	95	164
Veneer logs and bolts	110	188
Cooperage, piling, poles, posts, ties, etc.	14	49

It is evident from these tabulations that demand for saw timber is not expected to increase in proportion to that of other uses for wood. The reasons are many and complex, and a discussion of them has no place in this chapter. We are here concerned primarily with the present and future demand for pulpwood and whether or not there is a sufficient supply of timber to meet that demand. Our concern is also with the measures being taken to assure the continuance of that supply.

To evaluate the pulpwood demand, it is necessary to refer again to Table 3.1. Reference to the year 1952 shows that the use of hardwoods was reported for the first time. Although such woods have been a part of the pulpwood mix prior to that year, they were not considered of sufficient importance to justify a separate statistical reporting.

Examining the record from 1952 to 1960, it is evident that hardwood consumption has increased from 14.36% of the total to 21.52%, thus reducing the demand on softwood species by approximately 5 million cords and changing the forest manager's emphasis on the growing of softwood.

While it may be that the reader is familiar with the terms "softwood" and "hardwood" as used in this chapter, their definitions will serve to clear up any possible misunderstanding.

Softwoods are those trees which bear needles, which are commonly known as "evergreens" and which generally bear cones. This latter characteristic gives them the designation of conifers. The physical property of the wood itself—whether hard or soft—has nothing to do with its broad classification. Spruce, balsam fir, the pines, hemlock, Douglas fir, tamarack and cypress are typical softwoods.

Hardwoods are those trees which bear broad leaves which fall off in the winter and bear fruit instead of cones. Typical examples of hardwoods are beech, birch, maple, the oaks, yellow poplar, tupelo gum, cottonwood and aspen. Since a piece of seasoned oak can hardly be dented with a hammer, while aspen can be deeply scratched with a thumbnail, it is evident that actual "hardness" is not the determining factor in the classification of the species.

Another factor of importance in evaluating the pulpwood drain on the forest resource is the growing use of pulpable chips produced from sawmill residuals. These residuals are the slabs, edgings and other material produced in the process of manufacturing merchantable lumber, which in the past were burned and, to some extent, used in the sawmill for the production of steam for power or heating. With the greatly accelerated demand for pulpwood which occurred between 1950 and 1960 and the introduction of efficient mechanical debarkers designed for use in comparatively small, as well as large, sawmills, the production of salable pulping chips became a matter of

economic importance to the producer of lumber.

Statistics on the use of so-called purchased chips have been kept only since 1957. The data presented in Table 3.2 brings sharply into focus the impact of this source of wood supply on the demand for "new" wood to produce total pulp tonnage. It is to be noted that while total softwood use in 1957 was 29,450,996 cords (Table 3.1), of this amount, 4,135,940 cords (Table 3.2) or 14.04% came from sawmill residuals. Of further significance is the fact that in 1960 when total softwood usage increased to 31,521,688 cords or by 7.3% over 1957, utilization of purchased chips had also increased to 6,387,228 cords or to 20.26% of total softwood use.

The statistics in Table 3.1 show that as the hardwood component of the pulpwood mix had increased more rapidly than had total use, so too had the use of chips increased (Table 3.2) from 2.37% of the total in 1957 to 5.19% in 1960.

TABLE 3.2. PULPWOOD CONSUMPTION 1957-1960 (CORDS) BY SPECIES CLASSIFICATION AND SOURCE OF SUPPLY †

	Softwood		Hardwood	
Year	Round Wood	Chips *	Round Wood	Chips *
1957	25,315,056	4,135,940	5,938,014	140,906
1958	23,525,116	5,212,173	6,014,493	208,620
1959	24,855,409	6,091,990	7,770,131	366,567
1960	25,134,460	6,387,228	8,217,159	426,455

† Source: Same as Table 3.1.
* Produced from sawmill residuals.

Total purchased chip usage, both hardwood and softwood, in 1960 totaled 6,813,683 cords or 16.96% of total wood consumed in the United States. The significance lies not so much in the quantity per se but in the fact that these chips came from timber already taken from the nation's wood pile in the form of sawlogs and were material which previously had had no economic value.

The statistics which have been cited show the phenomenal growth of the pulp and paper industry in the United States since 1940 and the resultant increase in the demand for pulpwood. Figures have also been given for projected usage by the years 1975 and 2000. Both past performance and projected demand are predicated upon the availability of wood fiber at a cost which will be competitive with other natural or man-made fibers. It is the responsibility of the forest manager to provide this wood fiber. The methods used in the several major forest regions of this country to accomplish this purpose will constitute the major portion of the balance of this chapter.

CONDITIONS ESSENTIAL FOR FOREST MANAGEMENT

A prerequisite to the inauguration of any system of forest management is adequate protection from fires, which is a responsibility of the public as well as the owner of timberland. This responsibility has been recognized by several federal laws but more particularly the Weeks Law passed in 1911 and the Clark-McNary Law of 1924. Under the authority of these laws all the forested states have enacted legislation providing for cooperative work with the U.S. Forest Service in the prevention, detection and control of forest fires. However, as late as 1933, there was so little concern about forest fires and their effect on the nation's wood needs, that nearly 44 million acres of timberlands were burned.[1]

As the demands for forest products increased and the impact of the reliance of the total economy of the country on its one renewable natural resource, wood, began to be realized, funds and personnel trained in forest fire detection and suppression became available. The result was that by the year 1950 total acreage burned had been reduced to 15.5 million acres and in 1961 total burn was down to approximately 3.0 million acres.

The risk to the timberland owner of total loss of his investment in growing timber is still greater than it should be, but the over-all picture is improving. The incidence of man-caused fires is decreasing,[1] and there is a growing public awareness that when timber burns, everyone is the loser. Eternal

vigilance is the watchword of fire prevention.

As the risk of loss from fire has diminished, losses from insect attack and tree diseases have increased in their importance to the forester. In the 1952 study of the Forest Service [10] it was estimated that insects and disease accounted for 50% of all timber mortality, whereas the toll from fire was but 7%. Working cooperatively, private agencies, the state and federal forestry forces and forest schools are meeting these challenges through intensive basic research on economic methods of control. To the forester in the field falls the responsibility of detecting and identifying an insect or disease epidemic and then applying such measures of control as will best fit the particular situation.

FOREST MANAGEMENT DEFINED

The words "forest management" have been used several times in prior parts of this chapter, but what is meant by that term as here used? There is no one definition which satisfies every situation, but to the author, forest management means the application of business methods and technical forestry principles to the operation of a forest property, the objective being to have the forest unit produce an annual or periodic maximum net value in timber and other products that can be maintained in perpetuity.

There are certain key phrases in this definition which call for emphasis:

(a) "application of business methods." Forestry is an enterprise which is subject to the laws of economics. The forest property must yield a return to the owner commensurate with the nature and purpose of the investment.

(b) "application of . . . technical forestry principles." There are many technologies in the handbook of the forester; silviculture, the chemistry of soils, engineering, ecology, aerial photo interpretation, game management and public relations are but a few of them.

(c) "in timber or other products." Veneer or peeler logs, poles, piling, sawlogs, pulpwood, and fence posts are timber products which may be available for harvest from any single acre of a managed forest property. Whether or not a specific tree can or will be put to a particular end use is determined by the characteristics of the individual specimen, and the price which can be obtained for it when brought to the market place. Other products may include lake or stream side campsite areas leased on an annual basis at established rates, leased hunting and fishing rights or areas for ski developments and simple picnic areas maintained for fire protection or public relations purposes. Into this "other" category will also fall large-scale Christmas-tree cutting, berry picking, fern or salad gathering, turpentine operations and, where compatible with timber growing, grazing rights.

From this definition it should be evident that the manager of a property owned by a pulp and paper company is concerned with more than just the growing, protecting and harvesting of a crop of timber suited primarily for conversion into pulpwood. It is his job to grow wood fiber at a cost which will be competitive with other natural or manmade fibers. To accomplish this objective, each resource will be so utilized as to make its maximum contribution to the enterprise.

BASIC DATA NEEDED

For any business enterprise to succeed, certain basic facts must be available for examination at regular intervals. In this respect, forest management is no different from any other business. Consider the following comparisons:

The Forest Business

The growth of wood (annual increment)
The mortality of trees
Ingrowth of small trees
Timber drain
Inoperable

Any Other Business

The interest earned
Losses
Capital increases
Disbursements
Write-off

The major difference between these two sets of economic yardsticks is in the frequency of their application. For most forms of business, a quarterly statement as to the health of the enterprise is the least that the owners will accept or can do without. A forest business, on the other hand, can succeed within the framework of periodic measurement of the changes taking place on the property. The more intensive the management of a forest, the greater is the need for regular and frequent reports on the progress of harvesting of various products against budget, on the accomplishment of regeneration objectives and on changes in demand for specific products which may affect current or future operating plans.

A forest enterprise is similar to any other in that if it is to succeed, it must have policies and goals clearly established, yet sufficiently flexible to be able to take advantage of changing conditions. These policies and goals are, in the language of the forester, the forest management plan; each such plan must be predicated on natural factors not associated with more frequently and better-known types of business ventures.

The first, and possibly most important, of these factors is the forest environment, for this combination of conditions determines the tree species best adapted to the area and the silvicultural systems to which they will satisfactorily respond. The forest environment is a complex of atmospheric, topographic and soil influences, complicated by the reactions of the forest and its inhabitants (both plant and animal) to the activities of man. Not only is environment far from uniform throughout a forest region, but it varies from place to place within a given forest area.

Included in the atmospheric or climatic

environment are the factors of temperature, moisture and light. Topographic or physiographic factors include angle of inclination and direction of slope, frequently referred to as aspect. Soil or edaphic environment is that complex of soil moisture, texture, composition and temperature which in large part determines several of the characteristics of tree growth. No one of these environmental factors can be considered as operating independently, for each affects and is affected by the other.

To aid the development of a management plan, information is available in published records on climatic and topographic conditions plus broadly based data on major soil classifications. However, the detailed knowledge required about the timber on the property at the time the plan is being initiated can be obtained only through skillful interpretation of aerial photographs supplemented by systematic data gathering. In this process, the necessary edaphic studies may be completed.

The techniques of interpreting aerial photographs had their beginnings in World War I. Both photographic techniques and interpretation have improved dramatically since then, as witness the U-2 pictures of Cuban military installations. While there are several types of photographs which can be used for purposes of forest management, those taken vertically at a scale of 1:15,840 feet based on sea level are most frequently utilized. When viewed in stereoscopic pairs, mapping of timber types by areas, identification of species, designation of merchantable vs. immature timber, and identification of dominant natural and man-made features (mountains, streams, roads, fences) are all possible for the initiated.[8]

Aerial photographs are indeed a useful tool for the forester, since they make it possible for him to reduce the time needed for detailed field work to provide information of the required accuracy. However, a very considerable amount of on-the-ground work is necessary which must be done in a thor-

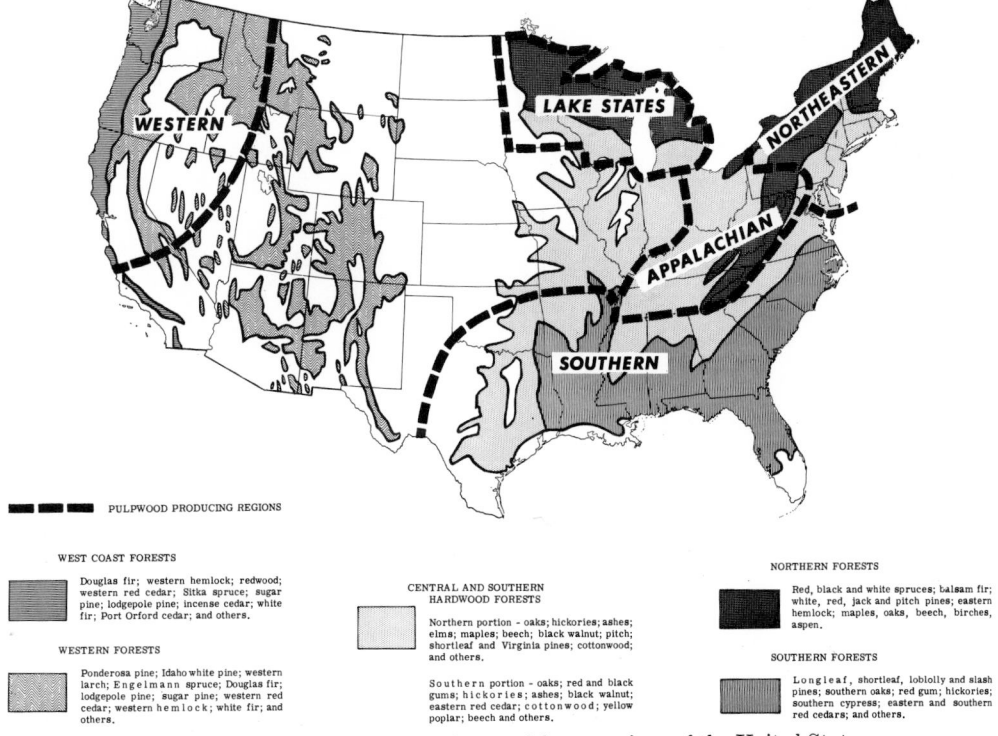

■ ■ ■ ■   PULPWOOD PRODUCING REGIONS

WEST COAST FORESTS

Douglas fir; western hemlock; redwood; western red cedar; Sitka spruce; sugar pine; lodgepole pine; incense cedar; white fir; Port Orford cedar; and others.

WESTERN FORESTS

Ponderosa pine; Idaho white pine; western larch; Engelmann spruce; Douglas fir; lodgepole pine; sugar pine; western red cedar; western hemlock; white fir; and others.

CENTRAL AND SOUTHERN HARDWOOD FORESTS

Northern portion - oaks; hickories; ashes; elms; maples; beech; black walnut; pitch; shortleaf and Virginia pines; cottonwood; and others.

Southern portion - oaks; red and black gums; hickories; ashes; black walnut; eastern red cedar; cottonwood; yellow poplar; beech and others.

NORTHERN FORESTS

Red, black and white spruces; balsam fir; white, red, jack and pitch pines; eastern hemlock; maples, oaks, beech, birches, aspen.

SOUTHERN FORESTS

Longleaf, shortleaf, loblolly and slash pines; southern oaks; red gum; hickories; southern cypress; eastern and southern red cedars; and others.

Fig. 3.1. Pulpwood producing regions and forest regions of the United States.

ough and conscientious manner under conditions which often are not conducive to human comfort.

A discussion of the several methods in use to obtain the needed field data would have to be in rather great detail to be informative and is therefore omitted. Some consideration of the nature and form of data to be gathered does, however, appear to be warranted, using as a typical example a property located in the Southern Forest Region (Figure 3.1).

It is known from a general reconnaissance of the property that the timber stand is predominantly pine but with some good hardwood on the ridge tops and in the sheltered coves. It is also known that pine sawlogs and pulpwood plus some of the better grades of hardwood have been taken from the property in the past five years. Investigation of markets showed that pine poles and piling are in good demand in the area, there is a steady market for pine sawlogs and pine pulpwood, while only the better grades of hardwood can be sold. With these facts in mind and assuming that a pulp and paper manufacturer is considering purchasing the tract, specifications for a cruise would include, though not necessarily be limited to, the following items:

(I) Timber Estimate—Tally by species groups and sizes.

  (A) *Longleaf and Slash Pine* (as a group)

  (B) *Loblolly, Shortleaf and Other Pine* (as a group)

  Trees 8 to 20 inch D.B.H.* by one-inch diameter classes, trees 20 inch D.B.H. and larger by two-inch diameter classes, all by 16-foot log lengths. Trees 8 to 10 inch D.B.H. will be estimated to a 5 inch minimum top diameter, outside bark, and the volumes computed in standard cords of 128 cubic feet. Trees 11 inch D.B.H. and larger will be estimated to a minimum 7 inch top diameter

* D.B.H.—Diameter Breast High.

and the volumes computed in board feet in accordance with the Doyle Log Scale. In addition the 11 and 12 inch trees will also be computed in standard cords.

(C) *Hardwood Sawtimber*
13 to 20 inch D.B.H. by one-inch diameter classes, 20 inch D.B.H. and larger by two-inch diameter classes, all by 16-foot log lengths and to a merchantable top diameter of not less than 9 inches. Board foot volumes will be computed on basis of Doyle Log Scale. Species to be tallied separately are:

> Red Oak
> White Oak
> Gum
> Cypress
> Hickory
> Poplar
> Bay-Magnolia-Maple
> Miscellaneous hardwood

(D) *Hardwood Pulpwood*
Only sound trees 8 to 12 inch D.B.H. will be tallied by diameter class only in accordance with the above species separation and the volumes computed in standard cords. No cull trees in this class will be tallied.

(E) *Cull Hardwood*
13 inch D.B.H. and larger trees containing at least 50% sound merchantable volume will be tallied by diameter class only and the volumes computed in standard cords. Tally will be kept separate in accordance with the following species breakdown:

> *Soft Cull*
> Gum
> Bay-Magnolia-Maple
> Poplar

> *Hard Cull*
> Oak
> Hickory
> Miscellaneous

(F) Timber Estimate—Reproduction and sub-merchantable stems.

(1) Tally by species groups and sizes.

(a) *Longleaf and Slash Pine* (as a group)

(b) *Loblolly, Shortleaf and Other Pine* (as a group)

Trees 2 to 7 inch D.B.H. by one-inch diameter classes. The 5, 6 and 7 inch trees will be computed in standard cords. (Note: Where there is an excess stocking of 2, 3 and 4 inch trees and the strip runs through such an area for 66 feet or more, tally of these stems will be made on the basis of 800 trees per acre and extra count will be disregarded.)

(c) *Red Oak, White Oak, Gum, Cypress, Bay-Magnolia-Maple, Poplar and Miscellaneous Hardwood*

Only sound trees 5 to 7 inch D.B.H. will be tallied by two-inch diameter classes and the volumes computed in standard cords. No cull trees in this class will be tallied.

All pine (11 inch D.B.H. and up) and hardwood (13 inch D.B.H. and up) sawlog volumes are to be reported in board feet, Doyle Log Scale in net volume after cull deductions.

Pine 5 to 10 inch and hardwood 5 to 12 inch to be reported in standard cords. Although the 11 inch and 12 inch pine is computed initially as sawtimber, this tree count will also be computed in cords.

(2) Summary sheets will be prepared for each section or summary unit, for each type at the grand summary level, and for the entire tract (all types combined).

(3) Stock and stand tables by diameter classes will be supplied for both pine and hardwood on the section or unit summaries, grand summary and type or condition class for the overall property.

(4) Acreage will be supplied by type or condition class for each section, unit summary and grand summary.

(II) Timber Type Map

To be a photo controlled ground cruise using aerial photographs as a basis for preliminary typing and preparation of a planimetric base map. Mapping procedure will be in accordance with standard practice.

The forest type and condition classes to be recognized in the preparation of the type map are outlined as follows:

(A) *Pine Types*

(1) Sawlogs (13 inch D.B.H. and larger in Doyle Log Scale)

(a) 3,000 feet per acre or more

(b) 1,000 to 3,000 feet per acre

(c) Less than 1,000 feet per acre

(2) Pulpwood (5 to 12 inch D.B.H. in standard cords)

(a) 10 or more cords per acre 9 to 12 inch D.B.H.

(b) 10 or more cords per acre 5 to 8 inch D.B.H.

(c) 3 to 10 cords per acre 9 to 12 inch D.B.H.

(d) 3 to 10 cords per acre 5 to 8 inch D.B.H.

(e) Less than 3 cords per acre 9 to 12 inch D.B.H.

(f) Less than 3 cords per acre 5 to 8 inch D.B.H.

(3) Natural Reproduction (under 5 inch D.B.H.)

(a) Over 500 trees per acre

(b) Less than 500 trees per acre

The pine types to be delineated on the basis of some combination of the above quantitative brackets for both sawlogs and pulpwood. Typed areas to be not less than 10 acres in size except in the case of open land which will be mapped as it occurs. All plantations, fields, etc., to be noted by appropriate symbols.

(B) *Hardwood Types*

Defined as being any area on which more than 80% of the dominant stems or 80% of the total volume are hardwood species.

  (1) Bottomland, including first and second bottoms (branch and creek bottoms)

    (a) 1,000 board feet per acre or more, Doyle Log Scale

    (b) Less than 1,000 board feet per acre, Doyle Log Scale

  (2) Upland Hardwood, includes all areas not covered by 1.a.&b.

    (a) 1,000 board feet per acre or more, Doyle Log Scale

    (b) Less than 1,000 board feet per acre, Doyle Log Scale

(C) *Pine-Hardwood Types*

Defined as being any pine-hardwood area on which 50 to 80% of the volume is hardwood.

    (a) 1,000 board feet per acre or more, Doyle Log Scale

    (b) Less than 1,000 board feet per acre, Doyle Log Scale

(III)   Reproduction Study

A sample of the pine tree stocking in the seedling and sapling classes (0 to 1.5 inch D.B.H.) is to be obtained using 16-foot square plots subdivided into quadrants. One or more established seedlings per quadrant is to be rated as full stocking.

(IV)   Site Index Map

Using stand procedures to identify site * from sample tree (not old

* Definition: Site or site quality—the capacity of an area to produce vegetation; it is the sum

growth) data and southern pine site index curves, site index classes in 10-foot intervals to be established for each sample tree location.

U.S. Department of Agriculture soil maps to be used in the preparation of an overlay map to show soil type and texture for the entire property.

From the above data and in collaboration with a soils consultant, plot a map showing the boundaries of all sites classified from 60 feet to 110 feet and up. This site index map to be prepared as an overlay to the timber type map.

Acres in each site class are to be summarized for each section, summary unit and grand summary.

(V)   Growth Study

Increment borings to be taken on pine in accordance with standard procedure, said borings to be measured for five year growth only and recorded by D.B.H. and by forest type and condition class. Tabular summaries to be prepared to show average five year growth for each diameter class. On the property as a whole, all borings will be summarized and curved and the data used to project the summary pine stand table ahead five years to compute current annual growth. To provide an estimate of current mortality, pine trees which have died in the year just passed will be tallied in conjunction with the tally of live pines required under I.A and B. (Timber Estimate)

total of the soil factors, biologic factors, and climatic factors affecting the plant or plants. The most commonly used measure of site quality is site index, the height reached by a forest stand at a given age in its development, as represented by the dominant or codominant trees. The standard age is generally fifty years in the eastern United States and one hundred years for the longer-lived species of the West Coast.) [9]

(VI) Final Report: To Include the Following:

(A) *Areas*

(1) Maps—scale 1:20,000 (3.168 inches per mile) Each set described to comprise **20** township sheets.

(a) One set of acetates—planimetric map.

(b) One set of B & W (black and white) check prints from (a).

(c) One set of acetates—timber type map.

(d) Two sets of B & W prints from (b) timber type map; one set showing run layout, one set showing acre count by type.

(e) One set of transloid negatives from (b) timber type map.

(f) Three sets of blueline prints from (d) timber type map; one set colored, two sets uncolored.

(g) One set of B & W prints from (a) showing site index sample tree data.

(h) One set of acetates—site index finished map.

(i) One set of tracing work map overlays—site index, soils and topographic data.

(2) Acreage Summaries

(a) Summary of timber type acreage (3 sets)—one for each section, summary unit and grand summary.

(b) Summary of site index acreage (3 sets)—list by sections, summary unit and grand summary.

(B) *Volumes*

(1) Field tally sheets—one set for each type within each section or fractional section.

(2) Timber estimate summaries.

(a) Tracings—one for each section, summary unit, forest type and condition class at the grand summary level and a grand summary of the entire property.

(b) Three sets of B & W prints from (a) in post binders.

(C) *Final Report*

Six cloth-bound copies, numbered consecutively from 1 to 6.

Before data-processing machines came into general use, the computing and accurate summarizing of all the accumulated field data was an arduous and time-consuming task. Today this work has been greatly simplified and made less subject to error through the field use of mark sensed cards which can be run directly through a computer system. Basic to the accuracy of any final report, however, is the meticulous attention which must have been given to the process of data gathering.

FOREST MANAGEMENT IN ACTION

With the receipt of the final report on the theoretical property just discussed, the owner has available the information needed on which to predicate a decision as to purchase and, if the property is acquired, the data needed to determine management objectives and goals. For further purposes of illustration, let it be assumed that the property is acquired by the pulp and paper manufacturer previously mentioned and that therefore the principal objective of ownership is the production of wood fiber suitable for conversion into pulp at a cost which will be competitive with fibers obtainable from other sources. A further objective is to produce income sufficient not only to pay operating expenses but to contribute to the per share earnings of the company.

Based on the data assembled in the cruise report and on information gathered separately as to markets for products other than pulpwood, it is determined that the present stand of timber best suited for poles, piling and sawlogs could most profitably be liquidated over a ten year period of normal markets. However, since the principal objective of ownership is to convert the property to pulpwood as the major crop at the earliest date possible, all related factors being given due consideration, it is decided to market current stands of poles, etc., in eight years.

To accomplish this goal, the forestry staff prepares a cutting schedule by areas predicated on the information supplied by the timber type map plus further data which

Fig. 3.2. A forester marks a tree for cutting in Florida. (*American Forest Products Industries*)

has been obtained in the field on the specific characteristics of particular stands. Decisions are also reached as to what methods should be used to regenerate the areas to be cut.

In order that there may be an appreciation of some of the economic factors controlling some of these decisions, relative values of different classes of standing timber must be considered. Poles and piling generally have the highest dollar value, because relatively few trees in any given stand meet the required specifications as to straightness, freedom from knots and other defects, and evenness of taper from the butt to the top of the tree. Sawlogs or logs which will produce veneers usually command the

next highest dollar value, for they too have standards of quality which must be met. Whereas pine trees suitable for pulpwood grow to merchantable size in the south in 15 to 20 years, depending upon site factors, trees suitable for other purposes take longer periods.

The stumpage (standing tree) value of pulpwood varies with many factors. The same is true of poles or sawlogs. Distance of the standing tree from its nearest market, whether or not it is near good roads and whether it is growing in flat or mountainous country all are factors in determining the price which it can command in the market.

Unless all the facts as to any particular situation are known, no actual comparison of the stumpage values of poles to sawlogs to pulpwood has any meaning.

Before any cutting is undertaken in any area, a forester will paint mark those pine trees suitable for poles or piling or sawlogs, using a different type of mark for each class. For this purpose he will use an especially designed paint gun in which only paints of specific characteristics and qualities can be used. No trees which are to be utilized for pulpwood need be identified, since it is assumed that all such timber will be cut after the removal of the poles or piling, followed by the sawlog cut.

If the area to be cut is in a part of the tract in which the topography is characterized by rather steep hillsides and narrow valleys with the timber being principally loblolly pine, it may be decided that satisfactory regeneration can be most economically obtained through the leaving of not less than four seed trees per acre. These trees will be selected by the forester, as he marks the other timber for removal. In order that the future stand may be of better quality than the old, only those trees giving indication of growing at the most rapid rate and with the best general form are left as a seed source. No scarification or other preparation of the site will be necessary as the duff or ground cover will be sufficiently disturbed in the logging operation to provide a satisfactory seed bed.

If this same area has been one from which the previous owner has removed some but not all of the merchantable timber, without having made provision for the regeneration of a new crop of trees, additional silvicultural treatment to that just described may be necessary. If, as all too frequently happens, undesirable and weed species of hardwoods such as the scrub varieties of oak (black jack, pin, turkey) dogwood or persimmon invade the area, they must be eliminated before desirable pine reproduction can be obtained. Should the area in such condition be fairly extensive, helicopters may be used to spray it with herbicides which will kill the hardwoods without harming the pine. On small areas, the herbicide may be applied with mistblowers transported by small tractors or even by a man on foot. Unselective but effective tree-killing chemicals may be applied directly to individual trees using girdling or tree injection techniques.

Proceeding upon another assumption, that the harvesting operation is to take place on a portion of the property which is rolling to flat and that the predominant species are longleaf and slash pines, other methods of obtaining the desired new crop can be utilized. However, the same sequence of removal of the present stand will be followed as in the situation previously cited, namely, poles and piling, then sawlogs and finally a clear cut of pulpwood.

Under the described conditions of topography and tree species, experience has proved the desirability of and economic justification for establishment of the new crop by planting seedlings of the desired species. If the ground cover is very heavy, a thorough and rather expensive job of preparing the site for planting is necessary to eliminate competition with the young seedlings for moisture. In this procedure, heavy

Fig. 3.3. Bulldozing and disking to control unwanted hardwood growth prior to planting pine. (*American Forest Products Industries*)

equipment pulled behind a large tractor breaks down and macerates the small trees and brush while, at the same, turning up the soil in much the same manner as a disk harrow in preparing agricultural land. Planting of the pine seedlings, which takes place between mid-December and mid-April in most of the southern pine range, is not done until the soil on the newly prepared area has had time to settle.

In those situations where the ground cover is light to moderately heavy, site preparation and its cost is reduced to a minimum. Here, under controlled conditions, fire is used as a silvicultural tool to kill as much as possible of the vegetation which would compete with the newly planted seedlings. In the planting process, attached to the front end of a light tractor there is a plow so designed that it scalps in the earth a furrow from four to six inches deep and about thirty inches wide. This has the effect of producing an area cleared of all vegetation. Following the tractor is a standard tree-planting machine. With this type of equipment and under fair operating conditions, three men can plant from 8,000 to 12,000 pine seedlings or between 11 and 17 acres in a nine-hour day. One man operates the tractor, another plants the trees from the planting machine, while the third services the equipment with seedlings and other necessary supplies.

The timber type map of the property, together with analysis of the cruise data, brings to light the existence of several areas of pine plantation which are between 15 and 18 years old. The growth data obtained on these plantings during the cruise, supplemented by further on-the-ground studies, show that the growth of the trees has been slowed by reason of too thick a stand. The data at hand might show a present stand of say 32 cords on the 18-year-old planting, but that projecting current increment, this rate of growth will not continue. A thinning operation to bring the stand into a free-to-grow condition is therefore needed. To set up this thinning operation, a forester is as-

signed the job of marking the timber to be removed. Keeping a tally of marked trees as he progresses and with a basic plan in mind of reducing the stand by approximately one-third of its present volume, he covers each acre in parallel strips. By regular reference to the tally, he determines whether the marking is too severe or too light and corrects accordingly.

Up to this point consideration has been given only to broad phases of the management of the pine component of this theoretical property. However, there is merchantable hardwood which can be marketed and, as has been discussed earlier in this chapter, hardwood pulpwood is becoming increasingly important to the pulp manufacturer. It is therefore to be assumed that our new owner will want to grow those hardwods most desirable for pulp manufacture on those sites best suited to that purpose. Parenthetically the observation is made that until recent years, emphasis has been given in most southern pulp and paper company forest management plans, to the conversion of hardwood lands to pine wherever economically feasible. That situation is now undergoing **marked** change.

The studies made of the market for pine sawlogs concluded that the good hardwood timber on the property can also be sold at a profit. Therefore such sales are integrated into the total timber marketing plan in order that the property may make maximum contributions to company earnings.

The silviculture of southern hardwoods is far from being as advanced as that of pine, simply because there has not been the need for its development. It appears that, for the most part a selection system of cutting to favor the growth of more desirable species plus the expenditure of limited funds to eradicate those less desirable, is the best practice. It is this policy which would be followed on our theoretical property until the results of experiments on other methods are made known.

The objective of this very broadly treated case study of a forest property, located in the southern pine region, has been to give the reader some understanding of the basic purposes of forest management. How those purposes could be accomplished have been illustrated by a few examples of common situations. No two forest properties are exactly alike and no two situations can be treated with the same prescription. The methodology utilized to develop a forest management plan varies only as to detail in the several forest regions in the United States. A discussion of some of those variations and silvicultural systems adopted to obtain desired regeneration follows.

That portion of the northern forest region (see Figure 3.1) lying in the northern parts of the states of Maine, New Hampshire, Vermont and New York, is of particular significance to the pulp and paper industry. It is in this area that are found the extensive tracts of spruce and balsam which have supplied the bulk of the pulpwood requirements of the region since the turn of the century. In these areas today, as in the South, hardwoods such as beech, birch, maple and aspen are assuming greater importance in the pulpwood mix and consequently more attention is being given to their management.

Because most of this softwood region is characterized by areas without publicly supported highway systems, a primary consideration in the forest management plan is a road location and construction program. This system must be designed to give maximum access for purposes of fire protection and the harvesting of the forest crop. At the same time construction costs must be held to a minimum for each dollar spent in this activity becomes a charge which must be amortized as timber is cut.

In this area, too, markets for timber products other than pulpwood are far less prevalent than in the South with the result that the major part of management costs must be borne by the pulpwood harvest. Intensive forest practices which are fully justified in the south are therefore not financially attractive to the northern forest manager,

for it is his responsibility to grow wood fiber at costs competitive with other regions.

Fortunately for the forest manager handling spruce and balsam, his problems of adequate regeneration are minimal. Whether his harvesting operations take place on steep mountain slopes where patch clear cutting is an economic necessity or on relatively flat lands where selective management using progressive cutting is desirable, nature provides prolific and satisfactory regeneration. The seed of both balsam and spruce will lie dormant in the soil for many years, ready to sprout when the shade of the overstory is removed. The one great hazard is fire, for when one occurs it destroys not only the standing timber, both young and mature, but also the soil cover in which the seeds have been stored. Regeneration of such areas can be obtained only by the expensive process of hand planting or by waiting for nature to ever so slowly rebuild the forest.

That part of the northern forest region lying in the area of the Great Lakes (see Figure 3.1) presents challenges to the forest manager different from those in the Northeast, due to an increasing predominance of red, jack and pitch pine in the softwood stand brought about by edaphic conditions and a series of disastrous fires in the early part of this century. Here, because of an established paper industry situated close to a large potential market for its products, a reduction in permitted pulpwood exports from the Province of Ontario and a diminishing wood supply at home, intensive forest management became an economic necessity.

In 1961, George B. Amidon, Director of Woodlands of the Minnesota and Ontario Paper Company, International Falls, Minnesota delivered at the University of Washington College of Forestry in Seattle, Washington, the fifth in a series of lectures on industrial forestry.[5] His subject covered the Lake States. Beginning on page 32 of the booklet containing Mr. Amidon's lectures is a section on "Trends in Industrial Forestry." It so succinctly describes the situation as it relates to the pulp and paper industry in the area that it is quoted below.

"Several surveys have been made by the author and the American Pulpwood Association, over the past ten years, of the mills in the region to determine progress being made in forest management. These have not given 100 per cent coverage, but the response to the surveys has been good and the information obtained a reliable indication of trends in forestry activities. The weakest part of this effort is the fact that most of the information is from the pulp and paper industry, and the other segments of the industry have not been adequately sampled. The major industry has, however, been well covered.

"The first survey was made in 1947, another one in 1950, a third one in 1953, and a smaller fourth survey was made in 1960 for use in this paper. All of these surveys which started with information in 1937 show impressive progress in number of technical foresters employed, in increased planting programs, and in the development of sustained yield management plans.

"The major conclusions from the 1947 survey, for example, were that the pulp and paper mills which reported (60 per cent by volume) employed nearly five times as many foresters in 1947 as in 1937, that land ownership had increased from 660,000 acres to nearly 1,200,000 acres during the ten-year period, and that plans were well under way for the acquisition of sufficient lands to produce under good management nearly one-third of the industry's annual requirements. The 1950 survey supported the earlier findings and showed in addition that the number of foresters employed in 1950 was over five times the 1937 figure and that land ownership had increased from 660,000 acres to nearly 1,600,000 acres.

"The 1953 survey was conducted under the auspices of the American Pulpwood Association. This was more complete than the previous surveys and gave additional information on forestry progress by the region's pulp and paper companies. The mills cooperating in this survey accounted for 90 per cent of the total pulpwood used in the region.

"The major results of this survey for the reporting mills were as follows:

(1) 77 per cent of the mills employed trained foresters in 1952, compared to 44 per cent in 1945.

(2) Sixty-seven graduate foresters were employed in forest management work in 1952, or one forester per 26,300 acres of company-owned forest land.

(3) 59 per cent of the mills owned forest land in 1952. The land owned by these mills was 1,760,000 acres.

(4) The mills had planted nearly 45,000 acres by 1952 and were planning to plant over 5,000 acres annually. (1952 Lake States Experiment Station figures show 276,000 acres of acceptable plantations on private lands. In 1960, the 31 major companies in the region planted over seven million trees on 7,541 acres.)

(5) The mills estimated average growth on company lands of .26 of a cord per acre in 1952 and .36 of a cord per acre by 1962.

(6) Expenditures for forest management averaged nearly 27 cents per acre on company lands or 17.5 cents per cord of pulpwood used in 1952.

(7) Taxes on company-owned lands averaged nearly 18 cents per acre in 1952.

"The survey conducted for this report (1960) covered only nine companies in the region, but these were the larger ones and represented two lumber and seven pulp and paper companies. The 1959 pulpwood consumption of the seven companies was nearly 45 per cent of the regional total. Some of the more interesting facts obtained from this survey are as follows:

(1) The nine companies own 2,221,000 acres of forest land or about 74 per cent of the total industrial forest land in the region as reported for 1952. (Actually, the industrial land is now probably greater than shown for 1952, so the percentage of these nine mills would not be this high.)

(2) The number of technical foresters employed on forestry or woods work by these companies was 19 in 1940, 66 in 1950 and 108 in 1960. This is a 470 per cent increase in twenty years and a 64 per cent increase in the last ten years.

(3) These nine companies have planted over 54,000 acres, to 1960.

"The record of these several surveys does not give precise or conclusive figures of forestry progress, but it does show that the industry has been making rapid gains in employment of foresters, in forest land ownership, in sustained yield management, and in planting, all of which are basic to an effective forestry program."

It was in the Lake States that the now widely accepted method of obtaining essential forest management data through the use of a Continuous Forest Inventory was first developed by the United States Forest Service and adopted for industrial use. It is here too that the demands of the public for recreational opportunity have been keenly felt by private owners and where progressive steps toward game management have been undertaken.

The growth in acreage of timberland owned and put under management by pulp and paper companies, the increase in number of foresters employed, and the strides made in the development of forest plantations in the Lake States since the close of World War II have not been peculiar to that region. Each of the major forest regions of the country can produce similar statistics.

The forest management practices discussed thus far have been applicable to sections of the country where the old growth timber had been harvested in years past and the challenge to the forester lies in the handling of second growth stands. However, in the Western forests, the opposite condition exists. There, the task is one of most efficiently and profitably liquidating the large old growth and of regenerating a new crop. Intensive management calls for prelogging or a thinning operation, a harvest cut and finally a salvage of the down, but merchantable timber. To keep this operation in proper perspective to those previously considered, it is necessary to keep in mind the very large size of the timber harvested and the stand of timber per acre of ground. It is not at all unusual to find a salvage operation in a western forest producing a greater volume of timber per acre than one would look

Fig. 3.4. View of patch cutting in Douglas Fir timber in Oregon. (*American Forest Products Industries*)

Fig. 3.5. Methodically criss-crossing tree farm lands scarred by forest fire near Vernonia, Oregon, a helicopter scatters Douglas fir seed for a new forest crop for the Long-Bell Division of International Paper Company. Snags have been cleared to reduce fire hazards and available timber has been salvaged. (*American Forest Products Industries*)

for as a good harvest cut of mature timber in any other forest region.

In considering forest management in the western regions, it is necessary that consideration be given to the end products of a timber harvest. Whereas in the Lake States, the Northeast and to a certain extent in the South, pulpwood comprises a major part of the cut, in the West sawlogs, peeler logs (veneer) and poles are the items of major interest. Pulpwood is principally a by-product, being derived from thinnings or salvage cuttings or from sawlogs which because of defects will not make salable lumber.

As in no other region, the raw material of the pulp and paper industry is derived from chips produced from sawmill residuals. Table 3.3 illustrates this point.

TABLE 3.3. PULPWOOD CONSUMPTION BY SOURCE OF SUPPLY (CORDS) *

| | Western Region | | Per Cent Purchased Chips | |
| | Purchased Total Wood | | | |
Year	Chips	Use	West	Total U.S.
1957	3,086,724	7,228,364	42.7	12.0
1958	3,623,798	7,030,368	51.5	12.7
1959	3,810,158	7,666,160	49.7	16.5
1960	3,821,175	7,940,188	48.0	15.2

* Source: Same as Table I.

In no other region is there the symbiotic relationship between sawmill and pulp mill. In fact many pulp mills of the Western area are owned and operated by companies which started as producers of lumber.

In the Douglas fir, western hemlock forests, patch cutting, with regeneration supplied from surrounding seed areas, is most common. In the ponderosa and lodgepole pine, western hemlock and western red cedar stands, selective cutting has been generally practiced but more recently the trend has been toward clear cutting with regeneration obtained by artificial means.

Natural regeneration is generally adequate in the Western forests, but where such is not the case, hand planting of seedlings or helicopter seeding is utilized. This latter technique has been brought to its most refined state in this region, a development made necessary by the rugged topography of the country and the consumption by rodents and birds of the dispersed seed.

As in every other forest region, the management of a forest property for the production of future timber crops was totally impractical until the risk of major fires had been reduced to a minimum. The history of forest fire prevention and suppression in the states of Washington, Oregon and California is an outstanding example of what can be accomplished when the efforts of federal, state and private forces are effectively combined.[6]

FORESTRY ON PRIVATELY OWNED LANDS

Up to this point the discussion has been directed to a consideration of forest management on lands owned or controlled by the pulp and paper industry. It is believed that the objectives of such ownership or control have been adequately demonstrated. But since the total industry obtains no more than 30% (and probably less) of its total round wood requirements—as opposed to chips obtained from sawmill residuals—from these lands, what about the management practiced on the balance of the properties from which this wood must be harvested?

To the best of the author's knowledge no statistics are available as to the quantities of pulpwood obtained from publicly owned and managed lands, such as the national, state and county forests. But whatever the amount, it is recognized that these properties too are dedicated to the growing of continuous crops of timber, and it is to be expected that they will contribute as fully to the nation's timber economy in the future as they have in the past.

The only remaining source of wood supply is the land in the hands of some 3,400,000 farmers and 1,100,000 other private owners.[2] In 1952, these farmers owned approximately 165,000,000 acres of commercial forest land and the "others" approximately 131,000,000 acres. These ownership figures are in contrast to the 62,000,000 acres owned by all the forest products industries and the 130,000,000 acres in public ownership.[10]

Recognizing its dependence on the lands in private ownership for a substantial part of its raw material needs, the pulp and paper industry has taken a leading role in fostering good forest management on "outside" ownerships. The economics of investing money in the growing of trees for future crops is of as much, if not more, importance to the farmer or other small timberland owner as it is to a corporation. A market for pulpwood has furnished the economic base and the cash incentive for private owners to undertake good forest practices where no such incentive had previously existed.

Lacking too, on the part of the small landowner, was a knowledge of how best to operate his timber property. To fill this vacuum in part, the Southern Pulpwood Conservation Association was organized in 1938 for the sole purpose of promoting good cutting practices on forest properties from which pulpwood was being harvested. It was then, and still is, supported by the majority of the pulp and paper mills of the South. The effectiveness of its work has been applauded by the United States Forest Service and the Forest Service of every southern state.

American Forest Products Industries, Inc., the public relations arm of the major forest-based industries, initiated the Tree Farm Program. A Tree Farm is a tract of taxpaying privately owned land in the United States on which the owner:

(1) protects his woods from fire, insects, disease and destructive grazing;

(2) harvests his trees in a manner that insures repeated crops; and

(3) reforests, through planting or seeding, portions of the Tree Farm that require it, thus maintaining full productivity of the land.

Out of the Tree Farm Program grew the Tree Farm Family which is a group of small private landowners who receive advice from a specific forest industry in the management of their lands on the premise they will carry out prescribed practices so as to qualify for tree farm certification. They in return have available preferential markets for their forest products.

As of December 31, 1961 there were 22,311 owners and 57,804,054 acres in the Tree Farm Program.[2]

PULPWOOD SUPPLIES

In 1935 there were 25 pulp and paper mills in the South, using annually about 2½ million cords of wood. It was estimated that in that year the total standing timber in the 12 Southern states was 120 billion cubic feet. In the 25 years that followed, while the number of pulp and paper mills was tripling, 147 billion cubic feet was harvested. During the same period, however, the timber resources of the South increased to 131 billion cubic feet—9% more in 1960 than existed in 1935.[7]

Using data for Maine in 1958 as a criterion for the Northeastern Region as a whole, it appears that the net annual growth of growing stock of all species has increased by some 50% over that found to be available in a previous survey. In softwood alone the increase is 83.7%. In other words, softwoods are growing eight times faster than they are being cut.[3]

Statistics for the states of Michigan and Minnesota indicate a gain of growth over cut in the area of 6% for all species, when compared to the data available in 1952.[3]

Inasmuch as the timber economy of the Western forest regions is predicated largely on the liquidation of old growth timber which is not adding significant growth, the picture there is one of greater drain than increment.

RESEARCH ACTIVITIES

Even though there is every indication that current and prospective pulpwood demands will be met through the growth of wood fiber at competitively attractive costs, the forest managers of the pulp and paper industry are quite aware of the challenges of substitute materials. To meet these challenges, a constant search is being carried on to improve the growing stock. This search is taking place in the laboratories of the Institute of Paper Chemistry, and of the Universities of California, Texas, Florida and North Carolina, to mention but a few. Both here and in the field, the science of genetics is being put to full use in an effort to grow trees to greater volumes, at faster rates, with cleaner boles and fewer limbs. At the same time the search goes on for stock that is disease- and insect-resistant.

Work in these fields has made rapid strides in the South in particular, where several companies have established seed orchards, the plants for which have been produced by the grafting of small branches shot from superior trees to healthy root stock of the same species. When these trees flower, controlled pollination will make available seed of a superior strain of tree for planting in nursery beds. Much of the seed used today in southern forest nurseries is gathered from trees selected for their rapid growth and generally desired qualities, thus assuring a finer planting stock for future generations of trees. Similar steps are being taken in other forest regions.

Much of the genetics work undertaken up to this time has been based on what the forester considered to be the type of tree he wants for the future. Research in the pulp and paper industry is now directing its attention to the type of fiber which the paper maker wants in his tree of the future. What the answer will be is still in the test tubes of the men in the laboratories.

MULTIPLE USE

Throughout this chapter, emphasis has been given to the techniques of forest management and the economics of producing economically wood fiber suitable for the manufacture of pulp. But there is another side to forest management which is also of great concern to the forester in the field and to the pulp and paper company which owns or controls a "timber factory," namely, the multiple benefits which can and do accrue to society and to the owner through the wise use of the land which is held in trust. These benefits inherent in the forest—water, forage, wild life, recreation as well as timber—are treated as a part of the total forest management plan by every forward-looking manager. The increasing demand for recreational space has placed the owners of large and attractive woodland areas in a position to supply a need, take a forward step in the field of public relations and at the same time reap some economic benefits. The growing of timber and the production of game are compatible in many areas and forest management plans of the pulp and paper industry are being directed to that end.

To close this chapter, the use of a statement made by Mr. Paul L. Phillips, President, United Papermakers and Paperworkers, AFL-CIO, at a Land Use Conference held in Washington, D.C. in September 1961, seems most fitting. Mr. Phillips said, "Forest management has brought a considerable degree of permanance to the paper industry. The paper industry finally is taking the lead in forest management and is making amazing progress. Continued availability of raw material, therefore, means the difference between production and annihilation."

REFERENCES

1. American Forest Products Industries, Inc., "Progress in Private Forestry in the United States," Table XVII, p. 46; Table XVIII, p. 87, 1961.
2. American Forest Products Industries, Inc., Memorandum, January 1, 1962.
3. American Forest Products Industries, Inc., "A New Look at the Wood Supply," p. 7, 1961.
4. American Pulpwood Association, "The Pulpwood Industry in the United States," Unpublished manuscript.
5. Amidon, George B., "The Development of Industrial Forestry in the Lake States," p. 34, Seattle, Washington, University of Washington, College of Forestry, 1961.
6. Cowan, Charles S., "The Enemy is Fire," Seattle, Washington, Superior Publishing Company, 1961.
7. McCaffrey, J. E., "Annual Report of the President," Vol. 92, (THE UNIT) p. 5, Atlanta, Georgia, Southern Pulpwood Conservation Association, 1962.
8. Spurr, Stephen H., "Aerial Photography in Forestry," p. 51, New York, The Ronald Press Company, 1948.
9. Spurr, Stephen H., "Forest Inventory," pp. 301 and 309, New York, The Ronald Press Company, 1952.
10. United States Department of Agriculture, U.S. Forest Service, "Timber Resources for America's Future," Table 5, p. 17; Table 6, p. 17; Table 41, p. 65; Table 16, p. 32, Jan. 1958.

CHAPTER 4

Pulpwood Procurement and Production

WILLIAM S. BROMLEY

Executive Secretary, American Pulpwood Association and Co-authors *

Wood in various forms of "pulpwood" is the dominant raw material base of the pulp and paper manufacturing industry. About 90% of all pulpwood consumed in the United States is purchased by pulp mills and only 10% is produced by logging operations of pulp and paper companies, but almost the reverse is true in Canada. It is essential therefore to understand how American pulp mills buy or "procure" the 90% of their pulpwood requirements and how pulpwood is logged or "produced" in the U.S. and in Canada.

Most pulpwood is prepared from sections of trees in lengths that range from 4 feet to as much as full tree length. The minimum diameters usually range from 4 to 14 inches, but may include logs or bolts up to 40 inches in diameter. When sold, pulpwood is usually measured in terms of "cords." A "cord" of pulpwood is 128 cubic feet of wood, bark and air space resulting when bolts are stacked in a space 4 by 4 by 8 feet, or in any dimensions resulting in this volume. A "rough" cord refers to unpeeled wood. A cord of "peeled" wood refers to bolts of wood from which the bark has been removed prior to its measurement.

Pulpwood is usually (about 80%) sold and bought in terms of "roundwood" in

* Co-authors—APA Forest Engineers, J. A. Altman, J. S. Hensel, J. A. Holekamp, K. S. Rolston, Jr. and D. A. Swan.

rough or peeled "cords." The unit of measure may be in terms of other units of volume such as "cunits" of 100 cubic feet; or "units" of 168 cubic feet; or if the wood is in chip form, as "chip units" equal to one cord of rough pulpwood. The "chip units" may vary from 190 to 210 cubic feet depending on the contractual agreement between the seller and buyer of the wood concerned, which may even include provisions for buying wood or wood chips by weight instead of by volume. Pulpwood received at mills in "chip" form accounts for about 20% of total consumption in the United States.

With this brief statement of what pulpwood is and how it is measured, we can now consider how pulpwood is "procured" or bought from dealers or producers or obtained directly from company operations or imports. To avoid confusion elsewhere in this chapter, these terms are defined in detail as follows:

Dealer: A supplier to the pulp company who buys domestic (U.S.) pulpwood, chips, or other pulping raw materials of forest origin from others for resale to the company. The dealer may own some logging equipment, but the majority of his sales volume is processed in the forest by producers who own their own equipment and employ their own logging workers but deliver wood to the dealer or to the mill under the dealer's contract or purchase order.

Producer: A producer may be a farmer or other individual who manages a domestic (U.S.) pulpwood harvesting operation or an operation processing other pulping raw material of forest origin, independent of a dealer and sells his products *directly* to the pulp company or to a dealer.

Company Operation: A domestic (U.S.) pulpwood-producing unit (or other pulping raw material-processing unit) wholly owned and operated by the pulp manufacturing company. The workers concerned are on the company payroll.

Imported Receipts: Pulpwood harvested outside of the continental limits of the United States.

Pulp companies usually provide for the procurement of pulpwood in a separate division, or as part of an overall "Wood Department." Some of the larger companies with Woodlands Departments may have separate subdivisions to cover such responsibilities as:

(1) Wood Procurement
(2) Woodlands Administration
(3) Woodlands Research
(4) Logging
(5) Land Acquisition or Examination.

Regardless of where or how pulpwood procurement is handled in each company, it is estimated that the proportion of pulpwood received at United States mill sites in 1961 was:

	Thousand Cords	Approximate Per Cent
(1) Dealer operation	26,700	63
(2) Producer operation	10,400	25
(3) Company operation	3,900	9
(4) Imported receipts	1,300	3
Totals	42,300	100

The balance of this chapter will deal first with the details of how pulpwood is procured or obtained by pulp mills, second with how pulpwood is produced or logged and finally with trends and research in pulpwood production.

PULPWOOD PROCUREMENT

Pulpwood Procurement Through Dealers

To understand the dealer system and how it works, it is necessary to know the origin and background of this method of procuring pulpwood and how it evolved to the system we know today, particularly as developed in the Appalachian and Southern Regions.

Prior to the turn of the century practically all pulpwood was produced by company-operated logging crews on company-owned or company-leased lands. This wood was taken out of the woods by company-owned railroads and flumes and by animal-drawn wagon trains or sled trains. The wood was then transferred to public railroads or to water for delivery direct to the mill.

Around 1920, as the demand for wood increased because of construction of new mills and increased capacity of existing mills, the demand for markets for forest products from the many small woodlots was also increasing. To satisfy these demands, the pulp companies began appointing local merchants as wood buyers. These merchants bought wood in wagon load lots (about 60 cubic feet per load) and transferred it to rail box cars. The hauling distance was seldom more than four to six miles, for with the existing road conditions and the slow pace of ox teams, this was about the maximum distance that could be covered with one load in a day. The merchant usually offered goods sold in his store in exchange for the wood. The volume of wood purchased at these buying stations initially was so small that the pulp companies could not justify full-time men to look after the purchases.

As the early trucks (usually Model T Fords with a capacity of about three quarters of a cord) started coming into the picture in the mid-twenties, the merchants changed from payment in goods to cash payments. The method of payment in goods was not satisfactory to people who must purchase gas, oil and tires, as well as household staples. The advent of trucks meant that the hauling distances could be increased along with the pay loads. This increased the volume of wood tributary to each merchant or buying station, which in turn permitted the pulp mills to increase their purchases from this source.

The Office of Price Administration (O.P.A.) during World War II recognized the dealer system and added stature to it by allocating given areas, some by states, some by counties, and some by certain lines of a railroad to these dealers. The wood was then purchased in carload lots and the dealer received a standard commission on each cord of wood shipped from his area regardless of the time and effort that he spent in seeing that the wood was produced. This same system has been expanded to the point that today most dealers devote full time to wood procurement and in many instances employ one or more full-time assistants.

Often a dealer has his own pulpwood crews working for him in addition to purchasing wood from independent suppliers on the open market. He sometimes assists these independent suppliers in locating pulpwood stumpage and in arranging financing for it. At times he also finds it necessary to arrange financing for logging equipment and the other incidentals necessary to producing wood.

Some dealers are large forest landowners and their headquarters or offices are headquarters for forest management information in their areas. Some of the newer dealers are graduate foresters and the larger dealers often employ graduate foresters to assist in forest management and wood procurement.

A dealer may sign a wood order or an agreement with a pulp company to supply a specified number of cords per year, but the vast majority of dealers operate on weekly wood orders. The wood order may be subject to frequent adjustments in volume subject to the needs of the particular mill. In most instances pulpwood is bought by the dealers at their own buying stations or pulpwood concentration yards. Inventories of pulpwood are stored in bundles or piles for shipment to the pulp mill. In most yards the wood is unloaded from pulpwood trucks by mechanical unloaders costing over $10,000 each. Wood is generally scaled on a volume basis, but weigh-scaling is gaining in use and acceptance. Payment is usually by check upon receipt of the wood from the producer. Dealers still arrange for railroad cars to be spotted at local sidings to be loaded by hand by the producers when the producers find it more convenient than delivering wood to the concentration yard.

Pulpwood production increased 93% from 1950 to 1960. It is safe to say that during this period purchases through the dealer system increased at about the same percentage rate as did the direct purchases from producers.

Pulpwood Procured from Producers

An estimated 25% of the annual pulpwood receipts are procured directly from producers. The success of this sort of procurement depends largely on the skill and ability of the pulp company employees assigned to act as liaison with producers. These employees are required to perform many of the same tasks described as functions of a dealer without the direct profit incentive upon which the dealer system is dependent.

The type of company employee involved in direct procurement varies in background and responsibility from region to region. In many cases these men have a background of practical experience in dealing with producers and landowners. In some areas, particularly in the South, wood procurement men are often trained professional foresters who have learned to weigh the factors influencing the delivery of pulpwood and have learned how to win the respect of the producers and landowners in their sphere of influence.

In some areas, specifically in the Northeast and Lake States, these men are often called "company wood buyers." In the Southern States a variety of titles ranging from "Conservation Forester" to "Area Superintendent" are used to describe a wood procurement employee.

The division or department head who has the responsibility for over-all wood procurement must have the administration skills necessary to direct and advise his field men, scalers, timber cruisers, logging superintendent, etc. The primary function of his organization is to furnish the required raw material in the necessary amounts at a competitive price. Careful daily analysis of the changing conditions of stumpage supply, labor availability, climatic prospects, mill woodyard inventory, transport availability, and fluctuation in mill requirements are needed to meet the demands of this primary function.

A wood procurement employee finds that he must make numerous on-the-spot decisions in the transaction of business between the pulp mill and the producer and sometimes with landowners. A dealer can speak for himself, but the company employee must keep the reputation and integrity of his employer in mind when he makes decisions or implements policy. Upon his ability and good judgment depend the good relations with producers, landowners, and the general public necessary to an efficient and profitable business.

The advantage of procuring wood directly from producers has become more apparent since the advent of the mechanized rail concentration yard. The company, through its wood procurement division, often can establish better control over the fluctuations in receipts, stimulate producers to improve their operating equipment and techniques, and promote conservation practices among landowners.

In some cases the company procurement employee will have additional duties with respect to the acquisition and management of company lands. A man with such responsibilities can often act in a most comprehensive fashion to prevent or overcome a shortage of supply.

Some companies feel that the administration and business functions with producers are best served through the dealer system. Many pulp mills are currently employing

Fig. 4.1. Hauling pulpwood longer distances is now economically possible with larger trucks and trailer units.

Fig. 4.2. Improvements in handling equipment will continue. This unit moves a cord of wood per trip from stump to road.

both systems. Generally this means procuring directly from producers in areas close to the mill and relying on dealer procurement for the areas further out.

Procurement from Company Operations— United States

In 1961, the last year for which a breakdown of consumption figures is available, of the 42,318,000 cords equivalent of round pulpwood consumed by United States pulp mills, about 9%, or approximately 4 million cords, came from company operations. A large percentage of this was wood in chip or slab form, produced from sawmill and veneer mill wastes. While figures are not available, it is known that a sizable percentage of this material was developed from saw mills operated by pulp and paper mills. This is particularly true in the West, but is not included in the amount of roundwood from company operations above.

We might at this point enlarge somewhat the definition of the term "company operation" previously given. It means simply that the workers producing the wood are on a pulp manufacturing company's payroll and supervised by company personnel

rather than on the payroll of a pulpwood producer, logging contractor, dealer or broker.

While only 9% of the pulpwood supply nationwide came from company operations, the ratio of operated wood to purchased wood does vary considerably between regions. In the Northeast, 16% of the wood is operated by the consuming companies, in the North Central region 11%, in the South only slightly over 2% and in the West 30% is company-operated.

The production from company operations varies even more widely between companies. Several companies particularly in the Northeast and West produce over half their wood supply by company operations, while others have no operations. This relationship between operated and purchased wood has been relatively stable for many years. In general the companies owning the most land do the most operating. When we consider that the pulp and paper companies own only 23.3 million acres (1956) of forest land in the United States and are currently using over 40,000,000 cords per year it becomes obvious that the industry's lands are not capable of growing the wood consumed. Using the most optimistic growth rate imaginable of one cord per acre per year, industry-owned lands could not supply much more than half the pulpwood consumed at present, even if they were fully stocked. Another factor is that many company operations are integrated, the higher quality material going into products other than pulpwood.

Practically all the land owned by the pulp and paper companies is now under good management and in general is being cut as heavily as practicable when it is considered that much of it is in small second growth or new plantations.

Company operations undoubtedly are the most reliable source of wood supply for the mills and the wood is of generally higher quality due to closer control of all phases of production.

Company operations from a production standpoint are usually more mechanized and seem more efficient than those of the small independent producer, but paradoxically often produce the most expensive wood. One reason for this is that the companies usually operate remote or difficult logging areas in which development and

transportation costs are inherently high and beyond the financial ability of the independent producers.

In some cases a pulp and paper company will buy stumpage and operate it as a company operation. There are usually special circumstances calling for such action, perhaps remoteness, size, or logging conditions of the area or lack of financially responsible producers. Most company operations in the northern United States today are smaller than those of 20 years ago, when large camps and cookrooms were a necessity and the latter are not even found in the South. Today the trend is to have the men commute from their homes or in more remote areas "housekeeping" camps are furnished. In the northern areas of course there are still many company-operated camps complete with cookrooms, but the trend is away from them.

The shift to more mechanization in the woods and the high capital cost involved in mechanizing will probably tend to increase the amount of company-operated wood or at least hold it at present levels. Few independent producers can afford to experiment with new equipment and meth-

Fig. 4.3. A mixed hardwood area, marked by a forester for thinning. Pulpwood shown has been taken out to improve the standing timber and accelerate growth.

ods; thus most equipment and method development work must be done on company operations.

Another factor that may increase the amount of wood produced by company operations is that much company-owned land will become more productive as plantations and second growth reaches maturity.

Procurement from Company Operations— Canada

We have seen that only 10% of the pulpwood produced in the United States is from company operations while 90% of it is purchased from a myriad suppliers. Almost the reverse is true in Canada where 78% of the wood is produced by company operations or large contractors operating on company-licensed limits, and 22% purchased from independent suppliers. For the purpose of this text, we will consider large contractors operating on pulp and paper company limits as company operations. They are very similar, the company usually owning the camps, doing all development work and the "contractor" simply working on a production bonus system for the actual pulpwood production.

When the ownership pattern of timberland in Canada is noted, it becomes clear why so much of the pulpwood supply is company-operated. Approximately 93% of the total forest area of Canada is publicly owned and administered as "Crown" lands by the Federal or Provincial Governments —usually the latter, although title rests with the Federal Government. There are 141,000,000 acres of commercial "Crown" land under license to private timber operators, of which 117,000,000 acres are held as pulpwood licenses. In addition to the above there are 231,000,000 acres of commercial forest land potentially available for pulpwood or other timber licenses. Much of the latter, though, is too inaccessible to be economically operable at present.

To put the United States-Canadian picture in perspective, then, consider that the Canadian pulp and paper industry—con-suming only some 13,000,000 cords annually, including approximately 1,000,000 cords equivalent of chips from sawmill residues—has 117,000,000 acres already under license and potential control to draw from, while the United States industry, consuming 40,000,000 cords plus, has only 23,000,000 acres (1956) under its control (ownership).

To produce and deliver pulpwood from these large unbroken areas of timber, large-scale company operations appear to be the most efficient method—indeed it is the only means of securing the needed wood.

An interesting aspect of Canadian operations is that some provinces, particularly Ontario, compel limit licensees to produce a certain percentage of sawlogs along with their pulpwood. Much of the pulpwood delivered to Canadian mills is by water, some drives involving distances of 200 miles or more. This too tends to require large-scale company operations.

It is unlikely that the pattern of wood development and procurement in Canada will change much in the foreseeable future, although pressure is now being exerted by the Quebec Government on the companies to buy more wood from farmers through cooperatives established by the government to provide for compulsory negotiations of prices and allocations of pulpwood from specific districts of the province.

There is not enough privately owned timber land to supply the industry with its pulpwood requirements, and large-scale company operations will continue to provide the best means of opening up and developing the forest resources of the vast and remote "limit" areas.

PULPWOOD PRODUCTION

The pattern of pulpwood production in each of the major forest regions in the United States and Canada is much more complex than that of procurement policies and procedures. The complexity of production methods is due to such important factors as:

(1) The species, size and density of timber,

(2) The historical background of initial cutting and logging methods,

(3) The nature of the topography and primary means of transportation,

(4) The quantity and nature of manpower available for woods work,

(5) The influence of climate and weather on tree growth and logging methods.

These important factors develop their most significant patterns in three major pulpwood producing regions. These regions are:

(1) *Northern Regions:* the Northeast, the Lake and Central States and eastern Canadian areas,

(2) *Southern Regions:* all the area from Virginia to Texas, including the Appalachian Mountain areas,

(3) *Western Regions:* all the coastal Western States, the timbered portion of the Rocky Mountains and the British Columbia timbered areas.

The relative consumption of pulpwood by the above regions for 1961, shown below, reveals the dominant position of the South in supplying the basic raw material of the pulp and paper industry in the United States.

PULPWOOD CONSUMED—1961

Region	Pulpwood Consumed (cords)
Northern	8,601,000
Southern	24,648,000
Western	9,069,000
Total	42,318,000

To fully understand how pulpwood is produced it is essential that the major characteristics of pulpwood logging in each of these major regions be clearly understood. We shall first consider the Northern Region.

Production in Northern Regions

United States. Most of the first pulp mills in the North were built by lumber interests late in the nineteenth century. It was therefore logical that the wood for the new mills was produced in the same form as for the saw mills—in log lengths of 12 to 16 feet. They were slashed into short lengths for the grinders and chippers at the pulp mills.

Fig. 4.4. Four-foot pulpwood.

Waterways and logging railroads were the primary means of transportation to the mills. Horses, of course, took the wood to the waterway or railway. As the timber was removed from the main river valleys and logging railroads became prohibitively expensive, it was discovered that by cutting the wood into shorter lengths (4 to 8 feet) much smaller streams could be driven. This change took place around 1920, making the minor valleys accessible to water transportation.

Successive steps in the evolution of pulpwood logging to its present state were: (1) In the early thirties motor trucks started appearing in the woods as prime transporters. This eliminated some river driving and made more remote areas accessible. (2) Shortly after World War II the bulldozer became a common woods tool. This in turn made trucks more versatile as truck roads could be built on almost any type of terrain. (3) The chain saw took over practically all cutting operations in the early fifties, increasing man-day production 30 to 40% for the felling and bucking operation.

Fig. 4.5. Typical modern bulldozer.

Until very recent years, northern pulpwood production was a highly seasonal operation, almost entirely dependent on frozen ground and snow cover to move the wood by horse and sleigh to the primary transportation artery, whether a waterway, truck road or railroad. Even most truck roads were constructed only after the freeze-up, using the winter elements for both foundation and surface. Water transportation, of course, was strictly a seasonal business. The climate of northern regions has until very recently dictated basic methods of woods operations for the whole region. Varying types of topography within the region have dictated methods to a lesser extent and, with equipment in use now and being developed, will continue to have even less effect on methods.

With the foregoing as a background of the development of pulpwood logging, it now seems feasible to describe a typical pulpwood operation in the north country. The trees are severed from the stump by one man using a chain saw. They are skidded by a single horse or tractor, either tracked or rubber-tired, to a truck road, which may or may not be an all-weather road. At roadside the are "bucked" into 4-foot lengths if in the Northeast, or into 8-foot lengths if in the North Central region. After bucking, the bolts are piled alongside the road for transfer to a truck, accomplished either manually or by a crane equipped with a pulpwood grapple, a hydraulic loader or fork-lift attachment on a tractor. The wood is probably trucked di-

Fig. 4.6. Typical winter haul road.

rectly to the mill, or if the distance is over 80 miles is likely to be transferred to a common carrier railroad for completion of the trip to the mill. In rare cases in the Northeast, it may be trucked to drivable water to complete its trip to the mill. In some areas it may be hauled by horse and sleigh or tractor and sleigh to drivable water or a truck road. For probably 90%

Fig. 4.7. A river full of pulpwood.

Fig. 4.8. Typical rubber tired skidder.

of the pulpwood produced in the North, the above methods or some slight variation or combination of them are still in general use.

Pulpwood production is in a stage of evolution as new machines and methods are being developed constantly. The following are a few generalizations as to current trends of northern pulpwood production.

(1) Logging in the North is becoming less and less seasonal. A large proportion of pulpwood already moves from stump to mill without benefit of winter conditions.

(2) *At least 90%* of all pulpwood makes some stage of its journey to the mills by truck and roughly **80%** makes the complete trip by truck after being skidded from stump to road.

Fig. 4.9. Loading truck with crane and pulpwood grapple.

(3) Driving waterways are rapidly disappearing as a means of pulpwood transportation. Only in the Northeast, by a few stragetically located mills, is it used at all today.

(4) Chips from sawmill residues account for a smaller percentage (4%) of total supply in the North than in other regions. This source of raw material will be further developed, but not to the extent it will be in the West and South.

(5) Labor for pulpwood production will continue to be in short supply. Only in fairly well settled areas near timbered areas is there sufficient native labor. Northern New England and northern New York are dependent on Canadian labor for a major portion of the woods work force. As mecha-

Fig. 4.10. Unsurfaced summer truck road.

of equipment is most efficient in tree-length logging.

(9) The last big increase in pulpwood prices occurred during the Korean War, just prior to their being frozen by the government. Since then pulpwood prices have remained reasonably stable. The increased use of hardwoods has had a restraining

Fig. 4.11. Logging a typical northern hardwood stand.

nization is further developed, the traditional method of paying woods labor in piece rates may tend to give way to payment by the hour. This will be necessary if the new high production machines are to lower or hold operating costs in line. The chain saw, while greatly increasing man-day production, primarily had the effect of raising the income of the piece workers. It did not lower cutting costs.

(6) The increased use of northern hardwoods, which are in plentiful supply, will permit expansion of the pulp and paper industry in northern regions—a logical and economically sound development.

(7) There is a strong trend now developing to shift from short wood to tree length logging, i.e., the tree is kept in full or one half merchantable length until it reaches the mill or a point as close to the mill as feasible, where it is cut into shorter lengths mechanically to fit into present-day grinders and chippers. This makes for more efficient handling, reduces labor requirements and promises to lower costs.

(8) The use of horses is steadily declining as better rubber-tired, all-wheel drive skidding equipment is developed. This type

Fig. 4.12. Tree length logging.

effect on over-all wood prices as they are in excess supply in close proximity to most mills. It is only logical to assume that costs and prices will follow the economic trend of the country as a whole in the future. However, the pulpwood industry does have an opportunity to reduce basic manpower requirements and to offset increasing basic costs through greater mechanization and more efficient methods.

Eastern Canada. The over-all picture of pulpwood production in eastern Canada is quite different from that in the northern regions of the United States. As we have pointed out, 78% of the wood is produced by large-scale company operations, and much of the 22% classified as purchased is produced by large contractors who run their own camps. Practically all company-operated wood in Canada is cut from large modern camps, housing and feeding as many as 250 men. Most companies build camps for 10 to 20 years occupancy rather than move every year or two into areas where the men can walk to the cutting areas. This is accomplished by building all-weather gravel roads radiating from the central camp over which the men are transported by bus or by means of their own cars to the work areas.

Waterways are still the prime movers of pulpwood in Canada; practically all mills are located on major rivers with their timber limits in the river's watershed. Most of the labor force producing pulpwood is made up of full or nearly full-time professionals, while the majority in the United States are part-time woods workers.

The situation described above applies quite generally to the mills on or north of the Great Lakes and the St. Lawrence River. There are a few mills south of the St. Lawrence where the procurement picture is very similar to that in the northern United States.

Basically, though, pulpwood is produced on large and small operations in eastern Canada by the same methods as in north-ern United States. It is cut and processed into desired lengths by one-man chain saw, most of it is moved by truck during some stage of its journey to the mill, often from an adjacent watershed to the watershed in which the mill is located.

The trend to mechanization is strong in Canada; in some cases Canadian operations are probably more highly mechanized than their American counterparts.

Fig. 4.13. Bombardier J5 with trailer.

Production in Southern Regions

The 1961 pulpwood harvest in the South reached an all-time high of 24,648,000 cords, roundwood, chips, and mill residues combined. Eighty-one pulp mills in the region having a total daily capacity of 50,000 tons of pulp and paper, plus the seven mills outside of the South that draw wood from this region, consumed 58% of the nation's total consumption of pulpwood. The Southern region has increased its consumption by 70% since 1951, when consumption totaled only 14.06 million cords.

Of 1960's total pulpwood harvest, 87.5% was delivered to southern mills in roundwood form. Of this total 80% was pine and the remainder hardwood. A majority of this roundwood consisted of bolts 5 to 6 feet in length, unbarked, and fresh from the forest—often harvested and manufactured into pulp and paper in the same day.

Production of Roundwood. *Stumpage Source.* Based on a recent pulpwood production survey in the states east of Mississippi, the 1960 harvest came from forest land ownerships as follows: Company-owned or leased, 19%; private holdings, 78%; governmental holdings owned and managed by federal, state, county and local governments, 3%. Thus the southern pulpwood industry is dependent on the lands of private ownership for its major source of pulpwood supply. Good forest practice is therefore being encouraged among this group of owners by the industry.

Crews. Most pulpwood in roundwood form in the South is produced by independent pulpwood producers, having crews of twelve men and less. The producer's workmen are largely compensated on a piece-work or a contract rate basis. Since they work out-of-doors and are subject to varying weather conditions, the full-time producers and their crews presently average a little more than 200 working days per year. Increased application of improved mechanical equipment and techniques of operation have raised man-day productivity among producers to the present average of 1.78 cords per man-day in 1960. This figure is an increase from 1.33 cords per man-day in 1956 and from .95 cord per man-day in 1950. The unit of measure in this case—cords per man-day—includes all work performed from the point of felling timber in the forest, to the point of delivery of pulpwood bolts by truck to a rail, barge or truck concentration yard, or to the mill proper.

Equipment: Without Tractor. Fully equipped pulpwood producers employ the following equipment: a one-man chain saw; a conventional two-ton truck with or without tandem wheels on the rear; a pulp-

wood rack and inexpensive yet effective hoist with boom, winch and cable; and an allied assortment of axes, measuring rods and minor maintenance tools. Such production units as described here are highly mobile. One such unit is easily capable of completing the harvesting of a small tract of pulpwood and within a few hours or the next day can become quickly engaged in the harvest of another forest tract located 20 to 30 miles away. Crew members live at home in towns or on farms, and travel to and from the forest, usually with the pulpwood truck as the principal form of transportation.

Crews with this equipment usually produce "stump loaded" pulpwood by felling trees and cutting them into bolts from 5 to 6 feet in length. This is done by a single crew member with a one-man, gasoline-powered chain saw, usually of the plunge bow design. A second crew member chops (or "lops") limbs and tops of fallen trees and marks the bole of each at proper intervals for subsequent cutting into bolts. Another worker drives the truck from stump to stump and, with the help of the remaining crew members, manually loads the truck or employs the truck hoist where heavy bolts are encountered.

After loading, the truck is driven to the nearest forest road and then onto county, state and federal highways. The destination is usually a rail concentration yard, although operators working within trucking distance of pulp mills deliver direct to these mills. At the concentration yard, the truck is scaled in terms of cords, or weighed. The load is then quickly transferred onto an awaiting pulpwood rack car, barge, or long-distance truck and trailer hauling unit. Sometimes this wood is put into storage and then loaded onto long-distance transportation equipment at some later date. This transfer is accomplished largely by rubber-tired loaders of the lift-truck design. Usually, when the truck returns for the next load of the day, sufficient wood has been cut ahead so all crew members can assist in loading the truck in the shortest time possible.

Equipment: With Tractor. In the coastal areas of the South and in the very hilly portions of the Piedmont Plateau, many producers employ small crawler or wheeled skidding tractors. In these localities the land ownership pattern is one of larger timber tracts and ground conditions of an

Fig. 4.14. View of crawler tractor ground skidding tree length pulpwood to gathering point.

adverse nature. Thus skidding tractors of some design are necessary. Such equipment keeps the pulpwood trucks on woods roads. Under this system of operation, felled pulpwood timber is usually de-limbed and topped and then skidded by tractor to a roadside gathering point. Here crew members measure and mark these stems for cutting into bolts, either by employment of one-man chain saws or by use of wheeled circular saws. The bolts are then loaded directly onto awaiting trucks or into steel U-shaped pallets. These steel pallets are winched onto the bed of the truck, thereby

eliminating much of the present physical effort in loading trucks.

Where tractors are used for skidding pulpwood, two trends are evident: (1) four-wheel-drive tractors with rubber tires, and rubber-wheel crawlers with rubber or steel tracks are being introduced in the South; (2) a mechanical loader, something like a mechanical hand, arm, and back is being tried to reduce or eliminate costly manual loading of pulpwod bolts onto trucks, tractor carts, or pallets. If these developments are widely applied, substantial economies in use of manpower will result.

More advanced techniques of harvesting involve the felling, skidding, loading, trucking and processing of pulpwood in tree lengths or in log lengths. When this is done, pulpwood is usually debarked by rotary ring-type debarkers and immediately passed into a chipper. This processing may be done

Fig. 4.15. A wheeled tractor and cart equipped with "human-like" loader for 5 foot bolts.

at some location away from the mill or at the mill proper.

Transportation, Handling at the Mill. Pulpwood moves to southern mills as follows: Truck delivery direct to the mill, 22 to 28%; rail car delivery, 66 to 74%; barge and miscellaneous means of transportation, 2 to 6%. Long-distance delivery of roundwood to southern mills is dominated by the railroad movement, but there is a growing interest in the use of trucks and truck-trailer transport up to distances of about 100 miles from the mill.

Rail cars and large truck-trailer units are usually loaded at a point of origin by mechanical means, as described previously. Unloading of roundwood at the mill is usually accomplished as follows: from rail cars,

Fig. 4.17. Transferring pulpwood from truck to rail car with lift-truck loader.

Fig. 4.16. A southern chip mill where tree length pulpwood is debarked and chipped-away from the pulp mill.

by locomotive or crawler cranes equipped with orange-peel grapples which can discharge wood directly into the woodyard system or into storage. Some mills employ rubber- or rail-mounted cranes with booms that move in and out, thereby enabling an attached paddle to avalanche wood from rack cars into the woodyard flume or conveyor in a more efficient manner and with a uniform rate of feed. Trucks are usually unloaded directly into a storage by means of large cranes equipped with cables and slings. These cranes often can handle loads as large as four cords. Occasionally, loads

Fig. 4.18. Trucks awaiting unloading by crane at a southern pulp mill.

of truck wood are dumped directly into woodyard flumes or conveyors by means of hydraulic truck dumping platforms. Barges are unloaded in a manner similar to that used for rail cars.

Wood Storage at the Mill. In recent years, southern mills are giving more and more consideration to storing and handling pulpwood in chip rather than in roundwood

Fig. 4.19. Bottom dump chip cars and chip trailer being unloaded at a southern mill.

form. This change-over has taken place for the following reasons: primarily to gain significant economies in pulpwood handling, processing and storage at the mills. It will also help to speed up research into closer utilization of wood fiber, bark and other by-products available from pulpwood and encourage woodlands and mill organizations to greater progress in finding faster and cheaper ways to grow, harvest and more closely utilize the forest crop.

Wood Storage at Outlying Concentration Points. Outlying concentration yards are largely rail loading points. Roundwood stored there is handled by rubber wheel loaders of the lift-truck design (see Figure 4.17). Some rubber-wheel cranes and even a few crawler cranes are still used for this purpose. Loads hoisted from each incoming

truck seldom exceed $2\frac{1}{4}$ cords in size. While the wood is held in the slings of the loader, a length of steel strapping with attached buckle is passed around and secured. Then when the bundle is placed in storage, the slings are removed and the wood is contained in bundle form. Bundles are usually reclaimed within a one- or two-week period. The re-usable strapping is removed and the wood is loaded onto long-distance transportation equipment.

Utilization of Forest Crop. Closer utilization of the forest crop—whether it be pulpwood, saw logs, or other forms of raw material for industry—provides a fertile field

Fig. 4.20. Mill storage of pulpwood in chip form.

for stimulating technological progress in more efficient machine and manpower application in all phases of pulpwood production, and for finding ways to keep total production costs in line. However, much of this effort toward higher utilization efficiency must first take place at the mill before efforts in the field can bear fruit. It is known that the cost of pulpwood can account for as much as 60% of the total cost of producing a ton of unbleached kraft pulp. In turn, as much as 75% of the total delivered cost of a cord of rough green pulpwood is incurred in the harvesting phase of forestry. Thus discovery of ways to increase the percentage of salable product from the basic raw material—pulpwood—by closer utilization can reduce this high percentage cost of raw material in terms of each ton of marketable product. Presently, only 30 to 40% of the original weight of rough pulpwood brought to the mill ends up as a finished salable product; thus, this vital field of more efficient wood utilization is a challenge to the entire industry.

Since more than one species of trees usually grows on a typical acre of forest land, the opportunity to utilize all these species is ever-present. This challenge is being met somewhat by an increasing use of hardwood, which only a very short time ago was not considered suitable for pulp manufacture. Logging left-overs and the presently non-commercial thinnings are wood volumes that are not now being fully utilized.

Utilization of Purchased Chips and Mill Residues. The southern mills increased their consumption of chips and other mill residues —once called "sawmill waste"—from 140,-000 chip units in 1954 to 3,731,000 chip units in 1961. Over 15% of the total 1961 consumption of pulpwood in the region was in form of purchased chips and other mill residues. This is to be contrasted with the 1960 figure of 12%. At least 900 sawmills and other wood-using plants were equipped to produce this material. The motivating force behind this increasing use of purchased chips and mill residues has been the advantage to the sawmills of utilizing at a profit material that had previously been wasted. Moreover, this provided the pulp mills with a steady flow of raw material at a reasonable cost. It did not drain the forests and required less manpower.

Types of Material. The principal sources of purchased chips are slabs, edgings and trimmings from the sawmills. Recently some mills took advantage of another waste product of lumber manufacture—sawdust. By using specially designed circular saws and exercising control over rate of feed of logs and lumber through them, it is possible to produce saw-kerf chips, i.e., chips $\frac{1}{4}$ to $\frac{3}{8}$ inch in width. Such chips are usually blended with those manufactured from slabs, edgings and trimmings. This is done as the material is loaded into waiting trailers or chip cars. To date, the greatest quantity of saw chips is utilized by southern mills manufacturing dissolving pulp.

Steps have been undertaken to develop machinery to produce "lumber sizing chips" or "Griffwood." These are high-quality chips which are produced as rough sawn lumber, are sized preparatory to drying and have a final run through the planer.

Some veneer plants in the South produce chips from bark-free material which is produced as veneer bolts are shaped into cylindrical form on the lathe. A specially designed veneer chipper is employed for this purpose.

Techniques of Manufacture. At sawmills, the bark on logs is removed by passing each log through a debarker which is usually one of the following designs: (1) a rotary ring-type with pressured tools which spirals off the bark by means of a cambium shear principle; (2) a debarker with traveling dolly and rotary rosser head which removes bark as it is rotated by bull wheels and as the dolly travels from one end of the log to the other; (3) a debarker similar to the one previously mentioned but incorporating either a chain flail or a rotary cutter head design; and (4) a debarker which cuts off the bark with a multitooth rotary cutter head as the log is spiraled past this debarking chamber. The resulting bark-free slabs, edgings and trimmings are then converted into chips by means of specially designed waste-wood chippers.

Transportation. Hopper-type chip cars with open tops are transporting a lion's share of chips to the southern mills. Truck-trailer transport direct to the mill is employed up to maximum distances permissible by competing rail freight rates. During 1956, the following modes of chip transport prevailed for mills in the Georgia, Florida, the Carolinas, Tennessee and Virginia area: trucks and trailers, 25.4%; hopper-type chip cars, 28.1%; and boxcars, barges, etc., 46.5%. By 1960, the respective percentage figures were about as follows: trucks and trailers, 17.4%; hopper-type chip cars, 72.4%; boxcars, barges, etc., 10.2%. This indicates a pronounced preference for usage of quick loading and unloading bottom-dump chip cars of open top design.

At the loading point, chips are blown into trailers, chip cars, boxcars and barges by pneumatic or mechanical throwing devices. Many mills use gravity loading systems which make use of the free fall of chips into these receptacles, except boxcars. At the mill, chips are discharged into large hoppers serving the chip system for the mill. Truck-trailer units are dumped by means of large hydraulically powered ramps or by an overhead cable hoist that dumps by picking up

the front end of the trailer. Hopper cars are discharged into these systems with the aid of top or sidecar shakers. The few remaining boxcars are principally unloaded by use of small scoop trucks.

Storage of Purchased Chips. Almost no storage of purchased chips takes place at the sawmill or wood-using plant where they are produced. Within the past several months more southern mills are going to outside chip storage and there is evidence that purchased chips are finding their way into these piles.

Production in Western Regions

In the West, the term "pulpwood" must include any wood which finds its way into the manufacture of pulp and paper. It may be derived from logs too poor in quality for veneer or lumber, or from chips manufactured from slabs and edgings from the sawmills, or small logs, limbs and other salvaged material following primary or old growth timber logging. After cutting of the old growth timber there has been a remarkable development of reproduction and sec-

Fig. 4.21. A typical over-mature stand in the west. Heart rot and other pathological action have reduced many of these trees to worthless shells. Logging has first priority to clean up the area and obtain a good healthy stand as soon as possible.

ond growth on hundreds of thousands of acres. Currently these second-growth stands contain large volumes of small pole and pulpwood size timber. From these areas there is springing an increasingly large supply of so-called 8 foot pulpwood or "farm" or "farmer" wood.

The Western Region produces approximately 20% of the total annual wood supply consumed by the pulp and paper industry in the United States. This production, in many respects, is unique and different from that produced in other regions. Such factors as extremely rough topography, land ownership patterns, timber sizes and other operating conditions, serve to place the area literally in a class by itself.

Currently, a large proportion of wood used by the industry is produced by logging contractors. Logging conditions and timber sizes require large and expensive equipment. Good forestry practice as well as economics demand clear cutting in the old over-mature timber stands. Large volumes of material must be handled to provide a logging profit and equipment investment return. Many types and qualities of wood are obtained from a single area. The highest-quality timber usually is sent to the peeler or veneer mill. The saw mill receives the better quality logs. Small straight stems may go to the pole or piling markets. The shingle industry accepts a portion of the cut. Obviously, there are many and varied ways to utilize these inter-grown materials.

The degree of wood utilization in the West is higher than in any other region. One third to one half of the wood consumed as pulpwood in this region is residual material in the form of chips, slabs and edgings. Many pulp and paper companies, for this very reason, operate both saw mill and pulp mill operations. Integrated operations of this type are therefore more commonly found in this region than in the Southern or Northern regions. A large proportion of pulpwood is produced as logs, ranging from 8 feet to as much as 40 feet in length. Generally speaking, this material is not economically useful to the other wood-using industries. Small logs, crooked logs, cull logs, and similar material are directed to the chippers in tremendous quantities.

Production of pulpwood, in small, short

Fig. 4.22. An aerial view of a large west coast pulp and paper mill. Note wood inventory in outside chip storage piles. Near center of photo is a small inventory of pulpwood.

Fig. 4.23. Residual chips from sawmill waste are delivered by truck, rail and water. This self-unloading van type of chip trailer plays an important role in transporting chips to the pulp and paper mills.

lengths as it is commonly known in the other wood-producing regions, is now beginning to assume increasing importance in the Western Region. Cut-over areas, both large and small, have reproduced well and remarkable second-growth stands are now ready for thinning and intensive forest management. Logging equipment so well adapted to large old-growth timber is neither economical nor practical. Herein lies the turning point.

First, it appears evident that sawmill residuals in the form of chips or slabs and edgings will continue to furnish a major share of the pulp and paper industry's wood requirements in the West. Secondly, as more and more second-growth timber stands reach pulpwood size, short round wood usage will increase, particularly from the more accessible areas and farm woodlots. Thirdly, equipment geared to Western logging conditions will continue to be developed for economic handling and processing of the smaller timber.

Any summary of pulpwood production in the West would be incomplete without reference to the pattern of land ownership

which prevails. Approximately two thirds of the commercial forest land in the Western Region * is in public ownership, either Federal or State. The combination of an expanding population and an apparent increasing recreational demand in this pattern of large public land holdings will limit acquisition and expansion of industrial forest lands. Intensive forest management of all land ownership will be required to assure a continuing pulpwood supply in the West.

RESEARCH IN PULPWOOD PRODUCTION

In all forest regions the opportunities of making full use of mill residuals, logging leftovers and thinnings in plantations and second growth stands will be explored most vigorously. The significant factors affecting pulpwood procurement and production will be studied more intensively than they have been in the past. These factors include:

* U.S. Dept. of Agriculture, Forest Service. 1958. Timber Resources for America's Future. Forest Resource Report No. 14, U.S. Government Printing Office, Washington 25, D.C.

(1) Stumpage availability

(2) Level of wood inventory

(3) Procurement policies

(4) Availability and quality of labor

(5) Status of existing harvesting and forest management equipment

(6) Fluctuations in pulpwood demand

(7) Weather.

In the Southeast, 17 pulpwood paper companies have pooled their resources and their interest in the above significant factors by organizing and sponsoring a three-year research project, referred to as the Southern Pulpwood Production Research Project. The project work is being conducted by the Battelle Memorial Institute at Columbus, Ohio. The financing and sponsor's administration of the project is being conducted under the auspices of the American Pulpwood Association.

Since 1947 the latter Association has had a technical program as its major function. This provides for the coordination of six APA regional Technical Committees. The exchange of ideas, the distribution of APA Technical releases and papers are a major factor in advancing the mechanization and technical progress of pulpwood production in the United States. A similar program is conducted in Canada by the Woodlands Section of the Canadian Pulp and Paper Association of Montreal.

Efforts to increase utilization of all pulpable species of wood are certain to be accelerated in the years ahead. As woods labor becomes scarce or should total wood costs go up with an inflated economy, the need for more research will become a more important phase of the Technical programs of the APA and the CPPA, and of the individual pulpwood consuming mills. Both associations are well organized and are prepared to meet this challenge of the immediate future even to the extent that they may have to explore more fully the use of time and cost studies, "operations research," work method studies, and other tools of modern management which are already being effectively applied in the pulp and paper mills and in most of the other industries.

CHAPTER 5

Wood Preparation

W. A. McKenzie

Simpson Timber Company

The pressure of ever-increasing costs of raw materials, labor, equipment and operating supplies has motivated the search for methods, machinery and techniques to reduce the cost of pulpwood in its final form ready for the pulp mill. This quest for lower pulpwood costs has kept pace with similar activities in all phases of the pulp and paper industry.

New methods, machinery and techniques, together with improvements on those already in use, have been developed along various lines in different parts of the United States and Canada, reflecting the particular influences in each area. For instance, large logs prevalent on the west coast made development of large chippers and hydraulic barking an economic necessity for the larger pulp mills and saw mills. As smaller mills could not justify the first cost and operating expense of hydraulic barkers, mechanical barkers were developed to handle logs of any length over 8 feet and up to 72 inches in diameter.

In the small tree areas of the North American continent, namely the United States and Canada east of the Rocky Mountains, manufacturers and operators alike improved the standard drum barkers in practically universal use to reduce maintenance costs and obtain better bark removal. Better log-handling devices and methods reduced hand labor. Developments in those fields

were necessary, if drum barkers were to retain their position as low-cost barking equipment.

Most mills find that chips made from sawmill and plywood plant waste material can usually be purchased at prices considerably lower than the cost of chips produced in their own plants. In fact a number of mills constructed recently on the west coast do not have chipping plants. All their pulpwood is purchased in the form of chips. This results in a very considerable reduction in both capital investment and chip costs.

Purchasing of all or even a large proportion of chip requirements usually makes a large chip inventory advisable. In view of the high first cost and the difficulties encountered with chips stored in bins or silos, outside chip storage was indicated. Equipment and methods were then developed for handling chips in the open, with the result that mills in practically all sections of both the United States and Canada are installing or already have outside chip storage facilities.

A most recent development, actually since 1960, is tree-length log barking and chipping. This began in the South, where most of the trees are relatively small, as compared to those on the West Coast. In this operation trees up to about 65 feet in length with tops as small as 4 inches are brought to a barking and chipping plant where they are processed full length through a mechanical barker and horizontal feed chipper at very substantial savings over the previous short-wood handling and processing methods.

Pneumatic conveying of chips over long distances is another recent development which has helped to reduce chip handling costs, as well as being a big factor in the economies obtainable from outside chip storage.

These are the more outstanding, even somewhat spectacular, developments whose favorable impact on chip costs has helped the pulp and paper industry materially in its battle against rising costs.

PULPWOOD MEASUREMENT

The following are measurements commonly used in the industry:

1 unit of chips or hogged refuse = 200 cubic feet.

81.38 cubic feet of solid wood will make 200 cubic feet of loose green, gravity-settled pulp chips, resulting in a conversion factor of 1 =2.46.

Using the Scribner log scaling rules, 1,000-foot board measure net scale of logs 40 feet long will produce 1.99 units of chips. Based on 32-foot logs, 1.89 units of chips were produced from 1,000-foot B.M. net scale of logs. It should be noted this is the Scribner log scale which for average smaller logs will show only about 53 to 55% actual log volume.

1 cord (piled 4 x 4 x 8 feet) = 128 cubic feet.

1 cord solid wood will produce 1.2 units of chips = 1.228 tons.

1 unit bone dry fir chips = 0.997 ton.

It might be well to point out that while the 128-cubic foot cord mentioned above is standard in most areas, there are some places where a piece of cord wood is longer than 48 inches, such as 56 inches or 60 inches, and the volume of wood in a cord is correspondingly greater. This is a result

of cutting wood into lengths most convenient for transportation in that particular area, such as piling at an angle crosswise on railroad cars or trucks to make unloading easier and to utilize the full allowable load width. The main point here is to be sure what units of wood measurement are being used and how much solid wood they represent when comparing wood costs, utilization and production figures for different mills. At best none of these measurements are precise; consequently, methods by which they are taken are also important factors.

Chips are often measured by weight. Here they are run over a weighing device and an average moisture content must be obtained, by scientific sampling and testing methods, before the actual weight of wood can be calculated.

An ingenious method in use at some eastern Canadian mills where pulpwood is cut into short lengths and transported in barges, is handling by large grapples and dumping into a hopper. From the hopper the wood is conveyed to a large steel cage-like elevator car. Gates on the cage are closed and the entire load lowered into a tank of water. Displacement is then registered on a chart and the wood volume is read directly. After measurement the cage is lifted, a side gate opened and the wood tumbles out into a hopper over a conveyor which takes the measured wood to storage.

While this system involves a rather high investment and requires some operating labor, it will handle large volumes of wood very rapidly with good accuracy and the cost per ton is relatively low.

LOG HAULS

Logs 8 to 60 inches in diameter are common in West Coast operations. These logs are received at the mill in lengths from 20 to 60 feet in log rafts, and up to 40 feet in cars and trucks with trailers. Some mills in the West also purchase wood in 8-foot lengths from private wood lot owners or wood cutters who are not equipped to handle long logs. However, in eastern Canada, midwestern, eastern and southern United States logs are smaller, generally less than 20 inches diameter, and usually are delivered in short lengths, that is, 48, 52, 60 inches or 8 feet, although recently a trend toward barking and chipping in tree lengths is developing in the South.

Large logs are most easily sorted and moved about when afloat; therefore, mills using them are located on natural waterways or where ponds can be constructed.

A single chain log slip is the most practical method for bringing large logs up from a pond or waterway. Inasmuch as the operating floor level of a mill should be 16 to 18 feet above the machinery or the basement floor to provide adequate headroom for conveyors, drives, etc., logs must be raised to a considerable elevation above water level. Where a mill is on tidewater or a river, level changes of 20 feet or more are not uncommon.

Experience indicates that it is wise to set the machinery floor level as high as practical above known high water because water levels have a bad habit of making new records from time to time. Three feet above absolute known high water should be a

minimum for tidal areas. On rivers more elevation should be allowed for reasonable safety from floods. As a result, logs must frequently be raised as much as 50 or 60 feet above low water to the log deck, which is usually about 5 feet above the mill floor. Consequently, the slip structure must be heavily built and strongly braced.

Briefly, a log slip consists of a single chain with heavy toothed attachments called chairs at about 10-foot intervals, running in a steel- or cast-iron-lined trough constructed of heavy timbers on timber bents, or all steel with cast-iron renewable liners to take the wear of chain and attachments. Figure 5.1 is a photo of a conventional log slip and Figure 5.2 shows a side lift.

Since the logs end up lying on the mill floor, the upper portion of the slip must be approximately tangent to the horizontal. This is accomplished by building the slip with a long radius convex sweep tangent to both the slope of its main portion and to the log deck at the upper end. It is not necessary to make this sweep a continuous curve. That can and has been done with laminated timber or with steel construction, but it is costly as well as being unnecessary. With the long sweeps possible, short straight

Fig. 5.1. Log slip. (*Courtesy Simpson Timber Co.*)

sections as chords of the true curve are entirely suitable and more economical. The maximum length of these sections depends, of course, on the length of the slip and its curvature. Ten- or 12-foot sections work out satisfactorily in most cases.

Fig. 5.2. Side lift. (*Courtesy Simpson Timber Co.*)

The lower twenty or thirty feet of the slip, called the apron, should be hinged to the main portion with its lower end resting on a piling bent so it can be raised with an overhead hoist when it becomes necessary to renew the lower chain idler drum, replace the chain if it jumps off the idler, or make other repairs. Provision should be made for hoisting the hinged end by providing suitable overhead framing and hoisting equipment, with lifting chains or cables permanently attached to lower end of the hinged apron. Figure 5.1 is a typical steel log haul trough clearly showing a 1¾ x 2½ x 8 inch cast manganese steel chain and log chairs, as well as the cast-iron liners on which the chairs and chain ride.

Where only smaller logs up to 24 to 36 inches in diameter are available to the mill, a side lift is usually more suitable than a slip, where mill and pond arrangement can be worked out. The side lift can be made steeper than a slip, does not require a sweep or point of tangency at the log deck; consequently, it requires much less length and ground area. It can also handle a much larger volume of logs at lower chain speeds because they are raised horizontally side by side, whereas a slip brings the logs up end to end.

The side lift consists essentially of a series of parallel transfer chains with high attachments running in suitable guides, usually with cast-iron renewable liners, the whole structure being installed at an angle as required by the location. Some of these side lifts are at angles up to 60 degrees with the horizontal.

Side lifts require only supports for the chainways, as compared to heavily constructed and lined troughs of log slips, and for same size logs are lower in first cost, so should be given most serious consideration when designing a log-lifting installation.

Here again the lower ends of the chainways should be arranged so they can be lifted out of the water for repairs.

Under some situations it is either not feasible or not economical to build and maintain a log pond. In such cases log-handling vehicles such as those developed by Le Tourneau, and others, during the past few years are the answer.

POWER REQUIREMENTS FOR LOG HAULS

The power required to operate a log slip can readily be calculated from information available after the slip or lift has been located, its maximum slope determined, its speed figured and the maximum weight of logs that will be on the slip at any one time determined. Daily averages mean nothing because the power required depends upon the weight that is actually on the slip, upon the chain speed and upon the acceleration. The maximum weight of logs on the slip and their necessary travel speed can be worked out, based on a knowledge of the type and size logs expected and the barker and chipper capacities. Where log sizes vary over wide limits, an a.c. wound-rotor motor or a d.c. drive should be used to power the log haul; then the motor will accelerate the load gradually and can be slowed down for large logs. The maximum chain speed would have to be enough to keep the mill supplied with the smaller logs expected. An induction motor driving through a hydraulic coupling, set for high slip to obtain low acceleration, has proved satisfactory, is relatively low in initial cost, and is practically trouble-free.

It must be realized that assumptions of log sizes, weights and chain speeds are vital in this case because results will directly reflect accuracy of those figures. For example, a particular West Coast mill handling hemlock logs for 200 tons of pulp production on two shifts originally had a 40 hp motor driving the log chain. It was soon changed to 75 hp, sufficient for the usual largest logs, but occasionally one was too heavy for the 75 hp motor and the deck winch was used as a helper. A design based on correct information, tempered by experience, would have called for 100 hp in the first place, with resultant obvious over-all savings in capital outlay and fewer operating troubles and interruptions.

Log hauls are usually provided with nonreversing devices such as a brake on the motor shaft and a pawl riding on the chain. Otherwise, a heavy load on the slip might go for a fast ride downhill at some very inconvenient time, damaging the drive motor or reduction gearing.

With figures for the basic data settled upon, the power requirements are readily calculated using a coefficient of friction for logs and chain of 0.33.

Various formulas have been presented for calculating the power requirements of conveyors running at any angle likely to be used. All are based on the law of sines. The chain pull is the combined load of the logs and resultant weight of logs, chain and attachments parallel to the conveyor, which are not counter-balanced by the return. In addition allowance must be made for the force required to start the load against friction resulting from component of total weight perpendicular to the conveyor.

A readily understood and easily used method is suggested by Chain Belt Company in their general catalog which the author has found to produce entirely satisfactory results, and to check quite closely with the above mentioned fundamental analysis.

The importance of judgment in selecting sizes and weight of logs or other conveyed material, as well as conveyor speeds to obtain satisfactory results, cannot be too strongly emphasized; if these are properly selected the application of safety or service factors is unnecessary. For large diameter logs, heavy chain such as $1\frac{3}{4}$-inch or 2 x 8-inch pitch round link is normally used, running at speeds up to 135 feet per minute; however, chain speeds should be held as slow as possible to minimize wear and power requirement.

It has been found by experience that manganese alloy steel in both chain and attachments, while higher in first cost, will outlast mild steel or dredge quality chain from two to five times.

SMALL LOG HANDLING

The method and technique used to harvest, load, transport, unload at the mill woodyard, store and handle from storage to the sawmill or woodroom as the case may be, is a broad subject with many variations, ramifications and details which materially affect the cost of pulp wood delivered to the mill. Much study has been put into these operations, and equipment has been developed for this purpose in various sections of this country and Canada. Much worthwhile information and data on pulpwood procurement and handling has been published by the American Pulpwood Association (New York), the Institute of Forest Products (Seattle, Washington), and by the Forest Products Research Society (Madison, Wisconsin). Publications by these organizations cover practically all phases of pulpwood harvesting procedures, from small diameter trees bucked to short length in the woods, to large trees hauled to the millpond in lengths up to 40 feet or more, with intermediate phases, such as small-diameter trees bundled with steel strapping for transportation. Details of those operations are covered in Chapter 4.

Mills often purchase small-diameter, 8-foot wood which is delivered on flat bed trucks. An interesting unloading method for this wood, shown in Figure 5.3, has been developed during recent years. In this operation two cables are led from a winch around the load on either side of the truck and brought back and attached to anchors located below the deck. The winch, in pulling the cables, rolls the entire load off the back of the truck and onto the transfer. A similar arrangement can be used to unload long logs from the side of a truck and trailer and onto a deck of suitable width. The overhead frame at the end of the transfer in this photo carries the winch. A small log-handling vehicle also unloads and piles logs.

In the case of mills in eastern Canada, and in middlewestern, eastern and southern United States, pulpwood is usually of a size that lends itself well to cutting into short lengths in the forest; hence most wood requirements are delivered to the millyard in cordwood lengths. The diameter is such that no breakdown or sawmilling operation is necessary ahead of the barkers. A well engineered and operated shortwood storage and reclaiming installation is shown in Figure 5.4.

Occasionally it may be advantageous to transport small-diameter pulpwood to the mill in lengths longer than is suitable for the barkers or grinders in use; consequently, these logs or small trees can be cut into

Fig. 5.3. Unloading 8-foot logs from trucks. (*Courtesy Link Belt Co.*)

Fig. 5.4. Short wood storage piles with stacking and reclaiming conveyors. (*Courtesy Link Belt Co.*)

suitable lengths by running them through a multiple saw slasher table with saws staggered in a V arrangement, or dropped one by one onto either a roll or chain conveyor which takes the logs past a swing cutoff saw where they are bucked to the desired lengths for barking. For obvious reasons, multiple saws have much greater potential capacity than a swing saw. The reason for the V arrangement is to have only one saw cutting on any one piece, thus avoiding binding or rolling which would occur if all saws were on the same arbor.

With a straight line barking and chipping setup, as outlined later in this chapter, long logs are cut off only when they are trimmed for recovery and sale of saw logs, or if they have sweeps or crooks which might interfere with barking or chipping.

In either case logs can be handled from a dry storage or cold deck onto transfer chains ahead of the saws or barker by any one of various types of cranes or log-handling devices. Another method is to set logs into a pond with a crane, whence they are

lifted either end to end by means of a chain conveyor, or side by side with transfer chains having attachments long enough to cradle each log as it is lifted from the water onto the log deck.

In the case of small logs it frequently happens that some will be too large for the chippers or grinders, in which case they can be split after barking. This is accomplished by cutting them to short lengths and transferring them sidewise through an air or steam axe splitter.

The splitter (see Figure 5.11) has a 54 inch stroke for 4-foot logs but they are built for longer or shorter logs, and with 8 to 18 inch cylinder bore, as required for the service intended.

Small logs and blocks can be handled and stored in water as well as larger logs, but handling methods must, of necessity, be quite different. With smaller wood, mass flow handling techniques are necessary to provide the volumes required by even medium-sized mills.

If, as is not uncommon in the West and

recently in the South, small logs of tree length are brought to the mill yard, they are usually bundled either with steel strapping or cable slings. The bundles are handled by cranes and can be broken down on a log deck ahead of slasher saws or in the pond for later movement up a log lift to the slashers. In the South, tree-length logs are beginning to be delivered on trucks and trailers without bundling, as mentioned previously.

Fig. 5.5. Short log lift conveyor from flume. (*Courtesy Link Belt Co.*)

In the East and South where small sizes are most usual and transportation considerations make it advisable, wood is usually delivered in short lengths. In that case dry storage is required for large volumes. In the North, long cold winters when logging is not possible necessitate huge wood stor-

age piles at the mill yard. At mills where ponds are not available or desirable, wood is handled from delivery, through barkers, into and out of storage piles with various types of conveyors, cranes, drag lines and grapples. Where ponds are available, wood can be dumped and stored there in quantities depending on pond areas. A typical short log-lifting conveyor for handling large volumes from a pond or from the end of a flume is shown in Figure 5.5. It discharges logs to a distributing belt ahead of barking drums, which are seen at the left. In the background is a barked wood storage pile. This general type of operation is typical of northern and southern United States and of Canadian mills.

Short wood in a pond can be moved to a lift conveyor or along a channel or flume by artificially created currents, using paddle wheels, propellers or pumps with surprisingly low power consumption (Figure 5.6). Some groundwood mills use this idea to float blocks to grinder loading positions in flumes with slow-moving water currents. If this is done, provision should be made to remove any bark that may fall off the blocks even though they have been through a barker. Some bark will float, but a lot of it sinks. Both create considerable nuisance, which require attention of the designer to avoid future operating problems.

After a drag conveyor is designed to remove bark from a flume or pond, the real problem of disposal is still to be solved. The bark should be de-watered by some means such as screening, or a bark press. The degree of screening depends on whether the water is re-used. After de-watering, the bark must be disposed of by burning or hauled to a refuse dump. This is no simple, inexpensive installation, but requires a great deal of thought on the part of the designer to devise an installation of minimum first cost, trouble-free, efficient operation, and low maintenance expense.

It may be possible to mix the wet bark with dry refuse from barking drums for burning in the boiler plant. If wet barking

Fig. 5.6. Log pond and flume. (*Courtesy Impco*)

methods are used, bark removed from ponds and flumes can be mixed with the wet material and run to presses, or other processes can be used to condition bark for burning.

HYDRAULIC BARKING

The effects of a solid jet of water backed by 1,400 pounds pressure impinging on bark, as shown in Figure 5.7, is truly spectacular. As a result, nozzles designed to produce the many intricate and often fearsome shapes and arrangements of water jets conceived by fertile imaginations have been built and tried. These vary from a wide, thin sheet striking the logs tangentially to superheated, high-pressure steam, with varying success at achieving the goal of more and faster bark removal with less water and power. However, it unfortunately seems to require a specific amount of energy applied with good efficiency to remove a square inch of bark per minute. This figure varies but little in successful hydraulic barkers. Round jets

produced by converging short tubes or sharp-edged orifices appear to be the most satisfactory. The jets in hydraulic barkers (Figure 5.7) have the appearance of wide, flat sheets, but are actually one or two rows of round jets emerging from closely spaced $3/32$-inch diameter nozzles at 1,400 or 1,500 psi. Due to their large surface areas, thin, flat jets and those of very small diameter dissipate so much energy and water in friction and fog against the air through which they travel that the energy of the jets at impact is greatly reduced, and, thus, operating efficiency is low.

In general, hydraulic barkers readily remove bark from practically all species, some more easily than others. Trees growing in the South are normally more difficult to bark than those from the North and West. Some of the southern hardwoods, such as gum, are the most difficult of all.

Hydraulic barkers require large amounts of power to drive the high-pressure pumps. The pump for a barker serving a 200-ton

Fig. 5.7. Hydraulic barker showing jet and trunnion wheels infeed with logs top and loader on right. (*Courtesy of Sumner Iron Works*)

mill will normally deliver 1,000 gpm at 1,200 to 1,500 psi and require a 1,200 hp, 3,600 rpm drive motor or turbine. Incidentally, steam turbines are almost ideal prime movers for this service, if their exhaust can be used as process steam.

Obviously, the capital investment in a hydraulic barking plant is high. Such plants use large volumes of dirt-free water and have high power requirements. The potential capacity is likewise large and must be utilized sufficiently to amortize the investment and justify the operating cost. The jet consumes the same amount of power, whether barking logs or not. One man can feed logs into and out of the barker as well as operate it. No additional help is needed to handle rejects, because logs are held in the barker until completely barked. Thus, a minimum of labor per ton is used.

Figure 5.8 is a shop photograph of a hydraulic barker of the Bellingham type, manufactured by the Sumner Iron Works,

now a division of Black-Clawson Co. (Everett, Washington). This has proved to be one of the best and highest capacity hydraulic barking units in operation and many of them have been installed to bark fir, hemlock, spruce, pine and even redwood.

The logs will come in from the rear on a log deck not shown in Figure 5.8. The log stop and loader for feeding logs into the barker one at a time is at the rear edge of the frame. It is standing with stop arms down. From the log stop and loader heavy cast-steel skids allow logs to roll over the first row of toothed trunnion wheels into the crotch formed by the two parallel rows of wheels. These two rows of wheels are mounted on shafts which are driven under variable-speed control to revolve the log in either direction. The nozzle is mounted on its raising and lowering arm, attached to an overhead carriage which travels from end to end of the barker. It too is under full variable-speed control in both directions.

Fig. 5.8. Hydraulic barker shop view, control house at right infeed on left.—Housing removed. (*Courtesy Sumner Iron Works*)

Water is fed to the barker through a pipe with swivel joints mounted on top of the frame, then to the nozzle through multiple hoses. After the log is barked, it is pushed out of the barker over the skids along the front edge of the frame by unloading arms which are retracted, and not visible in the photograph. At the same time another log is fed into the barker from the back by the stop and loader.

These hydraulic barkers are built in several sizes. A small one will take logs up to 10 feet long and 48 inches in diameter. One of these small units has actually debarked logs averaging 12 to 16 inches in diameter at the rate of five per minute for an 8-hour shift. A large barker of this type will handle logs 16 to 42 feet long, up to 7 feet in diameter and has barked 1,204 logs averaging 36 inches in diameter in one 8-hour shift.

While hydraulic barkers do sliver off some of the softer sap wood, the loss is surprisingly small. They clean up around knots very well, and do a bit better all-around cleaning job on the logs than can be accomplished with mechanical barkers unless they bite too deeply and remove good wood.

There are other types and designs of hydraulic barkers operating quite satisfactorily. The Hensel ring barker consists primarily of an annular ring with four or more nozzles mounted on the inner face discharging radially inward. This ring is revolved at 150 to 300 rpm, depending on size, by V belts on the outside of the ring. Logs are passed through the ring on fluted V rolls having a variable-speed reversible drive. The main features of this barker are the fixed nozzles, which cannot be brought in or out for various log sizes, the large diameter of the water seal in the revolving ring, and the necessity for filtered water to avoid packing wear. This design can be installed directly on a log slip with consequent minimum space and capital requirements.

The Simonds barker consists of two discs

Fig. 5.9. Nicholson barker. Infeed end.

revolving in parallel horizontal planes above and below the log. Each disc has four or more nozzles mounted on the face next to the log. The upper disc can be raised or lowered as necessary for logs of different sizes.

The Allis Chalmers stream barker, designed primarily for small logs, has stationary jets and two long parallel, spiral-fluted rolls close together, which revolve the logs when fed into the crotch between the rolls. The spiral flutes on one roll move the log along past the nozzles, which remove the bark by impact, as with other hydraulic barkers.

It is interesting to note that high relative speeds of the jet over the log surface do the most effective bark removal with least slivering and wood loss.

Bark and water from these barkers drop into a drag conveyor below, which has high

Fig. 5.10. Cambio barker out feed end. (*Courtesy Soderham Manufacturing Co.*)

sides and a perforated bottom for initial de-watering and screening. Large pieces go directly to a hog and then to the boilers for fuel. The water and fines run by gravity or are pumped to vibrating or oscillating screens to remove the water and the fines are then conveyed to the fuel pile.

Refuse from hydraulic barkers contains so much water that its value as a fuel is relatively small, but it will burn and sustain its own combustion under suitable conditions of furnace design and operation, rate of feed, temperature of air and combustion. However, it is best to mix this refuse with good hogged fuel. The more hogged fuel in relation to wet bark, the better. Bark soaks up more water than does solid wood but, if logs have been afloat for several days, that part of the bark in contact with water has become saturated before going through the barker. Water picked up in the barker can be rather completely shaken off, if fines are run over a vibrating screen or other type that jostles the wood particles sufficiently to release the surface water. As there is very little solid wood in refuse from hydraulic barkers, the water soaked up in the bark results in a higher average moisture content than in the usual wood refuse.

Presses to reduce the water content of bark and make it more suitable for fuel have been installed in a number of mills.

THE BREAKDOWN MILL

When mills receive logs of diameters and lengths that are too large for the chippers in use, they must be broken down into suitable sizes. Sometimes large-diameter logs are only a small percentage of the total. Such logs are cut up into pieces short enough to be split and by-passed through a steam or air-powered splitter, as mentioned previously.

Splitters

Splitters have been built to take blocks up to 8 feet long, but the most usual size is 4 or 5 feet, both for ease of handling the shorter pieces and for the convenience of a less cumbersome machine. Figure 5.11 is a shop view of a 4-foot steam-powered splitter with a single-blade axe. Some splitters use a four-bladed axe in the shape of a right-angled cross, the idea being to quarter a log at one stroke, whereas a single axe requires at least three strokes and some re-

Fig. 5.11. Steam powered single blade axe splitter. (*Courtesy Sumner Iron Works*)

Fig. 5.12. Wood being split by a cross blade axe. (*Courtesy Sumner Iron Works*)

handling of pieces. The cross-blade type works very well on reasonably uniform diameter blocks where the center of the blade coincides fairly well with block centers (see Fig. 5.12). However, the single blade type makes fewer slivers from large-diameter logs and the sizes of the split pieces are easier to control. It is a more versatile tool for the larger sizes.

Blocks are spotted in the single blade splitter by means of a transfer having multiple strands of chains spaced about 4 inches apart. The section of transfer across the splitter bed is divided down the centerline, each half being driven separately by reversible drives so that the two halves can be stopped or run either in the same or opposite directions independently of each other. Thus the operator can straighten blocks or split pieces to line them up for splitting.

Large Log Handling

If most of the logs are of large size, or the volume is too great for a splitter, the breakdown plant takes the shape of the head end of a basic sawmill with a log deck, headrig, carriage and edger with the necessary log and cant handling rolls, transfers and conveyors. Fig. 15.20 is a typical large log barking and chipping plant layout.

Log Deck Saws

When logs arrive at the deck on a slip or log lift, they are usually carried past a cut-off saw to reduce them to the lengths required by the mill barkers or chippers. Swing cut-off saws up to about 108 inches in diameter are in use for this purpose, V belt-driven by motors up to 75 hp, depending on size. The swing frame is moved by a long-stroke air cylinder under control of an operator.

Usually a drag saw is installed together with a circular saw. While slower, a drag saw blade can be long enough to cut off the largest logs too big for the circular. Drag saws are driven by a slow-speed crankshaft and connecting rod which takes its power from a motor and reduction gear or V belt and spur gear drive from motors of 15 to 25 hp, depending on size of logs and cutting speed required. The saw frame is raised and lowered by either a small winch or an air cylinder. If occasional logs are too large for the circular saw, the small section uncut by a large circular saw can be quickly cut through with a short one-man chain saw, thus avoiding the cost of installing a drag saw.

Two chain-driven Vee rolls can be set at an elevation that will raise the log 6 or 8 inches above the following section of conveyor, ensuring that the log will break away from the saw when cut. When a large number of small logs are expected, a set of dogging jaws operated by linkage and an air cylinder from below the deck can be justified. Another method of raising the log at the cut is a raised center section of the log haul trough ahead of the saw and a Vee-shaped cast-iron pillow behind the saw.

Cutting long logs into shorter lengths, say 20 feet, makes it possible to build a short mill with really worthwhile savings in capital costs.

Log Kicker

The cut lengths are then even-ended by a second conveyor section behind the saws and kicked out of the conveyor onto either a log transfer or log deck skids sloping downward away from the conveyor at about a 10° angle. The kicker consists of a heavy shaft set to rotate up to a maximum of about 90° operated by an arm near its middle. From 2 to 4 additional arms are keyed to the shaft with their upper ends pin-connected to approximately horizontal pusher bars which contact the logs. The power arm is connected by a link to an air or steam cylinder or to a crank driven by an electric motor with controls set so the crank will turn only one full revolution at slow speed, thus turning the shaft 90° or less and back to its starting point.

Electrical drive mechanisms for this type of application are manufactured by Westinghouse and sold under the trade name of "Motocylinder." These are built in a wide variety of sizes and provide a way to aid in complete electrification of a mill through their application to loaders, jump skids, drop-outs, etc., as well as to log kickers.

The logs roll down the inclined skids or are carried by the transfer and are stopped by a log stop and loader. This consists of another heavy shaft under the deck on which are mounted short cast-steel arms with crescent-shaped segments on one end and hooked teeth on the other. When the toothed ends of these arms are toward the logs, they act as stops. Then, when the shaft is turned, one log is rolled down the skids while the rounded segment turns up and prevents the next log from following. At the same time the heel kicks the released log off the transfer into a conveyor or onto a carriage. A log stop and loader are shown at the left in Figure 5.13 with the stops up to hold logs back; when the shaft is rotated it will release one log, kick it off the skids onto the carriage and still keep others from following.

In a standard sawmill the log would roll onto a carriage, but in a breakdown plant for a pulp or paper mill a log deck, such as described above, would be ahead of a log barker, and the logs could be discharged from the deck into the barker.

Often log deck skids are set horizontally with cast-iron chain channel liners bolted on their tops to transfer logs sidewise, forming a so-called live deck. The usual practice is to run these chains at about 40 feet per minute.

Logs drop off the lower end of a sloping deck or discharge end of a live deck onto a toothed Vee roll case of heavy construction which feeds them into the barker in

Fig. 5.13. Log deck with log stop and loader, skids and Simondson turning a log. (*Courtesy Filer and Stowell*)

some installations. With other types of barkers the logs discharge from a live deck directly into the barker.

In either case it is necessary to have a point of size selection between barker and chipper. This usually consists of a set of Vee rolls and lift arms to set logs out of the rolls onto another set of transfer skids, or live log deck, ahead of a carriage and head-rig for reducing them to size suitable for the chipper (Figure 5.14).

Log Turners

As a log rolls down the deck after release by the log stop, it will usually make contact with the carriage knees and be dogged into place. Often the log does not stop squarely against the knees, or rebounds. A Simondson combination log turner or a "Hill" nigger pushes the log against the knees and holds it in place for dogging. A Simondson turning a log is shown in Figure 5.13 with the push arms up and the hook in the top of the log. It should be noted the push arms are keyed to the shaft and operated by one

oscillating cylinder piston rod, whereas the hook arm is free on the shaft and can turn independently of it when operated by the other cylinder. Both cylinders are under control of the sawyer by means of a "joy stick" control lever.

The push arms will load a log on the carriage and hold it for dogging. The hook can reach out, hook into the top of a log and pull it away from the carriage, turning it 90° by letting it drop on the skids or against the push arms (Figure 5.13). The push arms will lower the sawed face onto the skids, then push the log back onto the carriage.

Most designers are now equipping their deck skids with lift sections at the discharge ends. These are raised by a jump cylinder, linkage and shaft. When above the carriage head blocks they will prevent the bottom of a log from sliding off the carriage when being turned. They also help slide a log onto the carriage by raising it above the head blocks, avoiding possibility of hitting their front edge.

Fig. 5.14. Vee roll section with lift arms. (*Courtesy Sumner Iron Works*)

A steam or air operated "Hill" nigger is used instead of, or in combination with, a Simondson where a large number of small logs are to be sawed. Its action is a combination of lifting (with a bar having hinged teeth) and crowding which rotates the log against the carriage knees.

Log Carriage

In a new wood mill, including large chippers, the number of logs requiring breakdown before chipping is relatively small. In operation, the breakdown mill will run intermittently, and economics dictate use of equipment requiring a minimum of labor. The new no-man carriages fit into this picture admirably; in these, the log is held in place by air-operated or motor-driven dogs. All functions of the breakdown operation are under remote control of the sawyer, who loads the logs, dogs, sets, saws and operates an air-powered set of off-bearing arms which catch the cant when it breaks clear after being sawn, then lowers it to the off-bearing rolls flat side down. It should be noted that taper sawing is unnecessary in this type of operation, so that knees are not equipped with taper attachments.

Carriage Feeds

The designer must select a carriage feed drive most suitable for the particular installation under consideration.

There are three general types of carriage drives now in use. The first is the twin steam-feed engine of various cylinder sizes. The engine crankshaft is geared to the cable drum shaft. Cables run from the drum to both ends of the carriage over suitable sheaves and tighteners. The matter of adequate cable tensioning and equalizing devices is vital to cable life. Incorrect tension will cause early failure of cables.

Experience has shown definitely that two cables driving a carriage will stand up from three to nine times as long as a single cable. For instance, in one mill having the cable drum grooved for $1\frac{1}{8}$-inch cables, single cables lasted only 20 to 22 days. When the cables were doubled up, they had to be replaced only every nine months. In another mill single cable life was eight to nine weeks at best, while the life of two cables in parallel was six months. Another point to keep in mind is to locate the feed engine at about the middle of the carriage travel so that the spring of the feed and haulback cables will be the same.

The second type of drive is the steam shotgun, which is simply a long cylinder having a stroke equal to carriage travel, with the piston rod coupled directly to an end of the carriage. These shotgun cylinders are normally of either 12- or 14-inch standard bore and can be made of any practical length by bolting together additional sections of cylinders and piston rods.

The third type of drive is electric. Usually these use d.c. motors either geared or direct-connected to a cable drum. This type has proved very successful with the advent of modernized control circuits which eliminate large contactors interrupting heavy currents. Usually control is accomplished by regulating excitation of the main d.c. motor and generator exciter fields. These currents are small and no problems are involved. The main problem in selecting electric carriage drives is to size the equipment so that it will provide acceleration and deceleration of the heavy carriage at a rate sufficient to obtain required speed and reversal well within the limits of carriage travel available.

Power requirements will depend on number of logs to be sawn, their size and weight, the weight of the carriage, its travel and speed desired. Installations vary from 65 hp for the a.c. motor driving the main m.g. set up to 400 hp in large complete sawmills. However, it is difficult to see where such large power could be justified in a breakdown mill.

For a mill built for 24- or 32-foot logs the author's preference is a shotgun carriage drive where low-cost steam is available for the following reasons:

1. Lowest initial cost,
2. Lowest maintenance (no cables),
3. Fastest action.

When a mill is built for longer logs, a cable drive is best. Here the selection of steam engine or motor drive for the cable drum depends again on steam cost and availability.

When installing a shotgun feed it is advisable to fully insulate the cylinder, as well as all piping and valves. Cylinder temperatures will then be kept more uniform, initial condensation of entering steam will be reduced, economy increased, and better lubrication and less wear will result.

Band Mills

In a pulpwood breakdown operation one of the main objectives is to get the logs ready for chipping with as little loss of wood as possible. Therefore, the use of band saws wherever practical is indicated, because even a large band mill will have its saws swaged to only 8 or 9 gauge, equal to $\frac{11}{64}$ and $\frac{5}{32}$ inch respectively. Edger saws large enough to rip heavy cants up to 12 inches thick will have $\frac{3}{8}$-inch wide teeth, thereby making a kerf over twice as wide as the band head rig. The large savings in wood are obvious.

The selection of a band head rig depends primarily on the maximum size logs it will be called upon to cut and the minimum thickness at which it is desirable to take the initial slab. Nominal head rig sizes, such as 9 or 10 feet, have little real significance with respect to the size of logs it can saw. Those sizes refer to diameter of the band wheels. Heavy-gauge saws will fatigue and crack when run on small wheels and it has been found that 9-foot wheels are about the minimum when using 10 to 12 gauge saws which, in turn, are swaged to 8 or 9 gauge.

Band Mill Drives

All band mills drive on the bottom wheel arbor, either direct- or V belt-connected to individual motors. If direct-connected, the motor speed must be right to result in a saw speed of from 9,000 to 10,000 fpm (feet per minute). With a 327 rpm motor and a 10-foot wheel the saw speed would be 10,200 fpm. If the band mill had 9-foot wheels, the same motor would run the saw at 9,200 fpm.

Experiments indicate that speeds on the low side of 9,000 fpm and relatively wide tooth spacing result in somewhat lower power consumption. However, these factors vary with wood species, density, moisture content, etc., but 9,000 to 10,000 fpm is about right for most cases.

Some sawmills have installed two-speed motors. Others use wound-rotor motors to provide the sawyer with a speed selection to obtain higher production. In a breakdown plant, either synchronous or constant-speed induction motors are used for simplicity and economy.

Motor power requirements for band mills vary from 250 to 400 hp, depending on mill size, feed speed and wood species. Here again, the designer's judgment coupled with his own and the experience of others will enable him to select the most suitable drive and motor size for the particular conditions.

MECHANICAL BARKERS

It has long been recognized that mechanical bark removal is less expensive both in first cost and sometimes in operating cost; but most machines designed for this purpose have shortcomings, such as incomplete cleaning of the logs, capacity for only short logs, removal of too much sound wood, etc. Wet barking, either hydraulic or mechanical, causes a disposal problem. Bark has a good fuel value but absorbs so much water that in wet barking processes it will hardly sustain its own combustion. Some tremendous and costly installations of bark presses have been made to de-water and make this wet bark suitable for fuel.

In addition to continual improvement of drum barkers, a goodly number of mechanical barkers have been developed, in an endeavor to take advantage of the economies inherent in barking long logs. These include abrasion, impact, chain and scraper types. Most of these are more or less limited in use by low capacity and high maintenance cost. However, scraper-type barkers have recently been developed, such as the Nicholson (see Figure 5.9) and the Cambio (see Figure 5.10), which appear to have overcome or minimized most of the weaknesses of mechanical barkers. These scraper types will handle logs fed through them continuously end to end of various sizes, lengths, tapers and nominal sweeps in any sequence, at speeds up to 125 linear fpm, depending on size. The largest will take logs from 10 to 60 inches in diameter in lengths from 8 to 60 or more feet. The barker, log deck, infeed and outfeed are all under control of one operator, as with hydraulic barkers. After two years of operation, maintenance has proved to be nominal. They require about a 150 hp motor and a 75 hp air compressor, so power costs per ton are also low. The Nicholson barker will clean up 100 logs per hour averaging 12-inches in diameter at the butt and 32 feet long.

Bark is collected in a conveyor below the barker, fed to a hog and then to the fuel pile or boiler house without further treatment. Various amounts of broken up bark will lay on top of a log as it comes out of the barker. Therefore logs should be run through a washer or other device to remove loose bark and dirt, and then through either a cutoff or slasher saws to the chippers; if too large for the chippers, the bolts can be side tracked through a splitter and returned to the chipper conveyor.

A point often overlooked when designing a mechanical barking plant is that a surprising number of pieces of loose bark fall on top of logs at the outfeed of these barkers. This bark will cling to the top of logs and ride them into the chipper unless some means for removal is provided. When logs are conveyed directly into a chipper some means of scraping or washing off the loose bark is necessary. All manner of devices, such as a curtain of chains, spring-loaded plates, strips of stiff belting, etc, have been used. A washer will clean the logs but the wash water and wet bark present additional problems.

If logs are kicked onto a deck then rolled one by one on to a chipper feed conveyor the loose bark will fall off. In this case hoppers must be placed under openings in the deck and under conveyor discharge sprockets to collect and direct the bark pieces into refuse conveyors.

HANDLING OF CANTS

Upon being sawn off the logs, the cants will fall onto a set of power-driven flat off-bearing rolls behind the band mill. These rolls should be wide enough to carry the widest slab that can be sawn on the band mill with but little overhang. Thus if there is falldown room for a 5-foot slab or cant, the off-bearing rolls should be a full 60 inches long and 16 inches in diameter. However, if such wide slabs are sawn very infrequently, the rolls can be reduced to 54 x 16 inches as a measure of economy, or even 48 x 12 inches if that is indicated as a necessity, but it is certainly not advisable.

Power Requirement of Roll Cases

$$\text{hp} = \frac{(0.15)\ (S)\ (W_R + W_C)}{(33,000)\ (0.85)}$$

Where

    hp = Horsepower of drive motor

    S = Surface speed of rolls (fpm)

    W_R = Total weight of rolls, sprockets and drive chain or miter gearing, and drive shafting (pounds)

    W_C = Weight of largest cant to be expected on the roll case (pounds).

In the above, 0.15 represents the friction coefficient of all rotating parts in the roll-case; 0.85 is taken as efficiency of the power transmission equipment, such as reduction gearing, chain drive, etc.

Normally a surface speed of about 300 fpm would be about right for off-bearing rolls, but the designer can choose a speed fast enough to keep cants out of the way of the band mill output without running them faster than necessary.

Cants are picked up from the off-bearing rolls by lift skids or skid arms onto a transfer which carries them to a roll conveyor feeding the chipper. The lift skids are controlled either manually or by a limit switch actuated by the cants as they progress down the off-bearing rolls.

At the transfer point to the chipper feed rolls several loading methods are used to control the rate at which cants drop into the feed conveyor so as not to interfere with logs coming directly from the barker. Both the log-loading and cant-loading machinery is normally under control of the chipper operator. In the design it is important to locate these points where they can be seen by the chipper feeder. Feeding cants onto the rolls is accomplished with a combination of lift skids and cant stop pins as previously mentioned.

In some mills, for one reason or another, only small-diameter round logs can be chipped. In that case the larger logs are broken down into cants 6 to 8 inches thick and full width of the log. These cants are then "ripped" to a width no greater than can be fed into the chipper.

As mentioned above, because the ⅜-inch wide kerf taken by edger saws is wasteful of good wood, band edgers can be used to rip the wide cants. A machine of this type consists of two 6-foot band mills of opposite hands set on a common base, one mill being adjustable so that the space between the saws can be varied. The edged cants are then transferred to the chipper feed conveyor as before.

Sometimes cants prepared in this manner are to be cut into short blocks for grinders. They are then transferred through slasher saws and dropped into a conveyor below the slasher for transportation to the grinder room.

A set of slasher saws can be installed with its table in line with the cant transfer to the chipper conveyor with lift arms or skids over the conveyor so that cants can be selected for slashing into blocks or run to the chipper. With this installation a round link cast manganese steel chain of about 1¼ x 8 inches with 30-inch flights spaced about 4 feet apart and running 60 fpm should handle the blocks. Power requirements can be calculated from the conveyor power formula outlined under log hauls. Usually 25 hp would be ample to take care of intermittent heavy volumes being slashed.

DRUM BARKING

Drum barkers have been greatly improved over the years, principally by use of new bar shapes and better methods of fastening the bars to the rings, thus increasing capacity and reducing maintenance.

Actually the operating cost of a drum barker installation is relatively low in both power and labor. A 12 x 45-foot drum will require only 125 hp to drive it and usually can be run unattended. With the proper conveyor set-up, two or more drums can operate in parallel without individual attendance.

In older mills wood going to drum barkers is usually cut into short lengths to fit the magazines of grinders or for feeding relatively small, low-powered chippers. Where wood comes to the mill in cordwood lengths it is fed to the barkers without cutting, unless it is for grinders. In mills making both chemical and groundwood pulp, wood for the grinders is cut to length after the barkers, while full-length wood goes to the chippers. It was believed by many that wood over 4 or 5 feet long would not bark well in a drum. However, installations using 8-foot wood are operating successfully with 45-foot barkers. A 65-foot drum will do a better barking job on 8-foot wood.

The ends of short wood tend to broom considerably in drum barkers, trapping bark particles, and the slivers are lost in screening. A chipper does not reduce the ends to as uniform chips as it does the rest of a bolt; hence chipping short wood results in more dust and undersized and odd shaped chips than an equal volume of longer pieces. Hence, chip recovery from short wood is lower.

When designing a drum barker installation every consideration should be given to taking advantage of barking in longer lengths. This favorably affects the economics of yard handling, storage, transportation and harvesting. Obviously fewer saw cuts through a tree will result in less sawdust loss, fewer ends to broom, and higher chip recovery. Thus, where possible and practical, the use of longer wood in a drum barker is the more economical arrangement, even though the cost of conveyors and wood handling equipment may be somewhat higher.

A good installation of conveyor and diversion plows for feeding two or more drums is shown in Figure 5.15. The plows are manually set from time to time as re-

Fig. 5.15. Belt conveyor and diversion plows (open) feeding multiple barking drums. (*Courtesy Link Belt*)

quired, but could readily be power-operated and remote-controlled. Both chains and belts have proved quite satisfactory for take-away conveyors. The chain conveyor trough section opposite the drums should be lined with at least ⅝-inch plate and preferably backed up under the bottom liner with heavy timbers at least 8 inches thick to take the shock of falling blocks. If belts in that area are run over rubber-covered or pneumatic-tired idlers on about 6-foot centers, the falling bolts will not damage the belt as they would if the belt was solidly backed.

CHIPPERS

Chippers are simply large forged or cast-steel disks bolted to a flange on a suitable arbor and mounted on a heavy cast-steel base. From 4 to 16 knives are mounted in pockets in the disk, with cutting edges pro-jecting ⅝ to ¾ inch from its face. The extent of this projection determines the chip length. A feed chute is set at a steep angle to the face of the disk in a standard chipper and carries a bed knife in the bottom and one side. Knives on the revolving disk pass across the inner or cutting edges of the bed knives at an angle, resulting in a combined shearing and cutting action; the wood is thus forced into the corner of the chute formed by the bottom and side bed knives. Clearance between bed and rotating knives is readily adjustable by means of set screws and locks bearing on the bed knives. Arbor thrust bearings can also be moved to change disk location for preliminary setting of clearances. Bed knife holders and main feed chute are carried on the chipper bed plate. The upper end of the feed chute is built of steel plate and installed on a separate support structure.

Chipper drive motors can be direct-connected, belted or engine type mounted on an extended arbor.

A removable sheet-metal housing covers the upper half of the disk, the lower portion being left open below the base, for bottom discharge.

If chippers are covered both above and below the frame, a tangential pipe built into the cover, and short plates welded to the outer edge and back of the disk, we have a top discharge chipper. These act like fans, and blow chips to considerable heights and distances. Chips from this type are blown into a cyclone which drops them onto a distributing conveyor feeding one or more screens, as required. Sometimes chips go directly from the cyclone to storage via belt conveyors or a pneumatic conveying system discharging to outside storage piles. This arrangement eliminates chip conveyors under bottom discharge chippers, at a very considerable saving in first cost.

Figure 5.16 is a large bottom-discharge chipper viewed from the side opposite the drive. The bed knife adjusting screws can be seen at the outer edge and under the bottom of the feed chute. This particular unit

has a 153-inch diameter cast-steel disk with 8 knives, and will chip logs up to 32 inches in diameter at a feed rate of 170 fpm. Figure 5.17 is a shop view of a 66-inch, horizontal-feed, top-discharge, 16-knife slab chipper (300 hp, 600 r.p.m.). A rounded bottom feed chute is used when chipping round wood.

Where possible the feed chute extension is usually carried up far enough so that the longest log to be fed will tip into the chute off the end of the feed conveyor. This is not always possible or desirable with large chippers, due to their height and the usual desire to feed 24-foot logs. This combination would result in an impractically high machinery floor elevation. If large, heavy logs were allowed to slide freely down the chute, they would damage the knives, knife holders and possibly the arbor bearings. Hence feeding devices are used to tip long logs into the feed chute from a lower level to reduce machinery floor elevations and to control the rate of feed of large logs. After a log is conveyed onto its fluted rolls, the outer end of that section is raised by an air cylinder; the log is tipped into the chipper chute at

Fig. 5.16. 153-inch 8-knife bottom discharge chipper 1,200 to 1,500 HP-257 rpm 32-inch spout. (*Courtesy Sumner Iron Works*)

the correct angle for chipping, and is fed in at the speed of the rolls.

Chips from a bottom-discharge chipper drop onto either a belt or chain conveyor running through openings in the ends of the foundation. Ample clearance between disk and conveyor is required to avoid a pile of chips building up to the disk.

Belt conveyors operate very satisfactorily under chippers up to about 84-inch diameter disks. For larger chippers, a wide multiple-chain conveyor will be needed to handle the huge volume of chips produced from a full-sized cant or log by these larger chippers. They are also easier to install and operate in the wider widths from the standpoint of conveyor troughs, shielding, skirting and leakage, and do not slip through under a pile of chips.

The disks of modern chippers are fitted with renewable wearing plates over the entire area of their faces. Knife pockets also are equipped with renewable liners. With a full complement of renewable wearing surfaces one of these disks should last indefinitely, barring a serious accident. While tramp iron, such as railroad spikes, boom dogs, broken machinery parts, etc. nick or break knives and cut the replaceable wearing surfaces, they do not damage the disk itself.

A number of nationally known concerns manufacture chipper knives to fit any chipper. All have numerous steel compositions and heat-treating combinations which they will tailor, as required, to produce knives most suitable for any condition encountered in chipper operation. For example, knives that stand up well on northern soft wood are entirely unsatisfactory when used on southern pine. Frequently a mill has to work with a knife manufacturer to develop a combination of steel composition, heat treatment and knife grinding angle for its particular chippers and wood. Sometimes two chippers in the same mill require different combinations for best results.

One of the most surprising things about chipper knives is that they stay as sharp and make as good clean chips for as long continuous periods as they do. Dull knives make ragged chips and increase the volume of cards and slivers. A regular program for changing knives should be set up, based on operating experience with the equipment and economics of the situation with all factors included. A good starting program is a complete change of disk knives every four hours and a change of bed knives every week.

Chipper knives should be ground in sets, each set being kept together during its entire life. Thus, all knives will be the same width, making knife setting easier and faster. If backup shims are used behind knives in their pockets, the shims for each knife should be kept with it, so that once all the knives have been set to correct projections, the addition of shims of equal thickness behind them will maintain equal projection when they are ground together.

As mentioned previously, some variations of angle for the back bevel are in use for various reasons, such as cutting edge support, power consumption on various species, card breaking, etc. Some operators use a double bevel with a short section back from the cutting edge ground with a greater included angle than the remainder for more support of the cutting edge. This practice consumes more power, but it does seem to reduce nicking of the cutting edges and may be justified if the wood is hard and dense.

With knives set out a given distance from the disk face, practically all cuts are the same length except for tail ends and some bouncing of small and short pieces. However, as the knives shear across the face of logs being chipped, wide sections are cut off. These are usually broken up by irregularities on the back of the disk, such as nuts on knife and face wearing plate bolts. Occasionally wide sections are discharged from the chipper along with fines and slivers of various sizes and lengths, depending on knife bevel angle, sharpness, and clearances, and on the species, shape, and condition of the wood. Odd-size pieces are unsuitable for chips and must be screened out.

It is interesting to consider progress in chipper design over the past 25 years. In the early 1930's most chips were cut from hand-barked sawmill refuse, slabs and edgings and small round short logs in 4-knife machines, some with as small as 45-inch diameter disks. As the years went by, economics dictated the use of larger pieces of wood and greater capacities per machine. Thus, the trend has been toward larger disks and more knives, until 15-knife units for high capacity are in use. Ten- and 12-knife machines are more common, however, and whole log chippers having 175-inch diameter disks are in use for large logs.

Paralleling the development of high-capacity, multiple-knife and large-diameter machines has been the search for better and more uniform chips. Strange as it may seem, there is evidence to indicate that chip quality has not been improved with the advent of these machines. There are cases where direct comparisons in a mill show less bruising and better uniformity from small 4-knife chippers, even when handling short blocks, than in chips produced by modern high-speed multi-knife chippers cutting long logs. The evidence is there but the reasons are not clear.

The backs of chipper disks are studded with nuts and bolt ends protruding through them, which anchor the knives and disk face wearing plates. The chips ejected from the knife slots collide with these projections; the more projections and the higher the speed, the worse is the battering received by the chips. The addition of blades for top discharge very likely further aggravates the situation. It is well known that bruised chips produce weaker pulp, and that they are almost impossible to get rid of. This problem of bruised chips is brought up here, not as an axiomatic, irrefutable chipper characteristic, but rather as a mat-

ter to be approached with caution and some apprehension.

The search for better chips and less power per ton has led to development of the Norman chipper with its spiral-faced disk. This design has been in successful operation in a large number of plants for several years, apparently with some improvement in chip quality and reduction in power consumption.

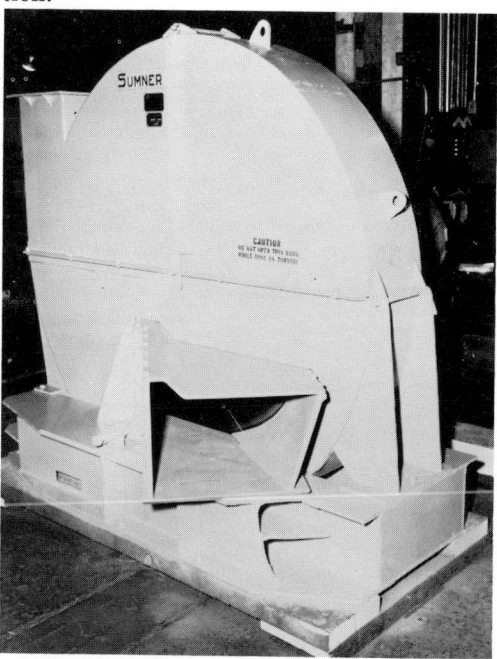

Fig. 5.17. 66-inch 16-knife top discharge, horizontal feed slab chipper. (*Courtesy Sumner Iron Works*)

A new concept in chipper design, which has promise of considerably less bruising along with more uniform chip length, width and thickness, is the drum type under development by the Anglo Paper Products, Ltd. of Quebec, Canada. This unit has knives mounted on the exterior surface of a revolving drum. The knives are arranged to score and peel a log held against the drum parallel to its surface. Log lengths are limited to the length of the drum. The experimental unit will handle logs up to about 30 inches in diameter by 4 feet long.

The feed chutes of the usual chipper design slope at a steeply downward angle to

Fig. 5.18.   72-inch top-discharge 6-knife veneer chipper. (*Courtesy Sumner Iron Works*)

the disk face, both horizontally and vertically. As previously pointed out, this design requires a large difference in elevation from chipper bed plate to the top of feed chute; this creates difficulties in laying out equipment arrangements, and adds to building costs. In the last two or three years a number of horizontal-feed chippers of medium size have been installed.

The horizontal feed chipper was originally designed and installed to chip waste veneer in plywood plants. Most waste veneer is sapwood, which is ideal for pulping. With feed speed controlled by toothed or spike rolls, veneer chips are exceptionally uniform and of high quality.

A 72-inch top discharge veneer chipper is shown in Figure 5.18. The heavy fluted feed roll which acts to pull veneer into the chipper, its drive, and feed roll loading linkage are clearly shown. Chips are discharged from the outlet on top of the housing. This chipper is direct-connected to a 600 rpm, 150 hp motor and has a rated capacity of 25 to 30 units of chips per hour.

Horizontal veneer chippers were tried on small wood with good success. Modification of the feed trough and rolls to properly handle round wood, slabs and edgings has resulted in a unit with some real advantages over the older types for many applications.

Another innovation is the top-discharge chipper already mentioned. This type can be set close to the ground and, if it is provided with horizontal feeding arrangements, such as the chipper in Fig. 5.17, the combination requires a minimum of head room and feed conveyor elevation. So far, only small and medium-size chippers up to about 84-inch disk diameter have been built for top discharge, primarily because the terrific volume of chips produced by large, multiple-knife whole log chippers is difficult to blow cleanly, and those chips remaining inside the housing for a few revolutions would be seriously damaged.

Horizontal-feed, top-discharge chippers combined with a mechanical barker made it possible to design the relatively low-cost, tree-length barking and chipping plants, which have been operating so successfully for the past year at two pulp mills in the South.

CHIP SCREENING

As proper cooking requires chips of reasonably uniform size, all chips must be screened before entering the digesters. Chip screens can be installed either between chippers and storage or between storage and digesters. The main advantages of the first arrangement is that oversized chips or cards, slivers, strips, fines and dust are kept out of storage bins, where they increase the tendency of the chips to "hang up" in the bins and jam in the feeders. In this location, screens must be sized to take the output of the chippers and must run as long as the chippers are operating. When installed after the storage bins, the screens must be sized to handle chips as fast as they are used to fill digesters. In most cases, but not always, this flow rate is considerably higher than chipper production rate; thus larger screens are required. The screens are then running only while the digesters are being filled. They start and stop automatically in sequence with feeders and chip belts, which are under remote control from the operating floor of the digester building.

There are numerous designs of chip screens in use, e.g., vibrating, oscillating and gyratory. In all cases it is necessary to make two separations. The first takes out the oversize chips, which go to a re-chipper. The second separates the fines from accepted chips, the fines usually going into a refuse conveyor.

Chip screens are set up singly or in batteries, depending on capacity of the individual units and total maximum requirements. Figure 5.19 is a close up of a 7-foot 6-inch by 18-foot oscillating or "shaker" screen. This screen has a capacity of 25 units of chips per hour and is driven by a 7½ hp motor. As can be seen, the screens have two decks driven by an eccentric shaft and connecting rods producing about 6-inch movement of the decks in opposite directions. Chips are fed from a conveyor at the upper left through rotary star feeders set in the bottom of hoppers over the upper ends of the screens, to regulate the feed and spread the chips evenly across the screens.

Oversize pieces drop off the end of the upper deck onto a belt conveyor which takes them to a re-chipper. They are recycled over the screens, and no oversize pieces are

Fig. 5.19. Oscillating chip screen. (*Courtesy Black-Clawson Co.*)

lost. Accepted chips drop over the end of the fine screen on the lower deck onto a belt conveyor to storage or digesters as the case may be. Or they could be discharged into the boot of a bucket elevator to raise them to the top of storage bins, or into a surge bin over a feeder of an air-conveying system. Fines and dust drop through the fine screen into a pan hung below and are shaken out onto a third conveyor (which in this illustration is below the floor) and then to refuse.

Several types of re-chippers or chip-breakers are in use. Some are adaptations of a revolving cage having pins or bars which run close to similar stationary pins. Oversize chips and slivers are broken up between the pins. However, the type most commonly used and apparently the most satisfactory is simply a small chipper. Experience indicates that a small-diameter (down to 36-inch) multiple-knife, top-discharge chipper with a V type feed chute built especially for chips running at 1200 rpm is probably the machine best suited for this application.

Chip breakers or bottom discharge re-chippers must be set over conveyors. Although they are narrow and light, these re-cycling conveyors often have to be rather long and a bit complicated due to relative locations of screens and re-chippers. With a top-discharge chipper, however, it is only necessary to run a small sheet-metal duct overhead directly to a cyclone set over one screen or the main feed conveyor. Maintenance of such a set-up is low, and no operating attendance is needed.

The drive motor on a re-chipper need be only large enough to start the chipper and bring it up to speed. A 25-hp motor will handle a 36-inch re-chipper without difficulty.

TREE-LENGTH BARKING AND CHIPPING

So called whole-log barking and chipping has been standard practice on the northwest coast of the United States and Canada since the middle 1940's, although trees were bucked in the woods and brought to the mills in lengths limited by transportation facilities or design of the barkers, chipper feed chutes, or other mill equipment. Logs above about 18 inches in diameter went through the newly developed big barkers and chippers. Smaller logs were cut in short lengths suitable for handling and feeding small barkers and chippers.

Some mills bundled small logs in full tree lengths for rapid handling by cranes, then broke down the bundles on a table. Logs were cut to short lengths, usually 8 feet, ahead of barkers and chippers. A good many mills have continued this practice.

Practically all other areas of both the United States and Canada purchased, stored, barked and chipped small-diameter wood in short lengths, 4 feet and 8 feet being standard lengths in the North and 4 feet 6 inches standard in the South. Probably the primary reason for this practice was the small diameters and the use of drum barkers. These methods are still prevalent in those areas.

The development and successful operation of several types of mechanical barkers, such as the Impco, Cambio and Nicholson to name the three leaders in this field, has made it evident that barking in long lengths materially reduces costs.

The standard, so called vertical or gravity feed chippers limited lengths of wood so that tree-length barked logs had to be cut ahead of the chippers. This obviously added an operation, with its equipment, operating and maintenance costs. It also added time, reducing possible production and made some sawdust instead of chips.

A horizontal feed chipper was first installed for chipping veneer because of the greater convenience compared with the usual practice of changing the flow of waste veneer from horizontal conveyors to the downward-angling chipper feed spout. Within the last few years the horizontal feed veneer chipper has been adapted to round-log chipping, mainly by changing the feed chute and using a standard log chipper disk, frame, bearings, etc.

Since practicability of the horizontal log chipper and its capability of producing satisfactory chips has been proved in operation, the next logical step is to combine it with a mechanical barker in a continuous line. Such an arrangement reduces costs and saves wood for chips instead of sawdust, from the forest right through to the production of chips. Some new chipping plants have been built recently in the South, using this concept with outstanding results.

Table 5.1 lists production rates of identical Impco No. 5-20-5 mechanical barkers installed in different mills. One mill uses short wood, the other barks and chips in tree lengths. The cost savings are obvious.

TABLE 5.1. BARKER PRODUCTION IMPCO MODEL S20-5 BARKER.

	Mill A		Mill B *
	Wet Logs in Pond 20 min	Dry Logs	Dry Logs
Log lengths, ft	10	10	20 to 65
			southern
Species	pine	pine	pine
Feed speed, fpm	100	100	100
128 cu ft cords/hr	11.73	8.73	26.8
128 cu ft cords/ 16-hr day	183	140	430

* Mill B uses tree length log barking and chipping techniques.

There are of course any number of various arrangements and relative locations of equipment where this straight-line principle of barking and chipping can be used. The simplest arrangement is to use only logs small enough to pass through the barker; these are brought to the mill in full lengths up to about 65 feet. Logs are unloaded from trucks and trailers directly onto a wide transfer deck either by cables and winches, a crane or a log-handling vehicle. Logs are fed one by one from the transfer deck onto a chain conveyor section in line with the barker. It is fast enough to keep logs butted

end to end in the barker feed conveyor so that no barker time is lost.

An off-bearing conveyor takes logs discharged from the barker straight into the chipper feeder with no sidetracking and no lost time when all equipment is operating. When trouble develops anywhere along the line, production stops. For that reason some operators prefer to install storage transfers ahead of the barker and between barker and chipper, so when one machine is down for a period the other can continue to operate. The economic justification for the added cost and operating expense of these storage provisions is questionable. No general observation can be made in that respect. Each operation should be analyzed on the basis of the particular conditions which exist and can be foreseen over whatever expenditure amortization period is required by company policy.

A considerable percentage of tree-length logs will have crooks or sweeps which prevent their ready feeding through the barker and will have to be sawn into shorter lengths. Those logs can be cut on the conveyor ahead of the barker with a swing- or carriage-mounted cut-off saw during a momentary stop of the conveyor. Due to its higher speed the conveyor can catch up with the barker feeder and keep logs butted or their ends very close together.

More elaborate arrangements include yard storage of logs where trucks are unloaded by a log-handling vehicle which also takes logs from storage and places them on a transfer table ahead of the barker or equipment set up to cut saw logs off the butts of larger trees for resale to sawmills.

Most pulp mills purchase chips from sawmills in the surrounding territory, often several hundred miles away. Where whole-log barking is practiced, it may be profitable to bring in trees whose butts are too large for the mill barker or chipper. These butts can be trimmed to saw log lengths and sold to sawmills supplying chips. However, unless the sawmill has a barker, it saws these logs with the bark on, which of course reduces lumber and chip recovery at the saw-mill. Here again possible combinations of arrangements are numerous and available savings justify careful economic analysis.

It may be more profitable to trim saw logs from a certain percentage of tree lengths after they have been barked. In this case, of course, the barker must be large enough to take the biggest log.

Another possibility is to install two bark-ers, one large enough to take the saw logs, which are trimmed from the trees and by-passed through the large barker. This com-bination can be justified only if both bark-ers can be kept busy. Barked saw logs would be discharged onto a storage transfer for reloading on railroad cars or trucks go-ing to a sawmill and returning with chips. A simple arrangement of tree length small diameter log barking and chipping plant is shown in Figure 5.22.

It is obvious that straight-line installa-tions, such as these, require a very long piece of ground. However, there is no rea-son why barked logs cannot be transferred sidewise and fed back into a chipper along-side the barker, if length for a tandem ar-rangement is not available. This arrange-ment would make it easier for one man to look after both barker and chipper.

When considering the design of a mechani-cal barking installation it should be kept in mind that with a properly located central control house one man can handle the con-trol of the entire operation after logs have been placed on the storage transfer table. Normally only an operator, a man to han-dle log unloading, and a man at the barker would be required. The chipper can usually be run unattended but should be located so it can be under observation from the con-trol house or the barker operator's station, with the necessary control buttons within instant reach.

Another point easily overlooked is that bark and slivers of various sizes get knocked off logs all along their route to the barker; provision should be made to collect this bark in ample refuse conveyors for trans-portation to a hog and then to the fuel pile or refuse burner along with bark from the barker.

A surprising amount of loose bark stays on top of logs when they leave the barker, and cleaning this off is not easy. Various types of scrapers have been used with more or less success. These take the form of weighted hinged plates, sections of chain forming a curtain, sections of rubber belt-ing, etc., hanging down on top of the logs. Curtains of water jets are also in use. How-ever, this practice causes a problem with dewatering the wetted bark, disposing of the water, etc., and is to be avoided if pos-sible. Violently rolling the logs or kicking them out of a conveyor onto a storage transfer will free them of bark.

There is nothing particularly special about the log-handling equipment used in a tree length small log barking and chipping installation. Log deck machinery of stand-ard design is used except as it may require modification due to the length and diameter of the logs being handled.

Further economies are realized in tree-length operations, as they make it possible to use tops down to 4 inches in diameter which would otherwise be trimmed off and left in the woods. Small wood of that diam-eter splits badly in drum barkers and can-not be handled in short lengths through mechanical barkers. Furthermore, it is be-ing demonstrated in several mills that a long log operation reduces costs in logging, transportation, handling and storage, as has been covered in detail in Chapter 4.

CHAIN CONVEYORS

A wide variety of standard conveyor chain is available in a multitude of sizes and designs made by a number of manufac-turers, most of them being interchangeable. The major chain manufacturers issue cata-logs containing much technical data on sizes, strengths and applications of chain which are extremely useful in designing conveyors. Rather than try to cover con-

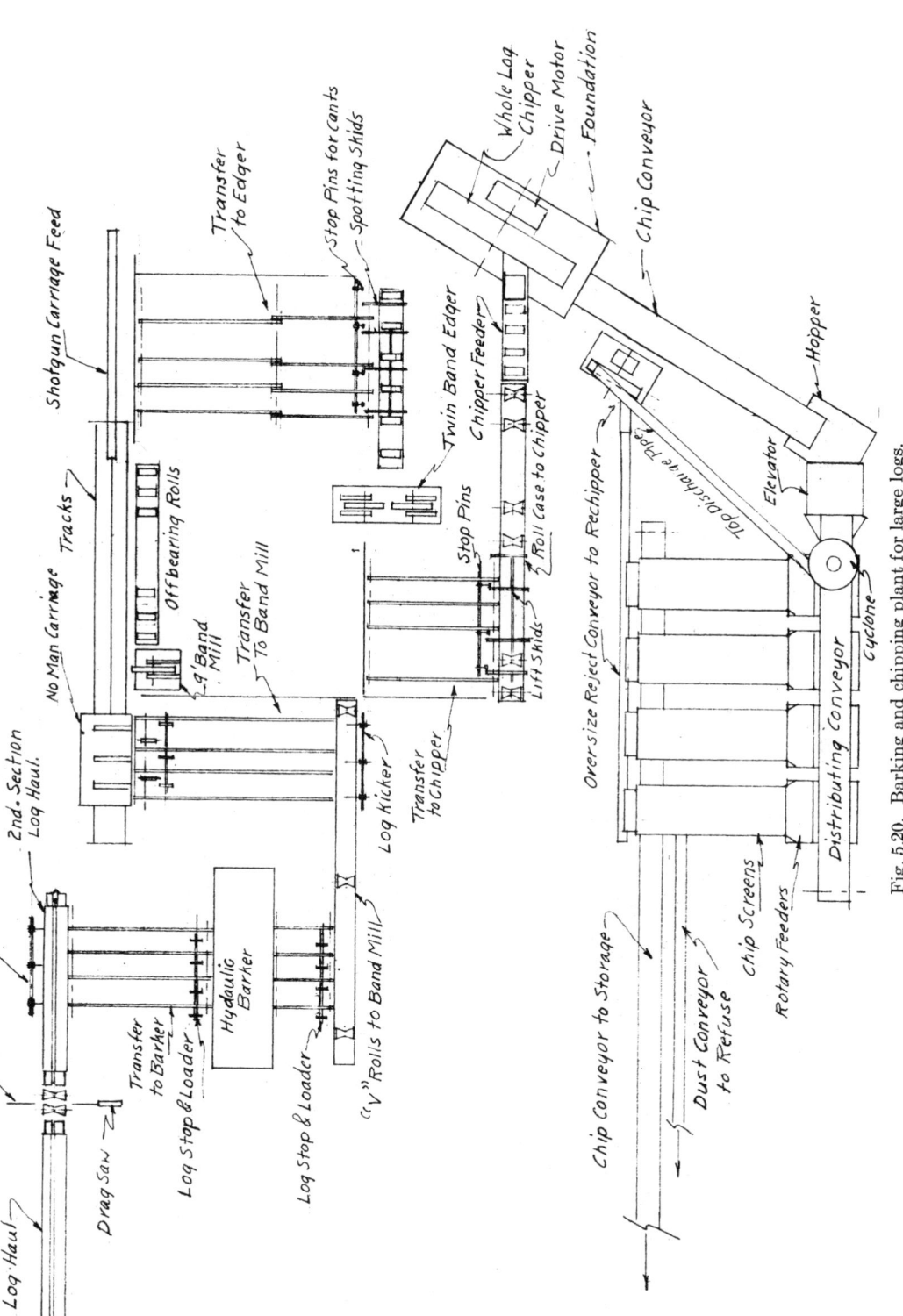

Fig. 5.20. Barking and chipping plant for large logs.

Fig. 5.21. Box link chains on small log haul. (*Courtesy IMPCO*)

veyor chain in detail in this chapter, the reader is referred to the manufacturers' literature.

It can be said that conveyor chain is one of the most versatile pieces of machinery available to the wood mill designer. Some types are more suitable than others for particular uses, but usually numerous types can be successfully applied, limited only by the designer's imagination or experience and the purchaser's pocketbook. All chain conveyors must run in a trough with a wear-resisting bottom or rails. Cast iron is an almost ideal material for this purpose, but while its life is long, its initial cost is high. Hardwood, such as maple, is frequently used: it wears well, is easily changed, and its cost is low. However, most chain conveyor troughs are lined with steel plate at least $\frac{1}{4}$ inch thick, depending on material handled, life desired, etc. Interestingly enough, an unlined concrete trough makes one of the very best conveyors. The concrete soon becomes very smooth and slick

and does not wear the chain noticeably more than a steel lining, nor does it show much wear itself. Where concrete troughs can be worked into the building or installed outside, they should be given consideration.

As examples of uses, single-strand box-link chain picks small logs out of the flumes (Figure 5.21) end to end and carries them up to barkers. Figure 5.5 shows a multiple strand conveyor of similar chain also picking logs out of a flume, but handles short wood on the basis of mass flow.

Practically all types of chain can be supplied with attachments of various shapes to which wood or metal flights can be bolted. Two parallel strands of forged chain with 6- or 8-inch high wood flights between them are used to distribute chips over screen feeders.

Refuse Conveyors

Chain conveyors are admirably suited to handling wood mill refuse, such as sawdust, bark, slivers, etc. A number of types can be adapted for this service, depending upon volumes and material to be handled. Either single or double-strand box-link chain with attachment links about 1 inch high every 2 or 3 feet works very well. Single-strand malleable or forged chain with attachments for bolting on angle-iron cross flights has high capacity for bark, chunks and other material of similar nature.

Sometimes it is necessary to lubricate conveyor chains to keep them flexible and reduce wear of the pins. A little crankcase or old transformer oil works quite satisfactorily. If chains run in a wet environment, such as picking logs or bark out of ponds and flumes, or if water sprays are used to reduce noise and lubricate chain ways, no oil is necessary.

The power required to operate chain conveyors depends on arrangement of the conveyor, type of chain, material handled, speed, slope, etc. A method for thorough analysis of chain conveyors is offered by Link Belt Company which has been found to produce entirely satisfactory results. In this connection a point to be kept in mind is that allowances for exceptional starting requirements are not made; consequently enough power should be installed to start the conveyors under the most severe anticipated conditions. Here is another case requiring the application of judgment and use of experience as guides.

Pneumatic Conveyors

Chips are readily handled by air over distances up to 1000 to 1200 feet, but this method consumes relatively large amounts of power, and the wear on bends in blow pipes is a factor. Surprising as it may seem, there is so little wear on the blow pipes that relatively light-gage sheet metal is used in straight sections. Usually bends are as long radius as possible and have a U cross section with the open side of the U on the outside of the bend. With this arrangement a flat abrasion-resistant plate can be bolted to the lighter U section to take the wear, and is easily replaced.

While pneumatic systems have proved highly successful for handling large volumes of chips, especially in connection with outdoor storage, operating experience with several installations has shown they are not particularly suited to unloading directly from railroad cars, barges or trucks. The suction pipes are too difficult to handle, and unloading time is so long as to be uneconomical. In cases where railroad cars or trucks are dumped into a track hopper with chips carried out of the hopper to a feed bin of a pneumatic system, the arrangement has proved extremely satisfactory.

Pneumatic systems are relatively simple in general concept but careful attention to detail design of the components backed by experience and judgment are absolutely necessary for successful installation. Briefly they consist of a large positive displacement blower discharging through a venturi tube into sheet-metal piping, which is low in first cost and easy to install. A surge bin with an enclosed variable-speed star feeder under it is set over the venturi, and chips are discharged by the feeder through a pipe connected to the venturi throat. The venturi is designed so its throat pressure is at or below atmospheric, so that chips will be picked up by the air stream and carried along the discharge pipe.

These systems are designed with chip loading such that they are in actual suspension and thus do not rub along pipe surfaces, which is the reason for the low rate of wear in the piping. Similar systems have been used for many years handling grain, cement, clay, salt cake, etc., but the design factors are different for each.

CHIP STORAGE

While it would seem that the design of a chip storage bin, in which the chips are dumped into the top from a conveyor or bucket elevator and withdrawn from the bottom by other conveyors, is a rather simple problem, actually it is extremely tricky, primarily because of the peculiar characteristics of chips.

The usual arrangement in older mills was to install rather large bins or hoppers above the digesters, which were filled directly from these bins. The structural requirements imposed by the heavy loads of overhead bins with attendant additional building costs have resulted in virtual abandonment of that arrangement in favor of wide, high-speed belt conveyors from the main storage discharging directly into the digesters, using trippers or plows at rates of feed even greater than could be obtained from overhead bins. With this newer arrangement, all feeders and conveyors from storage to the digester building and their controls can be set up in automatic sequence, with necessary interlocks and telltales or indicators to shut the system down in case of trouble and avoid spillage, overloading, etc. Television has recently been tried successfully as an aid to remote control of a chip-handling system.

The discharge of chips to storage and distribution in the bins is relatively simple, and deserves no unusual treatment by the designer. However, there are many possible arrangements and designs of the bins and withdrawal equipment. These are available to the designer, and are limited only by his experience and ingenuity. Practically all of them can develop troubles of one kind or another which often cause such costly operating problems as to deserve the most careful investigation before completing the design.

Chips have the pernicious characteristic of "hanging up" and arching over even wide spans with what appears to be little reason. To minimize this tendency, vibrators, steam or air jets, internal chains, etc. have been installed with more or less success. However, tight, hard jams will develop where hand poking is required to break the chips loose. So far as the writer knows, an entirely satisfactory chip storage bin of large capacity has not yet been developed that can be built at reasonable cost. Hence compromise is resorted to with results that are imperfect, but still not impossible to accept.

It would seem that the only way to prevent arching of chips in storage would be to slope the sides inward at the top, thus giving the form of a steep truncated cone or pyramid. This bin would then have a live bottom over the entire area consisting of screws or chain conveyors with variable-speed drives. Even then, there is some room for doubt that chips would flow freely after having been in storage for three or four days. Such an arrangement would be costly and uneconomical in utilization of space.

In recent years there has been a trend toward use of vertical cylindrical storage bins, often called silos, having conical bottom sections terminating over circular, rotating table feeders. The height of the conical bottom section is usually equal to the bin diameter and these table feeders are made in various diameters. The normal size is 12 feet in diameter.

When chips are dumped onto a pile or into bins of any shape they slide over one another at their angle of repose, approximately 45°; in general each chip comes to rest at an angle with the horizontal overlapped on the chips below. This is called "shingling" because of the pattern resembling shingles on a roof, and is one of the main causes of arching against the sides of bins at any internal roughness or a reduction in section. An inverted conical bin with a full-sized table feeder should be an approach to the ideal; but, as mentioned above, it is costly to build and uneconomical space-wise.

If chips are not allowed to stay long in a silo-type bin, they will usually feed out with only occasional hang-ups, but after several days in storage, full bins can be expected to hang up quite tightly, and much time, effort and expense is required to free them.

Some success has been attained with relatively long narrow bins having the ends and one side vertical and the other side sloping in at the bottom to sectional star-type rotary feeders. Bins of this type operate especially well if the shingling effect of the chips is utilized during withdrawal by loading from one end toward the other and taking out in the reverse direction. In this way chips will all be shingled in one direction, the last chips being withdrawn first, as they slide readily over the ones under them. Loading can be done from both ends toward the middle, unloading beginning at the middle; or the bin can be loaded from the middle toward the ends, unloading starting at the ends.

Storage bins of this type can be built of concrete, steel or wood. In the latter case a lining of hardwood flooring placed vertically will allow chips to slide quite freely. Even with this arrangement occasional hang-ups do develop under the best of operation and design precautions.

Outside Chip Storage

The storage of chips in the open began to be a significant factor in pulp-mill wood supply and storage operations about 1950 on the West Coast. Its advantages over round wood storage and handling were soon recognized, and outside chip storage facilities were installed in many of the West Coast mills, both old and new.

As a matter of interest, the Simpson Timber Co. used a spare planing mill fan and blow pipe system to store chips outside and to reclaim them at its insulating board mill in 1948 to build up chip inventory in anticipation of a strike in adjacent sawmills where the chips were produced. Contamination by cinders spewing out of the sawmill boilers and sand and gravel picked up in reclaiming, in addition to nuisance from wind carried fines and some chips, as well as inadequate equipment and little necessity for a larger chip inventory during normal operations, indicated the inadvisability of continuing this practice. Most of those factors are still important when considering new outside chip storage (O.C.S.) facilities.

At mills where a relatively large inventory of pulpwood is a necessity for various reasons, O.C.S. can be integrated into the operation at a reasonable first cost, compared to bins or silos, where the situation is favorable, and will show a real saving in operating expense from all indications so far. Figure 5.22 shows a straight line, long log wood preparation system featuring O.C.S.

Advantages. (1) Reduces pulp wood handling costs about 50% over round wood.

(2) More wood can be stored per acre because chips can be piled high, normally up to 90 and 100 feet, with one reported instance of a pile 160 feet high, and no ground area lost to roadways for trucks, railroad trackage or crawler cranes.

(3) Greater yield than from stored hardwood or pine round wood of 3 to 4 percentage points. This is primarily due to greater loss in fines when barking and chipping wood after drying out in storage than from similar green wood.

(4) Species can be kept segregated without much difficulty or added installation or operating expense.

(5) So far, O.C.S. chips processed green and stored as chips show no indication of insect damage.

(6) There has been no measurable loss after storage periods up to two years in the West and North and up to 3 months in the South, although some minor deterioration has been noticed there after 4 months.

(7) A goodly share of bark falls off round wood in storage and in handling, particularly after drying out. This creates a nuisance, and a house-cleaning and collection problem. Much of this dislodged bark is pulverized when run over by trucks and crawlers a few times so is lost as a fuel. When logs are barked and chipped green, most of the bark comes off in barkers, can be collected and burned economically in most cases.

(8) Chip storage piles can be more easily and accurately measured than random-piled round wood.

(9) The huge storage volumes possible reduces or eliminates chip procurement scheduling problems.

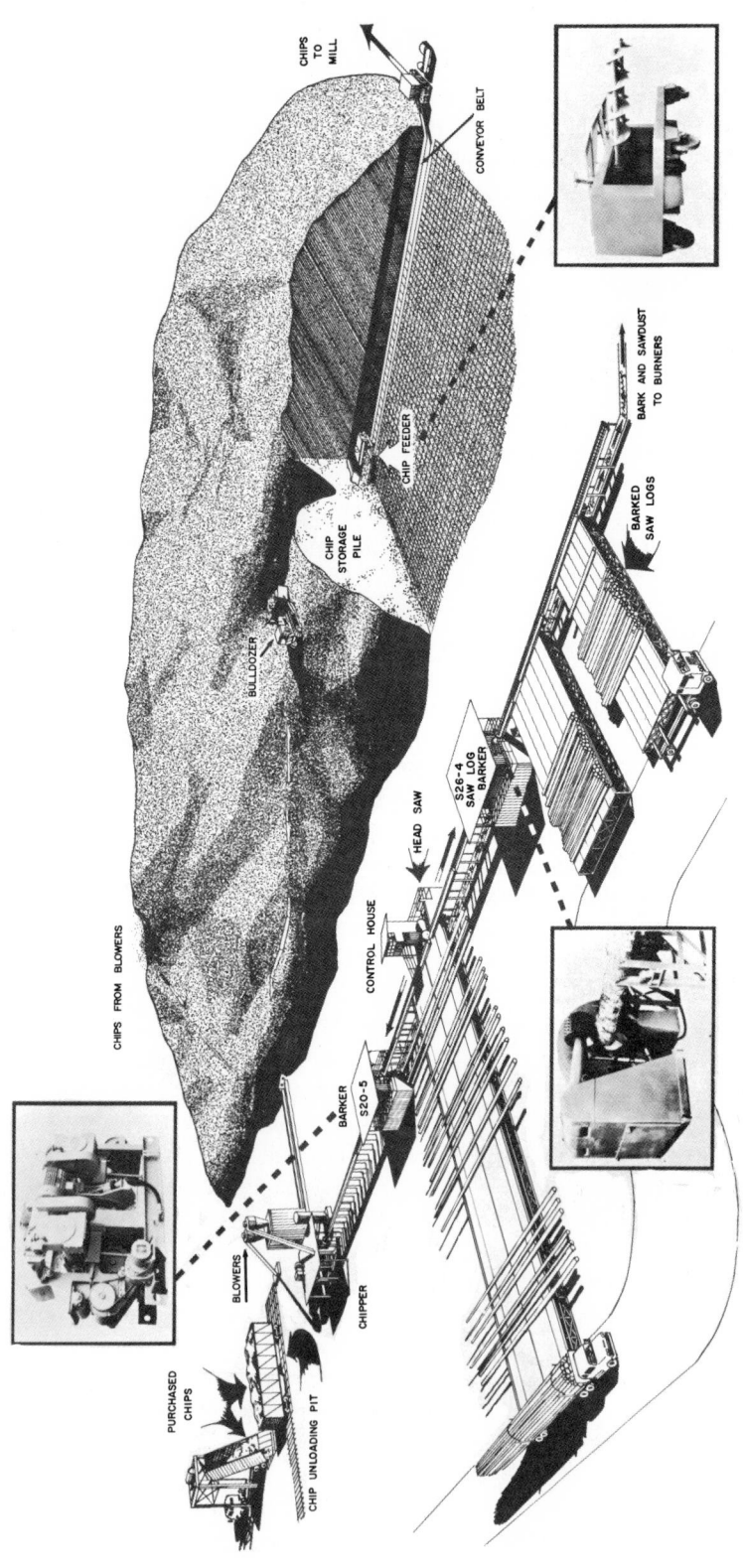

Fig. 5.22. Outside chip storage.

Disadvantages. (1) Fines carried by wind can create a nuisance to surrounding property owners and residents at very considerable distances with some chips joining in when winds are strong. Usually the chip piles can be located to minimize this problem.

(2) Wood dust settles on power transmission line poles, insulators and transformers, causing flashovers when rains come unless they are washed frequently.

(3) Dust also settles in and over mill buildings, parked vehicles and the ground in the surrounding area.

(4) Air-borne contaminants settle on chip piles and can cause trouble in plants producing high purity or brightness pulps or fine papers. This is particularly a factor in sulphite mills.

(5) Noise from the blowers can seriously disturb people in homes in a surprisingly large area down wind. This can be practically eliminated by mufflers on blower inlets.

General. Chips may be routed to storage bins or to outside storage piles from either a chipping plant or from a dumping point of incoming car and truck loads of purchased chips.

Both cars and trucks or trailers can be end-dumped into a pit with a tilting platform dumper operated by hydraulic cylinders, as explained in Chapter 4. Most recent installations use this system because it has been found to be the fastest and lowest cost per unit of chips unloaded. With properly arranged trackage and car moving facilities, such as slopes, car pullers and trackmobiles, as the case may warrant, a car can be in dumping position almost continuously. Economies resulting from dumping all incoming chips into a single pit are obvious, and with reasonable attention to scheduling a single dumping platform will handle both trucks and cars without difficulty, if truck drivers avoid backing trailers into the pit when the platform is tilted up. This has actually happened, and the whole operation was down for a half day or so while digging the trailer out of that deep pit.

Track Hoppers. The size of an under-track chip hopper is obviously important to the rapid and almost continuous dumping of cars and chips, as are the chip conveyors from the hopper and the transporting system to storage. It is easy to let costs overshadow judgment when designing a track hopper, as has been evidenced in some installations. A track hopper should be large enough to take at least two full rail cars.

Chip removal conveyors in the hopper bottom should have size and speed enough to take the chips away at a rate equal or greater than the contents of the largest car in the time required for a complete dumping cycle.

Chip hopper bottom conveyors usually consist of multiple strands with attachments 4 to 6 inches high, depending on the slope from the hopper bottom, to discharge over a high-speed belt which transports the chips to storage silos or to a surge bin over a feeder into a pneumatic conveying system discharging onto an outside storage pile.

Transportation to Storage. While chips have been transported to storage on belt conveyors on elevated structures and removed on the bottom run, installations of this type are high in first cost, require considerable maintenance, and the size and location of the piles are definitely limited. Consequently these have been superseded by pneumatic systems.

The blow pipes of most pneumatic systems have thin walls with quickly detachable couplings between sections, so they can be readily moved around on the chip piles, as required, in building them.

However, there are some large installations where the discharge ends of blowpipes are carried on high permanent structures over pile locations. Each pipe discharge is equipped with a swivel end section or a hood which can be directed up and down or from side to side by remote control, thus directing the chip streams for pile build-up.

Fig. 5.23. Elevated pneumatic conveyors discharging to O.C.S. piles over tunnel housings. (*Courtesy IMPCO*)

One of these elevated installations is shown in Figure 5.23.

One of the main problems in building chip piles is to control the chip stream so as to minimize dust and chips carrying beyond assigned storage borders. With portable discharge pipes lying directly on the chip pile surface, dispersal is confined to a smaller area than with elevated discharges. Frequent relocation of blowpipes on the pile is required.

After chips have settled on the piles they are distributed by bulldozers having large blades, usually about 4 x 12 feet. There are diametrically opposite opinions from mill to mill relative to whether crawler track or rubber-tired wheeled equipment is preferable. Results of investigations of various operations prior to equipment selection should lead to an intelligent and reasonable decision on the type most suitable for a particular application.

A boom and winch installed on the chip distributing bulldozer readily handles moving of blowpipes around the pile.

Chip Pile Foundations. A number of types of pile foundations are in use, such as fine-graded, tamped and rolled-soil, a similar bed covered with black top, rolled pit run gravel mixed with clay soil, and a bed of chips a foot or two deep over a rough graded area to be left on the ground when reclaiming.

While leveled, compacted and black-topped areas theoretically make it possible to completely remove and clean up stored chips during each pile turnover, the dirt, gravel or asphalt inadvertently picked up by the dozer blade with the last of the chips creates a dirt problem in the mill; hence such areas are not as practical as they at first appear. The cheapest and most effective method is a layer of chips to be left over the ground. If a few of these old chips do get mixed with those being reclaimed, no harm is done.

Reclaiming. Several reclaiming methods are in use. Some installations use a chain or a belt running longitudinally through the center of the pile area with the toe of chip piles along both sides of the conveyor. A bulldozer then pushes chips off the top of the pile, cascading it down onto the conveyor. This arrangement necessitates careful bulldozing operations to prevent chips from plugging the conveyor or arching over, if pushed into the valley between piles too fast.

The most popular reclaiming system consists of a rotary feeder table like those used

Fig. 5.24. Chip reclaiming augers and carriage dumping chips on belt. (*Courtesy IMPCO*)

under chip storage silos. These feeder units are set individually in pits over a belt conveyor running in an inclined tunnel emerging near one edge of the chip storage area. One or more of these reclaiming feeders are installed under the storage area. They should be located so a feeder is within economical bulldozing range from every point in the pile, if at all practical, taking into consideration the pile heights, slopes and volumes in each area.

Sometimes a steel cone over the feeder table, similar to that in the bottom of a chip silo, is used. The cone is installed in the center of a concrete slab about 50 to 75 feet in diameter. The top of the slab should be a foot or two above the surrounding grade with edges sloped to ground level. This arrangement will help to avoid pushing gravel or chip ground cover into the feeder cone when the pile is low. The steep cone of this installation makes a rather deep concrete lined pit necessary.

A simpler and less costly design sets the feeder up under a hole in the concrete slab without a cone. When chips are withdrawn they form their own cone at their angle of repose. Not only is this arrangement less costly because the pit can be 15 to 20 feet shallower, but the conveyor slope can be flatter and there should be fewer interruptions from chips bridging in the cone or slipping on the belt during wet or freezing weather.

A recent installation using elevated blowpipe discharges and a novel but very imaginative and practical reclaiming scheme is illustrated in Figures 5.24 and 5.25.

Here the reclaiming system uses large augers mounted horizontally on remote-controlled carriages, running lengthwise of the chip pile under a roof of 6-inch creosoted planks bolted to reinforced concrete rigid frames. The carriage tracks are above and parallel to a high-speed belt conveyor. Chips pulled from the pile under the roof edges by the augers are discharged onto the belt, which carries them to a screen room,

Fig. 5.25. Chip reclaiming augers on carriage. (*Courtesy IMPCO*)

to intermediate storage bins or directly to the digesters, if they were screened ahead of storage. This can be an extremely versatile and flexible chip storage arrangement because almost any desirable segregation of chips can be stored along the conveyor housing and reclaimed in any sequence or combination under remote central control. The rate of feed to the augers can be varied, if need be, by adding or removing planks along the roof edges. Another favorable feature is the shallow conveyor trench, only 3 or 4 feet below ground level, as compared to the deep pits and conveyor tunnels required with plate feeders.

WOODROOMS

Buildings

The development of whole-log barking and chipping has brought revolutionary changes in wood mill concept and design.

A whole-log barking and chipping installation involves a minimum investment approaching a million dollars. Such an expenditure, together with vibration and impact problems that accompany rapid traverse or rotation of the tremendous weights of large logs, and the high moisture conditions existing in a hydraulic barking plant, justifies careful and thorough analysis of the building and foundations and the use of structural framing of greater rigidity than that provided by the traditional wooden building. Almost without exception every major wood mill built since 1945 has been of steel and concrete construction.

Timber construction has worked out quite satisfactorily for wood rooms using mechanical barkers or dry drum barking when the building is well engineered structurally. The economies, versatility and ease of alteration inherent in timber construction are often overlooked by engineers. In the right environment timber construction will stand up far beyond any reasonable economic life of a wood room project. Most often they are torn down and rebuilt to suit changed conditions of raw material, technology or equipment long before that time. When an environment is adverse, pressure treatment will make wood as impervious to attack of fungi or insects as it is to acids and salts.

At the outset of a wood mill building design the suitability and economics of its construction using reinforced concrete, structural steel or wood and a possible combination of those materials should be thoroughly analyzed from the standpoints of suitability and economy, with consequent capital outlay and maintenance amortized over a reasonably anticipated life span, with obsolescence a properly weighed factor.

One combination frequently used consists of a reinforced concrete structure up to and including the operating floor, concrete columns with glue laminated timber roof trusses, timber purlines and a plywood or 2-inch T & G wood roof deck. This construction eliminates roof condensation and periodic scaling and painting of structural steel and is economical in first cost.

The steel and concrete woodmill requires a much greater amount of detailed engineering. The location of every shaft, bearing and sprocket must be known, fixed and called for on the drawings before the structural frame can be fabricated. Since the structural frame is prefabricated and erected ready to receive the machinery, field labor on the framing and equipment installation costs are materially reduced. Millwrighting skill has been largely transferred to the drafting board and steel fabricating shop, and field construction becomes primarily a matter of assembly and adjustment.

Because of the greater cost of steel construction and the higher strength available in steel beam sections, designers should endeavor to utilize structural parts as duplicate service members. Thus transfer skids which are self-supporting throughout their length can also carry concrete floors on their lower flanges.

Floor elevations are not carried at constant level but vary with elevations of main structural members carrying machinery. All floor areas should slope for drainage toward clean-up holes in the operating floor over refuse conveyors for easy waste disposal and the lower floor sloped toward sewer drains.

The lower floor is usually of reinforced concrete carried on a concrete beam system supported from the main column footings. Conveyors should be entirely of steel plate and structural shapes, the trough being of a simplified design that can be formed in about 12-foot sections by bending from flat plate with renewable liners to take the wear.

Here again wood construction has a place in conveyor trough and hopper backings for renewable steel linings, where the environment is suitable and economies attractive as with the building structure.

In designing a modern wood mill, sometimes representing an investment of more than two million dollars, the desirability of cleanliness should be kept in mind and made as easy as possible for the operators to achieve and maintain. Such an objective is difficult and sometimes costly, but it is justified in view of the magnitude of the total investment and worthwhile in future assistance toward lower operating and maintenance costs. Some recent mill designs have unfortunately overlooked this, and have fallen short of what should be reasonably expected.

Refuse Conveyors

In a standard sawmill cutting lumber from 35 to 45% of the gross volume of logs is rejected as unusable for lumber and goes out of the mill as refuse. Therefore, the designing of adequate, smooth operating refuse conveyors is just as important as well-designed log and lumber transfers, roll cases and conveyors. Actually, refuse conveyors are more difficult to design because of the wide variety of sizes and shapes they must handle, running from sawdust to slabs weighing 500 pounds or more.

A woodmill has the primary function of processing the logs in such a way as to send all the good wood in every log to the chipping plant. Therefore, it is to be expected that very little but bark and sawdust will be in the refuse conveyors and they should be designed accordingly, nevertheless still making provision for the conveyors to handle pieces of logs that may be slabbed off by the barker or its feed mechanism and drop into the conveyors. A conveyor as small as 12 inches wide will carry all the sawdust and practically any sliver or edging that is ripped off and can fall into it, but unless ample space is provided at turning points, a long sliver or edging is liable to punch on through the side of a building or jam and break the conveyor chain. However conveyors taking refuse from heavy machines such as head-rigs, resaws or edgers should be wide enough to handle the largest slab expected from logs to be sawn and then built with an oversize margin to spare. This applies particularly to sawmills as distinguished from wood mills feeding a pulp operation.

Malleable cast-iron box-link chain is quite satisfactory for sawdust. In a wood mill, bark will be removed before logs get to the head rig so the conveyor below will handle only sawdust with an occasional sliver provided slabs that sometimes break off large logs are kept out of the refuse conveyors and sent to the chippers as should be done in a wood mill. A box link chain 12 inches wide running in a trough with renewable steel liner plates will operate very satisfactorily in this service. There are many differing opinions on cross-section shapes for conveyor troughs, but vertical

sides up to 8 to 12 inches with the upper sides flared as necessary to cover the areas required, but kept steeper than 45°, will operate most satisfactorily.

Linings for the bottom should be $\frac{3}{8}$-inch or thicker and the sides $\frac{1}{4}$-inch plate.

If speeds are held down to 40 to 60 fpm, preferably below 50 feet, wear will be at a minimum and power requirements low. A 5- or $7\frac{1}{2}$-hp motor with reduction gear and roller chain drive to conveyor is normally ample, if heavy pieces are kept out.

A figure S drive on the return located near the discharge end with idler drums at both ends of the conveyor trough is normally used with chain of this type and operates with very little trouble. One of the idlers of the S drive should be mounted in a swing frame or on slide rails and weight loaded to keep the chain tight.

A belt conveyor running in troughing idlers would normally be used to collect discharge from conveyors directly under the saws and barkers for delivery to a fuel hog. Then a chain under the hog would discharge onto another belt conveyor carrying the hogged material to the boiler house or fuel pile, which usually are considerable distances from the wood mill.

It is good practice to run the refuse over a grid or a few spiked rolls ahead of the hog to separate sawdust and other fines which cause trouble by clogging knife pockets, sticking and building up on ledges in the back side of the rotor, around bolts, etc.; sometimes these get heavy enough to throw the rotor so far out of balance that it becomes advisable to shut down and clean out. This separated fine material can then be by-passed around the hog into the fuel conveyor.

CHAPTER 6

Sulfite Pulping

KENNETH W. BRITT

Scott Paper Company

HISTORICAL

As with many technical developments, it is difficult to single out an individual who deserves to be credited with the invention of the sulfite process for converting wood into paper pulp. The effect of sulfurous acid in softening and defibering wood was observed by Benjamin C. Tilghman, a chemist of Philadelphia as early as 1857. Some years later, as the result of visiting the paper mills of W. W. Harding at Manayunk, Pennsylvania, he was reminded of his earlier experiments and undertook a systematic study of the effect of sulfurous acid upon wood.

As a result of these experiments, Tilghman was granted U.S. Patent 70,485 in 1867 for "Treating Vegetable Substances for Making Paper Pulp." He carried out experiments exposing wood to high temperature and pressure and made the very important observation that the presence of a base, such as calcium, in the sulfurous acid cooking liquor would prevent the "burnt" or discolored cooks which were common when acid only was used. Tilghman ran into serious difficulties in developing suitable equipment for carrying out his pulping process, and after several failures he turned his attention to other activities without producing pulp commercially.

Shortly after 1870 several chemists in various countries were working on the use of the sulfite method for producing wood pulp. In 1872 Carl D. Ekman of Sweden produced laboratory samples of sulfite pulp using magnesium bisulfite as the base. In these experiments he was associated with George Fry, a British engineer. The first commercial sulfite pulp was made under Ekman's direction at the Bergvik Mill in Sweden in 1874 and shipped to the Ilford Mills in England where the first sulfite paper was made. Patents on the process were granted to Ekman in 1881. In 1883 Ekman moved to Northfleet, Kent, England, where he continued to collaborate with Fry and where one of the first sulfite pulp mills was erected and operated for many years under Ekman's direction.[1]

The first commercial application of the sulfite process in the United States was in 1882 by Charles S. Wheelwright in a mill located at East Providence, Rhode Island.

In 1874 Alexander Mitscherlich, professor of chemistry at the Forstakademie at Hannoversch-Munden, Germany, became interested in the pulping of wood with sulfite. Mitscherlich succeeded in making sulfite paper on a trial basis in 1874 almost simultaneously with the first conversion of Ekman's pulp into paper.

In 1877 Mitscherlich was operating a lined horizontal digester heated indirectly with steam. He also developed the limestone tower method of making cooking acid. The name Mitscherlich is still associated with that type of sulfite pulp which is cooked under mild conditions in horizontal digesters with indirect heating from steam coils within the digester. Pulp cooked in this manner retains a higher proportion of the hemicelluloses of the wood and hence it hydrates readily on beating. It is most suitable for dense, well-bonded papers. In common with many inventors, Mitscherlich faced many obstacles both in carrying his process to commercial success and in obtaining recognition for validity of his invention. Mitscherlich's German patent of 1878 was widely infringed in Germany and it was not until 1897 that he succeeded in establishing its validity in the courts and obtained a substantial financial settlement.[2]

During 1878-79 experiments in sulfite pulping were carried out at the mills of Baron Ritter, near Goertz in Austria, by Dr. Karl Kellner. The so-called Ritter-Kellner process, in which steam was directly injected into the digester, gave reduced cooking time and was widely adopted throughout the industry. The first installation of the Ritter-Kellner or "quick cook" process on the North American continent was at Merritton, Ontario.

For many decades following 1890 the sulfite process was the most important wood pulping method throughout the world. During this time, calcium bisulfite was the principal base used, together with free sulfurous acid. The coniferous woods of relatively low resin content, such as spruce, fir and hemlock, were chiefly utilized. The waste cooking liquor was discharged to the streams. For about 60 years following 1890 progress in the sulfite industry followed lines of improved equipment design and better operating and control methods, but with no basic changes in the chemistry of the process.

During the late 1930's the kraft process became the leading pulping method in terms of tonnage produced because of its ability to pulp resinous woods, such as pine, as well as other woods not suitable for sulfite. The development of practical bleaching methods during the 1930's and the great expansion in paper packaging were important factors in the growth of the kraft process. However, during the past twenty years, revolutionary developments have occurred in sulfite pulping through the use of bases other than calcium, namely, magnesium, ammonium and sodium. The use of these bases, together with the multi-stage and less acid processes, permits the pulping of woods not previously suitable for sulfite. They also give higher yields and pulps of new and unusual qualities. The use of the soluble bases permits the recovery of cooking chemicals because, unlike calcium, they do not cause scaling of evaporator surfaces. Also, because of the cost of the soluble bases, recovery of chemical is required for economic reasons. Chemical recovery greatly reduces the effluent load to the streams.

THE CHEMISTRY OF SULFITE PULPING

Because of the great industrial importance of the sulfite process, the chemistry of this process has been the subject of intensive study both in Europe and in America. These investigations have thrown much light upon the nature of the reactions that occur in sulfite pulping. The understanding so gained has contributed materially to technical progress. There still remains much to be learned about the chemistry of sulfite pulping, related as it is to the very complex subject of lignin chemistry.

It is not within the scope of this volume to review the chemistry of pulping in detail, but certain basic principles will be discussed in relation to the practical aspects of manufacturing sulfite pulp.

Composition and Structure of Wood

Wood is a porous material of cellular structure having a heterogeneous composition. In botanical terms, wood is that part of the tree known as the *xylem*. The porosity, the heterogeneity and the libriform structure are the properties of wood that make it a desirable raw material for pulp. The porosity permits the penetration of chemical reactants into the wood structure; the chemical heterogeneity permits selective chemical reaction, and the fibrous (libriform) nature of the cells is responsible for the fact that disintegrated wood forms a pulp.

The components of wood fall into three general classes as follows:

(1) *Holocellulose,* comprising 67 to 80% of the wood material, is a term designating the whole water-insoluble carbohydrate fraction. *Alpha-cellulose* is that portion of holocellulose that is insoluble in strong caustic soda; hemicellulose is that fraction that is soluble in mild caustic soda. Holocellulose contains both hexosan and pentosan polymers and shows wide variations in degree of crystallinity and in resistance to chemical reactants.

(2) *Lignin,* comprising 17 to 30% of the wood material, is considered to be a condensed phenylpropane polymer, amorphous in structure, and located principally in the layer of material between the individual wood cells (middle lamella). Lignin also occurs to some extent within the cell walls in intimate association with holocellulose.

(3) *Extractives,* 3 to 8%. This group comprises sugars, soluble mineral salts, resins, fats, tannins, etc. The amount and kind of extractives varies greatly among various species of trees and they are usually associated with particular locations within the wood. For example, resins are present in *resin ducts* of coniferous trees, and sugars, resins and fats are common constituents of *medullary ray* cells.

In coniferous wood, the chief structural elements are the tracheids. These are hollow tubes arranged vertically in the tree. The length of tracheids varies within the approximate limits of 2 to 4.5 mm. The number of tracheids per square millimeter of wood cross section varies from about 600 to about 3,000. The hollow cavities within the tracheids (lumen) communicate with each other by means of bordered pits. The tracheids serve both as support for the stem (bole) and for conduction of sap in the tree.

(See Figures 2.1, 2.2 and 2.3.) Less important from a pulping standpoint are the medullary rays, composed of short stubby cells, which furnish radial communication in the tree, and the vertical resins canals which are the source of resin in the wood.

In deciduous wood the functions of mechanical support and conduction of sap are differentiated into *wood fibers* and *vessels.* Deciduous woods generally have less lignin and more hemicellulose than coniferous woods. In all woods, the vertical cells have cell walls high in cellulose content and with a crystalline or oriented molecular structure. The individual fibers are separated by and cemented together by the *middle lamella* composed principally of lignin, which is amorphous in structure. It is the function of the pulping process to reach the middle lamella with chemical reagents capable of dissolving or softening the lignin. More detailed description of wood structure will be found in the literature.[3, 4]

The primary reaction of the sulfite process is that between bisulfite ions of the cooking liquor and the lignin of the wood to form lignin sulfonic acids, and also, in the presence of a base, the lignin sulfonic salts of that base. The rate of the sulfonation reaction is dependent upon the temperature and the sulfite ion concentration. Lignin sulfonic acids or salts are reported to represent about 65% of the solids content of spent sulfite liquor.[5]

In the sulfonation reaction, the weakly ionized sulfurous acid is replaced by the strongly ionized lignin sulfonic acid. In the presence of a strong acid and at elevated temperature, lignin undergoes poly-condensation reactions which result in the formation of dark-colored and insoluble compounds. Such a result is called a "burnt" cook, and this kind of cook results when sulfurous acid alone is used as a pulping agent. In the presence of a base, which may be calcium, magnesium, ammonium or sodium, the system is buffered to the extent that polycondensation of lignin is prevented. Even when the cooking liquor contains the proper amount of base, a too rapid rise in temperature in the initial period of the cooking cycle can result in poor yield and poor quality pulp. This is generally attributed to a more rapid penetration of SO_2 into the wood chip than of the slower-diffusing calcium bisulfite.

An alternative explanation has been offered for a burnt cook as being an autoxidation-reduction reaction of SO_2 at prolonged high temperature, resulting in the formation of sulfur trioxide (sulfuric acid) and colloidal sulfur.[6] The degradation of lignin is attributed to the excessive acidity due to sulfuric acid. Evidence of the presence of colloidal sulfur in the spent liquor from laboratory burnt cooks is claimed. Whatever the reason, the rate of temperature rise in the sulfite cook must be carefully controlled. Most mills control this temperature cycle automatically on the basis of actual experience.

It is well recognized that the acid bisulfite pulping process is not suitable for all species of wood, in particular, the pines and many hardwoods. The difficulty in pulping pines is generally attributed to the presence of phenolic compounds, especially in the heartwood; under conditions of acidity and high temperature these react with lignin to form resin-like polymers and thus prevent the normal sulfonation and dissolution of lignin. Likewise, woods containing large amounts of natural resinous and fatty acids obstruct the penetration of an acidic liquor to a greater extent than a neutral or alkaline liquor. As will be discussed more fully later, an important stimulus in exploring modifications of the sulfite process has been the desirability of pulping a wider range of wood species.

Penetration

The penetration of the cooking liquor into the wood chip with consequent contact between the bisulfite ion and the lignin under optimum conditions of concentration, temperature and time is a basic consideration both in the economy of the process and of the quality of the pulp produced. The time consumed in the penetration period of a sulfite cook, which may be as long as three hours at 110°C, has focussed attention on ways and means for reducing this time for economic reasons.

Among the methods found to be beneficial for penetration of liquor into chips has been the use of high pressure in the digester produced by pumping. By this method a digester is brought to maximum pressure practically at the start of the cook. Also, by pre-steaming the chips before contact with cooking liquor, especially by alternating cycles of high and low pressure (Va-Purge process),[7, 8] it is possible to remove air from the pores of the wood and hence gain a marked improvement in penetration. A similar removal of air may be accomplished by drawing a vacuum on the digester loaded with chips prior to injection of liquor.

In view of the importance of penetration as a factor in sulfite pulping, the size and shape of the wood chip is the subject of intensive study at the present time. It is obvious that liquid will completely saturate a small chip more quickly than it will a larger chip. It is equally obvious that cutting wood into smaller chips will result in more fiber damage from the mechanical action of chipping. The present commercial chips of $5/8$ to $3/4$ inch in the grain direction of the wood are a sort of compromise between fiber damage and penetration requirement (Chapter 5). A recent report[6] claims the elimination of the penetration period in laboratory sulfite cooks by the use of shredded chips consisting of slender pieces cut in the grain direction and less than $1/4$ inch in diameter.

Acidity and Temperature

Even when solubilizing groups, such as sulfonates, are introduced into a polymer such as lignin, true solubility still requires the cleavage of the polymer into smaller molecular fragments. This process, referred to as hydrolysis, plays an important role in the final dissolving and leaching out of lignin from wood chips. The acidity (pH) and temperature are the "aggressive" factors that create the hydrolytic conditions of the sulfite cook. To a certain extent, the rate of hydrolysis can be maintained under milder conditions of pH by using higher maximum temperature. Concomitant with the digestion of lignin, there occurs the hydrolysis of hemicellulose into soluble sugar and even some degradation of the resistant cellulose. In the hydrolytic attack upon cellulose, the effect is exhibited first by a decrease in the degree of polymerization (D.P.) of the fiber or pulp. The D.P. of wood pulps is indicated by the viscosity of a solution of the fiber in cupriethylene diamine (TAPPI Method T230 SM-50). In order that the fiber may possess maximum physical properties for paper, the D.P. should be maintained above 1500 glucose units in the cellulose molecular chain (viscosity above 80); values below 1000 units show marked loss in fiber quality, and at values below 200 the pulp is worthless.[9]

The pH conditions prevailing in an acid-bisulfite cook have been reported in a recent article.[10] A special high pressure glass electrode has been developed to measure the pH within a digester. Fortified cooking liquor at room temperature was found to have a pH value of 1.30. In raising the temperature to 80°C the pH increased to 2.24 due to reduced ionization of H_2SO_3 at elevated temperatures. During the penetration period with gradual increase in temperature, the pH rose to 2.9. This increase in pH was attributed to interaction between liquor and wood. With further heating at constant temperature the pH dropped to 2.7 due to the formation of acid reaction products (lignin sulfonic acids). Finally, during the period of top relief, the pH rose to 3.1.

In order that the digestion action be sufficiently rapid to be of practical interest, the maximum temperature of the sulfite cook must exceed 135°C. From that point, acid bisulfite cooks have been made at various maximum temperatures up to about 165°C. At such elevated temperatures, the acid-

bisulfite liquor attacks the cellulose polymer to an appreciable degree, resulting in reduced viscosity of the fiber in cupriethylene diamine solution. The following data illustrate the rapid drop in viscosity of an *acid bisulfite* cook held at maximum temperature.[11]

Wood: Western Hemlock

Cooking liquor: total SO_2—7%
                 combined SO_2—1%

Maximum temperature: 150° C

Total Cooking Time (hours)	Viscosity (centipoises), Tappi Method T230
5:30	337
5:45	213
5:55	160
5:55	140
6:05	79
6:05	78

Pulp below 80 viscosity is considered degraded to a point that is harmful for paper making. With less acid liquors it has been reported that temperatures as high as 180°C produce satisfactory pulps.[12]

The digestion of wood with sulfite liquors occurs throughout the pH range. However, the rate of pulping at a given temperature decreases steadily with rising pH at least to the neutral point.[13, 14] With less acid liquors it is customary to use higher maximum temperatures. The successive steps in degrees of acidity in sulfite cooking liquors, using sodium as the base, have been designated as follows: [13]

(1) acid-bisulfite ($NaHSO_3 + SO_2$)
(2) bisulfite ($NaHSO_3$)
(3) bisulfite-sulfite ($NaHSO_3 + Na_2SO_3$)
(4) sulfite (Na_2SO_3)
(5) neutral sulfite ($Na_2SO_3 + Na_2CO_3$)

Yield

In view of the above considerations, it is not practical to remove all the lignin in the digestion step because of the degrading action upon the cellulose. In the conventional sulfite cook, using spruce wood, the digestion is carried to the point of 44 to 46% yield of pulp based on wood, and with a lignin content of 2 to 5%. At that point a relatively light colored pulp of good strength properties is obtained suitable for use in the unbleached state, especially for admixture with a groundwood pulp for a variety of printing papers. For paper pulps where high brightness (whiteness) is required, the residual lignin is removed by bleaching. (Cf. Chapter 10.)

It follows further that no commercial digestion method is available to remove lignin from wood and leave all or nearly all the holocellulose fraction of wood as pulp. If conditions are such as to prevent loss of hemicellulose, then substantial amounts of lignin remain in the pulp. Also, when the digestion is carried to a point where the yield is approximately 50% or less of the wood, only mild mechanical action suffices to reduce the wood chips to completely defibered pulp. Such pulps are designated as "full chemical" pulps.

Sulfite cooking liquors, using soluble bases having little or no free SO_2, serve very well to digest wood in a high yield range (above 60%) where positive mechanical action is required to reduce the cooked wood to pulp. (Cf. Chapter 8.)

PREPARATION OF COOKING LIQUOR

Sulfite cooking liquor, as it is pumped into the digester at the start of the cook, consists of free sulfur dioxide dissolved in water at a concentration in the range of 4 to 8%, together with from 2 to 3% of sulfur dioxide in the form of a bisulfite. The preparation of this solution in the quantity and composition desired requires a chemical plant of considerable size. Precise control in the operation of the liquor preparation plant plays an important part in pulp cost and quality.

Chemistry of Sulfite Acid Preparation

Sulfur dioxide is obtained by the burning of sulfur or by roasting of iron pyrites, the former being the nearly universal source in the United States, while the latter source has found some use in Canada and Europe. Sulfur is recovered from sulfur beds deep in the earth in several areas in Texas, Louisiana and Mexico by injecting into the well superheated water which melts the sulfur permitting its pumping to the surface as liquid sulfur (Frasch Process).

Solid sulfur is delivered to the mills in coarse pulverized form and is stored in bins until used.

In recent years an increasing amount of sulfur has been shipped in molten form. Several advantages result from using liquid sulfur. (1) The labor of handling sulfur from tank car, tank truck or tank barge is greatly reduced as compared with bulk handling of solid sulfur. (2) Liquid handling eliminates substantial wind losses which may be 0.5% or more, and which lead to corrosion of exposed buildings and equipment. (3) Contamination with foreign substances, formation of acid in melters and pumps, and the danger of dust explosions are all minimized. (4) The sulfur melter, with its operating and maintenance costs, is eliminated.

Molten sulfur may be shipped in tank trucks, railway tank cars, tank barges and tank ships. The tanks are in all cases provided with either internal or external steam coils for heating and/or re-melting the sulfur, and with insulation to minimize loss of heat in transit.

The pumping and handling of liquid sulfur, the selection of piping, pumps, valves and fittings and the design of storage facilities are not difficult provided three basic considerations are followed: (1) that sulfur tends to solidify below an operating range of 265°-320°F; (2) that its specific gravity of 1.78 (14.79 pounds per gallon) is much higher than that most liquids encountered in industry; and (3) that the sulfur feed to a chemical process must be precisely controlled. Since liquid sulfur is troublesome to meter in continuous flow, positive displacement pumps are the preferred means of controlling rate of flow.

Viscosity is not a problem, being less than

8 centipoises within the temperature range of 280 to 315°F. Above 320°F the viscosity increases very rapidly to a point where the sulfur is no longer mobile. Dry liquid sulfur does not corrode mild steel and cast iron.

Sulfur burns in air to form sulfur dioxide according to the following equation:

$$S + O_2 \longrightarrow SO_2$$

In the manufacture of sulfite pulp it is essential that all sulfur is converted to SO_2 rather than to the higher sulfur oxidation product, SO_3, the anhydride of sulfuric acid. The accomplishment of this purpose depends upon maintaining a temperature in the range of 2100°-2400°F in the combustion chamber where complete burning of sulfur is attained followed by rapid cooling to 400°F.

The cooled SO_2 gas is absorbed in water containing a base chosen from the group calcium, magnesium, ammonium, and sodium. The proportions of sulfur dioxide and base are such that the greater amount of the sulfur dioxide is in the form of sulfurous acid. The chemical equations that apply follow:

(1) Formation of sulfurous acid:

$$SO_2 + H_2O \longrightarrow H_2SO_3$$

(2) Formation of calcium bisulfite from limestone:

$$CaCO_3 + 2H_2SO_3 \longrightarrow$$
$$Ca(HSO_3)_2 + CO_2 + H_2O$$

(3) Formation of calcium bisulfite from milk-of-lime:

$$CaO + H_2O \longrightarrow Ca(OH)_2$$
$$Ca(OH)_2 + 2H_2SO_3 \longrightarrow$$
$$Ca(HSO_3)_2 + 2H_2O$$

The equations of magnesium base liquor are similar to those for calcium.

(4) Formation of sodium bisulfite:

$$Na_2CO_3 + 2H_2SO_3 \longrightarrow$$
$$2NaHSO_3 + CO_2 + H_2O$$

(5) Formation of ammonium bisulfite:

$$NH_3 + H_2O \longrightarrow NH_4OH$$
$$NH_4OH + H_2SO_3 \longrightarrow NH_4HSO_3 + H_2O$$

A critical point in the preparation of sulfite cooking liquor is the solubility of SO_2 in water.

The following table shows the concentration of saturated solutions of SO_2 in H_2O at atmospheric pressure for various temperatures.

Temperature (°C)	% SO₂
0	22.5
20	11.1
40	5.3
90	0.58

In the early days of sulfite pulp manufacture the cooking liquor was made by absorption of gas at atmospheric pressure. This created the problem of keeping the liquor cool enough to make a solution of sufficient strength. To overcome this difficulty the modern sulfite mill prepares the cooking acid in a pressure vessel called an accumulator in which the acid from the absorption system is fortified in SO_2 content and heated by digester relief. By means of pressure of 35 to 40 psi, the cooking acid can hold 8 to 10% sulfur dioxide at a temperature of 80°C. By means of the pressure accumulator system, acid of any desired strength can be made. The normal practice uses an acid of 7½ to 8% concentration.

Definition of Mill Terms [15]

(1) *Total sulfur dioxide:* Total SO_2 as determined by an iodometric titration (TAPPI Standard Method T604m or Canadium Standard J-1, Palmrose Method) and expressed as percent total SO_2.

(2) *Free sulfur dioxide:* The free sulfur dioxide is the actual free sulfur dioxide plus half of the sulfur dioxide in the bisulfite of the base; it is more properly called the "available sulfur dioxide" because it indicates the sulfur dioxide in excess of the amount necessary to form monosulfite. The free sulfur dioxide is determined by titration with sodium hydroxide.

(3) *Combined sulfur dioxide:* This is calculated by determining the difference between the total sulfur dioxide and the free

sulfur dioxide. The combined sulfur dioxide, as thus calculated, represents the sulfur dioxide combined as monosulfite. More properly, it is termed "nonavailable sulfur dioxide."

Note: Because the terms "free" and "combined" SO_2 often lead to confusion, the following example is offered. Suppose that we have a solution in which the ratio is 5 molecules of H_2SO_3 to 1 molecule of $Ca(HSO_3)_2$. Then the ratio of free to combined SO_2 is 6 to 1. Observe that 1 molecule of $Ca(HSO_3)_2$ is equivalent to 1 molecule of $CaSO_3$ plus 1 molecule of H_2SO_3. The combined sulfur dioxide represents that part present as monosulfite, which is one half that present as bisulfite. Further, let us assume that the solution is one molar with respect to SO_2, i.e., 64 grams per liter. Then the actual concentration is 5.486% free SO_2 and 0.914% combined SO_2.

(4) *Sulfur dioxide:* SO_2 gas made by burning sulfur or a sulfur-bearing ore, such as pyrites.

(5) *Bisulfite liquor base:* The alkali or alkaline earth metal used in the preparation of bisulfite cooking liquor. This may include calcium and magnesium.

(6) *Storage acid:* Raw acid held in reserve for transfer to storage tanks for fortification with sulfur dioxide.

(7) *Accumulator acid:* Storage acid held in pressure containers (accumulators) during fortification by the sulfur dioxide digester relief gas, or by addition of liquid sulfur dioxide.

(8) *Cooking liquor:* Acid after being fortified and ready for use in the cooking operation. Also known as "strong acid."

(9) *Digester liquor:* Cooking liquor as it exists in the digester during the cooking operation.

(10) *Digester top relief:* Gas (or liquor, when the digester is heated with direct steam) withdrawn from the top of the digester during the early stage of the cooking operation and returned to the reclaiming system (accumulator) to conserve sulfur dioxide and heat.

(11) *Digester side relief:* Digester liquor withdrawn by side relief from the upper section of the digester in the early part of the cooking operation and returned to storage (accumulator) to conserve sulfur dioxide and heat.

(12) *Digester test:* Test of the digester liquor for total, free, and combined sulfur dioxide (SO_2) during the cooking process.

(13) *Spent sulfite liquor:* Liquor which is separated from the pulp after the cooking operation has been completed. This liquor contains the dissolved constituents of the wood and is also known as "red liquor" or "sulfite waste liquor."

(14) *Blow pit:* The blow pit is the receptacle for receiving the digester charge when the cook is complete.

SULFUR DIOXIDE PRODUCTION

There are two general methods for producing sulfur dioxide at the point of use: (1) the burning of sulfur and (2) the roasting of iron pyrites (FeS_2) or pyrrhotite (Fe_7S_8). Sulfur dioxide is also available commercially as liquefied gas in pressure containers and small quantities are used in the sulfite pulp industry in this form. The burning of sulfur is by far the most common method for the production of sulfur dioxide for pulp.

Formerly all sulfur used in the sulfite industry was delivered to the mills in bulk form (pulverized lumps) and stored in bins until required for use. Sulfur is stable and does not deteriorate with age, but must be protected from contamination from foreign material. In recent years a considerable quantity of sulfur has been delivered to the pulp mills in molten form.

Sulfur Burners

If the sulfur supply is in bulk form, it is first melted in a lined steel tank heated by steam coils to about 120°C (250°F) with automatic controls to maintain this temperature within close limits.

There are two general types of sulfur

burners: (1) the rotary drum and (2) the jet-spray burner.

A typical rotary burner with a diameter of 3 feet and length of 8 feet will handle about 7 tons of sulfur per 24 hours. The speed of rotation is about one revolution per minute, or at a rate to permit the entire inner surface to be covered with burning sulfur to provide maximum burning area. The burning molten sulfur is picked up from the pond in the bottom of the burner and carried up over the top and down until it meets the pool again. Molten sulfur is allowed to enter at one end to maintain a depth equal to about one quarter the diameter of the burner.

The primary air enters at the same place as the sulfur and provides sufficient oxygen to yield the necessary heat to vaporize the bulk of the sulfur. The burning is completed in the combustion chamber after the vaporized sulfur is mixed with the secondary air admitted at the discharge end of the burner. The volume of air admitted is important to the efficiency of the operation; too small a quantity may cause deposits of sublimed sulfur which tend to clog the system, and too large a volume decreases the strength of the sulfur dioxide gas and favors sulfur trioxide formation. With the use of automatic control instruments a more uniform product is attained than by manual control (Cf. Chapter 15).

The combustion chamber is a brick-lined structure which may be about 5 feet in diameter and 16 feet high. It is provided with a center baffle to assist in the proper combustion of the sulfur vapors. With proper adjustment a gas of 16 to 18% sulfur dioxide (by volume) should be maintained.

In burning sulfur with air, 1 volume of oxygen combines with sulfur to give 1 volume of sulfur dioxide. Because air contains about 79% nitrogen and 21% oxygen by volume, it is theoretically possible to obtain 21% sulfur dioxide. This is not realized in practice, however, for several reasons, one of which is the excess of air supplied to the burner. The volume of air at 68°F (20°C), and at atmospheric pressure, required for the combustion of sulfur to sulfur dioxide is given by the following equation:

Volume of air in cubic feet =

$$\frac{11.75}{\text{Per cent } SO_2 \text{ by volume}}$$

The percentage figure of sulfur dioxide (SO_2) should be expressed as a decimal in this formula.

Three conditions must be maintained to burn sulfur to sulfur dioxide at maximum efficiency.[16]

(1) A high and uniform combustion temperature not less than 1832°F (1000°C).

(2) An air supply at a carefully controlled temperature, properly distributed, and not exceeding theoretical requirements by more than 10%.

(3) A highly efficient cooling system in which the sulfur dioxide gas is cooled rapidly to below 392°F (200°C) to prevent the formation of sulfur trioxide.

A gas strength of 18 to 18.5% sulfur dioxide can be reached when proper conditions are maintained.

A more modern development in sulfur burning is the spray type, two examples of which are the Texas Gulf Sulfur burner and the Chemipulp-KC burner. The spray type burner gives close control of the amount of sulfur supplied to the atomizing nozzle, and uniform mixture of air and sulfur gives efficient combustion. Since no separate combustion chamber is required, the unit is compact and economical of floor space. With spray burners the start-up and shut-down can be accomplished quickly and rate of sulfur dioxide production is readily controlled.

Figure 6.1 shows the Chemipulp-KC jet type burner.[17] A burner with a capacity of 15 tons of sulfur per day has an over-all length of approximately 20 feet, height of 11 feet and diameter of combustion chamber of about 5 feet. These burners are available in a range of sizes from 2½ to 50 tons of sulfur per day.

Fig. 6.1. Chemipulp-KC jet-type sulfur burner. (*Courtesy Chemipulp Process Corp.*)

The relationship between sulfur consumption and tons of pulp produced varies considerably and is a very important measure of the efficiency of the pulping process and of the cost of pulp. A calculation based on total reported consumption of sulfur by the U.S. sulfite industry and total tonnage of pulp produced gives an average figure of 315 pounds of sulfur per ton, although this must be viewed as approximate. Many mills operate as low as 250 pounds of sulfur per ton. All these figures are for mills in which no sulfur is recovered from the spent cooking liquor.

In the operation of the Chemipulp-KC spray type burner, molten sulfur is pumped from the storage pit through steam-jacketed pipe to the burner nozzle where compressed air atomizes the sulfur, thereby enabling it to burn in suspension within the burner tube. Secondary air is admitted in several stages through a manifold and is preheated in the space between the outside of the burner and the surrounding jacket. This preheating assists in combustion and in maintaining a high percentage of SO_2. The burner operates at 2100° to 2400°F and the combustion at high temperature with high gas concentration prevents the formation of SO_3. The presence of SO_3 in the gas, which produces sulfuric acid in the liquor, is highly undesirable. The presence of this acid increases the corrosion of equipment, reduces pulp quality and leads to the formation of calcium sulfate scale.

Recording and controlling equipment is an essential part of a modern sulfur-burning installation. A SO_2 gas analyzer and recorder is used to control the operation of the burner. Temperature of the burner and the flow of combustion air are controlled by instruments. Further discussion of instrumentation will be found in Chapter 15.

Gas Coolers [18]

After the complete combustion of sulfur, it is necessary to cool the gas to promote the absorption of SO_2 in water to form the cooking acid; it is also important to cool the gas rapidly through the range of 900° to 200°C to minimize the formation of SO_3. Two general types of gas coolers are the surface type and the spray type.

Surface type coolers are formed by connecting several rows of vertical elliptical lead pipes to headers and flowing cooling water over the outside of these pipes. The gas is conveyed from the combustion chamber in a 20-inch cast-iron pipe to the top header, from which it passes downward to the bottom submerged header and alternately up and down the vertical sections of the cooler. All submerged or cool portions of the system must be of lead. SO_2 in the presence of water or condensed vapor rapidly dissolves iron. Iron is unaffected by dry or hot SO_2.

The spray-type system consists of two towers, a heat exchanger, circulating pump and a weir box for water level control. (See Figure 6.2.)

The primary tower is made of lead-lined carbon steel; inside the lead lining is a ceramic lining set in a silica type joint material. For inspection and repairs a manhole is provided in this primary tower as well as in the second tower. The second-ary tower, which is considerably larger than the primary, is made of chrome-nickel steel, and has a removable grating of chrome-nickel steel to support the ceramic packing, which normally consists of spiral packing rings or preferably cross-partition packing rings. The secondary tower is furnished with two manholes—one above the ceramic packing and one below. The connection between the two towers is made with a removable section, and is lined with lead and acid-proof tile similar to the lining in the primary tower.

Hot SO_2 gas enters at the top of the primary tower and is sprayed with cooling water as it travels down through the tower. Upon contacting the spray the temperature of the gas is instantaneously dropped through the critical range of SO_3 formation to the wet bulb temperature of the gas. A large percentage of any SO_3 which may be present is absorbed by the cooling water, which collects at the bottom of the tower

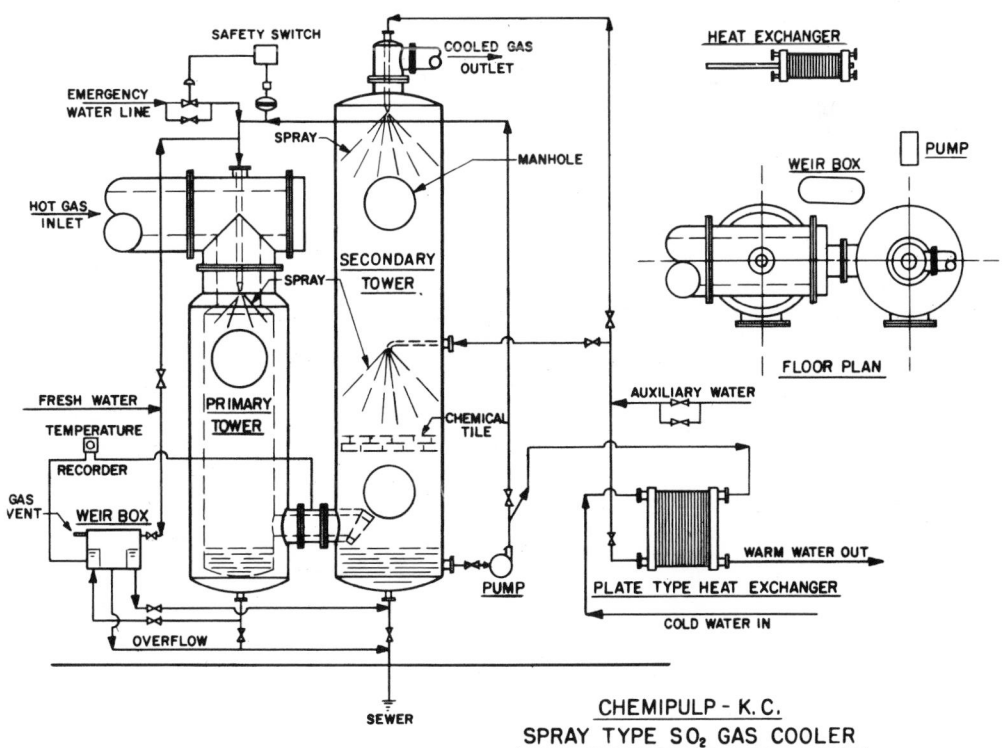

Fig. 6.2. Spray-type SO_2 gas cooler. (*Courtesy Chemipulp Process Corp.*)

where the level is controlled by means of a weir box, the overflow going to the sewer. Very little SO_2 is retained by the overflow water, and results from actual operation show that the loss is less than one pound of sulfur per ton of pulp.

The gas, cooled to approximately 155°F, passes into the lower portion of the secondary tower, where it is met with another spray, completing the cooling. Since the cooling water from this tower carries some SO_2, it is passed through a heat exchanger and the cooled water is recirculated through the tower. Part of this water, however, is used for the spray in the first tower. To maintain the water level in the secondary tower, make-up water is added in the weir box from the water supply and with normal operation the flow is always into the tower.

In case of either power failure or stoppage of the circulating pump for any reason, a safety switch and solenoid-operated valve are so arranged that the valve will open a fresh water supply for the spray in the primary tower to prevent damage to the equipment from overheating. Cooling at this time in the second tower is through a manually controlled valve in the cold water supply.

As previously stated, connections are made from both towers to a weir box fitted with a hood so that any gas which may be released can be removed through a vent. While sublimation has no effect on the operation of the system, its presence can be detected immediately by the condition of the water in the overflow from the primary tower. An observation glass is provided in the hood for inspection purposes.

The system has several advantages: it occupies very little space, is free from leaks, with all connections easily accessible, and operates with practically no maintenance or attention. Loss of SO_2 is extremely low and the rapid preliminary cooling reduces the formation of SO_3, the greater percentage of which is absorbed by the spray in the first tower. Very little make-up water is required and the hot water produced in the heat exchanger can be used for pulp wash-ing or for any other purpose where clean water is necessary.

Absorption of SO_2 Gas

The cooled burner gas is absorbed by water in the presence of a base, originally calcium in the form of carbonate or hydroxide, but in recent years magnesium, ammonium and sodium have come into use as bases in sulfite cooking. The resulting "raw acid" consists of the bisulfite of the base, for example, calcium bisulfite $Ca(HSO_3)_2$ plus free SO_2 in the form of sulfurous acid. The chemical equations that apply are as follows:

$$SO_2 + H_2O \longrightarrow H_2SO_3$$
$$\text{"free" sulfur dioxide}$$

$$2H_2SO_3 + CaCO_3 \longrightarrow Ca(HSO_3)_2 + CO_2 + H_2O$$
$$\text{½ "combined" sulfur dioxide}$$

The most widely used method for making raw acid is the so-called two tower (Jenssen) system. The towers are 60 to 100 feet high and 6 to 12 feet in diameter, and are constructed of reinforced concrete, lined with acid-resisting tile, and packed with limestone, with a wooden supporting rack at the bottom (see Figure 6.3). An elevator shaft to transport limestone is built alongside, and there are clean-cut doors and inlets and outlets for water, weak acid, strong acid and gas at appropriate points in the tower shell.

The towers are operated in series. The cooled burner gas enters the bottom of the "strong" tower, coming into contact first with the strongest acid descending over the limestone. Fresh water enters the top of the weak tower in contact with the exhausted ascending gas, which is then vented to the atmosphere. The acid at the bottom of the "weak" tower is pumped to the top of the strong tower and the gas from the top of the strong tower is conducted to the bottom of the weak tower. The stone in the tower receiving the strong gas is consumed rapidly and the level drops several feet per day. It is customary to reverse the flow of gas, water and acid each day by means of special multiple-direction valves so that the "strong" and "weak" towers alternate. Replenishment of limestone is done with the weak tower to minimize loss of gas when the tower is opened.

Fig. 6.3. Absorption towers for SO_2. (*Courtesy G. D. Jenssen Co.*)

A circulating fan is placed between the sulfur combustion system and the towers to draw air into the burners and blow gas through the towers. A connection may be made at the top of raw acid storage tanks to relieve any pressure on the tanks and restore the gas to the system. At the top of the towers there are also steam siphons or fans to vent spent gases from the weak tower to the atmosphere. The strength of the acid made is controlled by fan speed

(sulfur burned) and the water input to the towers. The ratio of free to combined SO_2 is less subject to direct control. It is affected by water temperature, colder water increasing the proportion of free SO_2 and warmer water resulting in a greater proportion of combined SO_2. Increasing the temperature of water is no great problem, but cooling it in summer is more complicated, and not all mills are equipped to exercise complete control of water temperature. In some mills, special pressure towers have been installed in which raw acids sprayed over tile packing is exposed to cooled burner gas under slight pressure, the gas then being conducted back to the main gas stream.

Chemical Absorption Systems

When the base is in the form of a slurry or a solution, another system of SO_2 absorption to form raw acid is frequently employed. For example, burnt lime (CaO) is slaked and diluted with water to form a slurry. Burner gas is bubbled through this slurry to form acid-bisulfite liquor similar to that obtained from limestone towers. The two best known types of absorption towers are the Barker and the Paulson types. These units consist essentially of five compartments one below another, containing tiling or perforated plates. The lime water enters the top compartment and flows downward countercurrent to the burner gas being pulled upward by a vacuum pump. The strong acid leaves the bottom compartment where it goes to absorption tower or acid storage.

The percentage of combined SO_2 is determined by the strength of the lime water. The sulfur dioxide first reacts with the base and all additional SO_2 forms "free" sulfurous acid.

In place of lime water, such a system may use a slurry of MgO to form magnesium base liquor, a solution of ammonium hydroxide (NH_4OH) to form ammonium base liquor or sodium hydroxide (NaOH) to form soda base liquor.

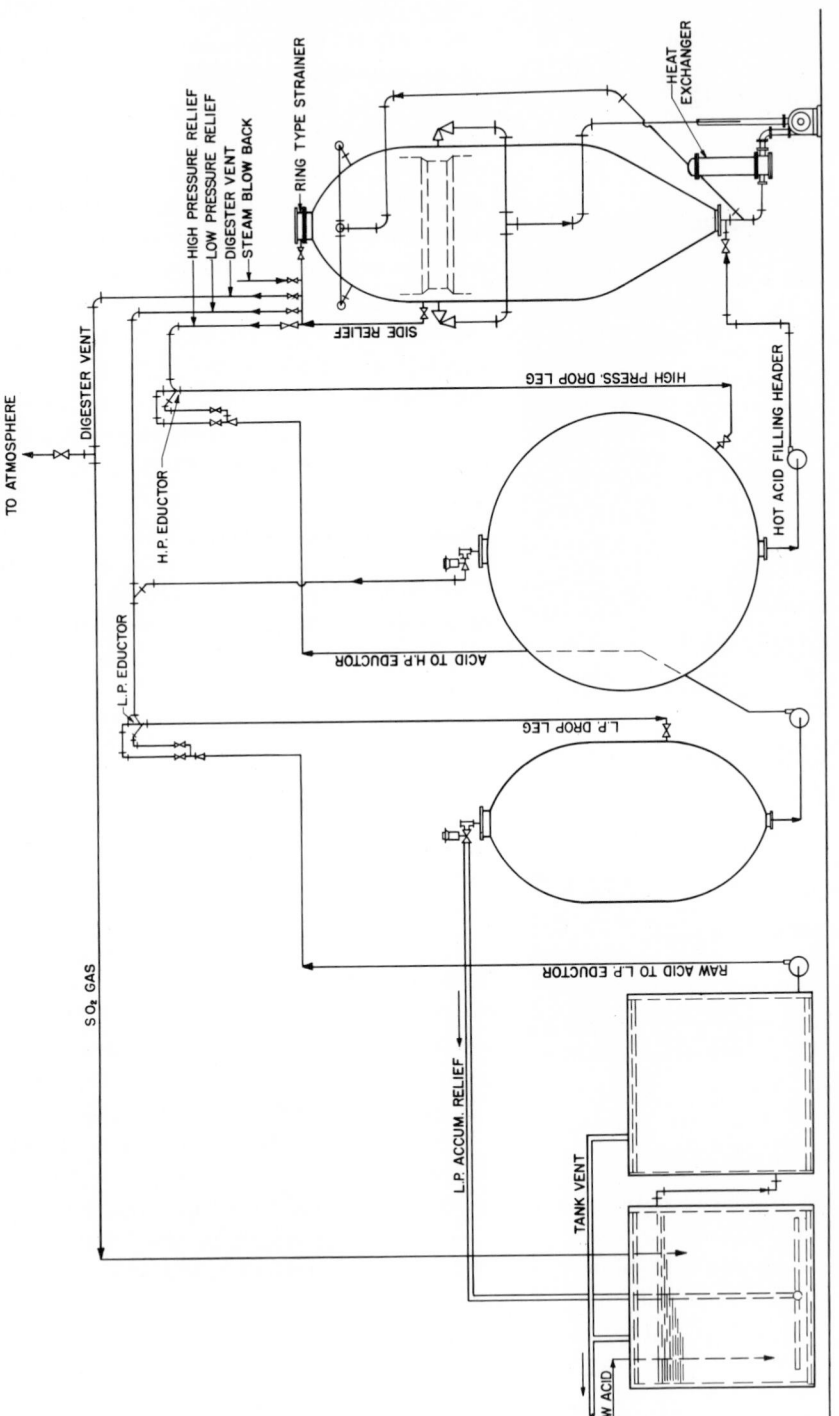

Fig. 6.4. Chemipulp hot acid cooking and recovery system. (*Courtesy Chemipulp Process Inc.*)

Fortification of Acid

In order to convert "raw acid" from the absorption system into the stronger "cooking acid" and also to recover SO_2 and heat contained in the digester relief, a process of absorption of relief gas in a pressure system is used. The Chemipulp or hot acid system is used in a great majority of North American sulfite mills.

As previously pointed out, the solubility of SO_2 in water decreases rapidly with increased temperature, and hence cooking liquor of sufficient strength must be at low temperature in order to hold SO_2 at atmospheric pressure. The hot acid system designed to overcome this difficulty is shown in simple form in Figure 6.4. A spherical pressure vessel, known as the "accumulator" contains the cooking acid at a temperature of about 80°C and at a pressure of 30 to 40 psi. The acid is made up by mixing under pressure the uncooled gas and liquor relief from the digester with the raw acid from the acid making system. The hot acid thus obtained passes into the accumulator and is there stored until required to fill a digester. One accumulator is used to recover the relief from all digesters.

Figure 6.4 shows a typical installation with both high- and low-pressure accumulators. When a low pressure accumulator (5 to 10 psi) is used, digester relief is sent to this vessel after the digester pressure is lowered to the point that the relief does not flow readily to the high pressure accumulater. The raw cold acid goes first to the low-pressure accumulator where the temperature and SO_2 content are increased before going to the high-pressure accumulator.

By use of the hot acid system there results a saving of about 2000 pounds of steam per ton of pulp and about two hours in cooking time.

THE COOKING OPERATION

The sulfite digestion process is carried out in a pressure vessel consisting of a steel shell with an acid-resistant lining which is either of ceramic tile set in acid-proof cement or of stainless steel. A common digester size is 16 feet in diameter and 50 feet high, with domed top and conical bottom and a capacity of 12 to 15 tons of pulp per cook. Digesters up to 35 tons capacity have been constructed. The rapid and efficient performance of the varied operations of a sulfite cook require carefully engineered design of fittings and controls (Figure 6.5).

Pulp mills normally have a series of digesters arranged in a *digester building,* in such a manner as to make handling of chips from storage and the discharge of cooked pulp as rapid and convenient as possible. Figure 6.6 is a view of the operating floor of a large sulfite mill showing the overhead chip bins, the top covers of the digesters and control mechanisms used by the operators.

After closing the blow valve at the bottom, the wood chips are allowed to flow into the top opening of the digester. A most important consideration in the economy of the pulping operation is the quantity or weight of pulp obtained per cook. Since the digester consists of a fixed volume, this means that the maximum weight of wood per cubic foot of digester space is desired. A further consideration in filling a digester with chips is to arrange them in such a way as to promote circulation of the liquor during the cook and to maintain uniform temperature throughout the digester and uniform contact of the liquor with the entire charge.

These considerations have led to the development of chip distribution to improve the packing of chips within a simple, free-flowing stream. Such a chip distributor (Chemipulp Process) is shown in Figure 6.7. The collecting hopper (A) receives the chips from the bin, and momentarily arrests them in their flow. Forming the bottom of the hopper is a metering plate (C) which has diametrically opposed outlet sectors, the degree of opening being adjustable. The plate is rotated at a speed of 20 to 30 rpm. The rate at which the chips are permitted

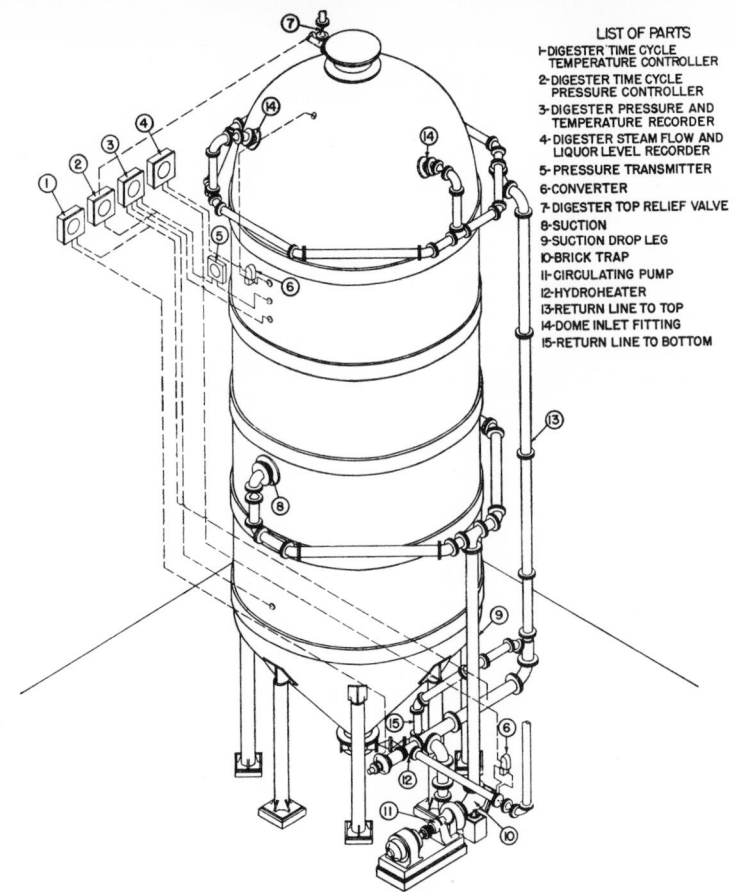

LIST OF PARTS
1-DIGESTER TIME CYCLE TEMPERATURE CONTROLLER
2-DIGESTER TIME CYCLE PRESSURE CONTROLLER
3-DIGESTER PRESSURE AND TEMPERATURE RECORDER
4-DIGESTER STEAM FLOW AND LIQUOR LEVEL RECORDER
5-PRESSURE TRANSMITTER
6-CONVERTER
7-DIGESTER TOP RELIEF VALVE
8-SUCTION
9-SUCTION DROP LEG
10-BRICK TRAP
11-CIRCULATING PUMP
12-HYDROHEATER
13-RETURN LINE TO TOP
14-DOME INLET FITTING
15-RETURN LINE TO BOTTOM

Fig. 6.5 Sulfite digester. (*Courtesy Chemipulp Process Corp.*)

Fig. 6.6. Operating floor of sulfite pulp mill. (*Courtesy Scott Paper Co.*)

to flow through metering plate (C) determines the filling rate of the digester. Spider (H) serves to support and position the rotatable distributing bats (K) just below the bottom of the digester top nozzle. The distributing bats, four in number, are in the shape of flat steel plates attached to a central hub by means of short shaft extensions, as shown in the sketch. Lock nuts permit adjustment of the angularity of the faces of the bat plates. This control of angularity is desirable for providing adjustment to suit operating conditions, such as species of wood being charged, wood moisture content and chip size. The bats are normally rotated at 700 to 900 rpm.

The advantages of chip packing are said to be as follows:

(1) The degree to which the chips are packed within the digester is determined by the rate of filling. At a rapid rate, an increase in chip content within the digester of 10 to 15% above that obtainable without the use of the distributor may be expected. Normally, with a moderate rate of filling, a 25% increase is readily obtainable, and this is the usual practice. The rate of filling is controlled by the openings in the metering plate.

(2) The shape of the chip pile within the digester is determined in part by the filling rate and in part by the angularity at which the blades are set. A fast filling rate produces convex piling. A slow filling rate produces flat piling.

Flat piling is the type to be sought. Convex piling in conjunction with forced circulation leads to centralized channels of liquor flow within the digester and the resultant possibility of non-uniform pulp. Flat piling results in uniform liquor flow through the digester and consequently more uniform pulp.

When the digester is filled, a gasket made from a lap of wet pulp is placed on the flange of the top digester nozzle, and the cover is lowered into place and bolted.

Hot acid from the high-pressure accumulator (Figure 6.4) is pumped into the digester until the latter is completely filled. The air replaced by the cooking liquor is vented through a valve for that purpose.

When the digester is filled, heating of the contents is started immediately either by direct injection of steam or by forced circulation through a heat exchanger. The pressure and temperature conditions at all

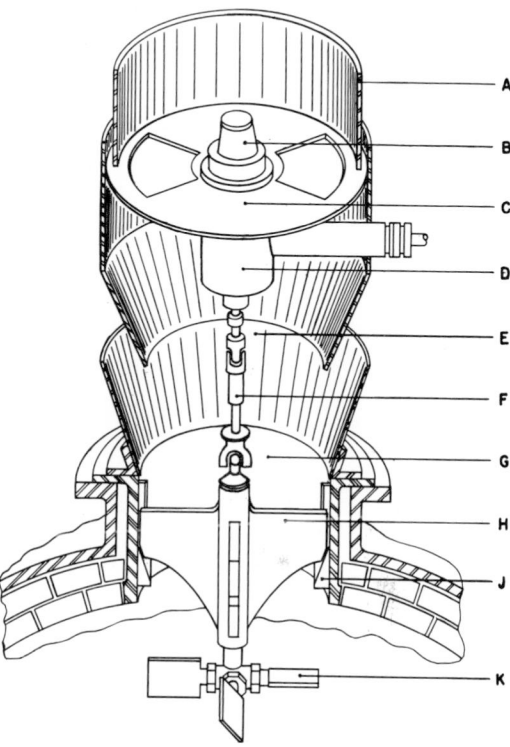

Fig. 6.7. Chip distributor for sulfite digester. (*Courtesy Chemipulp Process Corp.*)

times during the cook must follow a predetermined schedule, whether automatically or manually controlled.

There are no exact limits that apply universally in the sulfite process since variation in wood properties, acid-making equipment, and the variables inherent in digester design determine the optimum conditions in a given mill. Maximum pressure is 90 to 110 psi, fixed by insurance underwriter requirements and controlled by relief of SO_2 gas. Maximum temperature may range from 125° to 160°C and the total time of cook from 6 to 12 hours or longer, with 2 to

3 hours for attainment of maximum temperature. Higher maximum temperature is used with shorter cooking times and lower temperatures with longer cooking times. Sulfite cooks are generally designed as "hard" or "soft," the former indicating less delignification for such uses as newsprint paper, and the latter indicating a higher degree of delignification for pulp that is to be bleached. Figure 6.8 shows a typical sulfite cooking curve.

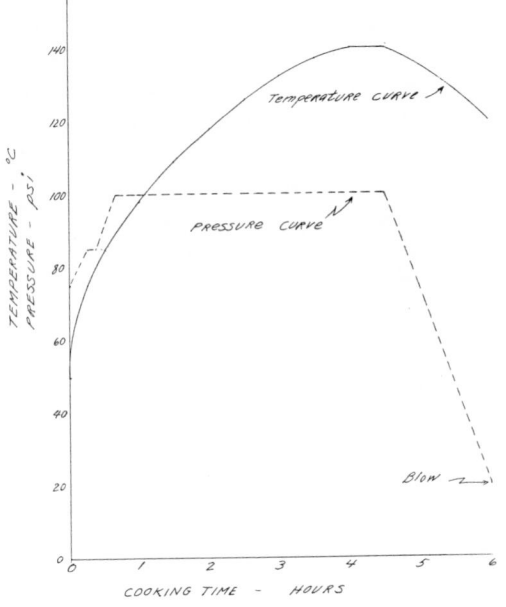

Fig. 6.8. Typical sulfite cooking curves.

A typical West Coast cooking operation with calcium-base and hot acid system would be:

Time of cook: 6 hours
Wood: Western hemlock
Cooking acid: 8.80% total SO_2, 1.10%, % combined SO_2, 70°C
Digester capacity: 40 tons wood (B.D. basis); 50,000 gallons acid
Temperature curve: Figure 6.8
Pressure curve: Figure 6.8
Pulp produced: TAPPI K No. of 12.0
Unbleached screened yield: 45 to 47%

The end of the cook is indicated by exhaustion of the SO_2 and by darkening of the color of the cooking liquor.

Satisfactory results in sulfite cooking require that the cooking liquor contain sufficient total SO_2 to complete the cook to a proper degree of delignification, in the time allotted, and sufficient combined SO_2 so that it will not be exhausted during the course of the cook. A total SO_2 content of 6.5 to 9.0% with a combined of 1.25% is customary in the modern sulfite mill.

In the preliminary phase of the cook, the temperature is raised gradually to about 130°C with a pressure of about 80 psi to permit complete penetration of the chips. At this point the side relief valve is opened and some of the liquor drained to the high-pressure accumulator. This results in a gas space over the cook at the top of the digester; this gas can be drawn off to the accumulator by the top relief valve. By means of relief, the temperature of the digester can be increased without increase in pressure and the SO_2 recovered can be used to fortify cooking liquor for subsequent cooks.

The progress of the cook is followed by testing the SO_2 content of the side relief. When 1 to 1½ hours of cooking time remain, the heating is discontinued and the pressure gradually reduced. During this period all possible SO_2 is recovered since gas that is discharged with the cook not only is lost to the system but also contaminates the surrounding atmosphere.

A typical blow pit [18] in a sulfite mill is a tank about equivalent in size to two digesters. It may be constructed of wood (yellow pine or cedar), of concrete lined with wood, or of stainless steel-clad plate. The blow pit has a false bottom of strainer plates constructed of acid-resisting material containing ⅛-inch or ³⁄₃₂-inch holes and supported by wooden grill work. The top of the blow pit is covered with a deck through which a tall vertical stack vents waste gases and steam to the atmosphere. Opposite the blow pipe leading from the digester, bronze or stainless steel plates are mounted to receive the impact of the blow. As the digester charge strikes this target at high velocity, the chips are reduced to pulp. Below the false bottom are outlets for the discharge of spent liquor and wash water. Immediately above the drainage plates is an outlet for discharging the washed pulp. Nozzles are provided for rapid flooding of the pulp charge with water, usually white water.

The digester charge is allowed to drain for 20 to 40 minutes and then is flooded with water, which again is allowed to drain. This process of flooding and draining is repeated several times, each cycle requiring one to three hours, until the operator is satisfied, on the basis of experience, that the pulp is well washed. The final operation is closing the drain valve and pumping the stock through the discharge valve to the storage chest. The evacuation of the stock must be assisted with high pressure hoses.

The Screen Room [18]

From 1 to 6% of the digester charge in the sulfite mill is undesirable material that must be removed from the pulp. Such material includes knots and uncooked chips, dirt and bark carried by the wood, and fiber bundles or shives. It is the function of the screen room to separate the unwanted particles (tailings or rejects) from the accepted fiber. Such separation is normally accomplished on the basis of particle size, although there is increasing use of the centrifugal principle which also separates particles on the basis of density.

A complete screen room contains the following equipment although, depending upon product requirement, one or several of these items may be omitted:

(1) Knotters
(2) Rifflers
(3) Flat screens or rotary screens
(4) Refiners
(5) Separators
(6) Thickeners.

Stock is received from the washers at 2.5 to 3.0% consistency and is diluted for screening to 0.75 to 1.25% consistency. Knotter screens may be rotary, flat, or vibratory, with openings of ¼ to ½ inch through which accepted stock passes and knots and uncooked chips are rejected.

Rifflers are long flow channels provided with baffles at the bottom over which the stock flows at a rate of about 50 fpm at a consistency of 0.5%. Grit, dirt particles and undefibered wood settle out in the pockets formed by the baffles.

RECENT DEVELOPMENTS IN SULFITE COOKING

For many years, from about 1890 to about 1950, the calcium base-acid bisulfite pulping process developed along conventional lines with improvements in technique but without basic changes in method. Since 1950 numerous innovations have produced a sort of revolution in sulfite pulping.

The stimulus for these innovations has been largely threefold. The calcium base-acid bisulfite process has been highly successful in pulping spruce, fir and hemlock among the softwoods and poplar among the hardwoods, but it has been far less successful with other species, notably the pines, Douglas fir and the mixed hardwood stands that are typical in most areas of the country. The ability of the kraft process to pulp a much greater variety of wood species gave that process an advantage over sulfite during the three decades following 1920.

Some of the reasons for poor results with acid bisulfite with certain species of wood are obvious. For example, wood high in resin offers great resistance to the penetration of acid liquor, but not to alkaline liquor. Certain wood constituents have been identified which react with lignin under acid conditions to form insoluble compounds. Much of the chemistry is obscure in what determines successful pulping of various wood species by acid bisulfite, but the desirability of a pulping process that is adaptable to a variety of species is self-evident.

The conventional calcium acid bisulfite process normally discharges spent cooking liquor as waste. The evaporation and burning of calcium-base spent liquor encounters some difficulty due to the scaling tendency of lime salts, particularly calcium sulfate, upon evaporator surfaces. Nevertheless, the process is carried out on a limited scale with recovery of heat from organic material in the spent liquor, the chief benefit being reduction of the pollution load on the stream. The principal inorganic products of the combustion, calcium sulfate and calcium sulfide, do not permit practical recovery of either the base or the sulfur.

With ammonia as the base, the residual liquor can be burned with recovery of most of the SO_2 and the heat value but with loss of the base as nitrogen and water vapor. The waste liquor from sodium base cooking can be burned and the heating values recovered as steam, while the chemical ash is recovered in the form of smelt consisting of sodium sulfide and sodium carbonate. The recovered chemicals are reprocessed in separate cycles to reproduce the cooking liquor. With magnesium as the base, the inorganic salts of combustion break down directly to magnesium oxide and sulfur dioxide, which may be recombined to form cooking liquor.

Just as economic necessity has dictated the use of greater diversity of wood species for pulping, so too has economic pressure developed for getting more tons of pulp from a given number of cords of wood. This has brought about the surge toward "high yield" pulping. There are no very sharp dividing lines in this area. The conventional "full chemical" pulp shows a yield of 44 to 48% in the digestion step and the cooked wood defibers with mild agitation and only moderate loss of undefibered wood at the screens. With yields much above 50% a positive mechanical action must be applied to prevent excessive loss as screenings.

A great variety of experimental pulps have been made in the range of 60 to 80% yield and some have attained commercial success. These are known as "semichemical" pulps (see Chapter 8). Modifications of the sulfite process have found a place in the high-yield area. These have included not only substitution of soluble bases for

calcium, but also such additional modifications as operating the digestion process at various points on the pH scale, all the way from the highly acid condition of the conventional acid bisulfite to alkaline liquors containing sodium sulfite. Further, digestion may occur in the so-called "vapor phase" where the chips are impregnated with liquor, then drained and digested in an atmosphere of steam or inert gas rather than being surrounded by liquid.

Thus there has been developed a wide choice of pulping variables beginning with the choice of base, then of pH, then of degree of removal or degree of softening of the encrusting materials, and finally a choice of defibering mechanism. Several of these processes have made the breakthrough to commercial utilization and, with the great surge of research going on all over the industry at the present time, it is to be expected that many developments in this field are in the offing.

Choice of Base

Many studies have been made to compare the various bases with each other in regard to yield, pulp qualities and pulping efficiency. Penetration into the wood is an important consideration. Here the indication is that sodium and ammonium show the greatest rate of penetration, calcium least, and magnesium intermediate. It would appear that the greatest factors in the choice of base would be the recovery system and the end use qualities of the pulp.

It has been pointed out that the time-honored sulfite pulping process has been passing through an era of change in recent years. Many of the innovations of this period have been touched upon in the preceding pages. Among the recent developments in the sulfite industry there are two which deserve special mention: (1) the so-called "Magnefite" process and (2) two-stage pulping as exemplified by the Stora and Sivola processes.

The Magnefite Process.[19, 20] The use of magnesium along with calcium as a base in sulfite pulping dates back to the early days of the industry when dolomite, consisting of the mixed carbonates of calcium and magnesium, was often used in absorption towers. The use of magnesium only as a base has two very important advantages over calcium. First, the greater solubility of magnesium salts permits the use of a greater proportion of combined SO_2 without encountering the danger of precipitation of insoluble salts during cooking, and also permits concentration of the cooking liquor by evaporation without scaling of equipment. Second, the incineration of magnesium sulfite results in the formation of magnesium oxide (MgO) and the release of SO_2, thus permitting simple recovery of a major proportion of the cooking chemicals.[20] Figure 6.9 illustrates a Magnefite pulping system.

Thus, several recovery systems have been installed for the use of magnesium base in the acid bisulfite system in which the savings in recovered chemical more than offset the greater cost of magnesium over calcium. The chief advantage of such a system is the reduction in stream pollution.

The "Magnefite" process developed at Howard Paper Mills, Ltd. Cornwall, Ontario provides the additional advantage of pulping species of wood that are not readily pulped by the acid bisulfite process, for example, the pines, Douglas fir, western cedar, and hardwoods. The cooking liquor for this process contains magnesium bisulfiite signifying that the total SO_2 consists of equal parts of combined and free. Such a cooking liquor does not release appreciable quantities of SO_2 even when hot, which means that pressure vessels are not required for the preparation of hot and concentrated cooking liquor and that the circulation and recovery of large volumes of SO_2 as relief gas is not necessary. The pH of the Magnefite cooking liquor is in the range of 3.5 to 4.5 and this higher pH value is credited with the ability of the process to delignify such woods as pine without encountering the re-

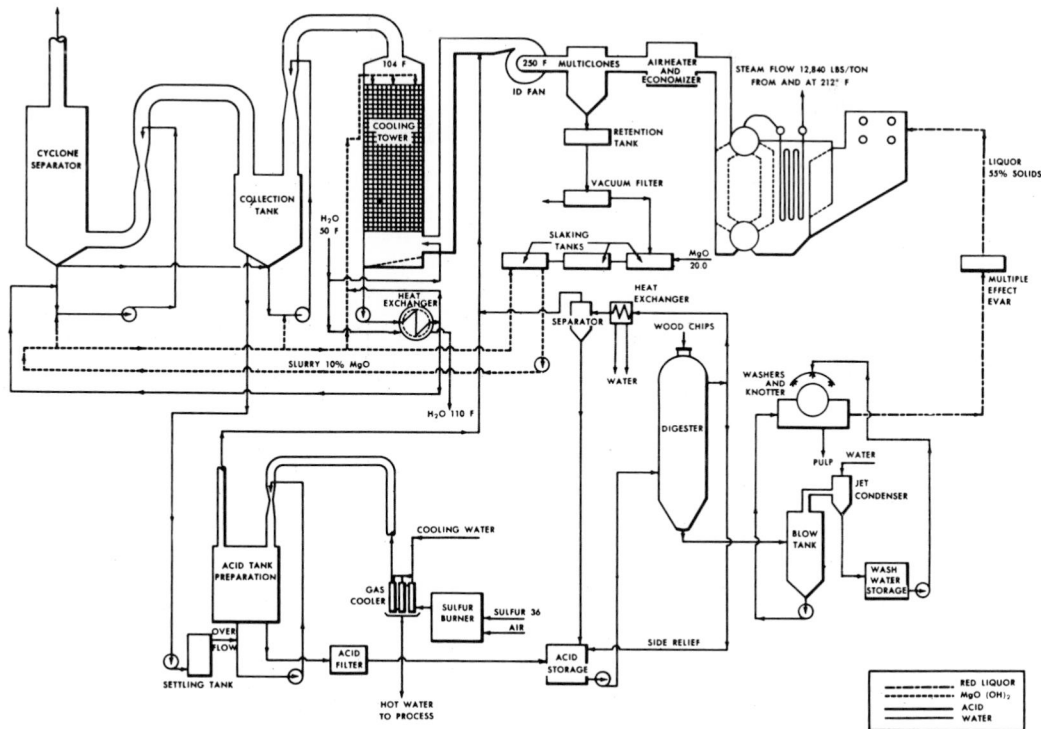

Fig. 6.9. Magnefite pulping and magnesium oxide recovery. (*Courtesy Babcock and Wilcox Co.*)

action between the phenolic compounds present in pine and lignin which seriously interferes with acid bisulfite pulping.

The outstanding characteristics of the Magnefite process have been summarized as follows: [20]

(1) It can be used to pulp a wide variety of wood species. It is not clear how closely the process can match kraft in a variety of species, but it has been demonstrated to be practical for many northern woods that are not suitable for calcium acid bisulfite.

(2) Pulp of higher yield and greater strength than presently produced by the acid bisulfite is obtained by this technique. The strength properties of Magnefite pulp apparently are intermediate between those of normal acid bisulfite and kraft.

(3) Full chemical and semichemical pulps may be produced with a single recovery process.

(4) Stream and air pollution are eliminated.

(5) Heat and chemical recovery are highly efficient. An 80 to 90% recovery of the magnesium base may be expected in this process. Since an equivalent of 240 pounds of magnesium hydroxide per ton of pulp is added to the digester, the required make-up of hydroxide should be 25 to 50 pounds. The make-up of sulfur is reported to be 50 pounds per ton of pulp compared with 220 to 280 pounds for a sulfite process without recovery. Figure 6.9 shows a flow diagram of Magnefite pulping and MgO recovery.

A further modification of the Magnefite process has recently been reported in which the cooking takes place in the "vapor phase." [16] In this study it was found that when using a sufficiently high concentration of liquor (3.5% combined SO_2 or higher) for impregnation, all free liquor could be withdrawn and a highly satisfactory cook could be done in the "vapor phase" using direct steam. As in normal Magnefite procedure, the total cooking times to normal pulp viscosity were about $4\frac{1}{2}$ hours, of which about 3 hours was at maximum temperature (166°C) and the remainder of $1\frac{1}{2}$ hours was equally divided between steaming and impregnation stages and the time for the temperature rise to maximum.

The current (1962) production of magnesia base sulfite pulp in the U.S. is estimated to be 790,000 tons out of a total sulfite capacity of 3,400,000 tons.

It is stated that a rate of temperature rise of 10 to 15°C per minute can be obtained without injury to the pulp. It is reported that a minimum combined SO_2 concentration of 3.5% is required and the most satisfactory liquor pH range is 2.5 to 4.5. Under these conditions yields of 49 to 53% were obtained compared with 43 to 47% for the same degree of delignification using the standard Magnefite process. The 6% gain in yield over standard Magnefite is attributed to less dissolution of lower order carbohydrates in vapor phase cooking. Strength properties of these pulps are said to be intermediate between normal sulfite and kraft pulps.

Multi-Stage Sulfite Pulping

One of the noteworthy developments in sulfite pulping in recent years has been that of multiple-stage cooking in which the stages differ from each other in degree of acidity or alkalinity. Thus, one stage is chosen for optimum conditions of penetration of the wood and initial sulfonation of lignin, and in the other stage conditions are chosen for dissolution and removal of reacted lignin. Multi-stage processes normally use sodium as the base and are associated with a recovery system which is an integral part of the pulping process. It is reported that multi-stage sulfite pulping gives more complete removal of lignin with greater retention of hemicellulose and less degradation of cellulose than can be accomplished by a single-stage cook. It is also claimed that a wide range of wood species can be pulped by multi-stage sulfite than by single stage even though soluble bases are used in the latter.

Two-stage sulfite pulping has been brought

to the point of commercial production by the Stora Kopparberg Company at Skutskar, Sweden. A new mill in Nova Scotia has recently gone into production using this pulping method and recovery system.[21] In the Stora process the cooking liquor for the first stage is composed of a mixture of liquor withdrawn from a previous cook together with a strong make-up liquor from the recovery system. This cooking liquor is a mixture of sodium bisulfite and sodium sulfite at a pH of about 6. The time and temperature of this stage are chosen in consideration of the wood used and the pulp requirements. The essential feature is that complete penetration is attained while avoiding the phenolic condensation which can occur under acid conditions with many species of pines.

At the conclusion of the first stage most of the free liquor is drained off and liquid SO_2 is injected and the cooking carried to completion in the presence of free SO_2. The pulp is then blown, washed and screened by conventional methods except that the waste cooking liquor is sent to the recovery plant.

The bleaching process for Stora pulp consists of six stages and is especially designed to preserve the high yield that is produced in the pulping process. The bleaching stages are:

(1) Chlorination
(2) Caustic extraction
(3) Chlorine dioxide
(4) Caustic extraction
(5) Chlorine dioxide
(6) Soaking.

It is of interest that no hypochlorite stage is used with this type of pulp and that the sequence is similar to that used in the bleaching of kraft.

Bleach plant operations are also designed for maximum removal of pitch and ash with the use of specially purified water and prevention of contact between pulp and metal. The brightness of the bleached pulp is reported to be 92 to 93.

The yield of Stora two-stage pulp is reported to be 5 to 10% greater than for regular sulfite. This additional yield is largely in the form of hemicellulose, or to put it another way a greater proportion of the holocellulose of the wood is retained in the pulp. It naturally follows that such pulp shows extraordinary strength and readily responds to beating and refining. The pulp compares favorably with kraft except for tearing strength.

The indispensable element in any pulping system using sodium as the base is the method of chemical recovery. In the Stora process the spent liquor is evaporated and burned. The smelt, consisting principally of sodium carbonate and sodium sulfide, is dissolved in water and the purified solution is treated with CO_2 which removes sulfide as H_2S gas. The gas from the carbonation tower consisting of CO_2 and H_2S is combined with SO_2 in a Claus reactor, in which the classic reaction (of SO_2 and H_2S) produces liquid sulfur and H_2O. The remaining CO_2 is returned to the carbonation tower and sulfur is burned to regenerate SO_2.

The "green liquor" from the carbonation tower now containing the sodium is a mixture of carbonate and bicarbonate. This solution is treated in a tower with sodium bisulfite to form sodium sulfite and CO_2, the former going partly to an SO_2 absorption tower and partly to cooking liquor make-up where it is mixed with sodium bisulfite to make liquor for the first cooking stage while the latter is recycled to the carbonation tower.

The SO_2 output of the sulfur burner is partially absorbed in water from which it is stripped by heat as a purification step in making liquid SO_2 for the second cooking stage and for use in the Claus reactor. The remaining SO_2 gas is absorbed in a solution rich in sodium sulfite which comes from the carbonation tower and which results in the formation of sodium bisulfite that may be sent to cooking liquor or to the carbonation tower.

At the Skutskar mill the make-up of sodium is added to the spent liquor as NaOH in order to furnish neutral solution for a yeast plant prior to evaporation and burning. The sulfur make-up is added as sulfur at the burner and is said to be about 30% of that used in a conventional calcuim-base sulfite mill.

The Sivola two-stage sulfite pulping method [22] proposes a first stage on the acid side followed by injection of sodium carbonate to produce an alkaline second stage. The pH range reported for the first stage is in the range of 3 to 4 and that for the second stage is in the range of 9 to 10. The smelt from the recovery furnace contains the sulfur in the form Na_2S and this is converted to H_2S by carbonation of the green liquor with CO_2. Sulfur dioxide is regenerated by burning H_2S in a special furnace.

Sivola two-stage sulfite pulps are reported to exhibit a wide range of properties depending upon the cooking conditions. The chemical recovery system can produce sodium-base sulfite cooking liquor for single and multi-stage cooking throughout the pH range as well as for semichemical pulp and for integration with kraft or soda pulp mills.

Chemical Recovery Systems for Sulfite Pulping

Mention has been made in the preceding pages of this chapter of some of the chemical reactions involved in certain of the sulfite recovery systems. The brevity of this description should not be interpreted to mean that these systems are simple either in terms of processes or equipment. The chemical engineering of these systems involves the handling of many materials that are highly corrosive and the prevention of side reactions such as formation of thiosulfates, polythionates and sulfur trioxide. Also, the accumulation of impurities from the pulpwood and from the water supplies must be controlled. Finally in addition to the efficient recycling of chemical materials, the system must conserve and recover process heat.

Because of all these factors, the problems of chemical recovery in the sulfite process has occupied much attention over a period of years from pulp manufacturers, engineering consultants and equipment manufacturers. At the present time there are various ideas and methods contending for adoption by the sulfite industry.

The reader who is interested in more detailed description of various recovery processes is referred to the August 1960 issue of Tappi Magazine. Pages 673 to 715 of that issue contain eight papers from a symposium devoted to sulfite chemical recovery systems.

It will be some time before a position of relative stability in the technology of this industry is attained. It is likely that several systems of cooking and chemical recovery will survive this competition. In any event, the time honored sulfite pulping industry is in a state of transition and gives every indication of vigorous and diversified future growth.

REFERENCES

1. Vroon, H., *Paper Maker* (U.S.), **29**, No. 2, 36 (1960).
2. Vroon, H., *Paper Maker* (U.S.), **23**, No. 1, 41 (1954).
3. Isenberg, I. H., "Pulp and Paper Microscopy," Third Edition, Appleton, Wisconsin, Institute of Paper Chemistry, 1958.
4. Brown, H. P., Panshin, A. J., Forsaith, C. C., "Textbook of Wood Technology," Vol. 1, New York, McGraw-Hill Book Company, Inc., 1949.
5. Felicetta, V. F., McCarthy, J. L., *Tappi*, **40**, No. 11, 851 (November, 1957).
6. Nolan, W. J., *Tappi*, **44**, No. 7, 484 (July, 1961).
7. Maas, O., *et al.*, The Va-Purge Process: A Symposium, *Pulp Paper Mag. of Can.*, **54**, No. 8, 98 (July, 1953).
8. Hart, J. S., *Tappi*, **37**, No. 8, 331 (August, 1954).
9. Tomlinson, G. H. II, *Tappi*, **44**, No. 1, 133A (January, 1961).
10. Ingruber, O. V., *Pulp Paper Mag. of Can.*, **58**, No. 10, 161 (1957).
11. Harris, G. R., *Pulp Paper Mag. of Can.*, **58**, No. 3—Convention Issue, 284 (1957).

12. Wilson, J. W., and O'Meara, D., Paper presented at Annual Meeting of the Technical Section, Canadian Pulp and Paper Association (January, 1960).

13. Peckham, J. R., and Van Drunen, V., *Tappi*, **44**, No. 5, 374 (May, 1961).

14. Yean, W. Q., Ross, J. H., and Vroon, K. E., *Pulp Paper Mag. of Can.*, **58**, No. 7, 197 (June, 1957).

15. Waste Committee, Proceedings Technical Section, Canadian Pulp and Paper Association, p. 277, 1952.

16. Chemipulp Process, Inc., "Chemipulp Sulfite Mill Operation," Watertown, New York, 1953.

17. Chemipulp Process, Inc., "Jet Type Sulphur Burner," Watertown, New York.

18. Sulphite Pulping Operating Manual, Canadian Pulp and Paper Association (July, 1955).

19. Tomlinson, G. H., and Wilcoxson, L. S., *Paper Trade J.*, **110**, 209 (1940).

20. Darmstadt, W. J., and Tomlinson, G. H. II, *Tappi*, **43**, No. 8, 674 (August, 1960).

21. Evans, John C. W., *Paper Trade J.*, **143**, No. 37, 50 (September 14, 1959).

22. Pascoe, T. A.; Buchanan, J. S.; Kennedy, E. H.; Sivola, G., *Tappi*, **42**, No. 4, 265 (April, 1959).

CHAPTER 7

Alkaline Pulping

GEORGE E. JACKSON

Bowater-Carolina Corporation

The rapidly increasing demand for paper during the nineteenth century spurred a vigorous search for an inexpensive and ample supply of fiber. Wood, although a logical source of such fiber, was found to be difficult to reduce to pulp by the dilute caustic soda solutions used in rag cooking. It was not until 1854 that Burgess and Watt in England succeeded in producing pulp commercially from hardwood by using a caustic soda cooking liquor at higher concentration and at higher temperature than used in rag cooking. The increased usage and cost of caustic soda led to the partial recovery of the spent cooking liquor by evaporation and incineration. Except for equipment modifications, the soda process of pulping wood has remained essentially the same to this day.

The soda ash (sodium carbonate) used as chemical make-up for the soda process has always been a more expensive material than the corresponding sulfate of soda, salt cake. According to tradition, a German chemist, Dahl, of Danzig, in 1884, substituted sodium sulfate for soda ash in the soda recovery process in order to reduce chemical cost. This experiment resulted in the introduction of a new ingredient, sodium sulfide, along with caustic soda in the cooking liquor. It was immediately apparent that a faster rate of pulping and a stronger pulp resulted. The new pulp became known as *kraft* from the German word meaning "strong." The process is also commonly called the *sulfate process* from the make-up chemical used.

The first manufacture of kraft pulp in North America occurred at the Brompton Paper Company, East Angus, Quebec in 1907. In February, 1909, the first kraft pulp made in the United States was "blown" at the Roanoke Rapids Paper Manufacturing Company (now Halifax Paper Company), in North Carolina. The pulp mill at that time consisted of two 30-cubic meter (about 425 cubic feet) tumbling digesters imported from Germany and having a rated capacity of 12 tons per day.

The sulfite pulping process developed commercially during the years 1874 to 1881 and hence was contemporary with the discovery of the kraft process. Sulfite pulp was both cheaper and stronger than soda pulp. The competition from sulfite pulp led to the conversion of many of the soda mills to kraft. However the dark color of the sulfate pulp was a definite hindrance to its use in fine papers. Efforts to bleach out the brown color with single-stage hypochlorite were only partially successful. Bleaching the pulp resulted in serious weakening of the fiber. However, a bright sheet was readily obtained by bleaching hardwood soda pulp. Since this pulp also had the necessary properties for book and writing papers, some soda mills continued to operate. Introduction of an electrolytic method of producing chlorine and caustic from a solution of salt was the salvation of the soda process, which now had an inexpensive supply of chlorine for bleaching the pulp as well as caustic soda for cooking. This was especially true where the soda pulp mill was located on a stream which could provide the hydroelectric power required.

Just prior to World War I, bleached soda pulp was used for book and writing paper because of its brightness and opacity; unbleached sulfate pulp was used for high strength where color was not of major importance, such as paper containers and wrappers; and sulfite pulp went into printing papers where an intermediate strength, brightness and low cost chemical pulp was called for.

Subsequent changes made in the process equipment significantly reduced the production cost of sulfate pulp. This has resulted in the majority of the recent chemical pulp mills being installed as sulfate process units. Coincidental to this was a change from bulk handling to individual packaging in the market place, using sulfate pulp as containers. Figure 7.1 shows the resulting growth in sulfate pulp production.

The superior strength of sulfate pulp has been the dominant factor for developing this process over the past 80 years. The equipment and methods of operating have been standardized to such an extent that even though other novel processes might yield a superior pulp, the cost and risk of introducing a new commercial pulping system are so great that few companies have taken this route. Some of the major factors influencing the decision to install sulfate pulp mills are:

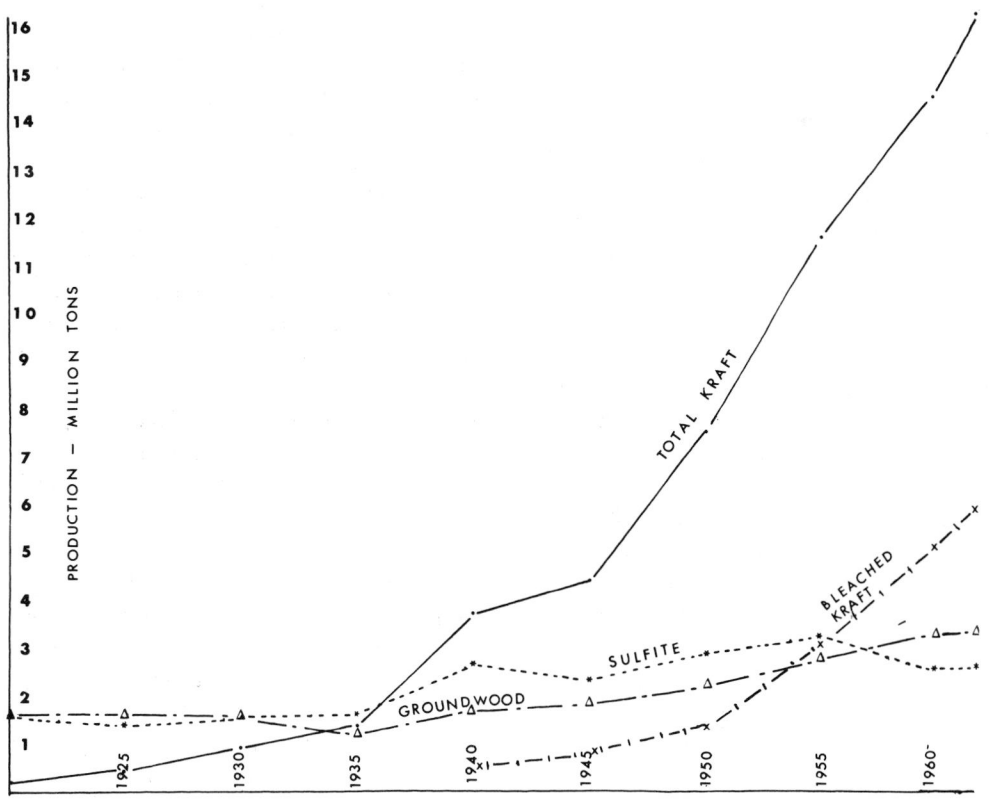

Fig. 7.1. Production of various pulp grades U.S. 1920-1960.

(1) High pulp strength
(2) Versatility of pulping different species of wood
(3) Inexpensive choice of several alternate chemical make-up raw materials
(4) Availability of standard process equipment
(5) Multiple choice of bleaching processes for type of paper product desired
(6) Relatively low stream pollution
(7) Efficient chemical recovery
(8) Efficient heat recovery
(9) Reduced pitch troubles with resinous wood
(10) Versatility of producing a wide range of pulps to meet end use requirements

Some of the disadvantages of the sulfate process are:

(1) Air pollution
(2) Dark color of the unbleached pulp
(3) Heavy capital investment for chemical recovery
(4) High cost of bleaching, when white pulp is required
(5) Lower yield of pulp in per cent of wood used as compared with sulfite process

The current expansion of technology in other phases of the industrial world has had its effect on the sulfate pulp process. The introduction of chlorine dioxide as a practical bleaching agent and the development of suitable materials to handle this corrosive chemical have finally opened the door to the use of sulfate pulp where the demands on fiber brightness and strength are greatest. Thus, sulfate pulp is now being used for chemical or rayon pulps (by prehydrolysis), fine papers, food packaging and other products which have created an ever-increasing demand for this type of pulp.

A number of pilot and full-scale continuous digesters are in various stages of development. The Kamyr continuous digester has been the most widely adopted in the sulfate process, and is now producing a pulp that is competitive in quality and cost with that from batch digesters.

The introduction of instrumentation in the pulp mill has been slow compared to that in the chemical industry. Giant strides have been made in recent years, spurred on by rising costs in the face of falling pulp prices, to automate the standard operations. Digesters, recovery boilers and evaporators have been well instrumented for semi-automatic control. The introduction of magnetic flowmeters and beta-ray gauges for density measurement and computer controls are helping to provide the automatic controls needed in the recausticizing of green liquor and lime mud recovery (see Chapter 15).

Changes in design and metallurgy of mechanical refiners have opened the door to successful high-yield pulping, resulting in improved fiber quality and savings in raw materials.

A number of improvements, none of which are radical in nature, have been made in the recovery boiler and its auxiliaries that now make it possible to operate under continuous heavy loads to furnish process steam without the necessity of a standby unit. Increased efficiency of chemical recovery has reduced the air pollution and chemical losses to the point where the sulfate process can now produce pulp that is economically competitive to sulfite pulp.

The recovery and purification of soap or crude tall oil has established a firm market for this product and it has proved to be a substantial source of revenue to the sulfate pulp mill. The majority of the recently constructed pulp mills in the Southeast have installed tall oil purification units.

The crude turpentine from sulfate pulp mills has suffered wide swings in price and demand, making it a by-product of variable success. Some mills burn the turpentine in the furnace as an auxiliary fuel whenever the supply is in excess of market demand.

The most significant stride in cost reduction has been the installation of larger processing equipment. This is true of every phase of the operation. The newer pulp mills are producing from 600 to 800 tons per day using a single line of equipment, and the trend is to still larger pulping units. It is no longer possible to build an economically sound mill in the United States with a production capacity of less than 300 tons per day.

KRAFT INDUSTRY ECONOMICS

The growth of the kraft pulp industry in the past 25 years has been spectacular. Figure 7.1 shows graphically the growth in production of various types of pulp in the United States for the 40-year period 1920 to 1960. In 1935, the three major types of pulp, sulfate (kraft), sulfite and groundwood, were very nearly equal in production at about one and one-half million tons. Since then, while sulfite and groundwood have approximately doubled in production, kraft has shown a tenfold growth. Of the total rated capacity of kraft pulp in 1960 of 15,892,000 tons, 12,687,000 or 80% was in the South. The abundance and rapid growth of both pines and hardwoods in the South and the adaptability of the kraft process to a variety of wood species have combined to produce this expansion. At the same time, the 20% of the industry outside of the South is also significant both in size and in rate of growth. In this connection, it is interesting to note the trend in Canadian pulp production. In the period from 1937 to 1959, the growth in production of paper grade sulfite pulp was from 1,208,956 tons to 2,158,064 tons, or somewhat less than double. In the same period, the increase in kraft production was 312,741 to 2,263,966, or approximately seven times. Thus, even in areas where the wood supply is composed of northern and western species, the rate of growth of kraft pulping closely matches that in southern United States. See Table 7.1.

TABLE 7.1. U.S. PRODUCTION OF PAPER GRADE PULP.*

	Total Sulfate	Fully Bleached Sulfate	Total Sulfite	Ground-wood
1920	188,651		1,585,834	1,583,914
1925	409,768		1,403,086	1,612,019
1930	949,513		1,567,063	1,560,221
1935	1,467,749		1,579,567	1,355,819
1940	3,747,992	453,282	2,607,789	1,632,727
1945	4,471,875	705,104	2,359,731	1,826,750
1950	7,506,329	1,432,945	2,843,536	2,221,910
1955	11,576,902	3,202,071	3,251,315	2,728,870
1960	14,516,000	5,060,000	2,567,000	3,291,895
1961	15,422,000	5,405,000	2,567,000	3,208,350
1962	16,299,000	5,852,000	2,574,000	3,362,000

* From Bureau of Census.

Another point of importance shown in Figure 7.1 is the growth of fully bleached kraft. Kraft pulp is difficult to bleach, and it was formerly considered uneconomical. With the development of multi-stage bleaching in the 1930's, and more recently with the use of chlorine dioxide, bleached kraft became an important commercial pulp. It is interesting to note that kraft became the leading unbleached chemical pulp in the United States as early as 1930; by 1938, it had become the leading chemical pulp in total production, and by 1958 it was the most important bleached pulp.

For 1959, the total production of kraft pulp in the United States is reported as 14,357,276 tons. The consumption of pulpwood for kraft pulp for that year is reported as 24,375,027 cords of 128 cubic feet of round wood. Accordingly, 1.7 cords of wood are required per ton of pulp. If we assume an average pulp yield of 45% based on wood, then 2,000/0.45 or 4,444 pounds of wood are required per ton of pulp, both calculated on an air-dry basis. Further, by dividing 4,444 by 1.7, an average value of air-dry wood per cord is obtained, namely 2,614 pounds. It is commonly assumed that a cord of round wood, occupying a volume of 128 cubic feet, contains 80 to 90 cubic feet of solid wood. Using the factor 90 cubic feet, we arrive at a value of **26.14** pounds of wood per cubic foot. Dividing this figure by 62.5, the weight of a cubic foot of water, gives an average density or specific gravity of **0.64**.

The calculations given above illustrate several important points in the economics of pulpwood. Although the traditional methods of wood measurement are by volume, expressed as cords or board feet, the weight of wood substance is of greater importance in pulp manufacture. The weight of wood substance is the product of the true solid volume times the density. For this reason, other factors being equivalent, high-density wood is preferred for pulping. The difficulty in using weight as a direct measurement of pulpwood is the variable moisture content. Wood may vary from about 10 to about 50% in water content with little change in volume. Hence, it is necessary to know this moisture content in order to determine the weight of solid fiber in a given weight of wood.

STANDARD TERMS USED IN THE SULFATE PULPING PROCESS [2]

(1) Total chemical: all sodium salts expressed as Na_2O.

(2) Active alkali: $NaOH + Na_2S + Na_2CO_3 + \frac{1}{2} Na_2SO_3$, all expressed as Na_2O.

(3) Active alkali: $NaOH + Na_2S$, expressed as Na_2O.

(4) Effective alkali: $NaOH + \frac{1}{2} Na_2S$, expressed as Na_2O.

(5) Activity: the percentage ratio of active alkali to total alkali.

(6) Causticizing efficiency: in white liquor, the percentage ratio of NaOH to NaOH $+ Na_2CO_3$, both items being expressed as Na_2O, and being corrected for NaOH content of the original green liquor in order to represent only the NaOH produced in the actual causticizing reaction.

(7) Causticity: the percentage ratio of NaOH to active alkali, expressed as Na_2O.

(8) Sulfidity: the percentage ratio of Na_2S to active alkali, expressed as Na_2O.

(9) Reduction: in green liquor the percentage ratio of Na_2S to $Na_2SO_4 + Na_2S +$ any other soda sulfur compounds, all expressed as Na_2O.

(10) Unreduced salt cake: Na_2SO_4 in the green liquor, expressed as Na_2SO_4.

(11) Make-up chemical consumption: the pounds of Na_2SO_4, or other sodium compounds expressed as Na_2SO_4, added as new chemical per ton of air dry pulp produced.

(12) Chemical recovery: the percentage ratio of total chemical to the digesters, less the total new chemical, to the total chemical to digesters (after correcting for any change in liquor inventory).

(13) Chemical loss: total, the ratio of total chemical in new chemical to total chemical to digesters.

(14) Green liquor: the name applied to liquor made by dissolving the recovered chemicals in water and weak liquor preparatory to causticizing.

(15) White liquor: the name applied to liquors made by causticizing green liquors. White liquor is ready for use in the digester.

(16) Black liquor: the name applied to liquors recovered from the digesters, up to the point of their incineration in the recovery plant.

DESCRIPTION OF PROCESS

Chemical pulp is made by dissolving the lignin and other material of the wood with a chemical solution, thus freeing the cellulose fibers so that they can be reformed into paper. The sulfate pulping process (Figure 7.2) uses an alkaline solution of caustic soda (sodium hydroxide) and sodium sulfide, termed white liquor, to remove the lignin binding the cellulose fibers together in the wood. This mixture of wood and liquor is steam-heated in a pressure vessel or digester; after completion of the cooking process, the charge is blown into a tank where the steam flashes off and the softened chips disintegrate. The loose fibers (pulp)

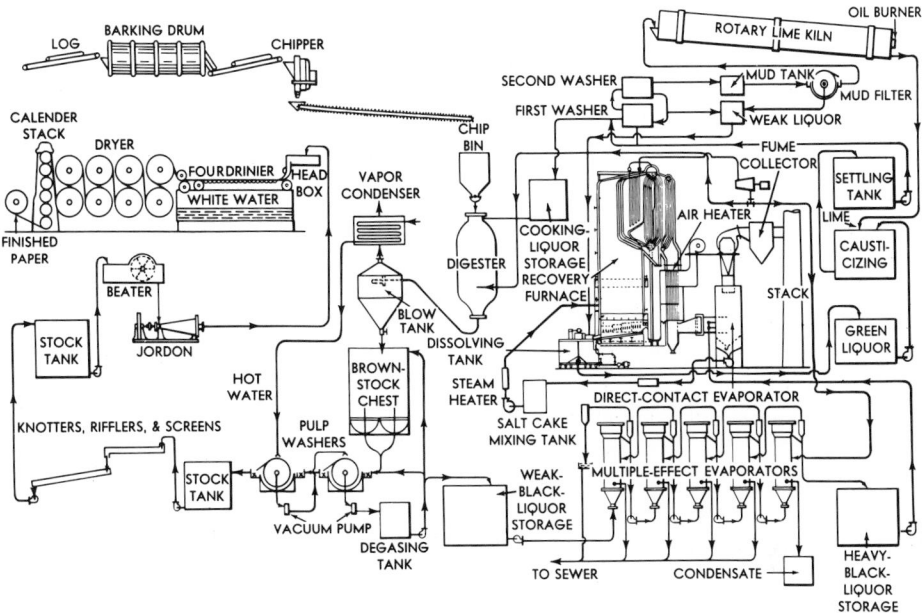

Fig. 7.2. Flow diagram of the kraft pulping process. (*Courtesy Babcock and Wilcox Co.*)

are separated from and washed free of the spent cooking solution (black liquor). The filtrate, containing most of the cooking liquor chemicals and the dissolved portion of the wood, is concentrated by evaporation and fired in a furnace. The dissolved portion of the wood in the black liquor burns, evolving heat to generate steam, leaving a molten residue of soda ash and sodium sulfide. This is dissolved in water to form green liquor. The latter is treated with lime (calcium oxide) to convert the soda ash (sodium carbonate) to caustic soda (sodium hydroxide). The sodium sulfide remains unchanged. The sludge or lime mud is settled out, leaving a clear solution of caustic soda and sodium sulfide, termed white liquor, ready for re-use in the digesters. The lime mud (calcium carbonate) is burned in a kiln to drive off carbon dioxide, thus regenerating the lime (calcium oxide) for use in treating green liquor once more.

The pulp, after separation from the black liquor, is screened to remove the knots and incompletely separated fiber bundles (shives) and other foreign material. It is then bleached or sent directly to the paper

machines or to the pulp dryer when bleaching is not required. The pulp may be mechanically treated to break up the fiber bundles that have been softened but not completely separated by cooking. The point at which the fiber bundles are mechanically treated or refined is variable. Some mills fiberize the hot stock as it is pumped from the blow tank to the brown stock washers; others refine the pulp after it has been washed. The choice depends on a number of factors, but appears to be primarily one of timing. Thus, the older mills have tended to install the refining equipment after washing, since the installed washer capacity would be limited in capacity with any serious effort to refine the pulp ahead of the washers. The introduction of pressurized refiners and screens has enabled the new high-yield pulp mills to take advantage of the new machinery made available by altering the process. Thus, the major undefibered particles are mechanically treated after leaving the blow tank, and the still oversize material is screened from the main stream to be separately refined and recirculated to the blow tank until sufficiently reduced in size to be accepted to the brown stock washers. This in effect combines the screening, refining and washing operations, eliminating the need for a separate screen room operation.

The cooking process removes the bonding material that holds the wood fibers firmly together, thus allowing the fibers to be separated to form pulp. During this process the cooking liquor attacks all the constituents of the wood to varying degrees, including the cellulose fibers. The soda process uses caustic soda or sodium hydroxide as the main component of the cooking liquor. The caustic dissolves the lignin between and within the fibers, while also attacking the cellulose. The principal difference in the sulfate process is the substitution of from 15 to 30% sodium sulfide for the active alkali in the cooking liquor. This increases the rate of attack on the interfiber lignin while buffering the effect of the caustic soda on the cellulose, which accounts for the superior strength of sulfate over soda pulp.

The cooking liquor also converts the fats, oils and resins present in the wood to soaps which are soluble in the liquor. This is one of the principal advantages of the sulfate over the sulfite process. Kraft pulp made from wood high in resin content still gives little or no pitch trouble on the paper machine.

The amount of lignin removed from the wood is dependent upon the end use of the pulp. Thus, for high-yield, medium-strength pulps such as are used to make liner board, the chips are cooked for a short time in dilute cooking liquor and mechanical defibration is required to complete the breakdown of the interfiber bonds. The yield of pulp is greater, for not only is the attack on the cellulose reduced but less lignin is removed.

Considerable improvement has been made in the mechanical equipment used to defiber partially cooked chips. This has increased the yield of fiber from 48 to over 60% on the basis of wood with satisfactory paper quality for many purposes. This is particularly true of integrated pulp and paper mills, where the inherent strength of the high-yield pulp can be utilized without the deterioration experienced when the fiber must be dried to reduce the transportation costs to a distant paper mill.

Pulps made by cooking the wood to a greater degree are used for making paper bags and heavy-weight papers. The cooking is continued to a still lower lignin content when higher strength is desired or when the pulp must be bleached, due primarily to the much higher cost of the bleaching chemicals to remove the remaining lignin. The introduction of new bleaching agents in the last few decades has materially changed the degree to which the pulp must be cooked to obtain the desired strength and brightness levels of the finished product (see Chapter 10).

Once the majority of the interfiber lignin has been removed, efforts to reduce the lignin content of the pulp by dissolving the cell wall lignin will result in an equal rate of attack on the cellulose itself. Thus, for bleaching grades of pulp the cooking process is stopped just prior to this, which means that the pulp entering the bleach plant has a TAPPI permanganate number of 16 to 22 (see Chapter 2).

The introduction of the multi-stage bleach plant and a plentiful supply of hardwood species has led to a rapid growth in production of sulfate hardwood pulp, using higher sulfidity cooking liquor to minimize the degradation of the short hardwood fibers. The result is an economical white pulp that approaches the strength of bleached sulfite pulp. The largest expansion of hardwood pulping has been in the Southeast using the plentiful supply of gum and oak wood. Maple, aspen, birch and beech are the principal species used in the mid-Atlantic and northeastern states.

The kraft cooking liquor consists of a mixture of white liquor from the recovery plant and black liquor from a previous cook. The chief ingredients of the cooking liquor are:

Sodium hydroxide, NaOH
Sodium sulfide, Na_2S
Sodium carbonate, Na_2CO_3
Sodium sulfate, Na_2SO_4
Sodium thiosulfate, $Na_2S_2O_3$.

The last three chemicals in the above list are not active in the cooking process, and are present because the chemical reactions in the preparation of the cooking liquor are imperfect or incomplete.

"Active alkali" is the sum total of the weight of sodium hydroxide and sodium sulfite expressed as Na_2O. Sulfidity is the ratio of sodium sulfide to the sum of the weights of NaOH, Na_2S, Na_2CO_3, all expressed as Na_2O.

Active alkali present in the cooking liquor varies considerably from mill to mill depending upon the type of pulp being made. A typical range for bleachable pulp is 18 to 20% based on oven dry wood. For board stock cooked to higher yield, the range might be 12 to 14%. Sulfidity may also vary over considerable limits, a typical value being 20%.

A typical kraft digester charge has been given as follows: [3]

Chips, bone dry basis	25 tons
Moisture content of chips	50%
Water in chips	6,000 gal.
Volume of digester	3,900 cu ft
Volume of cooking liquor	14,500 gal.
Black liquor in cooking liquor	4,500 gal.
White liquor in cooking liquor	10,000 gal.
Active alkali in white liquor	0.78 lb/gal.
Total active alkali	7,800 lb
Tons pulp produced	12 tons
Active alkali per ton of pulp	650 lb
Active alkali basis of dry wood	15.6%

It must be emphasized that the above data represent one example of kraft cooking and that there are wide variations from these conditions that are being used throughout the industry.

CHEMISTRY OF ALKALINE PULPING

The reactions that occur between wood and alkaline cooking liquors are extremely complex and incompletely understood. Black liquor from the soda process [4] contains two lignin derivatives precipitated by acid, denoted as alkali lignin A and alkali lignin B. Both of these fractions contain more acidic hydroxyl reacted with alkali during the cook than does native lignin. It appears that the single phenolic or enolic hydroxyl group in the highly polymerized lignin complex is not sufficient to bring about solubility when reacted with NaOH. Under cooking conditions, additional hydroxyl groups are formed, possibly from hydrolysis of the methoxyl, from the furan or pyran ring opening, or from the breaking of a linkage between lignin and carbohydrate. The liberation of methanol during the cook and decrease of methoxyl content of black liquor lignin are strong evidence of the occurrence of the first reaction.

During alkaline cooking, chemical attack upon hemicellulose and lignin occurs more or less simultaneously, as it does in all commercial pulping processes. Carbohydrates in the black liquor occur as sodium salts and highly degraded in terms of molecular weight such that these residues are not precipitated by acid.

The presence of Na_2S in the cooking liquor results in a distinct and measurable increase in rate of delignification [5] and also in retention of greater amounts of pentosan in the pulp. It appears that the sulfide brings about a specific reaction favorable to pulping rather than merely acting as a buffer, as first thought. Hägglund [5] reports that by increasing sulfidity from 0 to 16%, the rate of delignification is increased to the same degree as would be obtained by 7° to 8°C additional temperature. As another example, the lignin content of a pulp at 50% yield at zero sulfidity was 11.5% lignin, compared with 7.3% lignin content of a pulp cooked to the same yield at 31% sulfidity. All this means that soda fiber is exposed to more drastic conditions of temperature, chemical concentration and time, to effect a given degree of pulping, than is kraft fiber. In summary, Hägglund proposes that lignin first takes up sulfur in the solid phase, followed by molecular splitting that forms additional free hydroxyl groups thus producing soluble lignin fragments. Sulfidization of sensitive groups in the lignin molecule reduces or prevents the tendency to polymerize, thus keeping and promoting solubility.

Various investigators [6,7,8] have pointed out that kraft pulping is a topochemical reaction, that is, the reaction proceeds in successive steps in different areas of the wood substance. Thus, the lignin of the middle lamella is practically completely reacted while that of the cell wall is nearly untouched. Therefore, the last of the lignin is removed at a greatly reduced rate. This situation is different from sulfite delignification, where the reaction is essentially simultaneous on all lignin.

The amount of total alkali consumed is a direct function of amount of wood dissolved. At 50% yield this amounts to 15 to 17% total alkali consumed on basis of dry wood. The rate of pulping is highly temperature-dependent, an increase from 165°C to 175°C approximately doubling the rate.

In addition to the increased rate of delignification, the presence of sulfide in the cooking liquor has two other very specific and obvious effects—color and odor. The light brown color of unbleached kraft is attributed to sulfidized lignin residues, which make it difficult to bleach. The characteristic kraft mill odor is due to volatile sulfur compounds, the chief of which is methyl mercaptan.

It has been noted that kraft pulp has a high content of pentosan, a condition which for a long time made kraft pulp undesirable for dissolving pulp. This has led to the development of *pre-hydrolized* kraft, for which the digester of chips is subjected to a period of steaming or water cooking in the absence of cooking liquor. The action of the steam evolves organic acids from the wood which, at the elevated temperature, hydrolyze hemicellulose to soluble sugars. Subsequent pulping gives a product suitable for dissolving pulp.

PROPERTIES OF KRAFT PULP

The advantages of the kraft pulping process have been listed above. Kraft fiber tends to be less brittle, less transparent, more difficult to hydrate, but eventually capable of more strength development than sulfite pulps. Kraft pulps normally have greater pentosan, greater alpha-cellulose, and higher lignin contents than other pulps. McKinney [9] has suggested the formation of ether linkages of hemicellulose which would result in less swelling and slower beating but greater ultimate strength.

Peckham and Van Drunen [10] give extensive data on a variety of laboratory cooks over the entire pH range of acid sulfite to alkaline kraft. The greater rate of pulping is evident at both high and low pH. The long time and high temperature in the intermediate range of pH result in degradation of the pulp, which is revealed in reduced viscosity and lower zero span strength.

Pulping Process

The traditional method of cooking kraft pulp uses a batch digester illustrated in simple form in Figure 7.3. A typical kraft digester is a one-piece vessel of mild steel, of welded construction designed for 150 psi pressure. Such a vessel might have a typical hydrostatic test of 446 psi. Kraft digesters have been used having a wide range of capacities. A common size is 12 feet in diameter x 45 feet long, equivalent to a volume of about 4,000 cubic feet. A recent installation at Tennessee River Pulp and Paper Company has four digesters of 6,100 cubic feet capacity each.

Kraft digesters are not ordinarily lined, as originally corrosion was not considered to be a serious problem. In recent years, however, severe corrosion and consequent reduction in digester life have occurred in a number of mills. This has led to experimentation with stainless steel lining. Another method of prolonging the useful life of a digester is starting with a thicker steel wall.

With a digester 11 feet in diameter and an original wall thickness of 2 inches, a life of 12 to 15 years may be expected before the wall thickness reaches the permissible limit of ¾ inch. Digesters are tested for wall thickness periodically under the direction of insurance underwriters.

Digesters are normally provided with a circulating system and heat exchanger for bringing the contents to pulping temperature. However, direct heating by injection of steam into the digester as in Figure 7.3 is also common. Forced circulation, prop-erly carried out, affords better contact between liquor and chips and also minimizes the load on the evaporators by reducing dilution of the liquor. A common design draws liquor through a perforated ring near the midpoint of the digester and distributes the return flow from the heat exchanger to both the bottom and top of the digester.

The screened chips charged to the digester should be measured by Weightometer. In the turpentine areas of the South, tapping spouts may remain in the logs, hence tramp iron should be removed by a mag-

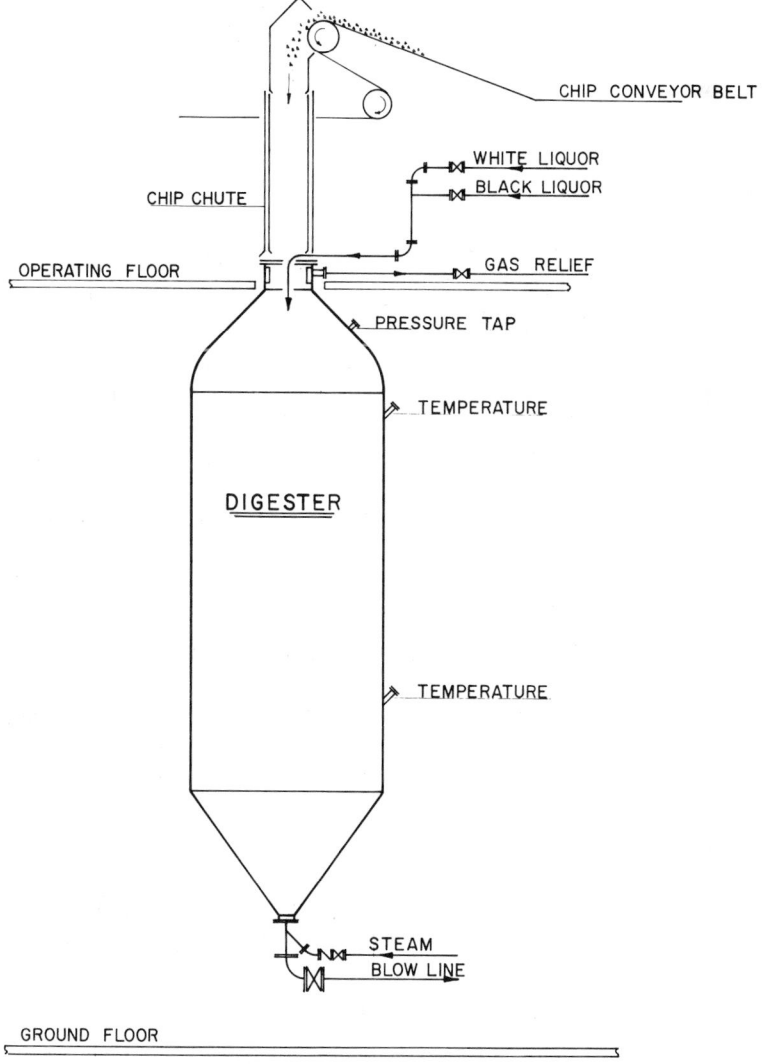

Fig. 7.3. Batch digester for kraft.

netic separator. It is important to know the actual weight of dry wood to assure a constant ratio of wood to alkali. The normal moisture content of green wood is 50%. In the short kraft cycle, the additional time required for the use of mechanical chip packers is not usually considered justified. The delay represents a greater loss of production than it does in the longer sulfite cycle.

The composition of a typical cooking liquor is given above. The general range of liquor volume is 3 to 5 pounds of liquor per pound of dry wood, with alkali concentration 40 to 80 grams per liter, and sulfidities from 15 to 35%.

The loaded digester is brought to maximum temperature and pressure as quickly as steam supply and transfer conditions permit. The chip penetration problem, which is characteristic of the sulfite process and limits the rate of temperature rise, does not exist for kraft. Maximum pressure is normally in the range of 100 to 135 psi and maximum temperature 170° to 176°C. The total length of the cooking cycle may range from $2\frac{1}{2}$ hours for a hard board stock to 5 hours for bleachable pulp. The cooking cycle itself varies considerably from mill to mill. The steaming rate is controlled by a clock-driven cam which is cut to the shape of the desired temperature curve. The digester is relieved during the initial steaming period to remove air and non-condensable gases. This relief is automatically controlled by temperature measurement, which distinguishes between false pressure due to inert gases and that due to saturated steam.

Continuous Digester

Continuous digesters have been in use for a number of years on lower grades of pulp, but it was not until about 1950 that a successful commercial unit built by Kamyr, Inc. was accepted by the sulfate pulp industry. Since then, Kamyr units have grown in capacity and numbers until continuous digesters of over 400 tons per day capacity are being operated. More than 50 such units are in operation representing production close to five million tons of pulp per year. Other manufacturers have also developed various types of continuous digesters, although relatively few commercial units are in operation.

The principal reasons for using a continuous digester are to lower manufacturing costs while producing a higher yield of a better quality pulp. The economic factors are:

(1) *Lower capital investment.* This is dependent on the size or capacity of the unit installed. Below 150 tons of pulp per day levels, the batch digester installation is usually less expensive to install, but as the capacity is increased, the continuous digester installation becomes more favorable. This is a result of fewer structural requirements and lower auxiliary costs due to elimination of peak loads on steam, chip handling and pumping equipment.

(2) *Reduced labor cost.* Batch digesters typically require several operators, whereas continuous units as large as 600 tons per day may be operated by one man.

(3) *Reduced digester shell corrosion.* The continuous digester shell is pressurized and remains at relatively constant pressure and temperature within the various zones, thus inhibiting corrosion. This is in contrast to the repeated temperature and pressure cycles of batch cooking.

(4) *Less steam demand.* The heat efficiency is better since (a) good liquor circulation means closer control of temperature within the digester; (b) flash steam from the black liquor is used to preheat the chips; (c) countercurrent heating of the fresh liquor with the spent liquor is utilized; and (d) there is steady steam demand for cooking, which promotes better steam boiler efficiency.

(5) *Lower bleaching costs.* The variations in bleachability occur gradually and are smaller in amplitude than with batch cooks.

The cycle of events that takes place in a batch digester is performed continuously in separate sections and the auxiliaries of a continuous digester (Figure 7.4). These are as follows:

(1) Chip metering,
(2) Chip preheating and air removal,
(3) Chip and liquor feeding,
(4) Impregnation of chips with liquor,
(5) Heating to cooking temperature,
(6) Retention at cooking temperature,
(7) Quenching and washing the cooked chips,
(8) Cooling and blowing the cooked chips to the blow tank.

The wood chips are fed from a small overhead surge bin through a chip meter and a rotary low-pressure feeder into a steaming vessel. The meter and feeder have oversized pockets to avoid pulp degradation by mechanical damage to the chips.

A slowly turning screw carries the chips through the horizontal steaming vessel to remove entrained air, while limiting the maximum temperature and dwell time to avoid hydrolysis of the cellulose. Flash steam from the digester waste liquor is used, together with make-up steam as required.

The chips are discharged from the steaming vessel into a chip chute connected to the high-pressure feeder. A successful method of feeding the chips continuously into a pressure vessel had been one of the main stumbling blocks in development of a continuous digester. In this feeder the cooking liquor is used to flush the chips from the rotor pocket and to seal the feeder.

The chips and flushing liquor enter the separator on top of the digester shell, where the liquor is screened from the chips and returned to the feeder, while the chips drop into the digester. The chips travel down through the digester at a rate established by the discharge of cooked chips to the blow tank.

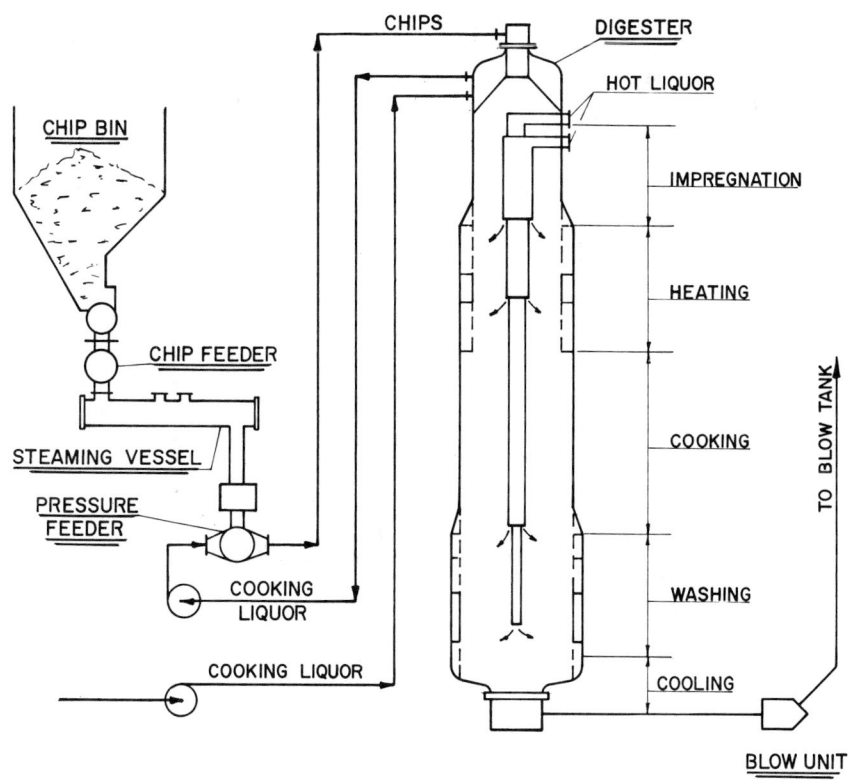

Fig. 7.4. Kamyr continuous kraft digester.

The internal digester pressure is maintained at 165 psi to eliminate flashing and boiling of the liquor between the different temperature zones. This pressure is maintained hydraulically by regulating the flow of cooking liquor entering the top of the digester as well as the black liquor used in the wash and blow sections at the bottom of the digester. The first zone at the top of the digester is sized to allow the chips to impregnate in the 240°F cooking liquor about 45 minutes.

The next zone below this is the cooking section, where the temperature is raised to 330°F in several steps, using indirect steam-heated circulating systems.

Once the mass is up to temperature, the third zone provides sufficient time for the descending column of chips and liquor to react. The retention in this zone is designed to suit the type of sulfate pulp being made. The cooking liquor temperature and strength are adjusted to meet variations in production rates.

The first Kamyr digesters discharged the cooked chips directly from the cooking zone to the blow tank. It was soon discovered that the mechanical action of the scraper used to move the chips to the discharge valve was seriously affecting the fibers at the high temperatures of the liquor in this area. The first attempts to reduce this damage were to flush the chips out of the bottom of the digester with cooler black liquor, while also reducing the mechanical action of the bottom scraper on the chips. Subsequent modifications to introduce larger quantities of cool liquor indicated that considerable lignin could be washed from the pulp by diffusion at the digester pressure and temperatures. Thus, the more recent continuous digesters have been increased in height to allow an additional retention time of about 1½ hours for washing by diffusion.

Washing is accomplished by pumping weak black liquor at 180°F (first brown stock vacuum washer filtrate) into the digester about 6 feet from the bottom. Two strainers are located near the top of the washing zone of the digesters, so that the wash liquor will flow upward, countercurrent to the chip flow. Even distribution of the wash liquor through the chips is maintained by a third extraction plate near the bottom of the digester. The flow here is controlled by a circulating pump that also injects the weak black liquor from the cold blow pump.

The hottest spent liquor from the top extractor plate in the wash zone is removed under flow control to a flash tank, the flashed steam being used to preheat the chips in the steaming vessel. The black liquor from the second extractor plate goes to a lower pressure flash tank, since the liquor from this point is first used to preheat the weak black liquor for washing.

Following the wash zone, cool wash liquor is introduced through the scraper arms at the digester outlet, reducing the temperature of the chip mass to about 200°F before blowing to the blow tank. This temperature has proved low enough to eliminate most of the pulp degradation formerly experienced.

The blow unit for regulating the rate of chip discharge from the digester consists of a small pressure vessel with a variable orifice valve that is kept from plugging by a rotating wiper.

Digester Relief and Turpentine Recovery

It is essential that the non-condensable gases be relieved from the batch digester during the period that the cook is coming up to temperature. A large surface area, heavy-duty strainer is located in the top neck of the digester, to allow these gases to escape while restraining the wood chips and pulp fibers.

The digester relief flow is regulated to avoid excessive steam losses once the digester is up to pressure, and to minimize the tendency for the liquor in the digester to foam and carry over with the relief gases. The flow of the relief gases is automatically controlled by several means. One method is to meter and limit the flow to a preset amount once the digester reaches a preset pressure. The use of steam to backflush and clean the strainer in the neck of the digester is frequently tied in to the relief flow control system (see Figure 7.5).

A cyclone is used to remove any liquor carried over, and the vapors are then condensed in a heat exchanger to remove the turpentine and steam. The non-condensable gases are vented to atmosphere or are treated to minimize air pollution. The mixture of turpentine and steam condensate flow by gravity from the condenser to a decanter, where the turpentine floats to the surface of the water and is skimmed off. The steam condensate is usually sewered.

Southern pine wood is rich in turpentine, and yields as high as four gallons of crude turpentine per ton of pulp have been experienced. The yield will depend on the wood species, the season and growing conditions of the species, the length of time the wood has been cut, and the turpentine recovery system used.

The crude turpentine contains small amounts of mercaptans as well as a mixture of other materials carried over with the digester relief gases. These can be removed by further purification, such as fractional steam distillation. In most cases the crude turpentine is sold to chemical processing plants that have developed markets for the purified products.

It is essential that all traces of black liquor carry-over be removed from the relief gases before the condenser, to minimize the possibility of emulsifying the turpentine in the steam condensate. For this reason, sight glasses are frequently mounted in the digester relief lines for the operator to check visually for black liquor entrainment. In

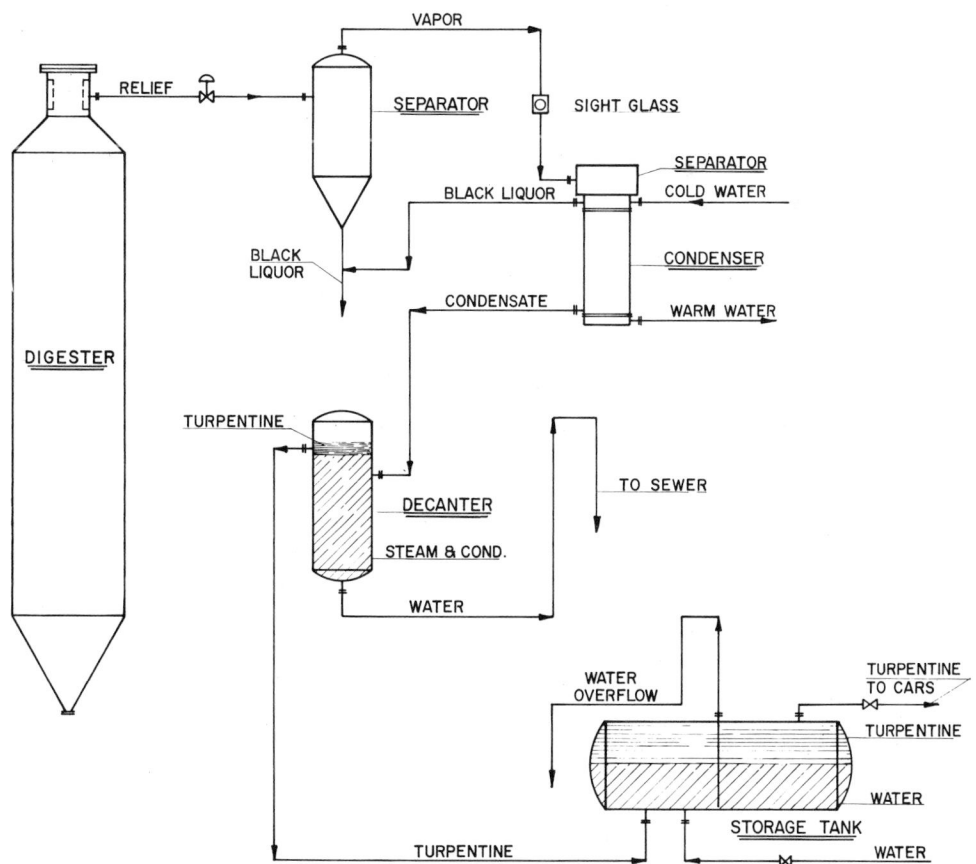

Fig. 7.5. Turpentine recovery in kraft cooking.

addition to this, individual cyclones are located in each digester relief line, and a second black liquor separator may be mounted immediately ahead of the condenser.

The turpentine is usually stored in a closed tank, which is filled by displacing water through the bottom as turpentine enters the tank. This in effect provides a second decanter. It also minimizes the explosion hazard of storing turpentine by elimination of a vapor phase in the storage tank.

Blow Tank

The digester is discharged to a blow tank at the end of the cooking cycle (see Figure 7.6). This tank is a closed steel vessel capable of holding several cooks, thus acting as a transfer point from batch cooking to continuous operation. The top section is baffled to minimize carry-over of pulp and liquor with the flashed steam that is evolved to the heat recovery system during the blow. A motor-driven vertical agitator is mounted in the conical bottom, and black liquor from the first brown stock washer filtrate is used to dilute the stock in this section to $3\frac{1}{2}$ to 4% consistency. The diluted stock is pumped from the blow tank to the brown stock washers. This same sequence of events takes place with either batch or continuous digesters, although the blow tank is smaller in the latter case.

The blow tank is a low-pressure vessel. It is equipped with vacuum and pressure relief valves, as well as a safety rupture disk. The greatest potential hazard is submitting the blow tank to digester pressure during a blow, should the flash steam outlet become plugged with pulp. The steam during a blow is piped to a condenser for heat recovery. The condensation of this steam is

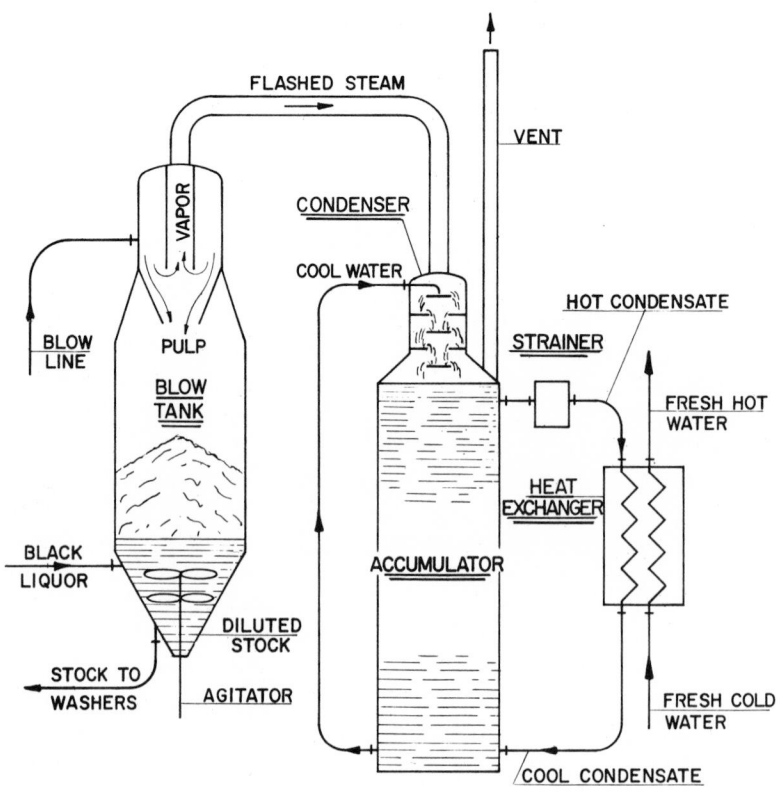

Fig. 7.6. Blow tank and heat recovery system.

sufficient to create a vacuum in the blow tank, which has been known to collapse the vessel under adverse conditions.

The pulp is normally diluted in two stages as it moves from the blow tank to the washer: to 3½ to 4½% consistency in the bottom section of the blow tank for pumping, refining and de-knotting the stock, followed by further dilution to 1% consistency at the washer headbox for good sheet formation on the cylinder mold. The amount of dilution in the first stage is regulated by the motor load on the vertical agitator mounted in the bottom section of the blow tank. The power requirements for a propeller-type agitator increase quite rapidly as the pulp consistency rises above 3%, and this serves as a convenient and effective means of indirectly measuring the dilution.

Efficient washing of the cooked pulp demands a uniform flow of pulp to the washers. This can be accomplished in several ways. A magnetic flowmeter is used to measure the flow of stock after the consistency has been regulated, and the pulp flow is then controlled either by varying the speed of the stock pump or by a control valve in the pipe line to the washers. The former is preferred, especially on high-yield pulps, for the partially softened chips can plug a throttled control valve.

Blow Heat Recovery

The recovery of more than two million Btu per ton of the pulp is the predominant reason for installing a blow heat recovery system for batch digesters. This heat is released as steam when the cook at 350°F is reduced from about 100 psi in the batch digester to atmospheric pressure in the blow tank. The evolution of large quantities of steam from the mixture of pulp and black liquor normally causes carry-over. The design of the blow tank is arranged to reduce this carry-over as much as possible by baffling and by a large vapor space at the top of the tank for minimum steam velocity. Another method of reducing the liquor and

pulp carry-over is to install a cyclone at the blow tank steam outlet.

The use of the blow steam will vary, depending upon the over-all heat balance in any particular mill. The most common use is for heating wash water used at the brown stock washers and the bleach plant. Continuous digesters normally preheat fresh cooking liquor with the spent cooking liquor, then use the flash steam from this cooled black liquor to preheat the chips entering the digester.

The non-condensable gases from the digester relief and blow contribute to the air pollution from a sulfate mill. Part of these gases can be dissolved in water when a direct contact shower is used to condense the blow steam. The remaining obnoxious gases can be disposed of by combustion, by a black liquor oxidation system or by treatment with waste bleach liquor.

The blow steam can be condensed in either a direct or an indirect condenser. The latter is more expensive to install but does give clean hot water. Other disadvantages are: fouling of the heat exchanger tubes with pulp on the outside and scale on the inside; low heat recovery, since the condensate is not cooled below 212°F; and variation in the flow of cooling water needed to condense the blow steam.

The direct-contact condenser has been most popular, as it is cheap to install, easy to operate and maintain, relatively flexible in loading, and does dissolve some of the evil-smelling gases that would normally escape to the atmosphere. The principal disadvantage is the resultant contamination of the water used to condense the blow steam (see Figure 7.6). A supply of clean hot water can be obtained from the direct-contact condenser by collecting it from the top of the accumulator by means of a heat exchanger. Clean water is thus heated, and the cooled dirty water is returned to the bottom of the accumulator. The hot dirty water accumulated during the blow is gradually cooled by the clean water between blows. The cooled dirty water from the bottom of the accumulator is used to condense the subsequent blow steam, reheating the dirty water in the accumulator once more. A strainer is located ahead of the dirty water inlet to the heat exchangers to avoid fouling the heating surfaces with pulp fibers carried over from the blow tank during the blow.

The use of heat exchangers on the water rather than an indirect condenser on the blow steam results in a considerable reduction in cost, since the former can be much smaller due to the longer time available to transfer the heat, together with considerably reduced heat exchanger peak load requirements by the use of the dirty hot water.

Some unbleached pulp mills omit the installation of heat exchangers, using the dirty hot water to wash the pulp on the brown stock washers. The cool water make-up to the accumulator frequently consists of white water from the screen room, so that the deckers are thus operated as an additional stage of countercurrent brown stock washing, minimizing raw water usage as well as stream pollution.

The blow heat is normally sufficient to meet the brown stock wash water requirements. Additional heat can be obtained from live steam and the digester relief gases.

Knotters

The knotter screens are located over the entrance or headbox to the first washer, so that the screened pulp can flow by gravity to the washers. This distance is kept at a minimum to abate the foam generated by cascading black liquor. The undefibered chips are removed by the knotter screens at this point, since they would accumulate in the bottom sections of the washer headbox and vat, eventually plugging off the flow of stock. The rejects from the screens are recirculated to the digesters to be recooked, or are reduced in size in a refiner and recirculated to the blow tank until small enough to be accepted through the screen.

The knotters are open-type vibrating screens, which generate a considerable amount of foam. For this reason effort has been spent to develop a screen that would minimize this tendency, since the foam seriously impairs pulp washing by restricting the rate at which the black liquor drains through the sheet on the cylinder mold. Vast improvement in screen and refiner designs has resulted in several methods of utilizing this equipment in a closed system under pressure so that relatively no foaming is experienced during transfer of the stock from the blow tank to the washer headbox. For soft pulps, uniform sized chips to the digester and uniform cooking have resulted in elimination of knotters ahead of the washers. However, installation ahead of the washers of a refiner set to reduce the occasional partially cooked chips to the maximum allowable size (about $5/16$-inch diameter) effectively eliminates any foam to the washers. It also avoids the need of recirculating partially cooked chips to the digesters, which aggravates the digester operation due to the non-uniformity of screen rejects in moisture content and size compared to fresh wood chips.

High or medium yield pulps require screening ahead of the washers due to the higher ratio of undefibered or partially softened chips in the stock from the blow tank. In this case several types of screens have now been developed that operate under pressure so that foaming can be effectively reduced. Several recent installations have successfully replaced the fine screens normally located after the pulp has been washed, thus performing all the stock screening ahead of the washers. The screen rejects are refined in hot black liquor and recirculated to the blow tank. For high-yield pulps, a refiner is used ahead of the screens also, to partially disintegrate the larger chips that would interfere with the screen operation.

Tramp iron, stones and other foreign material in the stock can result in serious damage to the screens and refiners. The use of magnets and traps are helpful, but have not proved to be reliable, primarily because the stock is too thick to separate out small foreign material.

Brown Stock Washers

The cooked pulp from the digesters is filtered and washed with water to remove the black liquor that would contaminate the end product made from pulp, and to recover the maximum amount of spent cooking chemicals with minimum dilution both as a matter of economy and to minimize stream pollution. Filtering and washing of brown stock was formerly performed in a false-bottom tank or diffuser into which the digester was discharged. The black liquor was drained through this false bottom, and the pulp washed by gravity displacement of the black liquor with wash water. The process was slow and inefficient, tending to dilute the black liquor excessively.

The introduction of the rotary vacuum cylinder in North America has replaced the diffuser described above. Reduced labor and space requirements, greater flexibility in rates of production, together with uniform, continuous, efficient washing have been the principal factors for converting to vacuum washers. The latter are normally operated with two to four washers, in series, depending on the amount of pulp being handled, for maximum washing efficiency. Between 98 and 99% of the spent chemicals are thus washed out of the pulp. The minimum loss of soda is about 15 pounds per ton of pulp, and this soda is so strongly held in the pulp that no reasonable amount of continuous washing will remove it.

The recent introduction of the continuous digester has restored interest in diffusion washing. However, in this case, the washing is continuous, and is performed in the digester at temperatures above 200°F and at operating pressures. Few installations have been made to date, but indications are that the washing efficiency is good, with a higher solids content of the weak black liquor to the evaporators, together with a reduction in the number of vacuum washers required.

The vacuum washer is a wire cloth-covered cylinder which rotates in a vat containing the pulp slurry, the lower section of the drum being submerged in the pulp (see Figure 7.7). By means of internal valving, vacuum is applied as the rotating drum en-

Fig. 7.7. Brown stock washers. (*Courtesy Improved Machinery Inc.*)

ters the pulp slurry. The black liquor drains through the wire cloth, leaving a layer of pulp on the face of the wire, and is held there by the vacuum inside the cylinder. The layer of pulp continues to build up as the submerged portion of the drum rotates through the pulp slurry in the vat. As the cylinder continues to rotate, the thick layer of pulp adhering to the face wire emerges from the slurry. Black liquor continues to drain from the pulp as a result of the differential pressure between the external atmosphere and the vacuum within the cylinder. Showers are located over the pulp sheet to displace the black liquor with water as the drum continues to rotate. Finally, the vacuum is cut off and the washed pulp is removed from the face wire of the drum just before the cycle is repeated.

There is a definite variation in the amount of chemical washed out of the pulp sheet on a vacuum cylinder, because the surface of the sheet where the wash water is applied is cleaner than the pulp adjacent to the wire cloth at the bottom of the pulp sheet; thus the wash water becomes richer in black liquor as it passes through the sheet. To overcome this, the pulp sheet discharged from the first vacuum washer is repulped or reslurried before travelling over the second vacuum filter. This is repeated between each vacuum filter in the washing sequence. The pulp and fresh water flow countercurrent to each other in multistage washing in order to minimize dilution of the black liquor. Thus, the hot water is used to wash the pulp on the last stage washer, and the filtrate or water that was pulled through the pulp sheet by the vacuum on this washer is used to wash the pulp on the preceding washer.

The wash water is heated for maximum solubility of the solids to be removed from the pulp. The upper limit in temperature of the wash water is determined by the vacuum carried on the first washer. Practical limits are 180 to 185°F, since higher temperatures will result in too high an evolution of steam from the black liquor, thus reducing the vacuum and, hence, the drain-

age of black liquor through the pulp sheet on the first washer. Figure 7.7a shows a brown stock washing system.

The wash water applied to the pulp sheet on the washer is kept at a low velocity by using multiple showers for two reasons: (1) to provide good distribution of the wash water over the pulp sheet without disturbing the sheet formation, and (2) to minimize the generation of foam on the first two stages of washing where the black liquor concentration of the wash water is higher. The foam has an adverse effect on washing efficiency, for the small bubbles not only impede the passage of wash showers through the pulp sheet, but also result in a greater carry-over of solids to the subsequent washer. Chemical agents are used to reduce the foam on some washers when they are operated beyond design capacity.

The filtrate leaves the washer through the hollow pipe axis of the cylinder, which also serves as the trunnion on which the cylinder rotates. This outlet is connected to a dropleg that discharges to the filtrate tank. The latter is of such size as to allow the entrained air to escape from the filtrate before pumping the latter back to the repulping stage and the preceding washer showers. The liquid level is kept at the halfway mark in the filtrate tank to allow ample room for the foam to separate from the liquor. Large pipe connections are made between the filtrate tanks at the foam-liquor interface to a central foam tower equipped with foam breakers; the black liquor and heavy soap are separated in the lower section of this tower. (Figure 7.7a.)

The most concentrated black liquor filtrate is transferred to the evaporators. This is the first filtrate in the case of the batch digester. Where diffusion washing is practical in continuous digesters, the first filtrate is used in the digester for washing before being pumped to the evaporators.

The weak black liquor will contain varying amounts of fiber, depending upon the condition of the face wires on the vacuum filters or the strainers in the continuous di-

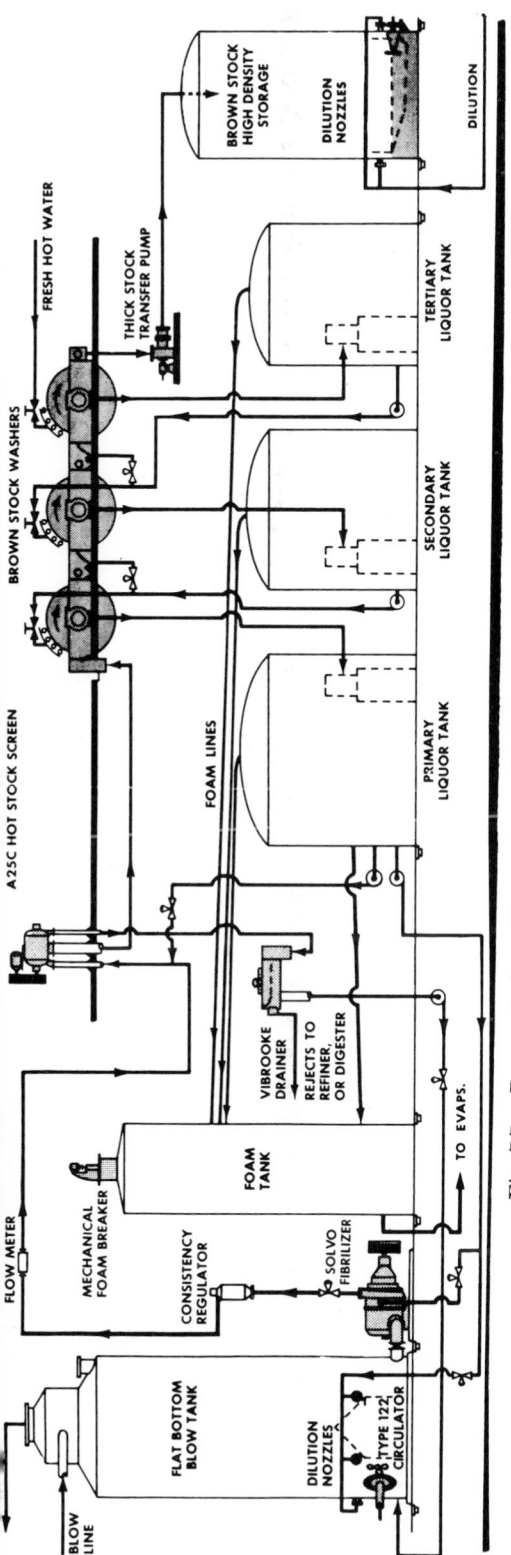

Fig. 7.7a. Brown stock washing system. (*Courtesy Improved Machinery Inc.*)

gester. This pulp will have a cumulative adverse effect on the black liquor evaporators, where it tends to accumulate and reduce the heating capacity. For this reason a black liquor filter is frequently used to minimize the amount of fiber going to the evaporators or black liquor oxidation tower.

The washed pulp discharged from the last stage washer is usually put in a surge tank to take care of minor changes in production rates between the washers and the subsequent operations. Storing the washed pulp at this point is common practice since the vacuum cylinder discharges the pulp at a relatively high consistency, so that a proportionately greater amount of pulp can be stored in a tank of a given size.

Screening

Sulfate pulp from the digesters contains incompletely cooked chips together with other foreign matter that enters the system, such as bolts, stones, sand, etc. To produce a top quality pulp, as well as to protect subsequent equipment, such material must be separated from the pulp. This is normally accomplished by using a perforated screen to remove the oversized material, the pulp being in a dilute solution so that it will pass through the perforations easily; or the foreign material can be removed from the pulp by centrifugal cleaners. The process of screening and cleaning the pulp usually takes place at a relatively low consistency (percentage by weight of pulp in liquid) in order to more readily separate the contamination from the pulp. This in turn means that the excess liquid must be removed after screening to avoid storing and pumping large quantities of liquid with the pulp.

As the oversized fibers and incompletely cooked chips are too expensive to waste, methods have been developed to reduce this material mechanically to acceptable size. Means of disposal are to recook the chips, burn them with the bark in the furnace, or use the screen rejects in some other product, such as hardboard.

The uncooked chips in the pulp from the digesters will vary in size and quantity. Thus, a cook made for a bleaching grade of pulp will contain very little uncooked wood that will be rejected by a screen with $5/16$-inch diameter perforations. However, a high-yield cook for unbleached liner board might reject as much as 30% on this screen. For this reason the equipment used will vary depending on the end use of the pulp. Thus, for well-cooked pulps that are to be bleached, the rejects are normally removed before the brown stock washers, and are either recirculated to the digesters or disposed of. High-yield pulps are mechanically refined before screening, and the screen rejects are either recirculated to the digester to be cooked again, or redirected to the blow tank for another pass through the refiners.

In all cases an effort is made to limit the maximum size of partially cooked chips going to the brown stock washers, since large particles will lower the washing efficiency and tend to plug the vat under the washer drum.

The *knotter* is usually a vibrating screen plate, that is formed or inclined so that the first section in which the stock enters is partially submerged in black liquor. The vibration of the screen keeps the perforations from plugging by agitating the liquor around the holes. The rejected material is pushed up to the dry section of the screen plate by the incoming stock, and black liquor showers are used to wash the remaining fibers off the oversized material. The latter drops off the end of the screen and is carried back to either the digesters or the blow tank. The accepted fiber and black liquor flow through the screen to the brown stock washers.

Several mills producing a bleached grade of pulp have eliminated the knotters by: (1) screening all chips to the digester to remove oversized pieces that would result in an incompletely cooked chip, and (2) installing refiners between the blow tank and the brown stock washers to break any over-sized uncooked chip that might come from the digester.

Thus, the screening after washing must reject all the oversize fibers or fiber bundles normally removed at the knotters. This is done in centrifugal screens, and their rejects are recirculated in a closed system through a disk refiner and a secondary fine screen until the fiber bundles are disintegrated. The accepted stock from this screen is centrifugally cleaned before proceeding to the primary fine screens, following which the stock is again centrifugally cleaned (see Figure 7.8). The fine screening of sulfate pulp on centrifugal screens is accomplished through holes varying from 0.090-inch diameter for soft pulps to 0.110-inch diameter for high-yield pulps.

The rejects from the fine screen represent as much as 25% of the feed. The majority of these rejects will be acceptable pulp fibers, but in order to prevent some of the objectionable material from being washed through the perforations in the primary screen, the rejects from the primary screen are rescreened on a plate with smaller perforations. This represents a balance between the reduced capacity of using more primary screens with smaller perforations and screening more rejects on the secondary screen.

The accepted pulp from the secondary screen contains more dirt than the accepted pulp from the primary screens. This is because screening works on a percentage basis, i.e., the more dirt present in the screen feed, the greater the amount that will be accepted. This is particularly true since the screen perforations are many times larger than the diameter of the pulp fibers.

As previously mentioned, another method of removing the dirt in the size range of the pulp fibers is by use of centrifugal cleaners. The pulp is pumped at a consistency of $\frac{1}{2}$ to $\frac{3}{4}$% through small cyclones in which the stock spins at high velocities. The higher-density material gyrates to the bottom of the cone and is discharged relatively free

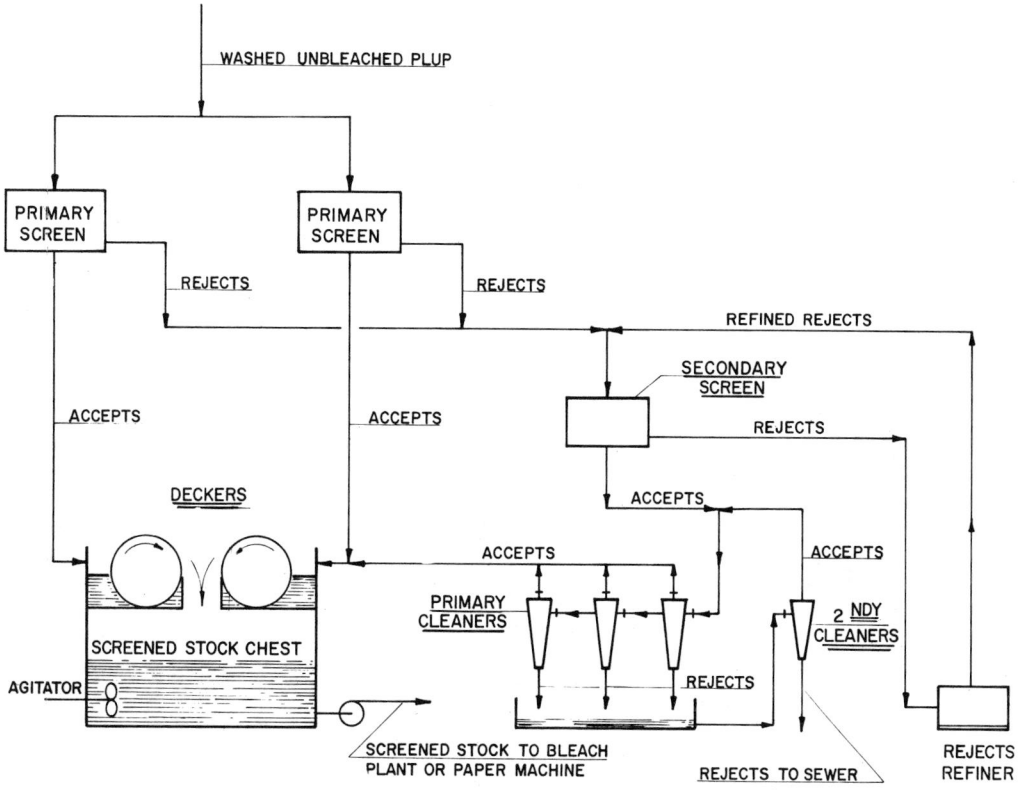

Fig. 7.8. Kraft pulp screening system.

of pulp fibers, while the stock moves towards the center of the upper part of the cone free of the foreign material.

The shape and size of these cleaners have been modified to create so fine a separation that most of the unseparated fiber bundles can be classified from the individual fibers in the stock.

Black Liquor Oxidation

The more volatile sulfur compounds formed in the sulfate process of cooking and liquor recovery are likely to escape to the atmosphere. The principal points of loss are digester relief, blow tank vent, evaporator condenser vent, and recovery furnace stack. Oxidation of the weak black liquor by exposure to air results in reduction of chemical loss and of the odor normally associated with a sulfate mill. The mercaptans and other sulfur compounds are oxidized into less volatile chemicals by treating the hot, weak black liquor from the brown stock washers with air. Relatively large black liquor surface area is required to have effective exposure to the air for oxidation. This is best accomplished in a tower filled with a large number of plates over which the black liquor is circulated countercurrent to an updraft of air. Another effect of black liquor oxidation in reducing sulfur loss is to raise the sulfidity of the white liquor. This can amount to several points, depending on the reduction in losses.

The method in which the recovery furnace is operated can nullify the benefits of black liquor oxidation. Too little secondary air in the furnace results in incomplete combustion of the volatiles, such as hydrogen sulfide, which then escape to the atmosphere. This is particularly true of an overloaded recovery furnace, where sufficient air fan capacity is not available, or where the secondary air has been reduced to avoid smelting slag on the boiler tubes.

The foamy nature of black liquor from southern pine has so far made the above method impractical. Black liquor oxidation has had best results in western United States and Canada where foam is not as great a problem. Studies are under way by various manufacturers and several testing organizations to overcome the foaming problem in southern mills. Moderate success has been achieved by bubbling compressed air from a network of pipes located in the bottom of a concentrated black liquor storage tank. This does not prevent the losses normally associated with the digesters nor the evaporators.

Location of the weak black liquor oxidation tower near the digesters means that some of the losses from the digester relief system and blow tank vent can be diminished by piping these gases with the air supply to the oxidation tower. This works quite well with a continuous digester, but recovery of the blow gases from a batch digester is more difficult in view of the large variations in gas flow that must be accommodated. Gas holders are in use in several plants for this purpose.

Although the usual point for installation of an oxidation system is following the brown stock washers, some mills are oxidizing the black liquor at the point in the multiple-effect evaporator system where the liquor is withdrawn for soap removal. This is usually the third or fourth effect.

CHEMICAL RECOVERY SYSTEM

The recovery of chemical in the spent cooking liquor of the kraft process and reconstitution of these chemicals to form fresh cooking liquor is a vital part of the pulping operation in providing maximum recovery of heat and chemical values as well as minimizing release of obnoxious wastes. The weak black liquor from the brown stock washers goes through the following steps:

(1) Concentration in multiple-effect evaporators,

(2) Further concentration in direct-contact evaporators,

(3) Incineration in recovery furnace with addition to salt cake (Na_2SO_4) to make up loss,

(4) Dissolving smelt from furnace in water to form green liquor,

(5) Causticizing of green liquor with lime to form white liquor which, after settling and filtering, is ready for next cooking cycle,

(6) Burning of lime mud to recover lime.

Multiple-effect Evaporators

Multiple-effect evaporators are installed in the liquor cycle between the brown stock washers and the direct contact evaporator; these are necessary to efficiently remove large amounts of water from the liquor so that the recovery boiler may economically produce steam from this liquor.

A multiple-effect evaporator is actually a series of evaporators arranged so that the vapor generated from one evaporator body becomes a steam supply to the next evaporator in series. The main advantage of the multiple-effect system is the efficiency with which it evaporates the water per pound of steam supplied. On an average, the multiple-effect evaporators installed in most mills will remove between 4 to 4.5 pounds of water per pound of steam.

The multiple-effect evaporators are supplied black liquor at between 12 to 18% solids and concentrate the liquor to between 40 and 55% solids. Most mills have multiple-effect evaporator systems using five to seven effects, the first two effects being contained in one evaporator body. Most evaporator systems are of the long tube, vertical type. The liquor is normally fed into one end of the system and the steam admitted at the other end to provide a counterflow arrangement. The final effect is usually under a vacuum in the vapor space which is maintained by a condenser. Normally, steam is supplied at 40 to 60 psi.

The liquor discharges from multiple-effect evaporators at an average of 45 to 55% solids and is concentrated in a direct-contact evaporator to between 62 and 70%. Because of dilution of heating steam in the burner lines, it is fired at approximately 1½ to 2% lower concentration than it is discharged from the direct-contact evaporator.

Direct Contact Evaporator

Recovery of the maximum amount of heat from combustion of the black liquor in the recovery furnace is of prime importance. The hot combustion gases leaving the boiler tube section of the furnace are too low in temperature for economical generation of steam relative to the boiler tube surface area required, so the heat at this point is usually extracted by preheating the feedwater to the boiler or the air used to support combustion of the black liquor in the furnace. The heat in the flue gas from the feedwater heater (economizer) or air heater is used to evaporate still more water from the black liquor by direct contact with the flue gas. The three types of equipment normally used are: (1) cyclone evaporator (Figure 7.9), (2) cascade evaporator, and (3) Venturi scrubber.

Direct-contact evaporation is used to further concentrate the black liquor from the multiple-effect evaporators. The liquor and gas are brought into intimate physical contact, resulting in a transfer of water from the black liquor to the gas and a reduction in the gas temperature.

The surface area of the black liquor must be extended to provide the desired heat transfer from the flue gas. If the black liquor is splashed or sprayed on hot metal, the volume must be sufficient for continuous washing. The black liquor must be agitated to prevent over-concentration, for the upper limits of solubility of the solids are being approached, which could result in a sludge that would plug the liquor-handling equipment. The flue gas velocity and flow pattern in the direct-contact evaporator must

be such that liquor entrainment in the gas exit is minimized.

Cascade Evaporator

A cascade evaporator consists of wheels that are partially submerged in a vat of black liquor, so that as they rotate they alternately dip into the liquor and emerge to present a wetted surface to the flue gas stream flowing through the wheel above the liquor level. The wheels are made of two circular side plates connected by tubes to provide an extended surface. The wheels are arranged in varying parallel and series configurations, depending upon the conditions of the flue gas and the quantity of water to be evaporated from the black liquor with each installation. The liquor is agitated by the paddle-wheel action of the rotating banks of tubes in the wheels. The concentrated black liquor is screened at the evaporator outlet to remove any solids that were caused by over-drying.

Cyclone Evaporator

The cyclone evaporator (Figure 7.9) is a vertical cylindrical vessel with a conical bottom. The flue gas enters tangentially near the bottom, and flows in a helical patch to the top, where it leaves through a baffled outlet. Black liquor from the evaporators is sprayed across the flue gas inlet, where the liquor droplets mix with gas and are then thrown by centrifugal force to the tank wall. Sufficient liquor from the bottom of the evaporator is recirculated to a ring of nozzles at the top of the vessel to keep the interior wall wet and to prevent localized drying on this surface. The evaporation or temperature drop of the flue gas is controlled by adjusting the quantity of spray liquor at the gas inlet.

Venturi Scrubber

This device serves the dual purpose of concentrating the black liquor by evaporation and collecting the fumes from the flue gas. The Venturi scrubber depends upon the collision of fume particles with liquid droplets, and in addition, serves to absorb heat from the flue gas to evaporate the black liquor. The flue gas is accelerated by a gradual restriction in the gas duct, and the black liquor is injected through steam atomizing nozzles at the point just before the duct tapers back to its original size. The black liquor is atomized by the steam and

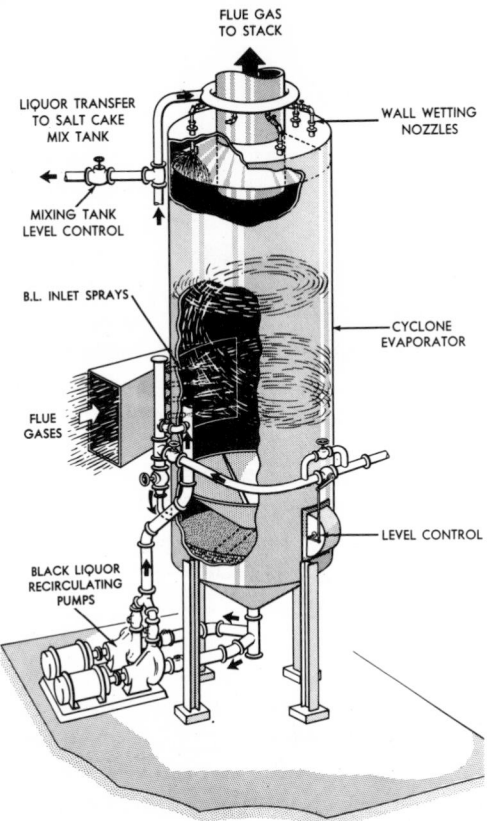

Fig. 7.9. Cyclone evaporator. (*Courtesy Babcock and Wilcox Co.*)

high-velocity flue gas, resulting in intimate mixing. The fume or dust particles collide with and adhere to the droplets, and the latter with their fume particles are centrifugally removed from the gas. Part of the concentrated liquor is recirculated to the nozzles to control the amount of evaporation. Fume collection efficiencies of 90 to 95% are continuously maintained, and a higher thermal efficiency is achieved since the outlet gas temperature can be reduced about

120°F lower than that permissible with an electrostatic precipitator to collect the fume. Offsetting this is the greater induced draft fan power required to obtain the high flue gas velocity through the throat where the black liquor is atomized.

Electrostatic Precipitator

An appreciable quantity of sodium is evaporated in the furnace in the form of salts. As the combustion gases cool, the sodium salts condense to a finely divided solid that is carried by the gas stream as a fume. Most of this fume is reclaimed from the heating surfaces of the recovery boiler and on the wetted surfaces of the direct-contact evaporator. The remainder, consisting of the smallest particles of sodium salts, not only would represent a costly chemical loss which must be replaced, but would also be a nuisance as an air pollutant, if allowed to escape with the flue gas. Many sulfate pulp mills are not collecting this fume from the flue gas with either an electrostatic precipitator or a Venturi scrubber.

The electrostatic precipitator operates on a principle that a particle, suspended in a gas subjected to a sufficiently strong electrostatic field, becomes charged electrically and travels toward an oppositely charged collection electrode to which it will adhere. The collection electrode is shaken periodically to remove the particles, which drop into a hopper below. The precipitator will remove from 85 to 95% of the fume. To energize the precipitator, between 50,000 and 100,000 volts are used. The voltage must be low enough to avoid sparking between the discharging and collecting electrodes. Care must be taken to see that the flue gas temperature entering the precipitator does not get low enough to cause moisture to condense on the electrodes, which would result in fouling and rapid corrosion.

Recovery Furnace (Figure 7.10)

The functions, objectives and requirements of the black liquor recovery furnace and its auxiliaries may be listed as follows:

(1) The black liquor is evaporated and the organic constituents are burned

(2) The ash (inorganic constituents) is recovered in molten form with as little contamination as possible

(3) The ash is heated with a deficiency of air to reduce the sodium sulfate to sodium sulfide

(4) The furnace floor must be tight to avoid leakage of the molten smelt except to the dissolving tank

(5) The combustion gases and fuel bed temperatures should be kept as low as practical to minimize fouling the heat-absorbing surfaces and loss of sodium to the flue gases by evaporation as a fume

(6) Gas velocities in the furnace should be kept low in the furnace bed and liquor spray zones to minimize chemical and fuel losses through entrainment as well as fouling of the heat-absorbing surfaces

(7) Water-cooled furnace walls and widely spaced slag screen tubes must have adequate surface to absorb sufficient heat from the furnace gas in the combustion area to reduce the temperature of the entrained ash, so that the latter will not be "sticky" or partially melted as it enters the closely spaced boiler tube section

(8) Hand lancing of the boiler tubes to keep their surfaces clean of ash deposits should be eliminated by minimizing the amount of carry-over and by arranging the boiler-unit heating surfaces so that automatic soot blowers can keep them clean

(9) The maximum quantity of steam should be generated from combustion of the black liquor; the steam is usually generated at a pressure and temperature sufficiently above that required for the digesters and evaporators that the electrical requirements of the mill may be produced as by-product power in a steam turbine electric generator

(10) The black liquor from the multiple-effect evaporators is concentrated to the feed values desired at the furnace by direct contact evaporation with the hot flue gas

(11) Reliability and ease of control and operation are necessary, for the recovery furnace is an integral part of the sulfate process supplying the cooking liquor, steam and electricity demands.

TABLE 7.2. TYPICAL BLACK LIQUOR FURNACE TEMPERATURE AND VELOCITY DATA.

	MHVT Temp. (°F)	Bare Thermo- couple Temp. (°F)	Velocity (ft/sec)
Furnace	2500	2210	10.0
Entering superheater	1600	1450	9.2
Entering boiler bank	1285	1195	16.0
Leaving boiler	775	765	16.0

In explanation of Table 7.2, a bare thermocouple which is measuring temperatures in a hot gas stream is affected not only by the heat transfer from the gas to the thermocouple junction, but also by radiant heat exchange with the surrounding surfaces. In a boiler or furnace, the bare thermocouple "sees" relatively cool boiler surface so that the loss of heat from the thermocouple junction due to this cold surface results in readings that are lower than the true gas temperature. To overcome this radiation error, it is common practice to use a multiple-shield, high-velocity thermocouple (*MHVT* in Table 7.2) with porcelain radiation shields around the thermocouple junctions. Hot gas is then aspirated over the thermocouple junction at a high velocity to increase the rate of heat transfer by convection. The shields greatly reduce the amount of colder boiler surface which the thermocouple sees. In this method, the radiation error is greatly decreased and the reading of the thermocouple caused to approach the true gas temperature.

Spray Nozzle

The concentrated black liquor from the direct-contact evaporator has the make-up salt cake added, then is heated and the mixture sprayed onto the furnace walls. The liquor dries and falls to the char bed in the bottom of the furnace. The spray is controlled to cover a greater or smaller area

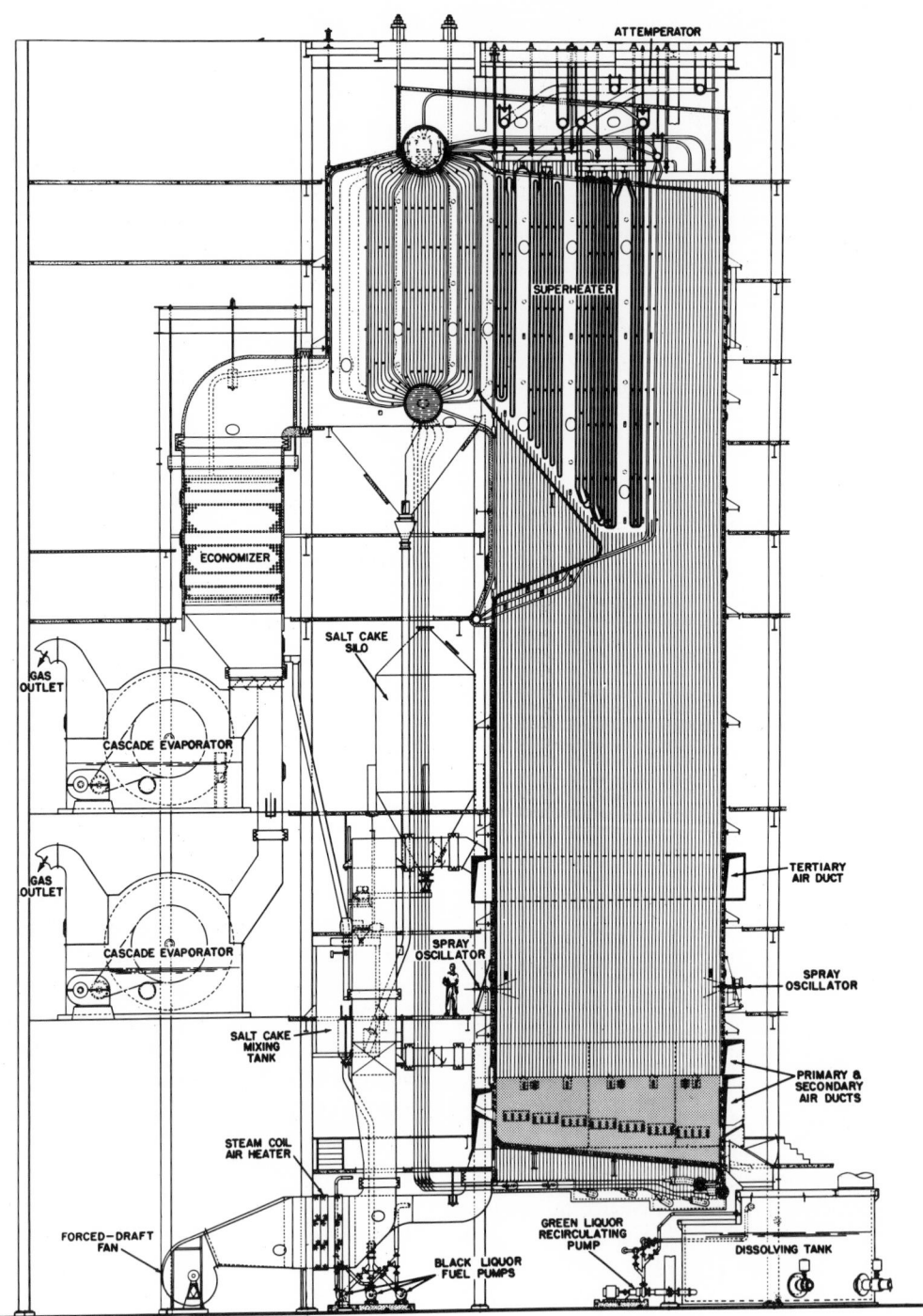

Fig. 7.10. Black liquor recovery unit. (*Courtesy Babcock and Wilcox Co.*)

of wall surface to compensate for the variations in concentration and quantity of black liquor handled.

Floor and Wall Construction

The lower part of the furnace is actually a chemical retort. Incomplete combustion of the char in the porous bed at the bottom of the furnace supplies carbon monoxide and incandescent carbon, which act as reducing agents to convert the sodium sulfate to sodium sulfide. The heat is sufficient to melt the sodium salts, which filter through the char to the floor of the furnace and flow by gravity from the furnace through the smelt spout to the dissolving tank.

The floor and walls of the furnace in this section consist of closely spaced water tubes. Those in the floor have metal fins or studs covered with plastic chrome-ore. This protects the tubes from wear and corrosion of the smelt flowing from the char bed to the smelt spout. The positive cooling of the studs provides the necessary medium to freeze the smelt and prevents leakage through the furnace floor. However, as a further precaution, a steel membrane is seal welded between the tubes to form a water tight floor.

The construction of the walls in the retort zone is similar to that used on the floor. The furnace walls above this zone consist of bare tubes, the area between the tubes being closed by flat studs. This is a fully water-cooled steel surface of the furnace and it is on this surface, at about the center third of the furnace height, that the black liquor from the spray is deposited.

Combustion Air

Air is admitted to the furnace through three sets of air ports, designated from the hearth or bottom of the furnace upward as primary, secondary and tertiary air. The primary air ports are located a few feet above the hearth and extend around the four walls of the furnace to provide as low a velocity as practical, while supplying about 60% of the air requirements. The secondary air ports are just over the char bed, and the tertiary air ports are in opposite walls just above the upper limit of the black liquor spray zone. The high-pressure air from the secondary ports allows complete penetration across the furnace to assure mixing with the combustible gases rising from the char bed. The combustion at the secondary level creates a high-temperature zone below the black liquor spray that aids in drying the liquor in flight from the spray nozzle to the furnace walls. The secondary air also effectively limits the depth of the char bed by providing heat and turbulence across the top of the bed. The tertiary air assures complete mixing and combustion of any unburned gases rising from the secondary air zone or any volatiles driven from the black liquor as it evaporates. Above the tertiary air zone sufficient gas travel is provided in the water-cooled furnace to cool the gases and entrain solids enough to permit removal of ash and fume from the heating surfaces by soot blowers. This temperature is about 1,450°F.

The steam-generating section of the boiler is protected from the high radiant heat in the combustion chamber of the furnace to prevent the ash and fume from slagging or fusing on the tubes. Thus, the hot gases are deflected by a nose baffle that shields the superheater section from the combustion chamber radiant heat, and causes them to enter the screen tube and superheater tube sections at a uniform temperature and velocity.

The screen tube section is made up of widely spaced tubes to reduce the gas temperatures in the zone where the greatest entrained load of ash and fume is encountered. The spacing is so great that it is difficult for the ash to build up and bridge the openings between the tubes.

The gases flow parallel to the superheater tubes, the tube spacing still being kept quite high to avoid plugging with ash. For the same reason, the adjacent elements are staggered. Both the screen and superheater surface arrangements are such that they can be cleaned by soot blowers.

In an attempt to reclaim further heat for use in the mill several mills have installed a low-temperature heat-reclaiming cyclone device to absorb heat from the recovery boiler exhaust gases before discharging to the atmosphere. The principle of these "heat savers" is to spray the gases with large quantities of water to reduce the gas temperatures to approximately 140°F before discharging to the atmosphere. The exhaust gases heat this water for use in other mill process systems. By means of a heat exchanger, the salt cake-contaminated water can be recycled through the boiler gases while fresh mill water is heated to approximately 140°F for use in boiler make-up, brown stock washers, and other miscellaneous points in the mill.

In addition to savings in mill heat requirements, the secondary scrubbing of the flue gases from the boiler in this cyclone further cleans the exhaust gases before discharging to the atmosphere, thereby contributing to the reduction in air contamination.

Capacity of a Recovery Unit

Increasing the amount of liquor completely burned in a given recovery unit will raise the gas temperature in the furnace and entering the screen and superheater sections. The maximum capacity of the furnace has been exceeded when the temperature of the gas entering the screen is so high that the soot blowers cannot keep these tube sections clean, and the gas passages become plugged with ash.

The capacity of a pulp mill is rated in tons of pulp produced in 24 hours. The object of a recovery unit is to reclaim the chemicals used and to generate steam by burning the liquor resulting from this pulp. Thus, the capacity of a recovery unit should be based on its ability to burn completely in 24 hours the dry solids contained in the black liquor from the pulp produced in that time. The capacity of a pulp mill, as well as the amount of organic material available in the black liquor per ton of pulp, will vary. For this reason, the capacity of the recovery furnace must be taken into account not only in reference to the capacity of the pulp mill, but also to the degree of cooking and the type of wood used. The capacity of a recovery unit is properly measured by the heat released in the furnace. Thus, a pulp mill producing 200 tons of pulp in 24 hours where the black liquor contained 3,000 pounds of solids from a ton of pulp at a heating value of 6,600 Btu per pound of solids would yield $(200 \times 3,000 \times 6,600 =)$ 3,960,000,000 Btu per 24 hours. In this example, 19,800,000 Btu are available per ton of pulp made.

Soot Blowing

Prior to 1940, soot blowers were generally ineffective in recovery boilers, and hand lancing was a necessary part of the recovery unit operation in keeping the heating surfaces clean. Even after mechanical soot blowers of improved design became available for cleaning the rear boiler tube passes and the economizer, cleaning of the screen tubes, superheater section and the front boiler passes still required the constant attention of hand lancers. The introduction of automatic sequential operation of the soot blowers, together with improved design to ensure superior cleaning ability, has almost eliminated the need of hand lancing. The soot blowers have been made retractable, so that they can be removed from the hot gas stream when not in operation, thus greatly reducing their maintenance. High-pressure steam has generally supplanted air as a cleaning medium, primarily because of the higher cost and limited availability of the latter.

Another method of cleaning the screen and superheater section of tubes involved the use of steel shot that was directed at the tubes to knock the ash collection off. The shot was collected at the bottom of this section of the furnace and recirculated.

Dissolving Tank

The smelt from the furnace hearth is molten and quite explosive in nature when exposed to water, primarily because the high temperature converts the water to steam so rapidly. The stream of molten smelt discharging from the furnace is broken up by a steam shower and/or a recirculated green liquor stream to disperse the smelt so that it will not explode when it hits the liquor surface in the dissolving tank. The latter is agitated to avoid localized overheating and to maintain uniform concentration of the dissolved smelt. A large vent on the dissolving tank is essential to remove both the steam and gases evolved, hydrogen (explosive) and hydrogen sulfide (poisonous).

A typical green liquor composition would be 20% sodium carbonate and 5% sodium sulfide, by weight, expressed as Na_2O. The density of green liquor is 15 to 20° Baumé, or 1.12 to 1.16 specific gravity.

Causticizing

The green liquor is treated with lime to convert the sodium carbonate to sodium hydroxide, the sodium sulfide remaining unchanged. The resultant solution, after removing the lime sludge, is called white liquor, and is ready for re-use in the digester as cooking liquor after dilution with black liquor.

Causticizing is actually divided into a number of separate functions in addition to the above prime function of converting the carbonate to sodium hydroxide.

(1) Clarification of green liquor to remove foreign material (dregs).

(2) Washing the green liquor dregs, before disposal, to remove entrained sodium salts.

(3) Slaking lime in green liquor.

(4) Removing and washing unreacted material from the green liquor slaker.

(5) Retaining the mixture of lime and green liquor in agitated tanks to allow the reaction to be completed.

(6) Settling out and separating the sludge from the white liquor.

(7) Washing the sludge to remove the entrained white liquor.

(8) Removing excess moisture from the sludge.

(9) Burning the sludge to form reburned lime ready to use in Step 3 above repeated.

The green liquor from the dissolving tank at the recovery furnace is regulated to a uniform concentration by controlling the amount of dilution added. Weak wash water from the causticizing process is used instead of fresh water to minimize dilution of the cooking liquor. The green liquor is clarified to remove the suspended solids, such as unburned carbon, plastic chrome ore and iron compounds. The solids removed by settling are called dregs. They are pumped with some of the green liquor to a washer, where they are washed with water to recover the entrained sodium carbonate and sulfide. The wash water is decanted and used as dilution at the smelt dissolving tank. The washed green liquor dregs are discharged to the sewer. In some cases the dregs are washed several times using countercurrent washing for maximum chemical recovery with a minimum of water.

Slaker

The batch process of causticizing green liquor has been replaced by the continuous method. In so doing, separate equipment has been designed to handle each step of the process more efficiently. The re-burned lime plus any make-up lime is metered into an agitated solution of hot green liquor to convert the quicklime to slaked lime. This reaction will not proceed with sufficient speed unless the temperature of the mixture is between 200 and 215°F. For this reason, steam is used to heat the green liquor feed, and the reburned lime from the kiln is kept as hot as possible to ensure maximum efficiency of reaction. In some recent installations the slaker was placed under the lime kiln discharge, so that red hot lime dropped directly into the green liquor primary slaker instead of being conveyed to a surge bin. Although theoretically this would give a maximum slaking efficiency, in actual practice the discharge of lime from the kiln cannot be regulated well enough to maintain a uniform strength of white liquor. The slaker consists of a cast iron-lined steel tank to resist the abrasion of the lime, with an agitator to ensure good mixing of the lime and green liquor. The green liquor-lime slurry flows by gravity to a grit removing section called a classifier. Here the unreacted particles (grit) settle out to the bottom of the tank and are raked out for disposal after washing.

Causticizers

The overflow of liquor from the classifier flows to a series of agitated tanks with about 1½ hours retention, where the chemical reaction of converting the sodium carbonate to sodium hydroxide takes place. Three to four tanks in series are used to minimize the possibility of the liquor short circuiting. Should the lime sludge continue to settle out of the white liquor after causticizing, a heavy build-up of lime and sodium carbonate would develop in the white liquor lines, pumps and digesters (carryover of lime and carbonate will frequently give the bleached pulp a green coloration that can normally be traced to having used cloudy or unclarified white liquor).

White Liquor Clarifier

The overflow from the last causticizer is transferred to the top and center of a vertical cylindrical tank where sufficient retention time is allowed for the lime sludge to settle out at the bottom and the clear white liquor to overflow at the circumference of the top. A large rake rotates close to the bottom of the tank to scrape the sludge to a central outlet, from which the white liquor mud is pumped to a mud washer.

As many as four settling tanks are integrally built one over the other, to conserve space, with the white liquor feed being equally divided to the different sections of the white liquor clarifier.

The size of the clarifier is dependent on the rate of settling of the lime mud. The following is a list of some of the more important variables affecting the settling rate.

(1) Strength of green liquor used, i.e., concentration of sodium carbonate and sodium sulfide. A high liquor concentration results in poor settling.

(2) Proportion of sodium carbonate and sodium sulfide. Greater amounts of the latter will require less slaking and lime sludge to settle out.

(3) Excess of lime used to the slaker. The causticizing reaction does not go to completion, and a slight excess of lime is added to obtain between 85 and 90% conversion of the carbonate to sodium hydroxide. Use of a large excess of lime will restrict the settling rate.

(4) Temperature of slaking. The temperature should be kept as close to 215°F as possible in the slaker to ensure maximum size crystal growth of the lime sludge in the causticizers for rapid settling in the white liquor clarifier.

(5) The make-up of the lime must be relatively free of silica and iron which form a gelatinous slow settling floc in white liquor that not only makes white liquor clarification difficult, but will also aggravate operation of the lime mud washing and kiln operation.

(6) Carry-over of soap or black liquor into the slaker with the green liquor as a result of poor recovery furnace operation will seriously retard settling. In some cases starch is added to help precipitate the lime mud in the white liquor clarifier.

The white liquor overflow from the clarifier may still contain small amounts of unsettled lime mud, and incompletely reacted lime and sodium carbonate. For this reason, white liquor filters are used to remove the last traces of solids that would contaminate the pulp, particularly serious with dissolving pulp.

White Liquor Mud Washer

In order to pump the lime sludge from the bottom of the white liquor clarifier, some of the white liquor is removed with it. To minimize the loss of white liquor, the mud is washed several times countercurrently with water to minimize the amount of water used. The thick mud from the white liquor clarifier is diluted, then allowed to settle out in a vertical cylindrical tank in the same manner as in the white liquor clarifier. Since the mud will settle out quickly in dilute solution, only half of the tank settling capacity is normally required. However, the mud washer usually consists of four sections, about the same size as the white liquor clarifier, the only difference among them being that the two top trays are operated in parallel as the first wash for the mud and the two bottom trays as the second wash. The washed mud is pumped to the kiln, and the wash water is combined with the wash water from the green liquor dregs to dissolve the smelt from the recovery furnace.

Some mills use the condensate from the black liquor multiple-effect evaporators to wash the mud from the white liquor clarifiers not only to economize on water consumption, but to minimize stream pollution, since this water contains mercaptans and other volatile sulfur compounds. Great care must be exercised to keep black liquor from entering this water, should operation of the evaporators become upset.

The washed mud is metered to a dewatering device before being fed to the lime kiln. This consists of either a continuous rotary vacuum filter or a centrifuge, the water removal being essential to minimize kiln fuel costs.

The vacuum filter has been recently operated with a precoat, the vacuum being left on during the full cycle of the turning cylinder. The cake of mud is washed by dilution in the filter vat and by water showers on the filter cake. The mud is removed by a doctor blade that cuts off the mud cake above the precoat layer. This gives a mud feed to the kiln of 60 to 65% consistency, compared to 55 to 60% when the filter is operated in the normal fashion of breaking the vacuum and blowing the mud cake off at the discharge point.

The centrifuge is a simpler piece of equipment to operate, and is capable of dewatering the mud as high as 70% consistency. Provision is made to wash the mud in the centrifuge. The wash water from the mud filter or centrifuge is used in the mud washer for countercurrent washing.

The greatest strides have been made in regulating the feed of lime mud to the dewatering devices. The first approach was to install an agitated surge tank between the mud wash and the mud filter or centrifuge, using the tank to even out variations in mud density. Introduction of radioisotopes to measure the consistency of the mud has opened the door to automatic dilution control for uniform mud density. The magnetic flowmeter has proven a better means of measuring the flow of mud than orifices or displacement meters that tended to cake or were worn by the mud. A combination of these instruments is being tried to control the density of mud being pumped from the white liquor clarifier for variations in the quantity of white liquor transferred with the mud have a decided effect on the washing efficiency as well as the settling rate in the mud washer (see Chapter 15). This operation is normally hand-controlled.

Kiln

The lime mud is washed to remove the sodium compounds, a maximum of $\frac{1}{4}\%$ being allowable in order to avoid ring and ball formation in the kiln. The kiln itself is a long inclined horizontal cylinder, mounted on rollers, through which the lime flows countercurrent to the heat. The latter is normally an oil or natural gas flame. Three things take place in the kiln:

(1) Drying of the lime mud,
(2) Rise in temperature of the mud, during which it passes through a plastic stage,

(3) The high-temperature zone during which the carbon dioxide is evolved to yield reburned lime or calcium oxide.

The kiln construction is modified to accommodate these varying conditions. At the mud feed end, different means are provided to transfer the heat from the gases to the mud by providing extended surface area; this is alternately heated by the gases and then by the mud as the kiln slowly rotates, the lime tending to remain near the bottom of the kiln. The most common method of providing the extended surface is by means of steel chains attached to the kiln shell and hang in the hot gases. The temperature of the gases entering the chain section must be kept below 1,000°F to avoid softening the metal.

A more recent method that was developed in Scandinavia uses sheet metal fabricated sectors that are made up of several sections, some fixed and others free to rotate but remain essentially fixed longitudinally in the kiln. As with the chain sections, precautions must be taken to avoid overheating the sheet metal and causing deformation or collapse of the sectors.

A third method is to build brick baffles in the lime and drying zone, in a trefoil pattern. Maintaining brick in a rotating kiln can be quite difficult, due to the occasional thermal shock load of cold mud on hot bricks, and the continual flexing of the long steel kiln shell, especially at the trunnions on which the kiln rides.

In the temperature rising section of the kiln following the drying of the mud, a brick lining 4 to 6 inches thick is used, made to withstand moderate temperatures. Wear is not excessive since the lime tends to form a thin film over the face of the brick in this area. As the lime rises in temperature, it goes through a semi-liquid or plastic state. The length of time it remains in this state is dependent on the amount of soda remaining in the lime and any changes that are made in the kiln operation. The plastic lime forms pellets or balls, the size of which will vary with the length of time the lime remains plastic. Under normal conditions the lime forms small pebbles up to one inch in diameter that will occasionally continue to grow in size until they reach the same diameter as the kiln. More frequently, the plastic lime will adhere to the brick and will build up a ring to such dimension that the internal diameter of the kiln is effectively reduced to a fraction of its normal size, thus acting as a dam to the flow of lime and the hot gases.

The high-temperature zone in the kiln where the carbon dioxide is driven from the lime is normally lined with 6-inch thick brick made to withstand temperatures of 2,400°F. Excessive temperatures in the hot zone of the kiln can result in fusion of the brick lining as well as the lime. Fused lime has a glasslike surface on the reburned pebbles that drastically reduces the rate of causticizing. The majority of this overburned lime is rejected to waste by the classifier following the slaker.

The gases leaving the kiln are laden with lime dust. Several methods are used to recover this dust, as well as the heat remaining in the exhaust gases. The most common methods are to use cyclones or baffled spray towers. The hot water containing the dust from these is normally used to wash the mud to the kiln.

Several kilns have been able to handle an increased amount of lime by utilizing the exhaust gases to flash-dry the mud feed before it enters the kiln. By drying the mud outside the kiln, the length of hot zone in the kiln could be extended to handle more lime without adversely affecting the heating efficiency.

The hot lime from the kiln is screened through a "grizzly" to remove large balls of lime or loose brick. The lime is either discharged direct to a primary slaker, as described earlier, or conveyed to a surge bin. The latter forms a very essential function of leveling out the variations in kiln discharge rates and causticizing lime requirements. The bin also serves as a reservoir to empty the kiln when the causticizing is interrupted.

The make-up of lime can be made as burned lime at the causticizer or as limestone at the kiln feed. The choice depends not only on the cost and availability of these materials, but on the capacity of the kiln. It is preferable to use the limestone since hot lime will react better in slaking than cold lime.

The kiln is usually driven by a variable-speed electric motor, to permit changing the length of time the load of lime is in the kiln as the feed rate is changed. It is common practice to install an auxiliary gasoline drive to continue rotating the kiln in event of electrical interruptions, for the kiln will warp out of shape if allowed to cook without rotating. This is especially true of kilns that could be exposed to a heavy rainfall.

The size of a kiln will vary with the pulp mill capacity and efficiency desired. Thus, kilns are made longer to more efficiently utilize the heat, and the diameter is increased to keep the gas velocities low and to increase the surface area of the lime bed in the kiln exposed to the radiant heat. An 11-foot diameter by 250-foot long kiln equipped with a chain section is capable of burning over 150 tons of lime per 24 hours.

In some countries where fuel is expensive, the air used for combustion is preheated by contacting the hot lime from the kiln. This feature has not been adopted to any extent in the United States, where the emphasis has been more on increased production than fuel economy. The heat exchanging equipment is subject to plugging with the large lime balls, and the interruption in production has been a deterrent to their installation.

The gases are pulled through the kiln by the combined effect of an induced draft fan and chimney. The latter is usually quite short, being high enough to dissipate the gases which are fairly corrosive, especially when oil is used as a fuel. The location of the induced draft fan can be either before the water sprays, in which case a larger drive motor and fan are required to handle the hotter gases, or after the gases are saturated with water, in which case some difficulty is experienced with lime depositing on the fan blades and causing an imbalance.

FUTURE DEVELOPMENTS IN ALKALINE PULPING

As with other areas of the pulp and paper industry, technical progress in alkaline pulping follows a course of gradual evolution. Thirty years ago bleached kraft pulp was a novelty, the use of hardwoods for kraft pulp was in its infancy, and the idea of continuous cooking was merely a dream. Today all of these and more are large-scale commercial realities. They have come about by slow and gradual steps. The amount of progress in any one year, viewed from a commercial standpoint, seems small indeed. But over a period of years, technical progress inevitably produces changes which, viewed in retrospect, are truly revolutionary.

There are two very important reasons for the gradualness of change in kraft pulping. First, the size of the capital investment in relation to the value of the product is such that fast write-off and quick changes are met with considerable reluctance. Second, the scale-up from laboratory or pilot plant to full-scale commercial equipment usually involves some unanswered questions and even buried surprises. It is not uncommon for new mills to have "shakedown" periods of months or even years during which "bugs," large and small, are ironed out and operating efficiency and product quality are brought to desirable levels. Recognition of the costly nature of these shakedown periods makes for a conservative approach in trying out innovations.

The kraft industry is a sort of showcase for the characteristic unit operations of chemical engineering. The material and energy balance involved in these operations is decisive in the economy of the process. It is expected that important progress will be made in design and operation of these systems, particularly in the direction of simplification and combination of unit operations.

Just as the industry has been changed dramatically by technical innovations in past years, so will the industry of the future be different from what we know today.

REFERENCES

1. Pulpwood Statistics, New York, U.S. Pulp Producers Association, Inc., 1962.
2. TAPPI Standard O 400, "Standard Terms of the Sulphate Pulping Process," p. 54. New York, Technical Association of the Pulp and Paper Industry.
3. Brainerd, F. W., "University of Maine Lecture on Pulp and Paper Manufacture," Series 2, p. 129, New York, Lockwood, 1953.
4. Marshall, H. B., Brauns, F., and Hibbert, H., *Canadian Journal of Research,* 13B, 103 (1935).
5. Hägglund, E., *Tappi,* 32, No. 6: 241 (1949).
6. Larocque, G. L., and Maass, O., *Canadian Journal of Research,* 19B, 1 (1941).
7. Bixler, L. A. M., *Paper Trade J.,* 107, No. 15, 29 (1938).
8. Mitchell, C. R., and Yorston, F. H., Forest Products Laboratory of Canada, *Quarterly Rev.,* No. 18, 6 (1934).
9. McKinney, J. W., *Paper Trade J.,* 122, No. 4, TS36 (1946).
10. Peckham, J. R., and Van Drunen, V., *Tappi,* 44, No. 5, 374 (May, 1961).

ADDITIONAL REFERENCE

W. F. Holzer, "Alkaline Delignification of Wood," in Jahn and Wise, "Wood Chemistry," Vol. 2, p. 975, New York, Reinhold Publishing Corp., 1952.

CHAPTER 8

Semichemical and Chemimechanical Pulping

J. N. McGovern

Parsons & Whittemore, Inc.

The development of semichemical and chemimechanical processes over the last three or four decades has been primarily for reasons of wood utilization and cost reduction. These processes have led to a desirable increase in hardwood use, sometimes where softwoods were not available and sometimes even to replace them. Naturally, the inherent high yields have resulted in reductions in the wood cost element in pulp manufacturing costs. The hardwood semichemical and chemimechanical pulps have also contributed materially to the advancement of short-fibered pulp technology and certain unique advantages in pulp properties have been realized in the course of the growth of the industry.

Before elaborating on the semichemical processes, it is necessary to define them, since there is no official system of nomenclature in the pulp industry, largely because of the radical changes introduced by these part-chemical and part-mechanical processes. The semichemical and chemimechanical pulping processes are those two-stage processes using (1) chemical energy with and without heat energy and (2) mechanical energy to cause separation of the fibers of lignocellulosic materials. These processes occupy a region between the classical chemical and groundwood processes. Chemimechanical pulping is distinguished from semichemical pulping in current pulping practice by the fact that there is no major change in the lignin of the fiber bond.

The semichemical processes are most readily characterized by their yields of pulp, which are taken at 85 to 95% for chemimechanical pulps and 65 to 85% for the semichemical pulps.

Within the scope of this chapter, there will be presented (1) a brief historical survey, (2) production statistics, (3) a discussion of the fibrous raw materials used, (4) an outline of the processes and their variables, (5) a brief description of the mechanism of the process, (6) a discussion of semichemical operations and equipment, (7) a mention of bleaching and brightening methods, (8) a discussion of pulp properties and uses, (9) a summary of spent liquor handling, (10) a reference to corrosion problems, and (11) an outline of test methods.

HISTORY

The idea of a part chemical and part mechanical pulping process was apparently first mentioned in 1874 by Mitscherlich, one of the originators of the sulfite process, using acid sulfite reagents. The employment of a neutral sodium sulfite solution for pulping in general and the base of the modern NSSC process goes back to Cross and Bevan, the famous cellulose chemists, in 1880. A number of other famous pulping researchers are associated with the early use of sodium sulfite.

The practical development and commercial installation of a true semichemical pulping mill was not realized until 1925 with the start-up of the Southern Extract Company based on experimental work conducted at the Forest Products Laboratory starting in 1921 and reported in the historical patent of Rue, Wells, Rawling and Staidl in 1927.[1] Several other mills followed closely in the next five years. Details of the operations of the earliest mill were given by Durgin and Small in the previous edition of this book.[2]

Several of the first mills used tannin-extracted chestnut chips as a means of utilization of this by-product material and the pulp end usage was corrugating board. This was the chestnut chip board which set the standard for corrugating board in the 1930's. Subsequently, the semichemical pulping industry diversified with production of pulps capable of being bleached and used in printing, writing, and glassine papers. This idea of making high-quality bleached pulps by continuing the removal of the fiber binding material with a multi-step chlorine-extraction-bleaching process was mentioned first by Tracquair and Rawling,[3] and the first bleached semichemical pulp installation was at the Consolidated Water Power and Paper Company in 1948.

The history of semichemical pulping shows a progressive change in the equipment used for the chemical and mechanical stages. The chemical treatment was first done in spherical rotary digesters. This was followed by adaptation of stationary vertical digesters of both the sulfite and sulfate type, and in the last fifteen years or so with continuous digesters of various types.

The fiberizing stage was originally done in the rod mill adapted from the metallurgical industry. This method did not prove satisfactory and was succeeded by the disc attrition mill, which is the preferred means for fiberizing in the modern mill.

The chemimechanical modification of semichemical pulping to produce pulps in the range between groundwood and semichemical pulping is a recent development which is now considered independent of semichemical pulping. The idea of mild treatment of wood chips to soften them and permit their defibering to produce pulps with essentially the same lignin content as the original wood was mentioned as early as 1919.[4] Again, the work leading to the commercial application of this type of chemical-mechanical pulping was conducted at the Forest Products Laboratory starting in 1951 and the first demonstration on a commercial scale was at the Green Bay Pulp & Paper Company in 1954. The first complete operating mill installation was at the Gould Paper Company in 1955. The work at the Forest Products Laboratory and the first commercial applications involved the cold soda chemimechanical process, in which the wood chips were treated at room temperature with caustic soda and then fiberized. More recently chemimechanical pulping has also involved neutral and acid sodium sulfite solutions.

PRODUCTION

As of late 1962, there were in the U.S. approximately 30 semichemical corrugating mills with a daily capacity of 7,500 to 8,000 tons, 8 bleached semichemical mills with a capacity near 900 tons per day, and 8 chemimechanical pulp mills with a daily capacity of about 700 tons for food and other boards and printing papers. The total capacity for semichemical pulping was over 9,000 tons per day.

Elsewhere in the world there is an active and growing industry for semichemical pulping and practically every important wood pulping country has one or more semichemical or chemimechanical pulping installation. Scandinavia, Italy, Japan, and Australia are among the leaders in this field.

The production of semichemical pulps is

now fourth in the U.S. among the major categories, as shown in statistics for 1960 in Table 8.1, amounting to approximately 9% of the total.

TABLE 8.1. PRODUCTION OF PULP IN THE U.S. IN 1961 [5]

Pulp Grade	Production (in 10³ tons)	% of Total
Sulfate	15,422	58.2
Groundwood	3,208	12.1
Sulfite	2,574	9.7
Semichemical and chemimechanical	2,352	8.9
Coarse fiber	1,225	4.6
Dissolving	1,195	4.5
Soda	436	1.6
Screenings	110	.4
Total	26,522	100.0

The pulping industry in the U.S. is plainly dominated by the sulfate or kraft process. It is of interest that the annual semichemical pulp production is now nearly that of sulfite pulp.

FIBROUS RAW MATERIALS

All fibrous materials can be pulped by the semichemical processes as far as is known, but the hardwoods of the temperate zone are chiefly used. However, eucalyptus, a semitropical hardwood, is used in several countries. Tropical hardwoods are used in one South American mill. In the U.S., hardwoods of all the major pulping areas are utilized, including the light-colored, low-density poplars, the "soft" hardwoods like sweetgum and tupelo, and the heavy hardwoods such as oak. The U.S. hardwoods used are listed by region in Table 8.2.

TABLE 8.2. HARDWOODS USED FOR SEMICHEMICAL PULPING

1. *Northeast:*   ash (*Fraxinus* sp.)
aspen (*Populus tremuloides*)
beech (*Fagus grandifolia*)
birch (*Betula* sp.)
cherry (*Prunus serotina*)
elm (*Ulmus americana*)
maple (*Acer sp.*)
oak (*Quercus* sp.)

2. *Northcentral:*   aspen (*Populus tremuloides*)
basswood (*Tilia americana*)
birch (*Betula* sp.)
cottonwood (*Populus deltoides*)
elm (*Ulmus americana*)
maple (*Acer sp.*)
oak (*Quercus* sp.)

3. *South:*   ash (*Fraxinus* sp.)
cottonwood (*Populus deltoides*)
elm (*Ulmus americana*)
gum (*Liquidambar styraciflua*)
hickory (*Carya* sp.)
oak (*Quercus* sp.)
tupelos (*Nyssa* sp.)
yellow-poplar (*Liriodendron tulipifera*)

4. *West:*   alder (*alnus rubra*)
cottonwood (*Populus* sp.)
eucalyptus (*Eucalyptus* sp.)
oak (*Quercus* sp.)

Softwoods, including balsam fir (*Abies balsamea*) and Douglas fir (*Pseudotsuga taxifolia*), are used to a small extent for semichemical pulping, but are generally pulped by the full chemical or high-yield sulfate and sulfite processes. The softwoods react less favorably to semichemical pulping, as discussed later.

In 1961, the total consumption of pulpwood in the U.S. was 39,000,000 cords. Of this, 2,180,000 cords or 5.6% was used for semichemical pulping. Out of this semichemical volume, 88%, or 1,920,000 cords, was hardwood.

SEMICHEMICAL PULPING

Processes Used

The chemical pulping stage can be conducted with any known pulping reagent and many have been tried. The first, as mentioned before, was acid sulfite, and there is now a minor use of soda and kraft liquor, the other common pulping reagents. However, the major portion of semichemical pulps and a part of the chemimechanical pulps are made with sodium sulfite buffered with sodium carbonate or bicarbonate or kraft green liquor. Ammonium sulfite has been used from time to time and magnesium bisulfite, a more recently applied reagent for chemical pulping, has received attention.

The largest production in chemimechanical pulps is by the cold soda process which applies sodium hydroxide to chips at room temperature. Chemimechanical pulps are also made with buffered sodium sulfite solutions and with a mixed solution of sodium sulfite and sodium bisulfite.

Variables Affecting Pulp Yield and Quality

The yield and quality of semichemical pulps are affected by the following variables:

Chemical stage: Physical and chemical properties of the wood, chip size, composition of pulping liquor and amount applied, time and temperature of pulping; the penetration of the cooking liquor into the chips is an important dependent variable.

Mechanical stage: Properties (including size) of the material from the chemical stage, consistency, temperature, number of passes, design of the fiberizing machine and its elements; these variables are considered briefly in the following paragraphs.

Wood Properties. The penetration of the pulping chemical into the fibrous material is especially important in semichemical pulping because otherwise woody fiber bundles or shives result. Physical properties, such as density, heartwood and inclusions, the botanical nature, e.g., hardwood, softwood or grass, and moisture and air contents affect the penetration of semichemical liquors. The fiber dimensions and relative contents of libriform fibers, tracheids, vessels, parenchyma and ray cells affect the strength, density, and opacity of pulps, just as with chemical pulps. The brightness of the wood has a direct effect on the brightness of the unbleached pulp. Bark, knots, and decay obviously decrease pulp quality. The chemical composition of the fibrous material affects the yield for a given lignin content, particularly the yield of bleached

pulp; materials high in cellulose and low in lignin, of course, give the highest yields. Materials with high extractives give lower yields than the others. The hemicelluloses, especially the pentosans, are high in hardwoods and so are their semichemical pulps, which tend to give stiff, dense papers relatively low in opacity.

Chip Size. Semichemical pulping requires smaller chips than chemical pulping for reasons of penetration and uniformity of feed in the fiberizing stage. A secondary reduction in chip size to approach match sticks is often used for cold soda pulping.

Digestion or Treating Variables. The composition and amount of the pulping liquor, the temperature (pressure) and time affect pulp yield and quality to the extent of their degree of application in accordance with normal chemical reactions.

An increase in the amount of chemical applied causes a decrease in yield in all processes. The amounts applied in semichemical pulping are less than for full chemical pulping. When Na_2SO_3 is used, the range on the wood basis is 8 to 20% (4.3 to 10.8% Na_2O). The range for alkaline semichemical and cold soda pulping is 5 to 8% Na_2O. Softwoods require more chemical than hardwoods for a given yield.

Chemical concentration, the amount of chemical applied, and the liquid-to-solid ratio are mutually dependent variables. A low liquid ratio gives a low steam consumption and a high solids content in the spent liquor.

Buffering to a pH range of 7 to 9 is particular to NSSC pulping. This controls corrosion as well as the pulping rate, which is naturally slower in this range than under strongly acid or alkaline conditions. As mentioned previously, the buffers are sodium carbonate, sodium bicarbonate and kraft green liquor. The amount of buffer used depends on the amount of acid-forming materials in the wood and amount of sodium sulfite applied, since it acts as a buffer when present in high amounts, as in making bleachable pulps. The final pH value, as controlled by the buffer, affects pulp brightness—pulps being brighter under acid conditions.

An increase in temperature increases the rate of pulping. The temperature coefficient for NSSC pulping is 2 to 3 for a 10°C rise. Because of the near-neutral condition in NSSC pulping, the temperatures are relatively high to bring about a reasonably rapid reaction rate, being in the range of 160°C to 185°C. Chemimechanical pulping based on sodium sulfite solutions is also conducted at high temperatures. Alkaline semichemical pulping is done at temperatures of 170 to 180°C. Cold soda pulping is done at ambient temperatures, since an elevated temperature causes darkening of the pulp.

The time of pulping in the high-temperature processes at a given temperature depends on the amount of chemical applied. Yield decreases with increase in time in the classical hyperbolic manner. In cold soda pulping, the time is consumed mainly in achieving penetration, and the optimum effect is obtained in a maximum of two hours with natural penetration.

The conditions used for the variables in semichemical pulping are given under the discussion on operation of these processes. **Fiberizing Variables.** Uniformity of operation, as obtained from uniformly sized and treated chips, results in improved pulp quality and reduced power consumption. The power consumed to a given freeness depends on the fibrous material and its degree and kind of chemical treatment. Hardwoods use less power than softwoods. Power generally decreases with yield. Cold soda pulping is reported to take less power than sodium sulfite chemimechanical pulping.

Optimum fiberizing is obtained at treated chip moisture contents of about 50% at the highest practical consistency and temperature. Improved pulp quality is reported for multipass fiberizing, although at the expense of power consumption.

This discussion is supplemented in the sections on operations and equipment.

MECHANISMS OF SEMICHEMICAL AND CHEMIMECHANICAL PULPING

The chemical and physical actions of semichemical and chemimechanical pulping involve mechanisms similar to conventional chemical and groundwood processes. In the chemical stage, the basic wood components of lignin, cellulose, hemicellulose and extractives are made soluble in amounts depending on the fibrous material, process, pulping conditions and end products. In the mechanical stage, the fiber separation results from forces of attrition under controlled conditions of consistency and temperature.

Chemical Stage

The wood components removed under various circumstances of pulping have been quite thoroughly investigated and typical results are given in Table 8.3. For a given yield in semichemical pulping, the lignin removal increases in proceeding from alkaline to acid conditions, and the order for the usual reagents is soda, kraft, neutral sulfite, bisulfite, and acid sulfite. The reverse order is found for hemicellulose removal. On the other hand, the resistant cellulose is least attacked in kraft and soda semichemical pulping. The extractives are more soluble in the alkaline than the neutral or acid reagents.

In the cold soda and sodium sulfite chemimechanical processes, there is little or no lignin solution, the losses being hemicelluloses and extraneous matter soluble in chemical and water.

The chemical attack on the fiber bond in NSSC pulping appears to involve lignin sulfonation and hemicellulose hydrolysis. The sulfonated lignin is partly dissolved and partly altered to allow the strength development of the carbohydrate fraction of the pulp. Hydrolysis of hemicellulose leads to the formation of sodium acetate and formate. These effects occur to a lesser extent in sulfite chemimechanical pulping, but not to the extent of lignin solution.

In soda and kraft semichemical pulping, it is believed that there is a certain degree of sodium lignate or thiolignin formation and solution after the initial strong alkaline action on the hemicelluloses which cause their dissolution.

Although the lignin is not modified in cold soda pulping, carbohydrate areas are exposed—a fact which permits strength development. This is an important difference between chemimechanical and groundwood pulps inasmuch as the latter does not develop strength on refining.

Mechanical Stage

The mechanical actions in the defibering stage of semichemical pulping involve chiefly the friction between fibers, fiber bundles, and the surface of the fiberizing plates and compression of the pulp slurry forced between the plates by centrifugal action. The actions apparently involved are heating to cause a further weakening of the fiber bond, disintegration into fiber bundles and individual fibers and refining of the fibers accompanied by final separation. This last action involves fibrillation, softening and formation of the mucilage-like material characteristics imparted by beating. Semi-chemical pulps appear under a microscope more like chemical than groundwood pulps, as shown in Figures 8.1, 8.2, 8.3, and 8.3a.

SEMICHEMICAL PULPING OPERATIONS AND EQUIPMENT

Although semichemical pulping has been practiced for over 35 years, the operations and equipment have not yet become standardized to the extent of the older sulfite and alkaline processes. This lack of standardized methods is also true for the newer chemimechanical pulping. It almost appears that the semichemical mills are tailor-made to meet particular circumstances and that there is an almost continuous change in operations and design as the industry advances. It can be said that the earlier semichemical mills established for making chestnut board did achieve a certain uniformity of design, but that this design, as described in the previous edition, has become nearly outmoded.

In the following paragraphs are given descriptions of the present operating systems for producing semichemical-type pulps.

Wood Preparation

The wood yard of the mill making semichemical pulps does not differ from that for

TABLE 8.3. CHEMICAL ANALYSES AND LOSSES IN CHEMIMECHANICAL AND SEMICHEMICAL PULPING

Wood Component	Typical Hardwood Analysis (%)	Chemimechanical Process (88% yield) Cold Soda Pulp Analysis (%)	Pulping Losses (lb/100 lb)	Acid Sulfite Pulp Analysis (%)	Pulping Losses (lb/100 lb)	Neutral Sulfite Pulp Analysis (%)	Pulping Losses (lb/100 lb)	Kraft Pulp Analysis (%)	Pulping Losses (lb/100 lb)	Soda Pulp Analysis (%)	Pulping Losses (lb/100 lb)
Lignin	22.5	25.0	— / —	13.8	— / 12.2	17.4	— / 9.5	20.7	— / 7.0	23.8	— / 4.6
Hemi-cellulose	24.0	15.9	10.0	21.1	8.2	17.8	10.7	15.9	12.1	13.5	13.9
Cellulose	50.0	56.7	—	62.6	3.0	62.5	3.0	62.1	3.4	61.4	4.0
Extractives & ash	3.5	2.4	2.0	2.5	1.6	2.3	1.8	1.3	2.5	1.3	2.5
Totals	100.0	100.0	12.0	100.0	25.0	100.0	25.0	100.0	25.0	100.0	25.0

Semichemical Process (75% yield) covers the Acid Sulfite, Neutral Sulfite, Kraft, and Soda columns.

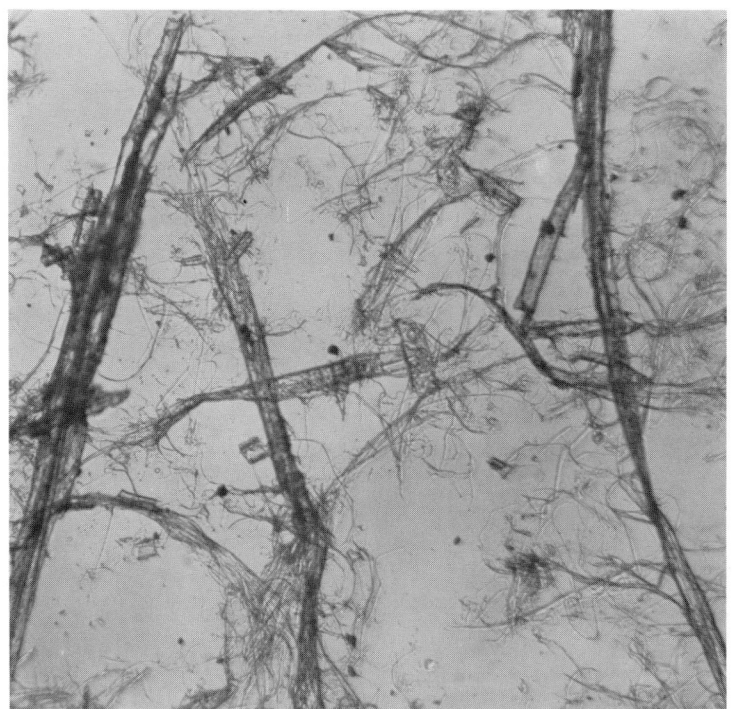

Fig. 8.1. Spruce groundwood pulp. 85×. (*Courtesy U.S. Forest Service, Forest Products Laboratory*)

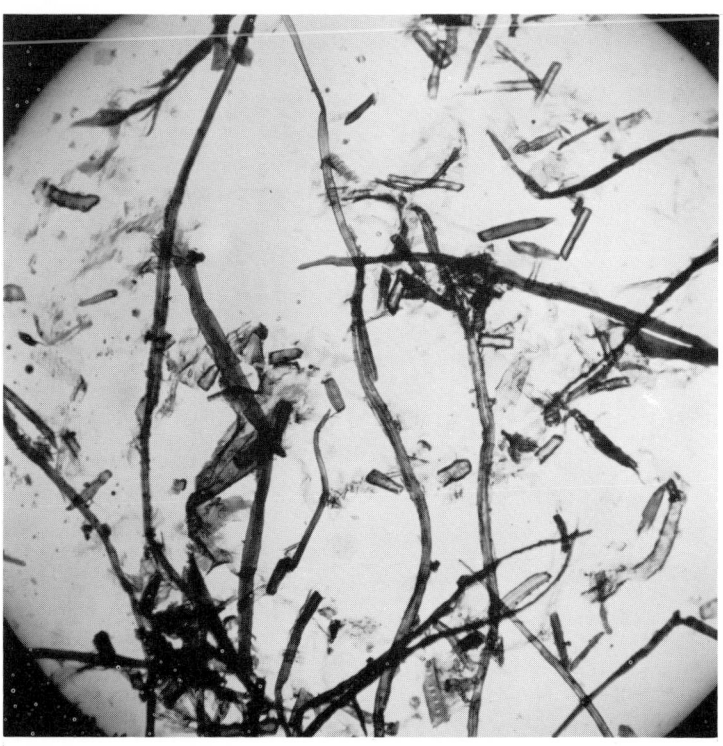

Fig. 8.2. Mixed hardwood cold soda pulp. 85×. (*Courtesy U.S. Forest Service, Forest Products Laboratory*)

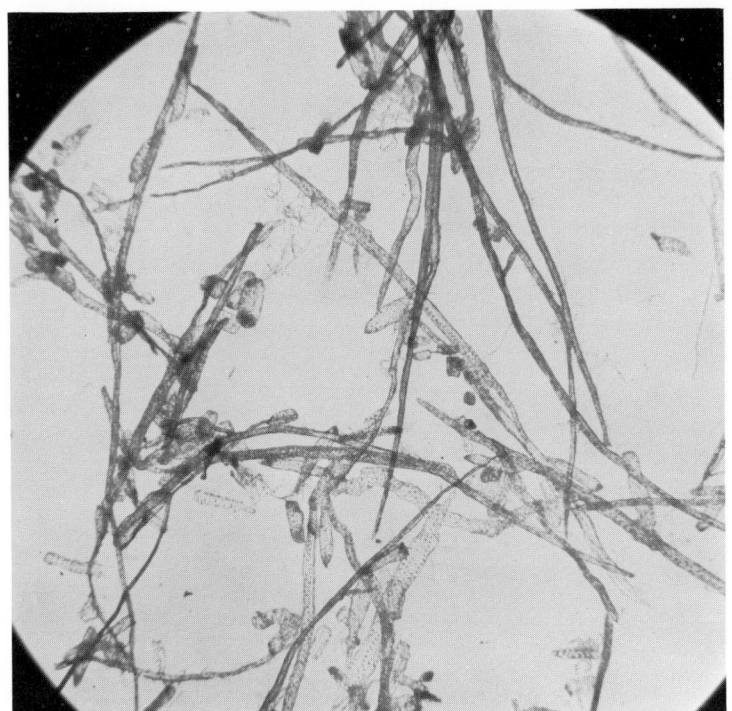

Fig. 8.3. Post oak sulfate pulp. 85×. (*Courtesy U.S. Forest Service, Forest Products Laboratory*)

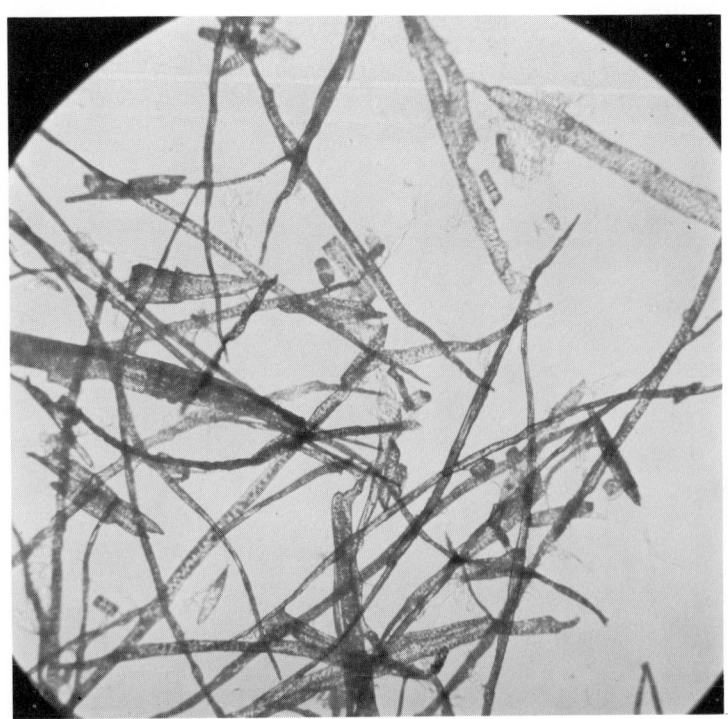

Fig. 8.3a. Post oak NSSC pulp. 85×. (*Courtesy U.S. Forest Service, Forest Products Laboratory*)

other pulp mills as described in Chapter 5. In preparing wood to be used for making bleached semichemical pulp, the bark is removed as completely as possible, since the NSSC process does not successfully reduce the bark. In making pulp for corrugating board, on the other hand, it is not necessary to use completely debarked wood.

Chip Preparation and Handling

The chips used in semichemical pulping are generally smaller than those for full chemical pulping to improve liquor penetration and uniformity of pulping. Thus, the chipper, which is normal equipment as described in Chapter 5, is set for a nominal chip length of $\frac{1}{2}$ inch. Typical ranges of values for chip classifications are as follows:

				Per Cent
Retained on 1-inch screen				1-6
"	" $\frac{3}{4}$ "	"		4-26
"	" $\frac{1}{2}$ "	"		40-55
"	" $\frac{1}{4}$ "	"		20-30
Fines				1-5

The fines are often included with the accepted chips. Oversized chips are reduced by rechippers or hogs. Sawmill chips are used in some mills and these chips are usually re-screened at the pulp mill.

Even with the relatively small chips used in semichemical pulping, it has been found desirable, especially in chemimechanical pulping, to reduce the chips further to a kind of match stick or pin chip by means of a single-disk attrition mill with pyramid-pattern plates, as shown in Figure 8.4.

The handling of the chips is conventional with weightometers in general use. Chip feeders are employed before continuous digesters and may be a star valve or a metering screw conveyor.

Liquor Preparation

As mentioned under pulping variables, several pulping liquors are used and they are prepared in different ways varying from direct batch solution of purchased chemicals to continuous reaction methods.

The NSSC liquor is made in some mills directly from market sodium sulfite and market sodium carbonate or other buffer. More often it is made by sulfiting of soda ash or caustic soda in batch or continuous methods. The reactions when soda ash is used are as follows:

$$S + O_2 \longrightarrow SO_2$$
$$Na_2CO_3 + SO_2 \longrightarrow Na_2SO_3 + CO_2$$
$$Na_2CO_3 + CO_2 + H_2O \longrightarrow 2NaHCO_3$$

The sulfur dioxide above is made by burning sulfur in a rotary or spray burner.

Fig. 8.4. Single-disk attrition mill. (*Courtesy Sprout Waldron Co.*)

In the batch method the sodium carbonate in solution is circulated in a packed tower during addition of the sulfur dioxide. The reaction is stopped when the desired concentration is reached and the liquor ("pink" liquor) is pumped to a storage tank. A flow diagram of liquor preparation is shown in Figure 8.5.

In the continuous method of NSSC liquor preparation rates of flow of sodium carbonate solution and sulfur dioxide to the reaction tower are controlled to permit the above reactions in a single pass through the reaction tower. The rates of sodium sulfite and sodium carbonate formation are controlled by a pH meter or periodic test. The volume of liquor produced is controlled by the rate of pumping the sodium carbonate solution which is coordinated with the stroke of the sulfur metering pump feeding the sulfur burner which supplies the sulfur dioxide to the reaction tower (Figure 8.5).

The reaction or absorption tower is usually of the packed tower design, but perforated plate and bubble-cap towers are also used.

NSSC liquor can also be made by sulfiting a sodium hydroxide solution in a tower as also shown in Figure 8.5.

The concentration of NSSC liquor from the absorption tower is 120 to 200 grams per liter Na_2SO_3 and 30 to 50 grams per liter Na_2CO_3 (as $NaHCO_3$). The ratio of sodium sulfite to sodium carbonate varies according to the acidic potential of the wood and the strength of the sodium sulfite itself, since the sodium sulfite can act as a buffer when present in sufficient quantity, as in making bleachable pulps. Thus, the ratio will vary from as high as 6:1 for bleachable pulps to 1.5:1 for corrugating grade pulps.

The cooking liquor is used at a concentration of 90 to 200 grams per liter sodium sulfite depending on the amount of chemical applied for pulping and the extent of brown liquor dilution.

In several of the mills NSSC liquor is prepared in a cyclic chemical recovery system. These systems are described later in this chapter.

A sodium sulfite-sodium bisulfite liquor

Fig. 8.4a. Chip fractionater. (*Courtesy Sprout Waldron Co.*)

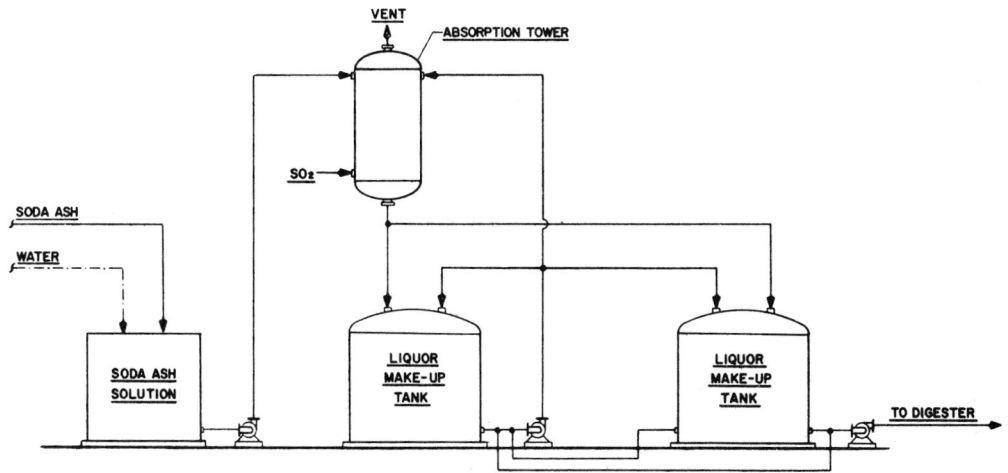

A) Batch NSSC liquor preparation system using soda ash.

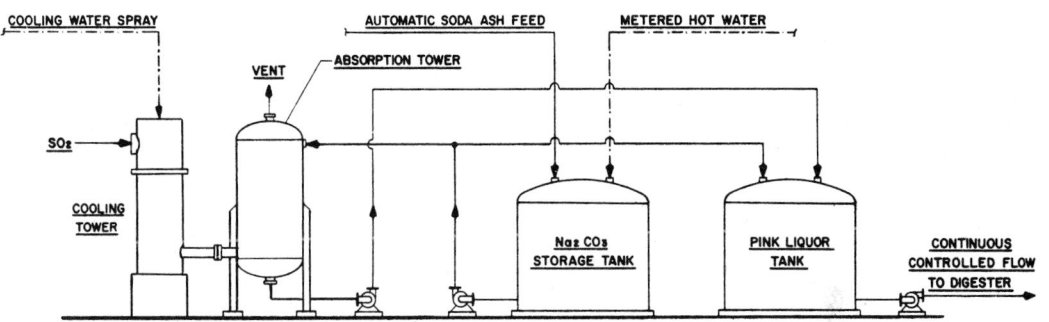

B) Continuous NSSC liquor preparation system.

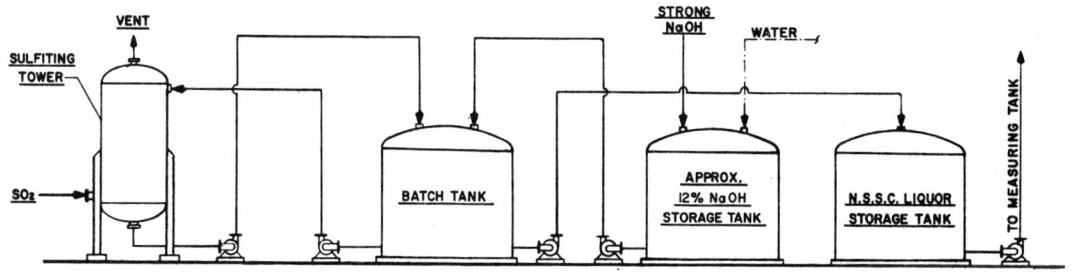

C) Batch NSSC liquor preparation system using caustic soda.

Fig. 8.5.

used in one mill for making a chemimechanical pulp is made up by dissolving the two chemicals in an automatic batch system using volumetric dry feeders.

Kraft semichemical pulping liquor is a weak white liquor from an associated kraft mill liquor system as described in Chapter 7.

The treating liquor for cold soda chemimechanical pulping is generally made from a strong caustic soda solution of 20% concentration which has been made from solid or concentrated caustic soda. The strong solution is diluted with water or recycled spent treating liquor to make a treating solution with a concentration of 20 to 50 grams per liter.

Digestion

An unusually wide variety of digestion equipment has been developed for semichemical and chemimechanical pulping. All the types used for full chemical pulping are used and a number of others in addition. In fact, developments in semichemical pulping equipment have found application in kraft pulping. Systems in use are depicted in Figure 8.6 for semichemical pulping and in Figure 8.7 for chemimechanical digestion.

The trend in semichemical pulping is toward continuous operation. However, a large portion of semichemical pulp production is still made in batch, kraft-type digesters.

The first semichemical pulp mills used globe rotary digesters (12 to 16 feet in diameter), probably because of the relative simplicity of charging and discharging and the mixing action of the rotary digester. In the first installations the chips were subjected to an impregnation stage of heating in strong NSSC liquor for 1 hour at 120°C. The liquor was then blown from the digester and the digestion conducted in the vapor phase. The digester contents were finally dumped into chests with a discharge mechanism, as described later.

In order to increase the productive capacity of a digestion unit the standard vertical digesters of chemical pulping, both sulfite and kraft, were next adapted to semichemical pulping. These digesters permitted larger charges of chips and shorter digestion cycles and blowing into blow tanks or blow pits. Actually, kraft and semichemical pulping can be conducted interchangeably in some installations.

Typical operating conditions for rotary and stationary batch digesters are given in Table 8.4.

Digesters of several designs for continuous pulping are used for semichemical pulping. Semichemical pulping to produce board and bleachable grades of pulp is conducted in digesters based on (a) horizontal flow, (b) upflow, (c) downflow, and (d) up-and-down flow in an inclined digester, as illustrated in Figure 8.6. A variety of inlet and outlet devices are used on these digesters to permit charging into the digesting zone under pressure and discharging from it. Brief descriptions of continuous semichemical pulping systems are as follows:

Horizontal-flow Digesters. Chips are introduced into horizonal tubes 3 to 5 feet in diameter under digestion pressure by means

TABLE 8.4

	Type of Digester			
	Rotary	*Rotary*	*Vertical*	*Vertical*
Grade of pulp	corrugating	bleachable	corrugating	bleachable
Wood species	gum-oak	aspen	alder-Douglas fir	gum-oak
Chips charged, lb	16,000	9,450	25,500	49,500
Chemicals charged Liquor concentration:				
Sodium sulfite, lb	1,600	1,980	2,500	9,400
Sodium carbonate, lb	800	220	kraft green liquor	1,570
Digester cycle, min.	120/163°C 150 @163°C	120/170°C 120 @120°C	140/174°C 30 @174°C	120/175°C 105 @175°C
Total digestion time, hr	4.5	4.5	2.3	4.5
Temperature, °C, max.	163	170	174	173
Pressure, psi	85	100	110	110
Pulp yield, %	79-82	68	70-75	66

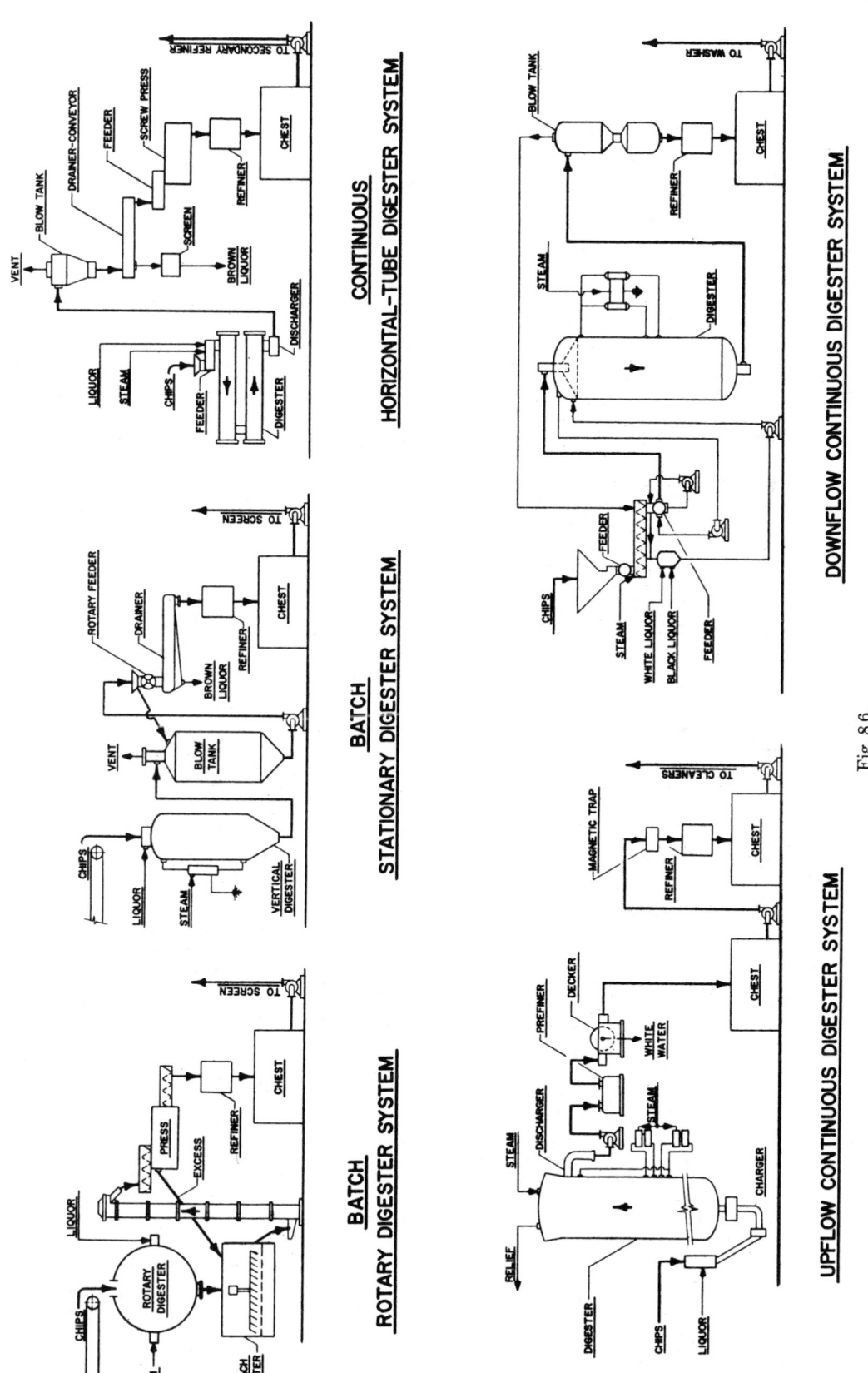

Fig. 8.6.

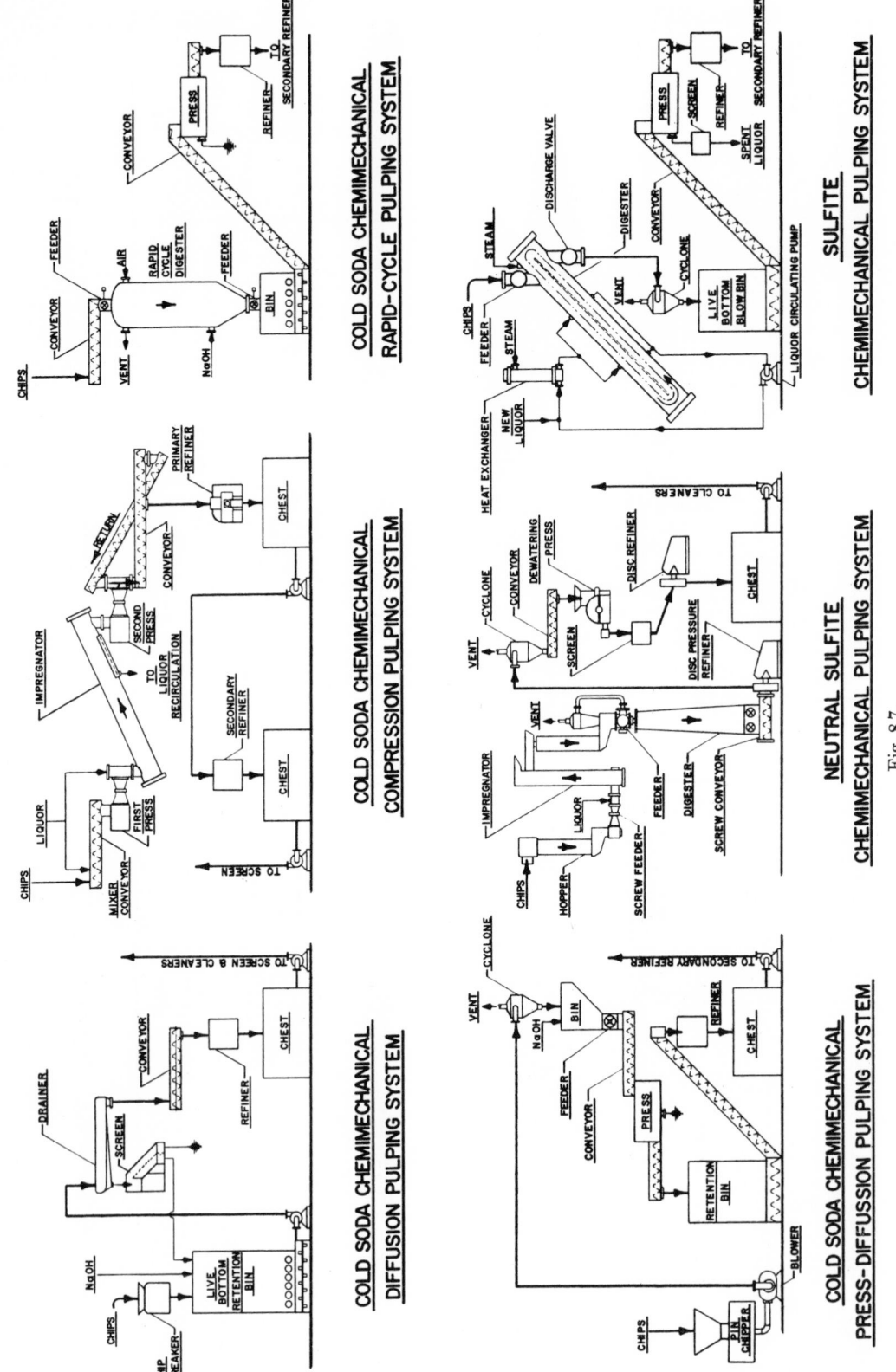

Fig. 8.7.

of compression screws or rotary-valve or rotary-vane feeders and are propelled forward by solid or broken-flight screw conveyors. There may be a multi-tube arrangement of parallel tubes mounted side-by-side or one above another. The discharge from the pressure zone is through an orifice or a rotary valve into a cyclone, as described later.

Upflow Digester. In this digester the chips are introduced into an atmospheric impregnator and then transferred into a vertical digester equipped with a special chip-lifting device and also designed for zone circulation and external liquor heating. At the top of the digester the cooked chips are scraped into a conveyor serving an orifice for discharge to a cyclone.

Downflow Digesters. In one design the chips are introduced into the vertical digestion zone by means of special low- and high-pressure rotary feeders with an intermediate steaming vessel. The digester is equipped for zone circulation and external heating and the flow is by gravity. The chips are discharged through a disk strainer into a blow tank.

Another design of downflow digester is preceded by pre-treatment involving successively pre-steaming, compression in a screw feeder, impregnation with hot NSSC liquor in a vertical upflow chamber and discharge into a hopper. The impregnated chips are fed from the hopper into the vertical pressure digester through a rotary feeder; the digester tapers out downward

and is heated by direct steam. The cooked chips are discharged through a single-disk refiner with a reciprocating valve to a cyclone.

Downflow-Upflow Digester. The chips enter the digester through a rotary valve. The digester itself, which is a tube 5 feet in diameter, is at an angle of 45° and is divided by a hollow midfeather into two sections. A drag conveyor carries the chips down the topside of the midfeather and up the underside. The cooked chips are discharged through another rotary valve to a cyclone. The cooking liquor is heated externally.

Operating conditions for several of the continuous digestion systems are given in Table 8.5.

CHEMIMECHANICAL PULPING

Chemimechanical pulping is conducted in equipment similar to that used for semichemical pulping, as described above, and also according to systems developed specifically for particular purposes. Several new systems in practice are shown in Figure 8.7. Although early installations used globe digesters in batch operations the trend is definitely toward continuous chemimechanical pulping.

The equipment used in chemimechanical pulping shows a natural separation into that used for neutral or acid sodium sulfite pulping under heat and pressure and cold soda pulping at atmospheric pressure and temperature. The former employs equip-

TABLE 8.5.

	Type of Digester				
	Horizontal	*Horizontal*	*Upflow*	*Downflow*	*Downflow*
Grade of pulp	corrugating	bleachable	bleachable	corrugating	bleachable
Wood species	mixed hardwoods	oak	mixed hardwoods	birch	mixed hardwoods
Chemical applied:					
Sodium sulfite, %	10	20	25	10	17
Sodium carbonate, %	3	3	3	3	4 ($NaHCO_3$)
Digestion time, min.	18	40	185	33	180-210
Temperature, °C	170	185	177	175	168-170
Pressure, psi	100	160	160	114	—
Yield, %	78	68	65	80	70-72

ment already described for semichemical pulping, including the inclined downflow-upflow digester and the tapered downflow digester. In addition, in an automatic batch system chips are metered into several parallel small vertical digesters and treated in two stages comprising first impregnation with NSSC liquor and second vapor phase cooking with discharge into a blow bin, as shown in Figure 8.7. Conditions used in sodium sulfite chemimechanical pulping are given in Table 8.6.

Cold soda chemimechanical pulping is conducted in globe rotary digesters, in the inclined-tube and automatic-batch digesters described above, and in equipment involving several steps of diffusion and compression actions for impregnation of the chips. The last-mentioned types are illustrated in Figure 8.7. The globe digesters are operated at atmospheric or under hydrostatic pressure using a 2-hour caustic soda treatment at slightly elevated temperature from the heat of solution of the caustic soda. The digesters are dumped in one mill into a bin with a table discharger and thence are conveyed to a press.

The inclined-tube digester is operated with open charge and discharge at a slightly elevated temperature or controlled by water circulated through the mid-feather. The treatment lasts for 1 hour and the treated chips discharge into a conveyor serving a chip disintegrator which discharges in turn into a live-bottom bin affording an additional retention time of 1 hour. The treated chips are then pressed.

Another diffusion-type treatment is conducted with matchstick chips which are treated in a continuous operation for 2 hours in an atmospheric tower with a live bottom. The concentration and level are kept constant by addition of fresh chemical and spent liquor. The treated chips are pumped to a drainer and the liquor returned to the tower after straining through a sidehill screen. The treated chips are then conveyed to the refiners.

In another system normal wood chips are first treated with a small amount of caustic soda before being reduced to pin chips which blow through a cyclone to a treating bin where additional caustic soda is added in a short diffusion step. The chips are then compressed in a screw press for further impregnation and preliminary fiberizing and are given a third treatment of caustic soda immediately on release from the press. The treated chips are then conveyed to a retention bin with a live bottom made up of parallel screw conveyors moving the material outwards to a receiving conveyor for a short diffusion period before fiberizing.

Double compression of chips in screw presses with an intervening inclined retention tube is used in a system under commercial trial. The chips from the first press discharge under a liquid level of the caustic soda treating solution in the retention tube which affords 30-minute treating. The treated chips are de-liquored and partly defiberized in the second press and are discharged into a conveyor feeding the fiberizing system.

TABLE 8.6

| | Type of Digester | | |
	Downflow	Downflow-Upflow	Automatic batch
Grade of pulp	newsprint	printing papers	newsprint
Wood species	birch	fir	birch and alder
Chemical applied:			
Sodium sulfite, %	10	12	10
Sodium carbonate, %	—*	—*	—*
Digestion time, min.	30-60	12-15	13
Temperature, °C	175	140	195
Pressure, psi	110-120	85	150
Yield, %	85-90	90	88-90

* Included with Na_2SO_3.

The conditions for cold soda chemimechanical pulping are summarized as follows:

Caustic soda concentration—15 to 45 grams per liter
Caustic soda consumption —5 to 9% on A.D. pulp
basis
Treating temperature   —30 to 50°C
Treating time   —30 to 240 minutes

Leach Casters, Blow Tanks, and Live-Bottom Cyclones

In the first semichemical mills the globe rotary digesters dumped the cooked chips into a wooden chest with a false bottom for liquor drainage and equipped with a leach caster, which comprises revolving arms with plows working downward to sweep the cooked chips to an outlet. Later, the digesters dumped into bins with conveyors or silos with rotary plate dischargers.

The vertical digesters discharge their contents into a blowpit equipped with a leach caster as above, or into a blowtank from which the chips are pumped to a drainer before fiberizing.

The continuous digesters operating under pressure generally blow into cyclones from which the cooked chips drop into tanks or bins with live bottoms (described above) of several designs or other chip discharging devices for removal to conveyors serving the fiberizing system.

Special handling and leaching systems are used in specific mills which are not sufficiently general for description.

Cooked Chip Handling and Pre-fiberizing Treatment

The hot cooked chips in semichemical-type pulping with heat are taken from the digester receiving system to the fiberizing system with a minimum of time elapsed in order to permit hot fiberizing and refining and possibly to prevent darkening. In between these two points there may be metal removal, metering, draining, pressing and pre-refining equipment for the purposes of liquor recovery at maximum solids content and conditioning of the chips for optimum fiberizing. However, in many mills the chips from the live-bottom tank, for example, are conveyed directly to the refiners.

In one general cooked chip handling system, the material is pumped from a blow

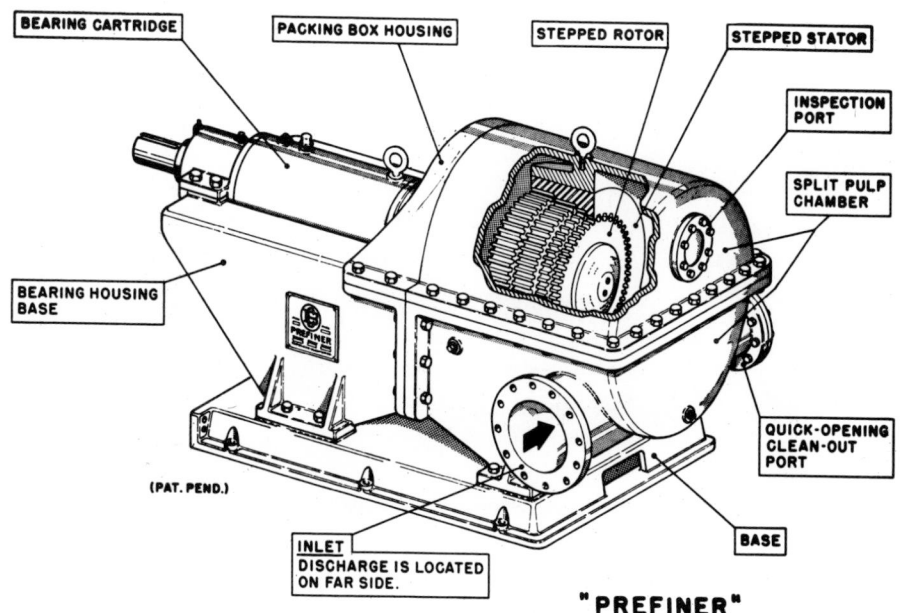

"PREFINER"

Fig. 8.8.

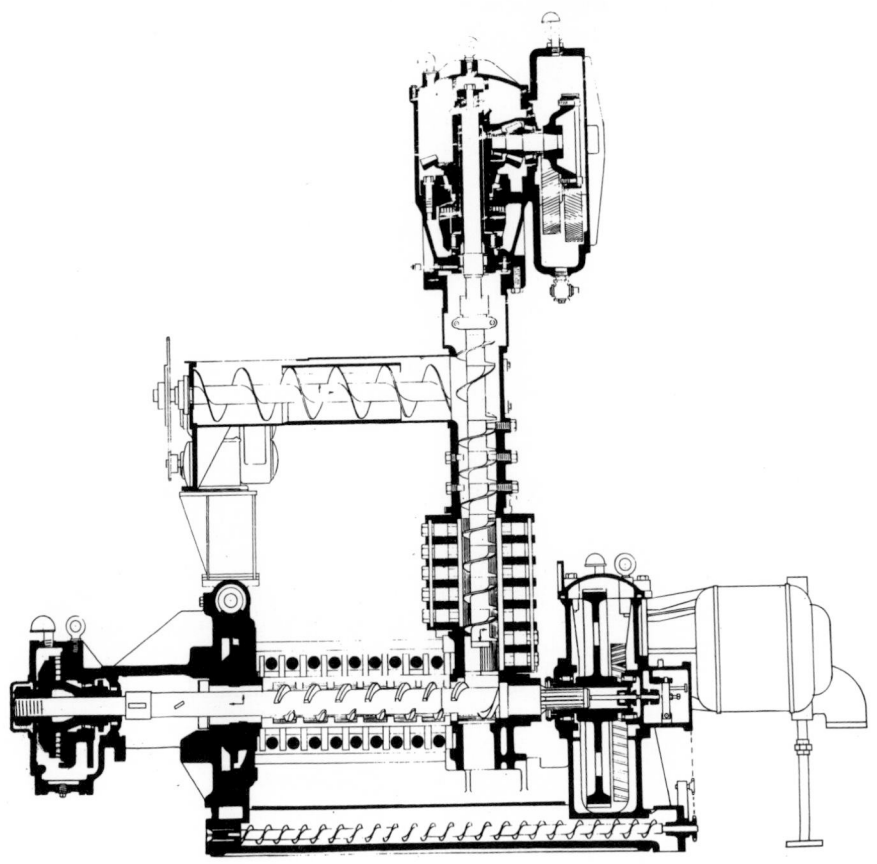

Fig. 8.9. Fiber Press 1307. (*Courtesy V. D. Anderson Co.*)

Fig. 8.9a. Pressofiner. (*Courtesy of The Bauer Bros. Co.*)

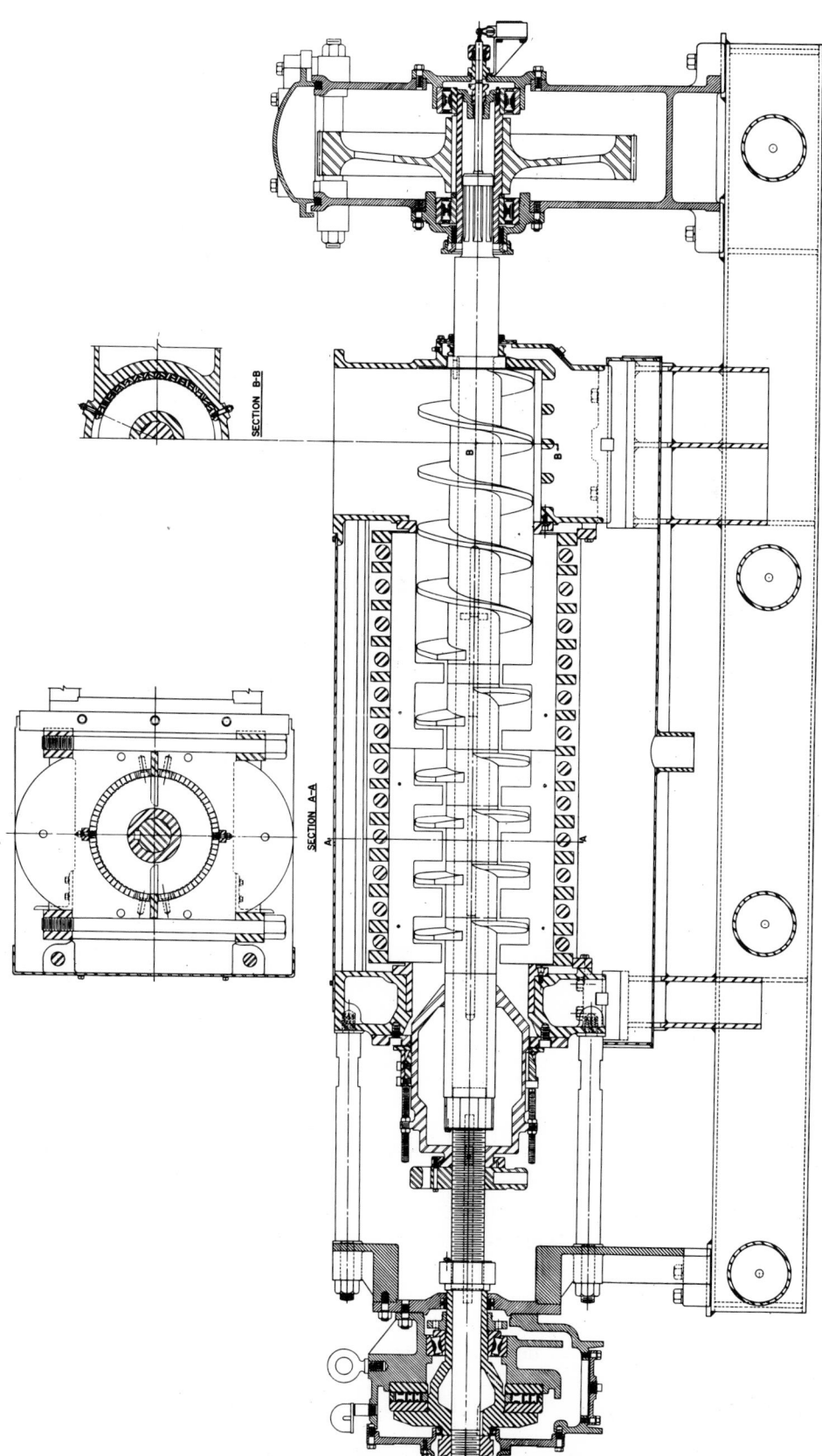

Fig. 8.9b. Anderson moisture expeller. (*Courtesy V. D. Anderson Co.*)

tank through a tramp metal trap to a distributing header serving parallel lines of rotary vane feeders and drainer-conveyors before dropping into the feed mechanism of the disk refiners over magnetic chutes.

In another typical system, the cooked chips are conveyed from a live-bottom bin to parallel metering screw feeders serving screw presses. The excess of chips not accepted by the feeders is recycled to the cooked chip bin.

In still another arrangement, the cooked chips are passed from a blowpit through refiners with a fixed clearance (Figure 8.8) before pumping to the primary refiners.

Several models of screw presses for deliquoring the semichemically cooked chips are used and are shown in Figure 8.9. One model is an expeller-type press in two stages, a vertical section to remove about 70% of the residual liquor at maximum concentration and a horizontal section to complete the liquor removal. Another model is a continuous screen press giving alternate twisting and compression forces at high pressure. A third type involves two-stage washing in one press. These presses impart a beneficial fiberizing action. The material is discharged at 65 to 75% solids and require 1.5 to 3 hp per ton daily output.

Chemimechanical pulps made with sodium sulfite solutions under heat and pressure are handled as above. The cold soda chips are generally subjected to pressing in between the treating and the fiberizing steps and the use of drainers is also common.

Fiberizing

Probably the single most important operation in semichemical-type pulping is the fiberizing of the partially pulped chips and the general success of these processes may be considered to stem from the introduction of the disk attrition mill for the fiberizing. The first fiberizing machine, the rod mill, was not satisfactory because of its small capacity batch operation, inadequate fiberizing and short rod life. Several designs of defibering and refining disk mills are used and these are illustrated in Figure 8.10

(a to c) and are described briefly below.

One fiberizer used considerably is a single-rotating disk model operated with fluid or high consistency feed by means of a throat feed screw. The rotating 42-inch disk runs at 900 or 1200 rpm, is powered by a synchronous or induction motor of up to 1200 hp, and is advanced or retracted by a geared mechanism to give a plate clearance within 0.001 inch. A feature is a peripheral control ring.

Another popular fiberizer is a double-rotating disk machine whose disks range from 24 to 40 inches in diameter, operate at speeds of 600 to 1800 rpm, and are powered with up to 1500 hp, synchronous or induction motors. The feed varies from pumpable consistency to chips with 50% solids content.

A third fiberizer of the single-rotation disk-type features a rugged construction and has a hydraulically controlled setting with hydraulic pressure applied along the center line of the down shaft. The machine is available in 24-, 36-, 42- and 48-inch diameter disks and rotates at 900 to 1800 rpm.

A newly introduced single-rotating disk refiner for secondary defibering operates at a high consistency of 30%. The principle of operation involves the application of two vertical opposed disks rotating in the same direction at approximately the same speed. One disk is driven at a constant speed and the other disk floats with a vertical axis adjustment imparting an orbital action.

The fiberizing of the cooked chips to a nominal freeness of 500 ml (Can. Std) takes 15 to 45 hp per daily ton, depending on the process wood species, yield, amount of prefiberizing action, temperature and other factors.

Pulp Washing and Screening

In the early mills making pulp for corrugating board the pulp from the fiberizing stage was usually passed through a coarse centrifugal screen before being pumped to the paper machine. The accepted pulp was used without washing and the effective yield

Fig. 8.10a. Single rotating disc refiner. (*Courtesy Sprout Waldron Co.*)

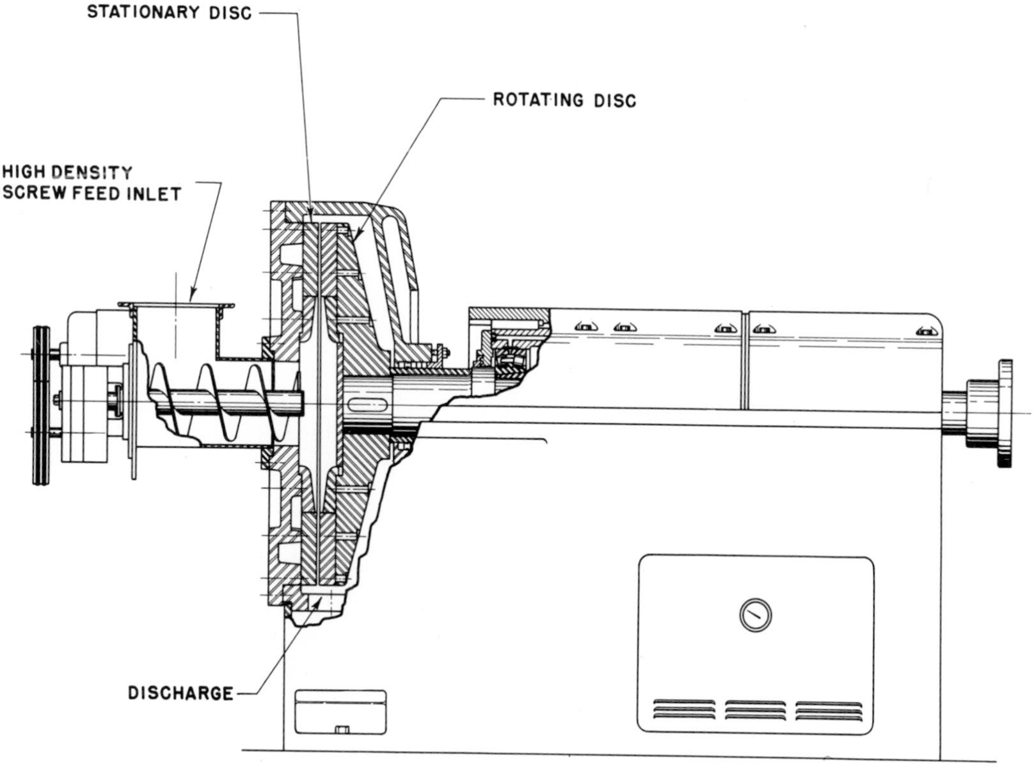

STATIONARY DISC

ROTATING DISC

HIGH DENSITY
SCREW FEED INLET

DISCHARGE

Fig. 8.10b. Hydradisc refiner. (*Courtesy of the Black-Clawson Co.*)

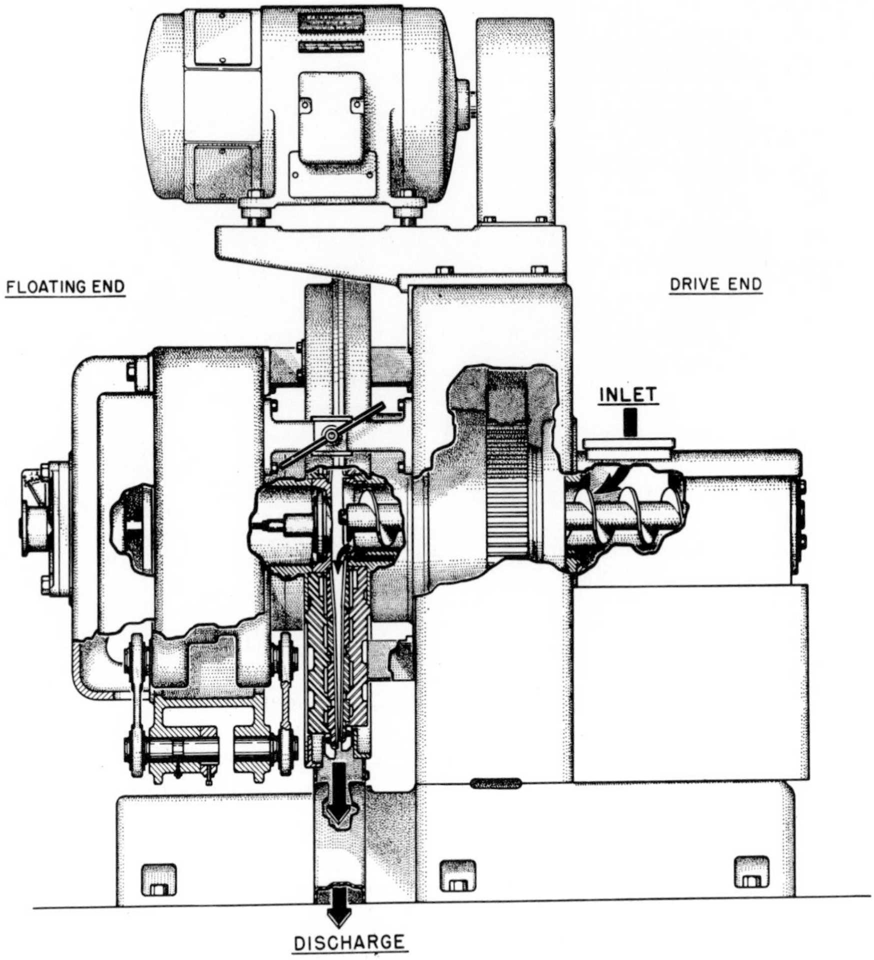

FLOATING END

DRIVE END

INLET

DISCHARGE

Fig. 8.10c. Chemifiner. (*Courtesy of the Black-Clawson Company*)

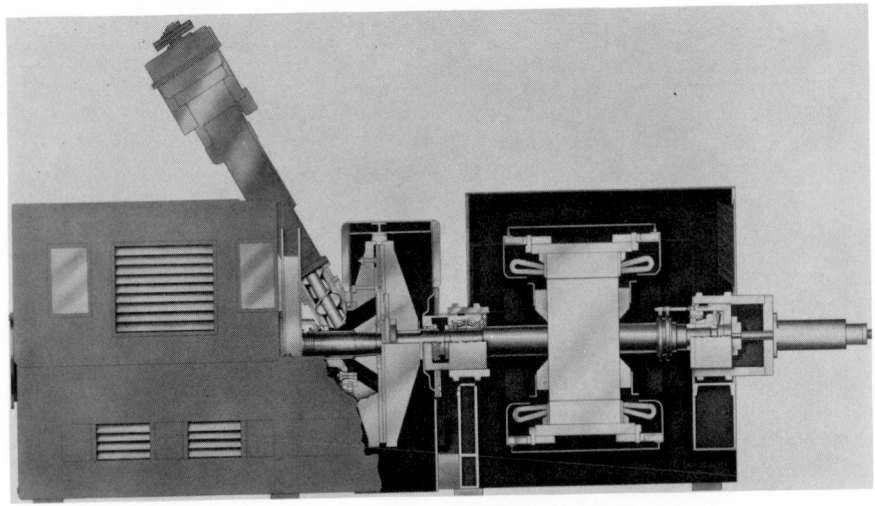

Fig. 8.10d. Double-disc refiner. (*Courtesy The Bauer Bros. Co.*)

was 85% or higher. The screen rejects were returned for refiberizing.

Later mills making bleachable pulps or recovering the brown (spent) liquor practiced conventional washing and screening procedures as used in chemical pulp production and described in Chapters 6 and 7.

An innovation in semichemical pulp washing has been the introduction of the horizontal or table-top washer as adapted from the cotton linters pulping industry. This washer, 19-foot diameter in one mill, offers complete brown stock washing in one piece of equipment. Screw press washers are used as well as standard vacuum filters.

Screening and cleaning of semichemical pulps is conducted by standard equipment, as described in Chapter 7.

A difference between chemical and semichemical pulp washing and screening is in the sequence of operation. NSSC pulps for bleaching may have pressure or rotary screens ahead or back of the washers with no trend apparently being established. NSSC board pulps may pass from the refiners directly to washers and thence to the paper mill.

The NSSC and chemimechanical pulps for bleaching or brightening generally include one or more stages of centrifugal cleaners.

BLEACHING AND BRIGHTENING SEMICHEMICAL PULPS

The semichemical pulps vary in brightness from 25 to 65%, depending on wood species, process, degree of pulping, and final pH value in cooking. The brightest pulps are made with sodium sulfite or sodium bisulfite slightly on the acid side. The darkest pulps are made under alkaline conditions. The chemimechanical pulps tend to be brighter than the corresponding semichemical pulps, although the NSSC pulps increase in brightness with decrease in yield within their defined yield range. The light-colored birch and aspen woods give the brightest semichemical pulps. An unbleached birch chemimechanical pulp made

by a sodium sulfite process is marketed with a brightness over 65%. Cold soda pulps may be as high as 45 to 50% in brightness and NSSC pulps are made up to 55%.

The bright semichemical pulps are used to a small extent unbleached in newsprint and other paper grades having minimum brightness requirement. However, the ordinary grades of bleached papers and boards make brightening or bleaching of the semichemical pulps necessary. The chemimechanical pulps are brightened by methods developed for groundwood pulps. Semichemical pulps are also brightened by these methods and in addition are fully bleached by conventional multistage methods. Details of the basic methods are given in Chapter 10.

Brightening procedures are applied mostly to cold soda pulps. The bleaching chemicals and methods employed include: single-stage peroxide, three-stage acidification-peroxide-hydrosulfite, two-stage chlorine-hypochlorite, and sulfur dioxide. The peroxide, which may be sodium or hydrogen peroxide, is applied in the fiberizing machine or in a tower or chest. The other brightening applications are in towers or chests. The peroxide methods generally require a final treatment with sulfur dioxide.

Brightness increases of 5 to 25 points are obtained by the methods above. The highest differential has been obtained with the three-stage process where the brightness level can be raised from 45 to 75 or 80%. The chlorine-hypochlorite increase is about 5%.

Typical amounts of bleaching chemicals applied are as follows:

Single-stage peroxide:
Refiner	—1.4% H_2O_2
Chest	—1.0% H_2O_2

Peroxide-Hydrosulfite
Na_2O_2 plus H_2O_2	—1.5% as H_2O_2
$Na_2S_2O_4$	— .8%

Chlorine-hypochlorite
Chlorine	—1.5%
Hypochlorite	—1.5% as Cl_2

Bleachable-grade semichemical pulps are readily bleached to a full brightness level of 85% by a conventional three-stage chlorination-alkaline extraction-hypochlorite bleaching procedure. The unbleached pulps have relatively high lignin contents of 10 to 14% and, therefore, have a high chlorine demand. Typical bleaching chemical requirements based on the unbleached pulp are:

Chlorine for chlorination —12 to 15%
Caustic soda for extraction—3%
Hypochlorite for bleaching—3 to 5% as Cl_2.

The bleaching of semichemical pulps is attended by a high bleaching shrinkage of up to 20%. The yield of bleached pulp is, however, 52 to 58% depending on wood species and the balance between yield reduction in pulping and in bleaching and the balance between cooking and bleaching chemicals. Each mill establishes its own compromise in these respects.

The bleached pulps are considerably stronger than the unbleached pulps, primarily because of the removal of lignin. The strength increase on bleaching is discussed in the following section on pulp properties.

PULP PROPERTIES AND USES

The first semichemical pulp made from the tannin-extracted chestnut chips would nowadays be considered very weak and the chestnut corrugating board would not meet present standards. Improvement in pulping and refining technology and diversification of wood species have led to improvements in pulp quality and to an increase in use of the semichemical pulps. The newer chemimechanical pulps have introduced these grades of pulps into wider fields of application. However, a very large percentage of the semichemical pulp is still used in corrugating board and these boards are considered the standard for their grade.

Properties of Semichemical Pulps

The semichemical pulps have chemical and strength properties intermediate to softwood groundwood and chemical pulps and tend to approach the chemical pulps, whereas the chemimechanical pulps tend to approach softwood groundwood pulps in properties and use. Therefore, the two grades are considered separately, although there is an overlapping in some areas.

Semichemical Pulps. The unbleached pulps are still lignified (15%) and are mostly high in pentosans (18%) due to their hardwood origin. The bleaching operation removes essentially all the lignin and elevates the pulps to a typical hardwood bleached pulp composition (18 to 20% pentosans and 75 to 80% alpha-cellulose). Softwood sulfite pulps of a bleachable grade in comparison have low lignin (0.7%), low pentosans (5%) and relatively high alpha-cellulose (82%) contents.

The yield and chemical composition of the semichemical pulps will vary with end usage and in the defined yield range of 65 to 85% the lignin content may be 10 to 20%, the pentosans within the rather narrow limits of 18 to 20%, and the alpha-cellulose from 70 to 55%, respectively.

The strength properties of selected unbleached and bleached semichemical pulps are shown in Table 8.7. In Table 8.8 there is given a general comparison of semichemical pulps with one of the highest quality chemical pulps, an unbleached northern softwood sulfate pulp. Also in Table 8.8 are given the relative strength properties for a typical hardwood sulfate pulp.

The considerable increase in strength resulting from lignin removed in bleaching is clearly shown in Tables 8.7 and 8.8. The bleached semichemical pulps actually approach bleached softwood pulps in quality and their main use has been as a substitute for the latter.

Bleached hardwood semichemical and sulfate pulps are considered to be on a par for strength, but the alkaline pulps tend to be softer and more bulky. The bleached semichemical pulps also tend toward low opacity.

The unbleached semichemical pulps are

TABLE 8.7. STRENGTH PROPERTIES OF NSSC PULPS

A. *Comparison of Unbleached and Bleached NSSC and Kraft Pulps from Southern Oak* [6]

	Freeness (C.S.) (ml)	Beating Time (min.)	Burst Factor	Tear Factor	Tensile (lb/in.)	Apparent Density (g/cc)	Brightness (%)
Unbleached							
NSSC, 58% yield	366	12	44	91	25	0.618	—
Kraft, 48% yield	388	25	56	98	31	.690	85-88
Bleached							
NSSC	356	8	67	98	32	.729	—
Kraft	359	25	54	84	30	.720	85-88

B. *Comparison of Bleached Hardwood NSSC, Hardwood Kraft and Pine Kraft Pulps* [7]

Properties Interpolated at 400 ml. (C.S.)

	Mullen (%)	Tear (%)	MIT Fold (folds)	Opacity (%)
Mixed hardwood, NSSC	190	325	250	73
Mixed hardwood, kraft	140	325	150	79
Southern pine, kraft	315	450	1,600	60

C. *Properties of Corrugating Grade NSSC Pulps from Several Woods* [8]

Values at 250 ml (C.S.)

	Pulp Yield (%)	Pulp Lignin (%)	Burst Factor	Tear Factor	Folds
Paper birch	79	13.4	46	67	315
Quaking aspen	77	11.6	46	61	161
Sweetgum	76	14.3	41	63	100

TABLE 8.8. YIELDS AND STRENGTH PROPERTIES OF HARDWOOD SEMICHEMICAL AND SULFATE PULPS RELATIVE TO SOFTWOOD SULFATE PULP

Pulp	Pulp Yield (%)	Bursting Strength (%)	Tearing Resist. (%)	Folding Endurance (%)	Tensile Strength (%)
Northern softwood, sulfate, KNo. 25	48	100	100	100	100
Hardwood NSSC, board grade	75-80	35-55	45-60	5-25	30-60
Hardwood NSSC, bleached	53-58	50-65	60-70	15-40	40-75
Hardwood sulfate, KNo. 14	47-54	40-60	60-65	10-35	35-80

mostly used in corrugating board where their strength properties are adequate for the purpose with their stiffness quality giving them a great advantage over other pulps.

The rapid beating characteristics of the NSSC pulps are shown in Table 8.7.

Chemimechanical Pulps. The chemimechanical pulps are usually classed as groundwood-grade pulps, although some approach softwood sulfite pulp in some strength properties. Properties of typical chemimechanical pulps are given in Table 8.9.

A comparison is made in Table 8.10 of typical chemimechanical and spruce groundwood pulps on a percentage basis.

The chemimechanical pulps have higher strength properties than groundwood pulp but are also more dense, less opaque, and darker, except for the birch neutral sulfite chemimechanical pulp shown in Table 8.9. As mentioned previously, the cold soda pulps are often brightened.

Cold soda pulps from woods like poplar and birch can be made with a range of properties. With relatively high applications of chemical and refining power, pulps having 65% of the bursting and tearing

TABLE 8.9. PROPERTIES OF CHEMIMECHANICAL PULPS

A. *Properties of Bleached and Unbleached Hardwood Cold Soda and Softwood Groundwood Pulps* [9]

	Freeness (C.S.) (ml)	Bulk (cc/gm)	Burst Factor	Tear Factor	Breaking Length (meters)	Brightness (%)
Cold Soda						
Unbleached mixed oaks	95	2.00	19.0	59	3750	41
Bleached mixed hardwoods	332	1.95	20.0	44	3580	59
Groundwood						
Southern pine	65	2.40	11.5	39	2350	58
Spruce-balsam fir	90	2.65	15.0	45	3400	58

B. *Properties of Birch Neutral Sulfite Chemimechanical Pulp* [10]

	Brightness (%)	Breaking Length	Folds
Birch N.S. chemimechanical	60-65	7,000-8,000	700-1,500
Spruce groundwood	55-60	3,300	35
Spruce sulfite	56-62	7,000-8,000	1,000-2,000

C. *Properties of Aspen and Balsam Neutral Sulfite Chemimechanical (NSCM) and other Pulps* [11]

	Freeness (C.S.) (ml)	Burst Factor	Tear Factor	Bulk (cc/gm)	Opacity (%)	Brightness (%)
Aspen						
Unbleached NSCM	495	6.9	27.5	2.9	92	48
Bleached NSCM	365	9.7	43.2	2.5	87	68
Groundwood	80-100	9-12	32-39	2.4-2.6	98	62-64
Balsam						
Bleached NSCM	300-310	22-24	88-98	2.4-2.6	89-91	66-68
Groundwood	60	15-17	42-48	2.2-2.3	97	61
Softwood						
Bleached kraft	525-540	44-50	165-190	—	73-75	26

TABLE 8.10. COMPARISON OF HARDWOOD CHEMIMECHANICAL AND SPRUCE SULFITE AND GROUNDWOOD PULPS [12]

Pulp	Freeness (ml) (C.S.)	Density (%)	Burst Factor (%)	Tear Factor (%)	Tensile Strength (%)	Opacity (%)	Brightness (%)
1. *Groundwood*							
Spruce	90	100	100	100	100	100	100
2. *Cold Soda*							
Poplar	250	160	240	125	185	80	85
Hardwood mixture *	180	140	170	100	140	—	70
3. *Sulfite*							
Poplar	180	150	150	100	135	90	70
Hardwood mixture *	180	115	135	110	100	100	85
4. *Sulfite*							
Spruce	450	180	260	200	240	80	90

* Northern hardwood mixture.

strengths of hardwood sulfite pulps have been reported, although the cold soda pulps are low in folding endurance.

Softwood chemimechanical pulps are made in small quantities using sodium sulfite or bisulfite and exceed considerably the strengths of groundwood pulps. Reported values are given in Table 8.9.

Uses of Semichemical Pulps

The semichemical and chemimechanical pulps are used in a fairly wide range of papers and boards. As mentioned previously, the major tonnage of semichemical pulp enters corrugating board. The semichemical component may comprise 100% of the fiber furnish but is usually 70 to 90% with the remainder being sulfate screenings or corrugating or other wastepaper.

A compilation of the approximate maximum commercial usage of hardwood semichemical pulps in major grades of paper and board is given in Table 8.11. These pulps have outlet in most paper products, except those requiring the highest strength, especially tearing strength. Undoubtedly, the list of papers and boards using the semichemical pulps will increase.

Softwood chemimechanical pulps are used in printing papers and groundwood molding products.

TABLE 8.11. USES OF SEMICHEMICAL PULPS

Type of Pulp	Grade of Paper or Board and Amount
A. *Hardwoods*	
1. Semichemical	
a. Unbleached	Corrugating (70-100%), newsprint (15%), specialty boards (25%), saturating paper (40%), wrapping paper (50%).
b. Bleached	Bond and writing (50-100%), greaseproof and glassine (60%), printing and coating base (30-50%), tissue and toweling (30%), ledger and envelope (25-50%), bristols (up to 50%), offset and mimeo (up to 50%).
2. Chemimechanical	
a. Unbleached	Newsprint (15-25%), corrugating (60%).
b. Brightened	Newsprint (15-25%), bond and writing (30-80%), printing (30-80%), coating base (30%), bleached food board (50%), tissue (25%), paper plate stock (65%).
B. *Softwoods*	
1. Semichemical	Corrugating (30-60%).
2. Chemimechanical (brightened)	Coating base (30%), molding products (50%).
C. *Possible Uses for Semichemical Pulps*	
Catalog, telephone directory, liner for folding box stock, linerboard, specialty boards, waxing and gumming.	

Spent Liquor Recovery and Utilization [13, 14, 15, 16]

Semichemical spent liquors from the first installations were discharged untreated into the streams. However, these effluents, as well as those from chemimechanical pulping, contain considerable pollutional loads, as shown in Table 8.12.

TABLE 8.12. POLLUTION LOADS FOR PULP MILL SPENT LIQUORS

Process	Yield (%)	Pollution Load, BOD * (lb/AD ton)
Groundwood	92	20
Cold soda	88	110
NSSC high yield	80	175
NSSC medium yield	65	400
Kraft (with recovery)	48	30
Sulfite (without recovery)	48	550

* Biochemical Oxygen Demand.

The untreated effluents also represent relatively high chemical losses, especially in making bleachable pulps.

Pollution alleviation and chemical recovery are readily accomplished in semichemical mills associated with kraft mills, as found frequently in the U.S. industry, but others are resorting to special recovery methods and by-product utilization, somewhat similar to the advances in the sulfite industry. The specific methods of treating the spent liquors are discussed in the following paragraphs.

The oxygen-consuming compounds in the neutral sulfite spent liquors have been found to be approximately 50% sodium acetate and formate and 50% wood sugars.

The cold soda spent liquor, although not precisely investigated as yet, probably owes its oxygen demand also to the dissolved hemicelluloses and water soluble gums and sugars.

Neutral Sulfite Spent Liquor Recovery

The recovery of the chemical values in the spent liquor from pulping with sodium sulfite has been under development for over 40 years. Complete cyclic recovery methods are now available for neutral sulfite semichemical spent liquors. Important tonnages are now handled by the integrated semichemical-kraft "cross recovery" method. The cyclic recovery of sodium sulfite in most processes involves a kraft-type evaporation and combustion operation with provision for conversion of the sulfide and carbonate compounds to sodium sulfite. On the other hand, the cross-recovery method depends on the use of the sodium and sulfur values of the semichemical spent liquor as make-up chemicals for the integrated kraft mill and the employment of fresh sodium sulfite for the semichemical mill.

Cross Recovery in an Associated Kraft Pulp Mill. In the U.S., 60% of the NSSC pulp production is made in association with kraft mills to whose chemical recovery system the NSSC brown liquor is added as described below. The cross recovery method depends on the utilization of the sodium and sulfur compounds in the NSSC brown liquor as a replacement of the salt cake make-up in the kraft recovery operation. Since a corrugating-grade NSSC spent liquor from cooking to a 78% yield using 10% Na_2SO_3 and 2% Na_2CO_3 (on the wood basis) has a Na_2O content of approximately 112 pounds per ton of pulp (assuming 80%

recovery in pressing and washing) and the Na_2O equivalent of 165 pounds of salt cake make-up normally used per ton of kraft pulp is 72 pounds, the theoretical ratio for a balanced kraft-semichemical operation is about 1.6 to 1. In commercial practice this ratio varies from 3 to 1 to 10 to 1. The theoretical ratio for a kraft-bleached semichemical mill is about 3 to 1.

NSSC and kraft black liquors have somewhat different compositions, the NSSC being lower in Na_2O and higher in sulfur than the kraft liquor.

The addition of the semichemical spent liquor to the kraft mill recovery system may introduce certain problems, especially in evaporation. There is a tendency for fouling of evaporation tubes with combined NSSC and kraft liquors due to short-fibered material and also due to calcium compounds, including calcium oxalate. Separate filtering of the semichemical and replacement of the kraft black liquor used for dilution in the digester with semichemical spent liquor are being used with subsequent filtering in the brown stock washing system. It is reported that a residue is found in the brown liquor storage tanks.

NSSC Cyclic Recovery Methods. In the carbonation (Mead) method, as practiced in two U.S. mills, the spent liquor is converted to a sulfide-high, kraft-type smelt. The flue gas, which is high in SO_2, is used for sulfitation of sodium carbonate in the carbonated green liquor. The carbonation is accomplished with the CO_2 in the flue gas, and the H_2S formed from Na_2S is returned to the furnace for burning to the SO_2 found in the flue gas.

In the direct sulfitation (Institute) method, as used in several mills, the green liquor from the kraft-type recovery is treated with SO_2 to form sodium sulfite for use in cooking. The H_2S produced is exhausted to the air, although it can be burned to SO_2.

In the crystallization (Western Precipitation) method, as demonstrated in a small mill-scale operation, the green liquor, again, is concentrated to the point of crystallization of Na_2CO_3, which is separated and subsequently sulfited. The filtrate is mixed with additional green liquor and aerated to fix the H_2S with the mixture then returning to the furnace to produce a flue gas high in SO_2 for sulfiting purposes.

In the oxidation (Zimmerman) process, as worked out in a pilot plant, the organic matter in the NSSC spent liquor is burned in flameless combustion to CO_2 and water with the energy being recovered through gas engines and turbines. The inorganic portion is oxidized to sodium sulfate, which is subjected to conversion to sodium sulfite.

Other NSSC spent liquor recovery methods are under development, including ion-exchange methods.

By-Product Recovery. Acetic and formic acid are recovered by one mill from the acidified spent liquor by means of solvent extraction with methyl ethyl ketone and subsequent separation of the mixed acids by azeotropic distillation with ethylene dichloride. The raffinate is used as a salt cake substitute in kraft mills.

Spent Liquor Utilization. NSSC spent liquor is utilized to some extent as a road binder or stabilizer in a manner similar to sulfite waste liquor disposal. There is also some movement of brown liquor to kraft mills elsewhere for cross recovery as described above.

Chemimechanical Pulping Spent Liquor Recovery

Cold soda spent liquor is used in at least one mill for dilution in associated kraft digesters as with NSSC spent liquor in supplying soda make-up for a kraft mill. Separate sulfur make-up is required. It is supposed that a cyclic soda recovery method could be developed with an economically-sized operation.

Chemimechanical operations using sulfite compounds are too new and few for recovery methods to have been developed and

the Na_2O equivalent of the spent liquor is low.

CORROSION AND MATERIALS OF CONSTRUCTION

Semichemical pulping by the neutral sulfite process is generally conducted under mildly alkaline conditions although the final pH may drop slightly below 7. In spite of the near neutral condition, serious corrosion problems are encountered in digesters and subsequent handling equipment. The main problems involved are: (a) corrosion and erosion, (b) pH conditions, and (c) vapor-zone action. In addition to the digesters, there are blow lines, conveyors, presses, washers, and refiners which need the protection of stainless steels especially suited for the service. Older rotary digesters have been restored by a metallizing application.

Semichemical pulping with kraft liquor uses essentially the same materials of construction as for the kraft process.

Cold soda chemimechanical operations are conducted under alkaline conditions, but equipment is subject to erosion by the nature of the process and the fibrous material.

Chemimechanical and semichemical pulping with acid sulfite liquors involves highly corrosive reagents and suitable protection with special stainless steels is required.

TESTING METHODS

TAPPI Standard Methods are available for most of the testing connected with semichemical pulping, the same as with full chemical pulping. However, unofficial methods are used for determining neutral sulfite liquor strength and the degrees of cooking and defibering. See Chapter 2.

The NSSC liquor is sometimes tested by an iodine-hydroxide method which includes back-titration of an excess of iodine with sodium thiosulfate for the sodium sulfite and back-titration of an excess of sodium hydroxide with acid after removing the carbon dioxide. The Palmrose method for sulfite acid testing has also been adapted to NSSC liquor.

The degree of lignin removal is determined by modified TAPPI permanganate number methods, as well as with a chlorine test and the use of the TAPPI Standard lignin test.

The degree of defibering is measured by the TAPPI Standard freeness test and also by standardized laboratory fiberizing procedures.

REFERENCES

1. Rue, John D., Wells, Sydney D., Rawling, Frances G., Staidl, Joseph A., *Tech. Assoc. Papers,* 10, No. 1, 90 (1927).
2. Durgin, A. G., and Small, Thaxter W. Jr., "Semichemical Pulping, Modern Pulp & Paper Making," New York, Reinhold Publishing Corp., 1957.
3. Tracqnair, John, and Rawling, F. G., U.S. Patent 1,843,467 (Feb. 2, 1932).
4. Woodhead, Robert, Australian Patent 17,342 (1934).
5. Wood Pulp Statistics, United States Pulp Producers Association, Inc., September, 1962.
6. Chesley, K. G., *Tappi,* 42, No. 2, 130 (February, 1959).
7. Lyon, M. G., *Paper Trade J.,* 145, No. 9, 23 (Feb. 27, 1961).
8. Wells, Sydney D., Libby, C. E., O'Neill, F. W., "Semichemical, High-yield Chemical, and Special Groundwood Processes" in "Pulp and Paper Manufacture" Vol. II, p. 547, New York, McGraw-Hill Book Co., Inc., 1951.
9. Swartz, J. N., *Paper Trade J.,* 140, No. 41, 44 (Oct. 10, 1960).
10. Evans, John C. W., *Paper Trade J.,* 143, No. 34, 36 (Aug. 24, 1959).
11. Richardson, C. A., *Tappi,* 45, No. 12, 139A (December, 1962).
12. Chidester, G. H., Laundrie, J. F., and Keller, E. L., Forest Products Laboratory Report, No. 2188 (May, 1960).
13. Rogers, Charles N., *Southern Pulp Paper Mfr.,* 21, No. 3, 80 (March, 1958).
14. Brown, Richard W., Jackson, Donald T., and Tongren, John C., *Pulp & Paper* 33, No. 6, 66 (June, 1959).
15. TAPPI Sixteenth Alkaline Pulping Conference, Savannah, Ga., 1962.
16. Private communications from mills employing semichemical recovery.

GENERAL REFERENCES

Bibliography of Papermaking and U.S. Patents, TAPPI, Various Publications through 1961.

The Institute of Paper Chemistry Bibliographic Series No. 175, "Pulping Processes," Part IV, "Semichemical Processes," 1955.

University of Maine, Lectures on Pulp and Paper Manufacture, Series I and II. New York, Lockwood Trade Journal Co., Inc., 1951, 1953.

Runkel, R. O. H., and Patt, K. F., "Semichemical Pulp" (in German), Germany, Gunter-Start-Verlag, 1958.

TAPPI, "Pulp and Paper Science and Technology," Vol. I, New York, McGraw-Hill Book Co., 1962.

CHAPTER 9

Groundwood

JOHN H. WHITE

Keyes Fibre Company

INTRODUCTION

Important forward strides have been made in the manufacture of groundwood pulp since 1955: the pitless grinding technique has come into international use; stone speeds have risen from 3200 fpm to 6500 to 7000 fpm, and pressures have increased far beyond the plans of the earlier grinder and stone manufacturers. Automatic grinder feeding has become commercially feasible in at least two mills, with more to come; instrument manufacturers are providing more automation for wood yards and grinders. Indeed it would be simple to peer into the future and see entire large production groundwood units operated by push buttons, which is not at all impossible.

However, while the large production mills in the 300-ton-per-day class have been able to justify the capital expense involved in modernizing and automating their mills, the smaller units, particularly in the less than 150-ton range, have been feeling the economic pressure of rising labor and wood costs and the constantly increasing demand for better quality. In fact, some of the large chemical and semichemical mills can now produce these pulps at a lower cost than a small groundwood mill, and techniques of stock preparation have been developed to make it possible to incorporate the benefits of groundwood pulp in the lower priced

chip, mechanical and semichemical pulps.

At the Fourth International Mechanical Pulping Conference held in Chicago in the fall of 1961, practically the entire theme was devoted to chip mechanical pulp and what it had to offer in place of groundwood. The balance of the meeting was taken up with the vast strides in the above mentioned techniques and the one new grinding development, the Bersano process, described in detail later in this chapter.

The feeling that small groundwood mills are fighting for their very existence was intensified by the fact that at least two American mills have abandoned their low production groundwood mills in favor of the far less expensive and more easily controlled chip mechanical pulp.

However, there are many small groundwood producing units throughout the world, and it is obvious that the great majority of these will continue to produce pulp and maintain their existence through improved techniques and the addition or substitution of equipment which will permit lower labor, power and maintenance costs. This chapter on groundwood pulp attempts to make definitive the modern trends in equipment and operating procedures.

In the province of Nova Scotia in 1838, Charles Fenerty, poet, student, and a young man of great inventiveness, decided that rags were too expensive a raw material for the manufacture of paper and that somewhere in the many vegetable substances of fibrous structure lay one which could supply the rapidly growing need for pulp and paper more cheaply and completely. Although Fenerty was classed as a dreamer by his contemporaries, he did not allow himself to be dissuaded. Because of the prevalence of spruce in his native province, he focused his attention on that wood, and in the same year of 1838, successfully turned it into paper. The method by which Fenerty reduced this spruce to fibrous form was simply that of pressing the stick, or section of wood, against a revolving grindstone with a stream of water to soften the fibers and to reduce the heat of friction in the grinding process.

In 1840, a German by the name of Keller, without prior knowledge of Fenerty's work, discovered the adaptability of softwood through reduction by the same grindstone technique to various forms of paper as a cheap and desirable substitute for the rags previously used. Both Fenerty and Keller were unable to sell their invention to the paper industry, and it was not until several years later that further experiments proved this early method of mechanical pulp manufacture to be practical and economically sound.

Groundwood, or mechanical pulp, although representing from 80 to 85% of the fiber for Canada's great newsprint industry and from 20 to 80% of the fiber for tissue, toweling, pulp book paper, hanging, and board paper business, has defied the efforts of experts in quality control to eliminate its constantly changing qualities caused by the fundamental variables in the wood moisture content, density, chemical constituents, and fiber length.* In fact, although the equipment is more modern, the process itself is exactly the same as it was in Fenerty's day. The development of the ESPRA process of wood pretreatment has been the only major

* Fiber length ranges from 1.0 mm in hardwoods to 7.0 mm in western redwood, with spruce and fir about 3.5 mm and poplar 1.25 mm.

change in the mechanical pulping industry in many years. However, this process cannot be classified as an improvement in grinding techniques but, rather, in wood preparation. The ESPRA process is described later in this chapter.

Thus, at the present time, there is no such thing as a standard mechanical pulp. Each mill determines what fiber characteristics provide the best results on the paper machine, and each operator develops his own controls to supply, within the range allowed by the many variables, a quality of pulp best suited to his mill and its product.

The most commonly used control in the manufacture of pulp is *freeness,* or measurement of the drainage characteristics. Since all pulp is at one time in the form of a water suspension, the water must be removed in order to make a sheet of paper, and the ease or lack of ease with which this mixture, or slurry, will drain is referred to as *freeness* or *slowness.* A free stock is usually composed of relatively long, coarse fibers, or is a stock from which the fines or flour (gelatinous bits of fractured fibers) have been removed; a slow stock consists of short, fine, well-fibrillated fibers well-intermixed with fines. In judging groundwood stock for freeness characteristics, the fines content must be taken into consideration, for a fine book paper groundwood will drain as readily as board stock if the fines are removed. A description of the instruments used in determining freeness is given in a subsequent section of this chapter.

In a paper presented at the 1944 annual meeting of the Technical Association of the Pulp and Paper Industry, Kent Rhodes remarked, "Groundwood has a remarkable and peculiar resiliency or compressibility which gives it outstanding printing qualities. In rotogravure, this quality removes the ink cleanly from the intaglio wells. In letterpress, it has the effect of levelling the surface and flattening out the hills and valleys. In coated and surfaced papers, the hard, tinny surface is compensated for by the soft, yielding interior. It seems to be the super quality base pulp from the printer's standpoint. In converting papers it is the ideal short fiber for extending and blending with long fibers and works well in percentages all the way from 20 to 80%. It gives bulk and body where desired; it gives absorbency where necessary for pasting or surfacing." In addition, its use is extensive in the manufacture of molded pulp products, pie plates, and packaging materials for eggs, fruits, and vegetables, as well as for light bulbs, bottles, and many other articles of a similar nature. There are, however, certain disadvantages in mechanical pulp. Chiefly, it is impermanent owing to the adverse effects of sunlight, heat, and air on its color and strength, and when compared with fully bleached chemical pulps, it is lacking in strength and brightness.

In recent years, through the addition of refining and bleaching equipment, the field of groundwood usage has been vastly increased. Treatments of the fibers following the grinding process and any of the numerous bleaching techniques not only fibrillate and develop the fiber to where it approximates the characteristics of chemical pulp, but also remove the tendency for a browned or reddened discoloration due to the lignin remaining in the pulp during its manufacture.

ECONOMICS OF THE GROUNDWOOD INDUSTRY

In the economy of the North American paper industry the manufacture of groundwood plays an important role. This is best indicated by the fact that in Canada, mechanical pulp in 1960 constituted 52.1% of the total pulp produced and in the United States, 12.9%. Tonnage is as follows:

Canada:

Total pulp produced (1960)	11,119,600 tons
Total gwd. produced (1960)	5,795,500 tons

United States:

Total pulp produced (1960)	25,188,000 tons
Total gwd. produced (1960)	3,247,000 tons

The far larger production of groundwood in Canada is the result of the large amount of newsprint manufactured there. For instance:

In 1960

Canada produced	6,738,611 tons news
Canada exported to United States	5,229,910 tons news

In 1960

United States produced	2,038,422 tons news
United States consumed	7,376,205 tons news

Thus, the United States produced only 27.6% of its requirement of newsprint.

However, while the United States is short on newsprint production, it is far stronger on the other grades of paper containing groundwood, for example, some book paper, many types of board, tissue and specialty papers such as toweling, low cost printing, writing, and tablet paper, "pulp magazines," and molded articles.

While there are not as many large modern groundwood mills in the United States as in Canada for the manufacture of newsprint, their place is taken by many small pocket grinder mills producing specialty stocks having widely divergent characteristics. In 1961 there were 84 groundwood mills and only 14 mills manufacturing newsprint in the United States, as compared to 72 groundwood mills and 40 newsprint mills in Canada.

In both Canada and the United States there are many market groundwood mills with but one or two grinders manufacturing specialty grades, such as shoe board and insulating material; there are many others also using pocket grinders in larger quantities supplying manufacturers of tissue, toweling, and toilet papers with both bleached and unbleached pulp. In fact, in early pulp and paper development, wherever there was a supply of suitable pulpwood and cheap water power, a mechanical pulp mill could usually be found. In recent years, many have succumbed to economic pressure. However, there are still enough to supply with pulp those converting mills located in areas nearer their immediate market.

In addition to these small market mills there are many groundwood mills, as integrated units of both small and large paper mills, manufacturing all the many types of groundwood paper: newsprint, hanging or wallpaper, book, board, tissue, toweling, printing, writing, tablet, molded, and pulp magazine.

So great is the demand for groundwood throughout the world that in practically every country, it has been discovered that certain woods lend themselves to this type of pulp, making possible local newsprint manufacture. The following countries either have built newsprint mills recently or have such mills in the planning stage: Yugoslavia, Colombia, Dominican Republic, Mexico, Egypt, India, Israel, Morocco, Pakistan, New Zealand, South Africa, Indonesia, Philippines and the state of Alaska.

THE WOOD USED

Spruce and fir constitute the most widely used woods in the manufacture of mechanical pulp north of the Mason-Dixon line and east of the Rockies. To a degree, poplar, hemlock, jackpine, and hackmatack (juniper) are used, but only because a mill may be forced to incorporate small percentages to complement its supply of the preferred spruce and fir. Of these woods, spruce, by any measure, is the best. Its longer fibers, strength characteristics, yield, and color have made it the first choice. However, outside of a few fortunate Canadian mills whose large timber holdings in northern Canada give them an ample supply of spruce, most mills use what their own timberlands have available or what pulpwood buyers procure for them. Small mills in the Northeast are still able to maintain averages of at least 50% spruce, but throughout

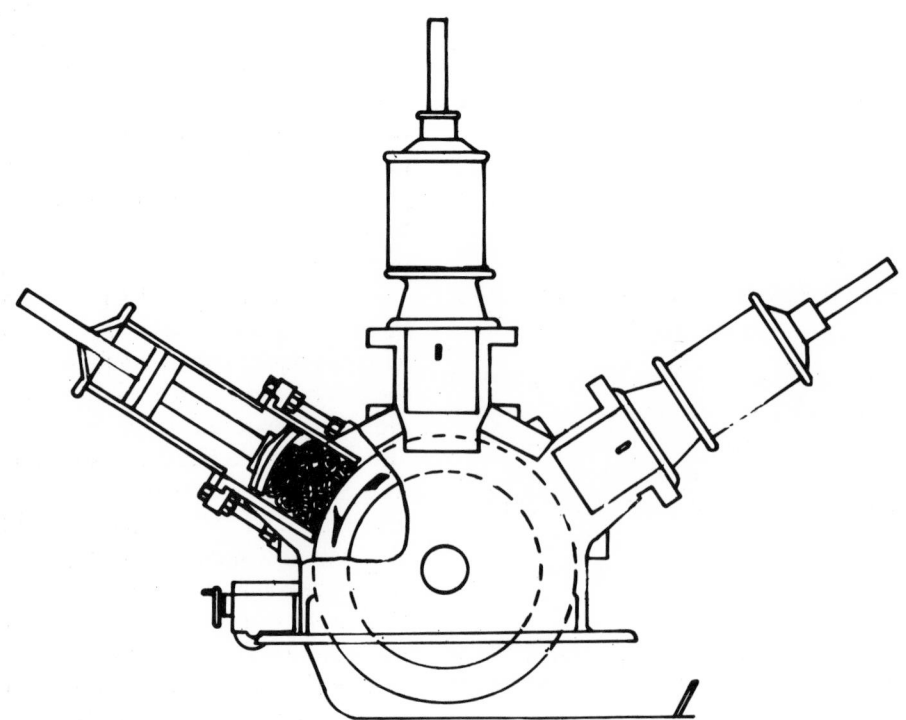

Fig. 9.1. Three-pocket grinder.

the Central and Great Lakes section, spruce content is small and percentages of balsam and poplar are high. The properties of certain pulpwoods in the United States are given in Table 9.1.

The South in recent years has become the largest source of newsprint in the U.S. as well as cheaper grades of book paper, insulating and building board due to the development of the grinding techniques on southern pine. The long growing season and the excellent soil characteristics allow this wood to mature to usable size in 15 to 25 years.

TABLE 9.1. SOME PROPERTIES OF CERTAIN WOODS IN THE UNITED STATES

	Specific Gravity	Shrinkage (%)	Bark (%)	Hardness		Cellulose (%)	Lignin (%)	Fiber Length (mm)
				Side	End			
Conifers								
Spruce:								
Engelmann	0.31	10.4	11.1	240	250	60.5	27.9	3.50
Sitka	0.37	11.5		350	430	60.5	29.6	5.50
White	0.37	13.7	12.4	320	350	60.4	29.0	3.50
Fir:								
Grand	0.37	10.6	9.1	360	420	63.0	27.0	5.00
White	0.35	9.4		330	380			3.50
Douglas fir:								
Coast type	0.45	11.8	10.6	480	510	59.7	30.3	5.50
Pine:								
Jack	0.39	10.4	9.8	370	380	58.7	28.5	3.50
Red	0.44	11.5		340	360			3.50
White eastern	0.34	8.2	12.5	310	310	60.0	27.5	3.50
Hemlock:								
Eastern	0.38	9.7	18.9	400	500	54.4	34.1	3.50
Western	0.38	11.9	9.7	430	520	59.6	30.2	4.00
Larch:								
Tamarack	0.49	13.6		380	400			4.00
Western	0.48	13.2	8.8	450	470	57.8		5.00
Hardwoods								
Ash:								
White	0.55	13.3		960	1010	51.0	26.4	1.20
Basswood	0.32	15.8		250	290	61.2		1.20
Beech	0.56	16.3		850	970			1.20
Birch:								
Paper	0.48	16.2	13.2	560	470	60.6	25.7	1.20
Yellow	0.55	16.7		780	810	61.3		1.50
Chestnut	0.40	11.6		420	530			1.00
Elm:								
American	0.46	14.6	9.6	620	680	58.3	24.3	1.50
Gum:								
Black	0.46	13.9	12.4	640	790	56.7	28.4	1.70
Maple:								
Red	0.49	13.1		700	780			1.00
Sugar	0.56	14.9	13.7	970	1070	60.8	23.2	1.00
Poplar:								
Quaking aspen	0.35	11.5	18.4	300	280	65.5	23.4	1.25
Large-toothed aspen	0.35	11.8		370	400			1.30

On the West Coast, Douglas fir, hemlock, Sitka spruce and cottonwood are most widely used for groundwood manufacture. The redness of some of these woods tends to make bleaching almost essential in order to give brightness comparable with that of eastern spruce, balsam, and the poplar pulps.

In the Northeast, wood arrives at the mill in 4-foot lengths, preferably more than 4 inches in diameter on the small end and less than 24 inches in diameter on the large. Throughout the Middle West it is usually in 8-foot lengths, on the West Coast in tree lengths, and in the South in 5-foot lengths. Custom has been the guide for the variations, but the 4-foot length lends itself to easy volume determination since a cord of wood, the most usual form of measurement, is 4 x 4 x 8 feet in volume. There is some pressure being brought in the Northeast area to produce pulpwood in 8-foot lengths, although up to the present the resistance to this change is strong because of the large job involved in converting all forms of pulp-handling equipment from 4-foot to 8-foot lengths.

The most important property of the wood is moisture content, since the wetter the wood, the easier the grinding. The fibers tend to separate more easily, the strength is greater, the power consumption lower. In general, it is desirable to have at least 30% moisture content, and preferably between 45 and 50%. Wood of low moisture content is sometimes presoaked by a water spray in the pile or by a soaking pond or with extremely hot water and grinding temperatures which tend to soften the lignin bonding the fibers together. Since lignin has certain thermoplastic characteristics it has been ascertained that when the moisture content of the wood drops below 30%, the lignin, or resins, tend to set or cure. This naturally makes defibering more difficult. So critical to pulp quality is the moisture condition of the wood that many operators state that with dry wood they cannot maintain the standards required in their product.

HISTORY OF GRINDERS AND THEIR DEVELOPMENT

Discussion of the mechanical pulping process should give a history of the development of pulpwood grinders from the original method of jackscrews and a car jack for maintaining pressure to the modern high production magazine grinders and continuous grinders of the ring or chain feed types.

Early stones were driven by water wheels, the speed of the wheel being regulated by the amount of pressure placed against the stone. There were no controls, and the ear of the operator was the only determination of the speed of the grinder. As it accelerated, the jackscrews were tightened, acting as a brake, or if the stone slowed down, tension was taken off the jackscrews to effect a speed-up. Obviously, it was difficult to regulate speed and pressure, and production was low.

Such an inefficient method of producing groundwood could not continue for long without change. A hydraulic cylinder was soon developed to accomplish the same results as the jackscrews through the use of water pressure for stability of applied force, a reduction valve throttling the pressure to the cylinder according to the available power driving the stone. In the case of water wheel-driven grinders, a governing effect was obtained by belting the pressure pump to the grinder shaft; this increased the pump speed as the grinder speeded up, increasing pressure on the cylinder and, conversely, decreasing the amount of pressure as the grinder slowed down.

In modern mill layouts the water wheels that still exist are usually used to generate electric power to drive the grinders at a constant speed and power input. Many mills owning river water rights generate power for entire mill consumption, and others purchase their power from local utilities, but whatever the source of power, the effort has been made to eliminate completely the old and inefficient straight water wheel drive.

Original grinders, such as shown in Figure

9.1, usually ground wood in 2-foot lengths, each grinder having three or four pockets. Early stones were 27 inches wide and 54 inches in diameter. Width was increased on certain units to 33 inches to handle the longer half of a stick which was over the usual 48-inch length or wood which was cut in 5-foot lengths before it arrived at the mill. Shortly after the development of the hydraulic three-pocket grinder, units were made which would handle 4-foot wood, eliminating the necessity for slashing the wood after its arrival at the mill.

The early grinders were fed by hand, one man usually handling two units. Charging of these grinders was accomplished by pushing the sticks one at a time through a door in the side of the pocket, the wood being arranged so that binding or wedging within the pocket was held to a minimum. If such binding occurred, the excessive power used to overcome it was wasted against the pocket sides rather than against the stone surface. Lowered quality and increased power consumption were the inevitable results.

As these early grinders produced only 5 to 6 tons per day on the 2-foot and 10 to 15 tons per day on the 4-foot size, increasing labor costs made necessary the development of units which would produce more tonnage with fewer man-hours and a lowered per ton cost. It became apparent that it would be necessary to automate the actual process of loading these grinders to some extent.

Early electric grinders of 2- or 4-foot size employed approximately 500 to 1000 hp per stone at speeds from 2800 to 3300 fpm—restrictions considered necessary not only because of the tendency of the early sandstones to fly to pieces if too much speed or pressure was applied, but because the quality of the groundwood usually suffered with increased production. Also, the physical limitations of hand feeding the old 3- or 4-pocket grinders sharply restricted any chance of reducing grinding labor costs by increased production through higher pressures or stone speeds, and it was obvious

that if labor was to be saved it must be done through quicker and more efficient pocket loading.

The easiest way to increase the number of tons loaded per man was to develop grinders in which the pockets would trip automatically and could be fed in such a manner that there would be a reserve supply ready to transfer to the grinding area upon completion of the preceding charge. If the difficulty in filling a grinder pocket properly were eliminated, the saving in the time of the operator would be available for maintaining reserve pockets at a fully loaded level. The result would be decreased labor cost and increased production. In addition, if structural weakness of stones and equipment could be eliminated, increased pressure and surface speed, both of which were logical steps to higher production, would be possible.

Consequently, it was not long before units complying with the higher production requirements of pulp manufacturers were on the market. Though the advent of the modern high-production magazine grinders antedated the development of the artificial stone by a few years, the combination of the two soon made the industry aware that early ideas of groundwood manufacture were outdated, since powerful tools for quality stabilization and increased production had suddenly found their way to this important part of the pulp and paper industry.

Types of Grinders

The Waterous Hydraulic Magazine Grinder. The earliest successful large grinder produced in North America (Figure 9.2), was the Waterous, developed in Canada. It was of the hydraulic cylinder type using a stone 54 x 54 inches. Two huge magazines, containing several cords of 4-foot pulpwood and extending to a floor above fed two grinding areas rather than pockets on opposite faces of the stone. Each area contained a pressure foot connected to a single heavy hydraulic cylinder. As the wood held against

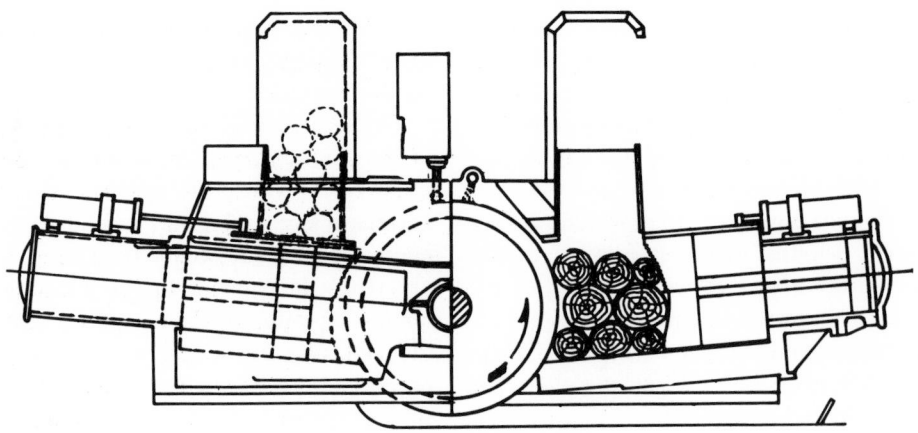

Fig. 9.2. Great Northern-Waterous grinder.

the stone surface by this pressure foot was ground out, a dog tripped a release and water pressure backed the foot off, allowing a fresh charge of wood to fall into the grinding area. As the cylinder piston returned to its limit of travel, another dog changed the valve position and started the pressure foot on its downward travel.

For those mills with ample area this was a great stride towards higher production and lower costs, since the location of the storage magazines made it possible for one man to feed several grinders, and the use of grinding areas rather than pockets elimi- nated loading grinders by hand. With stand- ard power input, production was increased to 25 to 30 tons per day and production per man-hour correspondingly increased by 300%.

The one weak point in this major change in grinding equipment was that it was diffi- cult to find an early sandstone that was large enough and able to stand up under the increased stress across the surface as the stone increased in width. It was not until the modern artificial pulpstone was developed that the efficiency of these mod- ern grinders became a reality. Subsequent

Fig. 9.3. Great Northern-Waterous grinder.

improvements have been made on this grinder so that it will take a stone 67 x 69 inches, with all working parts made more rugged to stand the high loads made possible by this size and by higher operating speeds.

Several years ago to provide a grinder adaptable to mills without sufficient head room for high magazines, the Great Northern (see below) low-head feed arrangement was engineered to this grinder by providing a similar low magazine over the grinding area (Figure 9.3, referred to as the Waterous-Great Northern). This became a very popular unit and has been installed in many grinder rooms throughout the United States and Canada.

The Warren Chain Grinder. In an effort to eliminate the shortcomings of hydraulic systems and to produce stock with no cessation of motion, a "continuous" grinder, called the Warren chain grinder, was developed (Figures 9.4 and 9.5).

Utilizing a single large pulpwood magazine which, like that of the Waterous, extends up to a second floor, this unit employs four heavy chains inside the magazine which pull the wood against the stone face. These

Fig. 9.5. Chain-type grinder.

chains are geared down to run very slowly, and spike points on the side of the chains make contact with the wood. The speed of the chains is regulated to vary the amount of pressure against the stone face, that is, if the chains are speeded up, the pressure increases, and it decreases as they slow down.

The Voith Grinder. The Voith grinder, developed in Germany, is a continuous grinder similar in construction and operation to the Warren grinder except that, instead of spike points, lugs are used on the chains.

One disadvantage of the chain grinder appears to be the high maintenance cost of chains, since there are four chains to a grinder and each chain costs several thousand dollars. Rapid wear on this equipment is not unusual. The hydraulic magazine grinder with properly installed packing or packing cups and some degree of filtration of the water supply to eliminate grit, perhaps with the addition of water-soluble oil, is superior in maintenance expense.

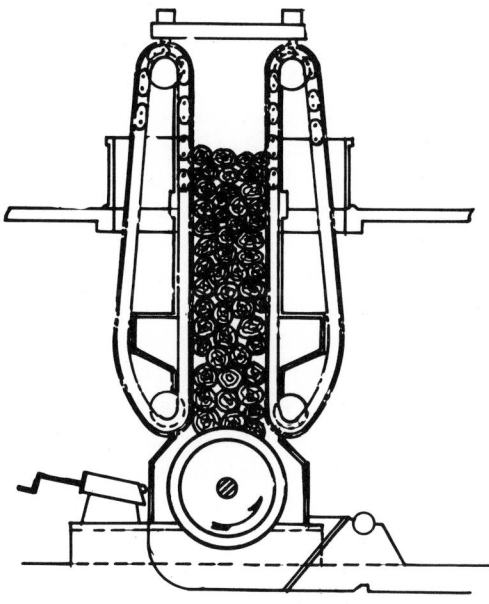

Fig. 9.4. Warren chain-type grinder.

One problem of continuous grinders is the difference in the quality, or type, of stock ground on different sections of the stone surface. As can be seen from the diagrams, the highest pressure comes as the wood is pulled directly into the nip between the grinder wall and the stone surface, but there is also much grinding done further back in the wood chamber under reduced pressure; consequently, it has been felt that continuous grinder stock is a blend of entirely different stocks rather than the more uniform stock of a magazine grinder.

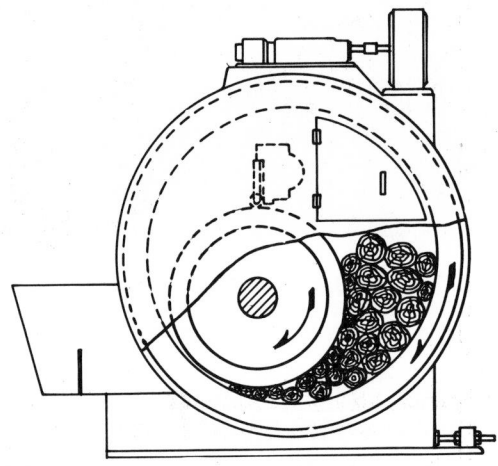

Fig. 9.6. Roberts ring-type grinder.

Because the chain grinder requires less room than does a hydraulic, either Waterous or Great Northern, available space in some mills would not permit the installation of anything but a chain grinder. However, since many modern mills are building new groundwood mills, this factor is not important and the grinders can be selected on their relative merits.

The Roberts Grinder. The Roberts grinder (Figure 9.6), the newest development in continuous grinding, showed early promise of overcoming some of the maintenance problems of the chain type. Pressure is generated by the friction between the stone and the ring. The inside surface of the ring is allowed to rotate at a speed which will ad-

vance the wood just fast enough to absorb the power for which the ring speed governor is set. Speed is controlled by a heavy gear on the outside of the ring which meshes with a worm gear; this, in turn, is connected through smaller, higher-speed gearing to the variable-speed governor motor. The sharpening lathe is located directly above the stone inside the ring. As has been the case with almost all the newer types of equipment, the early Roberts grinders had serious operating difficulties, which have been overcome with minor changes in design. These difficulties were largely concerned with the drive of the ring, and changes in mechanics have strengthened the weaknesses. An advantage of this type of grinder is that wood may be floated to the charging door in the side of the grinder in much the same way as it is brought to the Great Northern hydraulic grinders. A 5-foot Roberts grinder is shown in Figure 9.7.

The Great Northern Grinder. The Great Northern grinder, a development of the Great Northern Paper Company, was made necessary by the limitations of space when a modernization of their groundwood mills in Millinocket and East Millinocket, Maine, was contemplated.

These grinders (Figure 9.8) resemble the Waterous hydraulic except that they utilize two pockets with two cylinders and two pressure feet on each pocket. As the wood is ground out, a dog is tripped which opens a door at the foot of the auxiliary pocket and retracts the pressure foot, allowing the wood to drop through into the grinding area. Wood is supplied to a line of grinders by a water-filled trough in which sticks float parallel to each other and at right angles to the grinder, or by a belt or chains. It is a simple matter for the grinderman to flip the sticks with a short pickeroon from the trough to the auxiliary pocket. As is the case with the other modern units, this efficiency of operation makes possible increases in production to double and triple that of the earlier grinders, and as many as four grinders can be fed by one man.

Fig. 9.7. Roberts ring-type grinder.

Fig. 9.8. Great Northern grinder (for 4-foot wood).

Measurement of Production

A practical method of measuring accurately the number of pockets ground for any given period on a Waterous or Great Northern grinder was developed recently at the East Millinocket mill of the Great Northern Paper Company: the pressure foot backs off and moves forward on low pressure until it hits the wood. Then it goes onto high pressure for grinding. A pressure switch is installed on the cylinder head and is set to actuate an electric clutch to engage on high pressure and disengage on low pressure. The clutch is installed between a counter and the shaft of a sheave, which is caused to turn by a cable attached to the pressure foot. Once a factor is established for the counter by scaling wood ground, then the counter can be read whenever desired, and by applying the factor, the cubic feet of wood ground can be determined.

Automatic Grinder Feeding

Since automation within a grinder room is just as important as anywhere else in the manufacture of pulp and paper, an automatic method of feeding wood to magazine grinders was an inevitable development. In 1958 a groundwood mill in Sweden introduced such a method. Logs are carried by conveyor to a buffer bin outside the grinder room wall. Eight grinders are arranged in two rows with a conveyor running between them about three feet above the top of the charging magazines. This conveyor, starting as a "live bottom" in the buffer bin, feeds logs out through a slot on the side of the bin and will emerge from the bin filled with a continuous mat of pulpwood at right angles to the direction of travel. A series of stretcher rolls enables the conveyor sections to open, permitting the pulpwood to fall freely into the central magazine, and closes as this magazine is filled, allowing the wood to continue on the conveyor to the remainder of the magazines in the line. Refilling of an empty central magazine which in turn serves the two charging magazines is accomplished by automatically changing the position of the stretcher rolls. Complete operation is automated through a control panel which permits individual or total operation through a series of push buttons.

There are other makes of modern high production grinders, including the Kamyr, of Swedish manufacture, and the Tidmarsh, which is a variation of the continuous ring type.

Automatic Load Regulation

A natural result of the early developments in controlling changes in speed or load in water-powered grinders was the regulation of electric grinders. Although, with the latter, peripheral speed of the stone and pressure remained constant, a loss of production occurred each time a pocket was being loaded because, while the pockets were open and being charged, they were not grinding wood, and the power which could have been used for grinding was wasted.

Electrically, automatic load regulation was simply a matter of working out the necessary controls which, as a pocket was tripped, would distribute the excess power over the rest of the grinders or pockets, with an ensuing increase in pressure to absorb production loss. The specified electric load, or peak demand, must not be exceeded but should be utilized to its fullest extent.

These controls consist of a master governor and individual governors for each grinder. The master governor measures the total incoming mill load, and when the load exceeds the meter setting, the moving element overcomes the spring tension and energizes a relief magnetic valve which allows water to be forced by the weights from under the master cylinder. This causes a downward movement and cuts out resistance, allowing more current to flow in the individual electric governors. Thus, the grinder load is reduced the correct amount on a percentage basis on each grinder motor to suit the demand setting of the master governor. When the load is low, the torque of the wattmeter element is overcome by the spring tension and forces the swinging contact against the stationary contact, closing the circuit to the increasing magnetic valve and opening this valve. Water pressure forces the piston upward and adds resistance to the potential circuit of the regulated buss, supplying current to the moving elements of the individual wattmeters. Thus on all grinder motors, the load is increased the correct amount to bring the maximum demand to normal.

The master governor can be set so that any load dropped off in the mill will be applied to the grinders. This is done by adjusting the individual electric governors to carry more load; the master governor will immediately react and take the load off. This places the master governor in a position to apply surplus power to grinders when it is available.

Since approximately 60 to 90% of the total primary mill load is used in the grinding operation, it can readily be seen that close control can bring prompt returns in increased production and a lower over-all power cost due to a steadier power consumption.

Of course, with a grinder room containing only a few units, changes in pressure would have some adverse effect on stock quality. This would be more apparent as a new stick contacted the stone surface, since the pressure per square inch is much greater with a smaller arc of contact, such as would occur on a new stick, than it is with a stick ground halfway through and offering its full diameter in contact with the stone surface. However, this is not always a problem, for stock usually is well mixed or blended during the processes succeeding the grinding operation.

Lathes or Sharpening Devices

An early device for sharpening, or dressing, pulpstones consisted of a stick with a burr mounted on one end which was held manually against the stone surface and pulled across. Obviously, little control of the degree of penetration in the stone surface was possible, and chipping could not be prevented.

A later type of lathe was designed with a manually operated screw. A frame was bolted against the back of the grinder with a bronze screw in the center and parallel to the stone surface. Mounted on this screw, which was operated by a hand wheel, was a carriage which rode on the frame of the lathe. This, in turn, had an adjustable screw operated by a hand wheel, which permitted the burr to be brought into the stone surface. Rigidity was not a strong point of this equipment.

None of these early lathes, or sharpening devices, worked particularly well since, as mentioned above, they tended to chip the stone surface. Once a pattern is placed on a stone, the teeth of the burr mesh with the grooves on the stone and travel across, tracking perfectly unless the lack of rigidity of the lathe allows the burr to jump or skip, in which case it tends to break down the lands between the stone grooves. Since this condition allows choppy and coarse pulp to be ground, it is not one which promotes stock quality control. Fortunately, the early natural stones required burring at least every few hours since they tended to wear rapidly, so that the stone surface reconditioned itself in a short space of time. However, on the modern artificial stones which produce pulp by the cutting action of the grits themselves rather than the pattern, burring was held to not more frequently than every 24 hours and usually around 120 hours, and it was extremely important that the stone face be kept free from land breakdown. The only way to do this was to use lathes heavy enough in construction to withstand the chattering effect resulting from the contact of the burr with the stone surface. Hydraulic operation kept the speed of travel constant, minimizing variations which caused irregularities in the pattern.

Early efforts to develop a rugged hydraulic lathe produced one which had a single large cylinder in the center of the lathe frame on which the burr carriage rode, replaceable bronze gibs taking up the wear. This carriage was actuated by a hydraulically operated piston controlled by a valve in the center of the lathe. In this device, the burr was mounted on a roller-bearing mandrel in a heavy iron fork and fastened to the carriage with bolts. The carriage, in turn, was operated manually through a screw to make contact with the stone. Like its predecessors, this early lathe was not heavy enough for the precision burring necessary today for quality pulp, and it was supplanted by much heavier models.

In these new lathes, the burr carriage is mounted on two heavy cylinders with the hydraulic operating cylinder in the center and with a very rugged burr holder having an integral fork. This eliminates any motion as long as the equipment is kept in good condition.

In recent years lathes have been equipped with micrometer devices to measure in thousandths the actual penetration of the burr into the stone surface. This has made possible almost perfect control of burring, so that stock quality is changed very little after a stone dressing—a fact which makes it possible to burr every stone in a grinder room within a short time and cause very little change in stock characteristics. In the early days where degree of burring, or burr penetration, was controlled by the operator's ear or sense of feel, changes in stock quality were apparent most of the time. Many modern operators prefer to burr stones more frequently and lightly, maintaining top production and lower cost.

In addition to penetration measurement, at least one instrument company is designing pressure controls and charts to record the pressure used in each sharpening.

Modern grinders usually position the lathe on top of the stone, thus keeping it out of contact with the steam and spray water, with their corrosive effect. On grinders such as the Waterous, it is possible to stand on a platform between the magazines and ride the burr carriage across the stone surface; this permits constant close inspection of the burr action and penetration.

There is no doubt that the development of modern lathes with their tremendously rugged construction and pinpoint accuracy has helped materially to control some of the variables in the manufacture of groundwood pulp.

Motors and Horsepowers

When the first steps were taken to eliminate the old water wheels and replace them with electric motors, low horsepowers and relatively inefficient motors with low peripheral stone speed were the rule. For many years power input as low as 165 hp with speeds of 2660 peripheral fpm were used in some mills manufacturing newsprint pulp. These early mills had 2-foot pocket grinders. As 4-foot grinders became more common, horsepower increased along with motor efficiency. Until the advent of the artificial stone, top power was usually around 2400 hp, driving two 4-foot grinders at peripheral speeds of approximately 2600 to 3500 fpm. Horsepower per ton ran from 60 to 80 in the manufacture of newsprint with a low range of 25 to 40 on the freer, coarser pulps, and a high range of 100 to 120 on slow freeness book or specialty groundwood.

As artificial stones became increasingly popular, it was discovered that their construction would permit much more pressure and higher peripheral speeds, particularly when they were incorporated in grinders such as the Waterous and super-Waterous, Warren or Voith, Great Northern or Roberts. All these units were of massive construction as the groundwood industry moved towards high production through greater horsepower, pressure, and speed. In fact, whereas the early 2-foot grinders produced five tons a day, it is not unusual now to see modern grinders powered with 7200 hp producing as much as 70 tons of news groundwood per stone per day. Long-range planning for vastly increased grinder production in Europe has resulted in a request to the Norton Company, manufacturer of artificial pulpstones, to design a 90 x 84-inch stone, powered with a 9500 hp motor, to grind two meter or 80-inch wood.

Modern, high-horsepower motors are of the synchronous type and are used for their better torque at closer speeds, with high efficiency due to their unity power factor and no induction losses. They are far cheaper than motors of the induction type, despite the necessity for extra excitation equipment.

Although these tremendously high horsepowers produce high tonnages, it is not true that lower horsepowers per ton are the result, since 60 hp per ton is still considered excellent efficiency for news groundwood, and some mills in a recent survey have indicated power consumption as high as 85 to 90 under the modern high-load, high-speed grinding techniques.

Synchronous motors are usually wound today with inorganic binding substances, although earlier motors were wound with cotton, silk, paper or similar organic material either impregnated or immersed in a liquid dielectric. As it was discovered in some mills that it was possible to increase production with stable quality, it became common practice to operate synchronous grinder motors with overloads as high as 30%, and more heat-resistant, although more expensive, types of winding material became necessary. The latest type of insulation consists of mica, asbestos, "Fiberglas," and similar inorganic materials in built-up forms with binding substances composed of silicone compounds. Such insulation allows safe operation at temperatures far higher than with the cheaper materials and, consequently, horsepower increases beyond the rating of the motor.

Hydraulic Pressure Systems

To produce the pressure required for cylinder operation in hydraulic grinders, centrifugal pumps are usually used and systems are designed to develop pressures considerably in excess of that which the available power at the grinder can handle. For example, if 150 psi were practical, a pump would usually be furnished which could produce 250 psi so that at no time would there be any fluctuation of efficiency due to operating grinder pressures too close to pump capacity.

The Great Northern Paper Company in its new grinder room at East Millinocket, Maine, is now using some pitless grinding and greatly increased pressures, and has pumps developing 400 psi to allow this tremendous power to be transmitted to the stone.

Between the pump and the grinders are usually located pressure-reducing valves which control the input to the cylinders at the point where most efficient grinder operation results. If this pressure is controlled by automatic load regulation, the setting of the master governor would control any fluctuations or would maintain the setting at a predetermined point. However, in those mills not equipped with such regulation, it is necessary to adjust these valves by hand. Certain mills have made this easier by ballasting the valve with air or oil which, in turn, is controlled by a small valve located at each grinder and readily adjustable when necessary.

A recent improvement in power meters for those mills buying power on a peak demand basis is an indicating meter which will show the peak presently being produced against a predetermined high peak and which, if the high peak is being exceeded, will either give an alarm or energize a solenoid which, in turn, will cut the pressure to one or more pockets through an air-operated shut-off valve. This is a relatively inexpensive installation and is readily adaptable to those small mills unable to stand the high cost of automatic regulation.

Most grinders have cylinder valve systems so designed that the full pump pressure is used to back the cylinder off, thus speeding up the return travel of the pressure foot and cutting down the loss of grinding while the pockets are being loaded.

PULPSTONES

The actual defibering of a stick of pulpwood is, after all, done by the pulpstone, and the grinding equipment is simply the motive power. As early as the period from 1915 to 1920, it became apparent that the old sandstones were the weak link in the

Fig. 9.9. Early 54 x 27 in. pulpstone consisting of solid wheels laminated together.

chain. The manufactured pulpstone was originated in 1921, when the idea was conceived of using the abrasive silicon carbide. Two years later the first successful trial pulpstone was built. Originally consisting of solid wheels laminated to become a single 54 x 27-inch stone (Figure 9.9), this later gave way to the modern segmented type (Figure 9.10) to allow heat expansion at the joints.

In 1926 the artificial pulpstone had become an accepted tool of the paper industry for, almost concurrent with the first sale, the old sandstones began to be replaced rapidly. By 1933, pulp mills wanted more production per unit which meant increasing

power input and manufacturing larger pulpstones. About this time, the first 62 x 54-inch wheel was made to grind 4-foot wood. Then came a 67 x 54-inch and, by 1936, a 72 x 54-inch pulpstone requiring 2500 hp.

During the 10-year interval between 1923 and 1933, the artificial pulpstone allowed the paper industry to expand its production by permitting increased power inputs from the low of 150 hp per stone in 1923 to 2500 hp per stone in 1933. It was also during this period that pulpstones began to make an appearance in European and South American paper mills and the wide acceptance of their use in the United States and Canada proved their value to modern groundwood manufacture.

Along with the rapid advance in the paper mills of the southern United States came the 62 x 66-inch pulpstone in 1946 to grind 5-foot wood.

Porous (open structure) segments were developed in 1948 and proved particularly advantageous to the insulating board industry.

With mills asking for still more production and bigger motors with more power, a 67 x 69-inch giant was built in 1951. This pulpstone, the largest ever made (10½ tons), grinds wood longer than 5 feet in length. (See Figure 9.11).

Artificial pulpstones are tailor-made, that is, made to fit customers' specifications as to size and abrasive composition. There are now three abrasives available for use in pulpstones, in more than 100 grain and grade combinations of each to meet present requirements.

In order to determine the stress points and breaking limits of pulpstones, one large manufacturer recently designed a pulpstone with stress elements built in to determine what actually happens to a stone during the grinding operation. Electronic devices not unlike those used by psychologists to measure human brain waves were placed in and around the stone to measure the toughest grinding condition. Through this research, improvements were designed which helped

Fig. 9.10. 1924 version of a 54 x 27-in. pulpstone showing early segmental development which allows heat expansion at the joints.

Fig. 9.11. 67 x 69-in. Norton pulpstone.

reduce the result of high temperature and pressure, segment loss and breakage, and permitted dependence on these stones in recent experiments that have allowed successful trials of shaft speeds up to 375 rpm.

Burrs

To sharpen or dress a pulpstone, a cylindrical steel shell called a burr is used. Machined and hardened according to the specifications of each manufacturer, burrs are commonly made in four patterns: (1) spi-

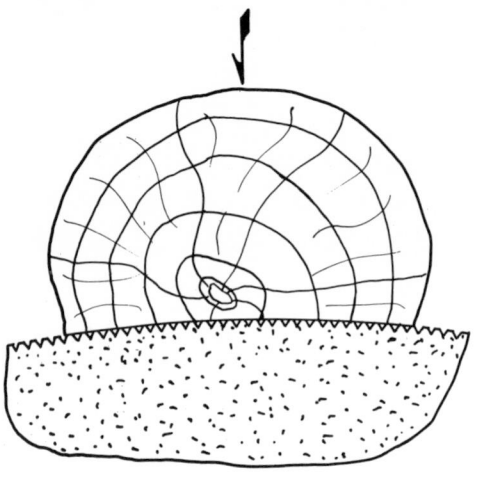

Fig. 9.12. Burr impression on the stone face and a log in contact with the stone.

ral; (2) fluted or straight-cut; (3) threaded, and (4) diamond.

The first of these is the most commonly used today and derives its name from the angular design of the burr lands which impart a diagonal impression to the face of the pulpstone. This spiral burr has patterns with leads from $\frac{1}{4}$ to 3 inches and spacing of the lands of from 2 to 18 to the inch. The fluted, or straight-cut, burr is patterned with the teeth parallel to the axis and, like the spiral, has pitches or spacing from 2 to 18 to the inch. The threaded burr, as suggested by its name, has teeth which are continuous, starting at one edge and running around and around on a very small angle or rate of advance until they run off

the opposite edge. Although this burr can be made with practically any number of teeth per inch, it is usually produced with only 8 and 10. The diamond burr is made by cutting grooves, or flutes, practically at right angles to each other and, again, with any number of teeth to the inch from 2 to 18.

At the beginning of this century, burrs were designed to impress on the surface of natural pulpstones, patterns which would cut or defiber different kinds of pulpwood. With the advent of the modern artificial stone in which the grits are varied in size and structure according to the type of pulp desired, the need for the fluted or thread burr disappeared. The grooves imparted to the modern pulpstones serve practically no purpose but to open up new grit to the grinding area and to remove the pulp without plugging the stone surface. (Figure 9.12.)

The majority of mills now use spiral patterns, in the spacing of from 8 to 12 per inch with leads from $1\frac{1}{4}$ to $2\frac{1}{2}$ inches. There are, of course, variations of this, and some mills have attained good results from cross burring, that is, using a wide spacing right-or left-hand lead, such as a #2, and a finer spacing with the opposite lead. In this technique, the wide-lead burr is used for a comparatively heavy impression which is reburred less often. The finer pattern is put on lightly and more frequently. It is claimed that the coarser, deeper impressions remove the pulp from the grinding area faster and more completely than a single finer impression, serving to reduce the amount of power required in regrinding.

The diamond point burr has a definite place in all grinder rooms, however, for it is used widely to clean the surface of the stone, either when a stone is first placed in operation or when the pattern has become so rough that sharpening will not remove the jagged edges of broken lands. Also, it is used to top off a dressing which is slightly too sharp or to smooth lightly a pattern which is in good condition but with slight peaks which tend to cut waste. Thread and straight-cut burrs are used very little in modern practice.

Burr patterns are usually the result of opinions within individual mills. The fact that it is not uncommon for mills identical in every respect to use different burrs substantiates the opinion that it is not the burr but the method of application which produces the pulp quality required.

GRINDING PRACTICES AND TECHNIQUES

Original grinding practices were simple ones in that, since the quality of pulp required was unknown and the pulp was used largely as a filler, no effort was made to control the type of fiber. The product of the grindstone was absorbed in pulp furnishes and its weaknesses were either overcome by blending with other types of pulp or compensated for by adjustment of paper machine operation.

As knowledge of groundwood was increased and operators became familiar with the type of fiber produced mechanically, efforts were made to produce acceptable fiber continuously. Of course, inherent weaknesses in the original grinding equipment handicapped operators to a considerable degree, but over a period of time and practice it was possible to produce good stock by changes in sharpening techniques or in the equipment itself.

Since the original stones were actually millstones and rotated horizontally rather than vertically, methods of sharpening were sketchy, if used at all. The stones themselves would not stand many changes in speed or pressure. With the advent of the newer types of pocket grinders and the 27 x 54-inch stone quarried exclusively for pulp grinding, it was not long before burring techniques were developed which would allow changes in quality to be produced from the stones themselves merely by changing the lead, or spacing, of the burr lands and the depth which the burr penetrated the stone surface. In addition, pulp was held in the grinding area or grinder pit by a variable height dam to a depth of from 6 to 24 inches; adjusting the stock level affected quality, depending on the degree of regrinding or fines production desired.

Early Burring Difficulties

In early grinders equipped with natural pulpstones, burring was necessary at least every four to six hours. This had a pronounced effect on pulp quality, since a stone would tend to cut free, coarse, and shivvy (groups of fiber bundles) stock immediately after burring—the fibers tending to shorten up and the stock to become slow as the surface became glazed or dull. If a stone were too sharp after burring, it was common practice to "knock it back," or dull it with an ordinary brick or a diamond point burr. Before this operation, however, an effort was made to control stock quality by again changing grinder consistency. As the stone became duller, with a consequent drop-off in production and freeness, additional pressure was placed against the stone surface which tended to overcome this. Since pulp mills are run on a 24-hour basis almost universally, graphs kept of the characteristics of the stock from these early grinders would show a surprising number of peaks and valleys, particularly since night operators, in the days before rigid quality control, anxious to make a production showing, would sometimes sharpen the stones at the start of their tour and dull them back at the finish so that quality would be up to standard when their relief showed up.

Consistency Regulation

As the consistency, usually from 6 to 8% on early grinders, was decreased and the dam raised to increase the submersion, pulp was carried in increasing quantities back through the grinding area, tending to regrind or refine the fibers, reducing their size, increasing the volume of fines, and decreasing the freeness. Decreasing the height of the dam with a consistency increase would tend to speed the exit of the pulp from the grinding areas, resulting in entirely different kind of fiber, less fibrillation, and usually a higher freeness. There were difficulties in this method of operation, since pulp tended to be thrown through the pockets as they were being loaded if the immersion of the stone in the pulp was too high or the consistency too low. Naturally, this would slow up production since the pockets would not be filled quickly if the operator were forced to stand back because of flying pulp. In addition, since it was necessary to burr a sandstone frequently, constant changes in water requirements occurred, because a freshly sharpened stone requires more water than one which has been running for a long time. Sharpened stones tend to thicken the stock quickly, and duller stones tend to become watery and hot, which makes the stock brittle, quite slow, and lacking in the color that characterizes good quality groundwood.

Changes in wood density or species would also cause changes in consistency or freeness, and it was a time-consuming part of a tour foreman's job to watch the many variables on these early grinders which could create sharp changes in stock quality.

Temperature Control

Since all grinders are equipped with a shower or showers to provide the water for stone washing and stock dilution, it was essential that a temperature controller be designed which would operate a thermally controlled water valve so that grinding temperature could be regulated and, with it, stock consistency. This instrument was successful immediately on any grinder from the old pocket type to the modern continuous.

The importance of controlling the temperature at any given point lies in the fact that quality of product is quickly changed by thermal variables. The actual surface grinding temperature has been measured as high as 800°F, and a change of 30 to 40°F would appear to have little effect; yet, if stone surface, speed, and pressure are set for a pit temperature of 170°F, a drop to 140°F may cause a detrimental change in quality. In order to develop pit and stock temperatures high enough to maintain these levels, a closed white water system is customary. All water removed during the thickening operation is returned to the grinding system. Constant heat of friction raises this water temperature to a level of about 130°F. There have been many experiments which indicate that hot grinding (180 to 200°F) is greatly responsible for high strength factors, but in European experiments of cold grinding (125 to 145°F), the pulps show fully as good strength as those produced under North American hot-grinding techniques.

So many other influences have an effect on strength that it is difficult to prove that the deciding factor is anything but a combination of all of them. For example, in a survey of Canadian newsprint mills, all of which are manufacturing under relatively the same conditions of temperature, pressure, and other factors, the burst test ranged from 11.5 to 16.4.

Actually, if groundwood pulp is to be used as a filler or additive in a small percentage, the bursting strength is not too important. It can be a part of a board furnish for stiffness and for book paper for printing benefits. In either case, where percentages are not too large, the far superior bursting and tear strength of the developed chemical pulp would not be affected by a slight strength increase or decrease in the groundwood.

Quality

To define quality with a specific character would be an impossible task since each groundwood mill has its own interpretation. What is required by the papermaker? Bulk, burst, tear, drainage rate, fines content— each has a dominant role in one mill or another and some mills require a combination of all.

Obviously then, practicality dictates a manufacturing method based on the limits of the raw material available equated to the specific type of groundwood demanded from experience gained over a period of years. As the potential of this pulp became apparent, individual mills have been able to gain production and improve the quality through a better knowledge of their product and advances in equipment and automation.

However, certain standards can be established for basic control. Still applicable to quality determination in older mills with pocket grinders is the visual evaluation of the pulp leaving the grinder. Pulp breaking smoothly over the dam, creamy in color with a fresh spruce smell, indicates that the stones are running smoothly, with no burned spots to char or impair the pulp. This same test applies to modern grinders of the hydraulic or continuous type with the exception of stock consistency, which is much lower. Here the stock flows, rather than breaks over the dam.

Examination in a blue glass—a technique mentioned elsewhere in this chapter—can indicate the quality of the pulp according to the required standards. The gamut of qualities from a slow, fines-heavy filler stock to the long coarse fibers required by insulating board manufacturers for dimensional stability are easily recognizable with practice; each stone can then be quickly examined and corrections can be made if necessary.

Past Grinding Practices

In an attempt to review grinding techniques as commonly employed prior to the advent of the artificial stones and newer, more powerful equipment, it would perhaps be advisable to quote from conclusions written by various investigators in the form of observations made at pulp and paper meetings or published in the technical press. Cline and Thickens [1] (1912): "Quality of groundwood decreased with increasing pressure; quality of groundwood increased with increase in pit temperature, but only slightly; production and energy consumption were not influenced by pit tem-

perature; production varied directly with grinding pressure, surface speed and sharpness of stone; factors in pulp quality were: greatest, stone surface; second, grinding pressure; third, surface speed."

Thickens [2] (1913): "Practically the same quality of pulp can be obtained under like conditions of pressure, speed and temperature if the surface of the stone is brought to the same conditions of sharpness of grit, irrespective of whether the design of the markings is diamond point, straight cut, or spiral; deep grooving of the stone causes more rapid production of pulp, but at the sacrifice of quality; the grit of the stone, more than any other factor, influences the quality of pulp produced under conditions of high power consumption."

Dickson [3] (1915): "The grooves put in a stone by burring simply provide a channel for the pulp to run off the surface and the fibers as first removed by an unburred stone are whole, but are ground between wood and stone until carried out from under the wood; the style of burring does not make much difference to the pulp; the grit of the stone determines the quality of the pulp; cool grinding (140°F) produces a hard stock, hot grinding (180°F) produces a pulp which shows distinctly curly fibers; if wood be ground on a trued but unburred stone, fluff or flour stock will be produced."

Gevers [4] (1916): "Pulp grinding is a combination of cutting, ripping and tearing accompanied by rubbing, brushing and stamping." McNaughton (1917): "The type of burr used is immaterial, provided the grit of the stone is raised to the same degree." And in 1926 it was said that a free pulp consists of a mixture of long, thick fibers and short, broken, thick fragments, while a slow pulp consists of long, thin fibers and short, mutilated thin fragments. In other words, the difference between slow and free pulps is one of thin and thick fibers, rather than of short and long ones.

Argy [5] (1926): "Cold groundwood is short, hard, and brittle, whereas hot groundwood is longer and softer; hot grinding showed an increased production over cold grinding."

Modern Grinding

It was about the middle 1920's that the big swing started toward more power in the grinders and artificial stones, and it can be noted from the next few excerpts that studies made on grinding with this modern equipment showed that, in many cases, the results were the same. Johnson [6] (1931) stated that coarse grit stones may cut on the grit and fine grit stones on the burr markings, which would indicate some variation of ideas with previous statements to the effect that the burr had relatively little effect on stock quality.

Schoengut,[7] in an article on the theory of wood grinding, in 1935, said: "Fresh cut wood requires less energy for grinding than does dry wood because it contains between its fibers more moisture, the vaporization of which causes a greater amount of disruption of the fiber than if less water were present." In this statement is summed up the consensus of opinion of groundwood producers that in order to obtain soft, well-fibrillated fibers, which are necessary to make a good sheet high in the strength properties required, the wood used in grinding must contain over 30% moisture and preferably between 40 and 50%.

Schafer and Pew [8] (1936): "In general, grinding is improved by increasing temperatures, provided consistency is not allowed to rise over 4%; (b) consistency rising over 4% decreases rate of production and increases unit energy required." Andrews [9] (1940): "At constant pressure, freeness rises with temperature at constant consistency," whereas "with constant surface the rise in temperature requires a decrease in grinding pressure if freeness is to remain constant." Brecht, et al. [10] (1940): "With a stone burred as for newsprint, increasing temperature causes an increase in production, decrease in energy requirements, and increase in pulp strength."

Modern or present groundwood mills follow very closely the procedure as outlined here; the major differences are in control methods which enable a closer watch to be kept on pulp quality, the use of high horsepower, and heavy construction of modern equipment to allow higher stone speed to produce more tonnage. Quality is controlled primarily by the selection of the proper grit stone, burring techniques, and pressures to handle the speed and power furnished and to cope with the species of wood, its moisture content, and its density. The accepted methods of controlling quality during the interval between sharpenings are the same today—that is, pressure and temperature compensate for dull or sharp stones, and bricks or stone rolls or heavy wire brushes "knock back" a stone if it is oversharpened or cutting waste.

Experiments have been made in longitudinal grinding and with stones made of metal and machined into a permanent pattern, but this has been laboratory work and has not been used in the field.

From a vast fund of experience in reference form, it is possible, as above, to trace definite agreement in conclusions drawn on all phases of the grinding process.

High Load Grinding

The tendency at the present time, particularly among the large producers of newsprint, is to increase production through the use of surface speeds as high as 6500 fpm and pressures as high as 100 psi on the stone surface.

In a survey by the 1952 Mechanical Pulping Committee of the Technical Section, Canadian Pulp and Paper Association, to determine the feasibility of this method, the following was reported: "Opinions as to whether high load grinding is a satisfactory means of meeting demands for increased production vary from a categorical no to an equally definite yes. When grinding at increased load, most mills burr lighter and more frequently but use the same burr. The majority found higher loads produce a bulkier, coarser, chunky type of stock, though one mill found an improvement in quality. Regarding effect on grinder operation, several mills found high load stock detrimental, one beneficial."

Recent experience with this technique necessitated by higher production requirements has solved the early problems and created complete agreement among operators that high load grinding is a practical, successful method of making existing equipment produce more and better pulp.

High load grinding can perhaps be described today as all unit pressure above 60 psi. As late as the middle 1940's large grinding units still restricted such pressures to a range under 40 psi, and only the newest equipment has the necessary horsepower and cylinder pressure to reach the established higher ranges.

Most Recent Improvements in Grinding Techniques

Probably the most dramatic and successful change in the accepted method of grinding is that of pitless grinding. Developed by Christian Anker, President of Risor Tremassifabrikor, Risor, Norway, this improvement eliminates a pit under the grinder and has greatly increased production per stone, increased pulp quality and decreased energy consumption. It requires a change in shower arrangement since, without the lubrication of the pulp slurry, the stone would quickly burn if it depended on the usual back pocket shower for water. Many mills have adopted this practice wholly or in part, and one of the most successful is that of the Great Northern mill at East Millinocket, Maine, where production per stone was increased 10% to 55 tons per 7500 hp, with 2 grinders to a line. These grinders are currently using three showers on Waterous-Great Northern grinders, and pocket production has been equalized and increased, whereas before the shower change the back pocket produced almost twice as much pulp as the front.

A different type of improvement is in use at one of the Bowater's mills in England,

where excellent results in newsprint groundwood are being obtained at 5500 fpm with a shaft speed of 295 rpm. These grinders have 3900 hp each and are producing 60 long tons per day per grinder with a horsepower demand of 68 horsepower-days per long ton (HD/T).

During the past five years these techniques have been developed beyond the experimental stages and are practical, dependable and well-tested improvements which are helping the large newsprint mills throughout the world to meet increasing demands.

Refining Coarse Groundwood

With the advent of improved refining equipment, experiments were conducted in an attempt to grind a coarser, freer stock with subsequent refining, using the ability of the refiner to improve pulp characteristics through the brushing and fibrillating action in the hope of producing a stock with sufficiently improved qualities to increase the use of groundwood in a furnish now restricted to chemical pulps, or a mixture of groundwood and chemical, in addition to lowering power costs and increasing production. Early investigations showed promise, at least on a laboratory scale, and Brown,[11] in 1941, published the satisfactory results of certain trials conducted in Canada.

Although some work has been done on a commercial scale the process has not been generally accepted, probably because of the high capital investment and power cost involved.

Cold Grinding

Until recently the Europeans made groundwood primarily by the cold-grinding methods and, through the use of screens as classifiers or blenders, have been able to isolate certain fibers to produce one type of paper, using the remainder in the manufacturing of another. In addition, they pioneered pitless grinding (described elsewhere) by eliminating the use of dams in grinders, allowing the pulp to drop directly to the grinder sink, thus eliminating re-grinding. Satisfactory pulps have been produced by this method with greatly decreased power consumption, since the re-grinding process consumes a great portion of the grinding power. The present trend abroad is toward hot grinding in the larger mills.

While there are many standard methods of producing groundwood pulp, the many variables involved in the process and the constant improvements in equipment have left doors open for constant research into methods more nearly approaching perfection.

Tips for Improving Grinder Room Efficiency

The following suggestions are made from the experience of a pocket grinder mill:

(1) Some grinder motors, with proper insulation, can be operated at overloads up to 30%. Remember that load tends to be infrequent.

(2) For those pocket grinder mills with no load controls, an ammeter at each grinder with desired operating position indicated will give operators a mark to shoot at and help to eliminate plugged pockets.

(3) Since burned stones are caused by faulty stone washing and/or shimming, a temperature regulator with properly designed showers will increase production and help eliminate this condition.

(4) If pulp packs between bridgetrees and stone sides, causing burning and segment breakage, widen the space slightly. This will improve the situation immeasurably.

(5) A stiff butcher's brush used lightly on a stone which produces slightly rough stock will overcome the tendency to cut waste and, in many cases, will eliminate the need for smoothing with a diamond, with the consequent loss of quality until the stone reconditions itself. Experiments have shown that about 9 pounds of abrasive are lost during a smoothing and sharpening operation as against 1½ pounds per sharpen-

ing, so that stone cost is drastically affected by the above procedure.

(6) Given a stable quality of wood there is considerable merit in frequent light burrings as a production aid without quality loss, and as a power saver.

(7) If the grit is properly designed for the quality desired, a fine burr is less damaging to the stone surface.

(8) Sharpening alternately from right to left and left to right insures proper truing of stone surface.

(9 Too deep stone immersion has only the effect of increasing power consumption. Actually all the regrinding necessary can be done with a 6-inch immersion or less and with properly designed temperature regulation for water control.

(10) Split wood will offset appreciably the effect of sudden freeness jump or a slightly too sharp stone. Any effort used to avoid manually dulling or "knocking back" a stone is worthwhile.

CONTROL METHODS

The blue glass—which is simply a sheet of glass dark blue in color and consequently opaque—contained in a frame with high sides, is probably the most universally used method of quality control in the grinder room. By placing a dilute slurry in this frame with a light shining on the pulp, the operator is able to see the fibers in suspension against a background clear enough to reveal an excessive amount of waste, or long fibers, when they should be short, or vice versa. To a trained operator, use of the blue glass also indicates to a small degree the amount of actual fibrillation of the fibers. Pulp manufacturers now realize that each fiber is surrounded by a skin and that rupturing this by rubbing or refining action, fibrillates, or allows to become exposed, the fine cottony fibers which produce a strong product. Also, increased fibrillation tends to lower the freeness, or drainage, characteristics of pulp and to lower the bulk of paper made therefrom.

Almost as widely used as a control method is the determination of freeness, or slowness. This is a measure of the drainage characteristics of the sheet. Since all pulp is at one time or another in liquid form with as little as one-half of 1% solids, the water must be removed in order to make a sheet of paper. The speed and facility with which this can be done is of prime importance. To make an analysis, a test known as the freeness, or slowness, test was developed. In mechanical pulp manufacture the most commonly used of several instruments is called the Canadian Standard Slowness Tester. A pulp mixture of 1000 ml is checked for temperature and drainage from the top chamber into the lower cone with a side outlet larger than the bottom outlet. Water from the side outlet is trapped and measured. The pad is dried, and weight and temperature are corrected to 3 grams and 20°C. Because of the sharp effect of temperature on drainage this correction must be made. Other freeness testers include the Green, Williams, and Schopper-Riegler. See Chapter 2.

Classifier

In order to make possible the determination of fiber length and size with a measurement of fines, or flour, an instrument called a "classifier" was developed.

A predetermined quantity of pulp slurry form is placed in the first chamber and floated through the succeeding ones, each of which has a mesh screen of different size at the outlet. Paddles keep the pulp blended until all the fiber has either been trapped on the screens or passed through. The screens are usually 20 or 28 mesh to the inch at the first chamber and 48,100 and 200, successively, on the others. Each pad is dried and weighed to give percentages of the total, and the difference, or "passed 200," is the measure of the fines or flour.

Since close control of stock variables is necessary before consistent results can be tabulated, this test today is usually done in the laboratory. Individual mills have found the classifications which produce the stock best suited to their needs and attempt to maintain them.

Photomicrographs

A relatively new and not widely accepted control method is the use of photomicrographs to compare visually fiber treatments and appearances. Very dilute slurries are placed on slides and photographed at magnifications of $100\times$. These pictures are compared with a standard, and attempts are made to duplicate it. However, owing to the drastic and sudden changes in stock caused by variables such as density and moisture content of the wood, reading of these pictures would serve only as a long-range guide since, in the time necessary to develop them, stock of completely different characteristics might be produced, resulting in divergent tests.

Other controls are Mullen, or pop, tests (burst factor), and bulk and tear tests, described earlier in this book. They are not, perhaps, as common, but are definite indications and controls of stock characteristics. See Chapter 2.

PRETREATMENT OF WOOD

To utilize the vast quantities of hardwoods as well as to improve the quality of softwood fibers, pretreatment of wood has been the subject of experimentation ever since the introduction of the grinding process. Earlier work was done mostly on spruce and other softwoods because the results from hardwood were so discouraging.

In 1869 it was discovered that steam at 90 to 150 psi softened the intercellular structure so that fibers could be separated by hand, although the resulting color was dark brown. While not patented, this process was used for many years to soften wood before grinding.

Subsequent work has produced variations of this process, including substitution of boiling for steaming, special burring following boiling, and the Bache-Wiig process of impregnating the wood with sulfur dioxide in a digester and adding a solution of bisulfite liquor. The resulting pulp is white enough and has sufficient strength to run as 100% newsprint furnish.

Until recently, the high cost of pretreatment plus the usually dark color of the pulp has made this process unattractive to the manufacturers, but the development of the ESPRA, or chemigroundwood, process has proved successful and is being used by a large Northeast news mill in conjunction with regular groundwood to utilize the vast quantities of hardwood available. Named for the Empire State Paper Research Associates, Incorporated, which sponsored the research, and developed by the New York State College of Forestry, this process is a procedure whereby billets of wood, generally hardwoods, are treated in a pressure vessel prior to grinding. The debarked logs are piled on cord racks to which wheels are attached. These racks are rolled on tracks into a horizontal or vertical treating chamber. After the cover is sealed, a vacuum of 28 inches of mercury is drawn on the vessel either by steam aspirators or vacuum pumps. After the vacuum of 28 inches has been maintained for a period of 30 minutes, the treating liquor, composed of six parts of sodium sulfite to one part of sodium bicarbonate at a concentration varying between 1 and 1.5 pounds per gallon (all chemicals calculated as sodium carbonate), is drawn into the digester with air excluded. The digester is heated to the desired temperature, varying between 135 and 150°C, as rapidly as possible. A high-pressure pump maintains a hydrostatic pressure of 100 to 150 psig by pumping liquor from the storage tank into the digester at a rate equivalent to the rate of absorption of the chemical by the logs. The temperature and pressure are maintained for a period of 5 to 6 hours, after which the liquor is blown into an accumulator. The logs are withdrawn from the pressure vessel in the same manner as they are loaded, and transported to the grinder room. The liquor may be refor-

tified by the addition of sodium bicarbonate and sodium sulfite. Experience has shown that this liquor may be re-used continuously.

The logs may be ground on any type of grinder. Experimental investigation has shown that natural or artificial stones produce very satisfactory pulps. The artificial stones used in the investigation at the New York State College of Forestry had an average grit size of 60 and was burred with a 9 x 1½-inch spiral burr. Burr patterns other than this were also investigated; although they produced a very satisfactory pulp, it was not of as high quality. The pulps from the grinder pit are treated in the normal manner of bull screening, centrifugal screens, and, if necessary, flat screens. The processing of the pulps after grinding depends entirely upon their end use.

The advantages obtained from this process are: exceedingly high yield (87%); excellent strength qualities (2 to 3 times those values obtained for spruce mechanical pulp); low power consumption (30 to 35 horsepower-days per ton); better woodlands management resulting from the utilization of beech, birch, maple, and aspen along with the coniferous species normally used in mill production; high yield of pulp per cord of dense hardwoods, and extreme versatility of the fiber. Pulps can be manufactured for use in grades ranging from newsprint and groundwood book through toweling and tissue to corrugating medium. This wide variety of pulps can readily be achieved by modifications of the treating techniques.

AFTER-TREATMENT OF GROUNDWOOD

Because conventional, i.e., hypochlorite, bleaching methods for groundwood pulp are impractical owing to the large amount of resinous noncellulosic materials present, it is necessary, in order to utilize the full value of a brighter mechanical pulp, to develop simple, cheap bleach techniques which would give a substantial brightness rise with a minimum of investment and operating costs.

The usual brightness level for good spruce and fir pulpwood ranges from 59 to 63 G.E., fresh-peeled green poplar occasionally getting to a top of 65. Provided dirt specks and shives are held to a minimum, this range is good enough for ordinary groundwood papers or products. However, most mills are not fortunate enough to have pulpwood of this quality available, and the use of inferior grades will cause a brightness drop of from 55 to 57 for old spruce and fir to 47 to 49 for southern pine and West Coast hemlock.

Obviously, regardless of the low cost of manufacturing mechanical pulp, in relation to chemical pulp, brightness must be increased by the market groundwood mills if they are to maintain a competitive position, or by mills manufacturing groundwood paper and specialties if they are to meet the demands of a buyer's market. Therefore, following bleaching attempts by the hypochlorite which tended to yellow the highly resinous softwoods, it was discovered that hydrosulfites, sodium or zinc, and later the peroxides, sodium or hydrogen, worked well on a single-stage bleaching and gave improvement of from 6 to 12 points, depending on wood, retention time, and pulp density, at a cost of approximately one dollar per brightness point.

On the West Coast, in raising the brightness of the widely used western hemlock to approach that of eastern softwoods, the easily applied zinc hydrosulfite has been successful when added to the stock at the grinder sink or immediately preceding the paper machine.

Problems in bleaching are being overcome as the position of bleached groundwood in the industry becomes stronger. It has definitely arrived to take its place with the bleached grades of semichemical and chemical pulps.

Full details on the mechanics of groundwood bleaching are given in a subsequent chapter.

CHIP MECHANICAL PULP

During the past several years an increasing amount of interest has been evident in the manufacture of mechanical pulp from chips. Many factors have contributed to this growth, but essentially the availability of chips from saw-mill waste and other wood by-products has made this most interesting to many mills, since the labor of operation is far less in an average mill than the grinder process. Also, the capital investment required to increase production is far less than for the addition of more grinders, motors, screens and other necessary components of a groundwood mill. As of 1962, there were at least three mills manufacturing this type of pulp which had discarded or added to the pure stone groundwood, and results on the paper machines fully justified the change.

In any given section of the United States at present, the chipping of long wood, either in the actual woodlands operations or at saw mills, has increased to the point that most mills plan their future wood storage in the form of chips obtained either as mentioned above or in chipping operations at their own mills, in which all long wood is chipped as it is accepted and is blown into piles to be used as necessary.

Again, almost any species of wood is available, from softwoods to the densest of hardwoods, and the new types of chemical pulping have made it possible to use woods never before considered economically possible for the manufacture of pulp and paper. Mild chemical pretreatments have resulted in semichemical types of pulps ranging from yields of about 65% to well over 90%, so that hardwoods and softwoods alike are finding uses in areas or in types of pulp heretofore reserved for groundwood made from softwoods or the soft hardwoods such as poplar and cottonwood.

The equipment used to manufacture mechanical pulp from chips is a disk refiner, either one or two stages, possibly a "pump-through" refiner and a centrifugal cleaner system to remove chop or shives which are quite commonly found in refiner pulp. Discussion of this process was given in a paper at the 4th International Mechanical Pulping Conference in Chicago in 1961, by Walter F. Holzer, John P. Henderson, William B. West, and Kenneth F. Byington of the Crown Zellerbach Company in Camas, Washington.[12] In their Central Research Institute, they developed a chip mechanical pulp giving all the properties of stone groundwood and even going beyond in burst and tear, with a pinpoint freeness control which would be impossible to obtain in the conventional grinding process.

These authors indicated that their work was done with a single double-disk refiner, followed with a "pump-through" refiner at a total applied horsepower of 85 HD/T vs. stone groundwood of 65 HD/T; the same freeness of 100 csf; a burst factor of 14 vs. stone groundwood at 10; and a tear factor of 50 vs. stone groundwood at 40. They also duplicated this work with two stages of refining giving them a total horsepower of 78 using 95% of power in the first stage and 5% on the "pump-through" refiner. The burst factor was reduced to 11,

the tear factor to 35, but the qualifications which they needed were still maintained.

They also discovered that it was not necessary to use conventional screens, since centrifugal cleaners will remove more effectively the undesirable dirt produced in refining. The refiner (Figure 9.13) which they put in commercial operation is a 48-inch double disk unit using 2,000 hp (1,000 on each disk) and a single conventional "pump-through" refiner which would handle all the tonnage produced by the larger unit. On the basis of 78 hp per ton such a unit could produce between 25 and 30 tons per day. See also Chapter 8.

These authors go on to describe the importance of accurate controlled feed to the refiner and controlled consistency, the disk being held as high as possible, i.e., in the range of 3 to 8%.

One large manufacturer of refining equipment used in two West Coast mills that have installed commercial production units has this to say about the technique of chip mechanical pulping following expansion in these mills: "It is our present opinion that two stages of double disk refiners (series) are preferable in the production of groundwood from chips."

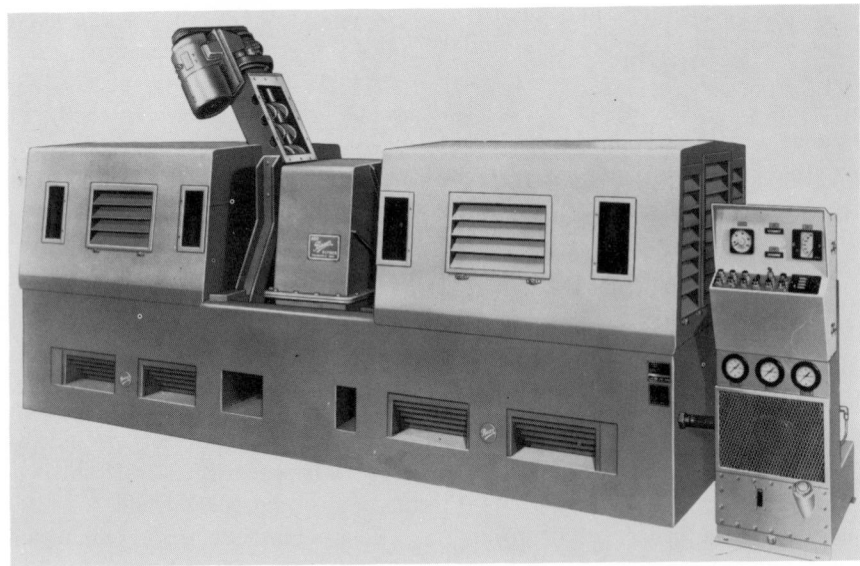

Fig. 9.13. Double revolving disk refiner. (*Courtesy Bauer Brothers Co.*)

Since the use of "pump-through" (Figure 9.14) refiners has been studied as a final stage in this new process and such refiners are being added to these systems, the above manufacturer adds, "It is pointed out that our data and information on the effect of the 'pump-through' refiner in the chip groundwood process are at present somewhat preliminary and we feel sure that the results to date are not the optimum that can be attained. Examination of data does indicate, however, that after a certain degree of fiberizing in the double disk, the 'pump-through' will reduce freeness and produce fineness in the pump at very low expenditure of power. There is also a good burst and tensile development with a very small loss in tear. We believe that this freeness reduction is accomplished at considerably less power input than would be required in the double disk over the same freeness range but that the double disk is required for the fiberizing of the chips and development of the inherent strength potential of the pulp." [13]

Labor advantages of the chip mechanical process over conventional grinding are numerous, and a properly designed chip mill would probably be able to move the chips from the storage pile to the refiners and the finished product into storage chests or thickening operations for shipping with no more than one or two men a shift. The size of the operation would have very little effect on the personnel required, because a single operator can control the desired quality and quantity from many refiners as easily as from one. With controlled feed and consistency there is little to change the quality of the product beyond the minor changes of wood density, moisture content, and so on. Automated mechanical movement of chips is already commonplace in new mills, and one man with an efficient front end loader can move all the chips required to the air flow system for mills up to 300 and 400 tons daily. From this point, flow is simple and can be controlled to the continuous refiner operation with no human effort.

Such a process eliminates the costly, involved screening systems required in stone groundwood as well as the multiplicity of pumps and thickening required to supply groundwood at lower than grinding consistency for screening; it also eliminates thickening the groundwood for storage or

Fig. 9.14. "Pump-through" refiner (up to 100 hp). (*Courtesy Bauer Brothers Co.*)

mixing with other pulps and chemicals for a paper machine or other operation.

It is apparent from the advantages of chip mechanical pulp and the success obtained thus far in commercial scale production that this process has gone beyond the experimental stage and offers an excellent future in pulping programs within its existing limitations.

ROTATIONAL GRINDING

A completely new application of fiber separation called "rotational grinding" using abrasive grinding wheels made its appearance in 1960 in Italy, and early samples of the pulp showed excellent qualities.

This new and unique method of pulp grinding was invented by Dr. Piero Bersano, Technical Director of Cartiere Burgo, Turin, Italy, and patented throughout the world. Assistance in development was given by the Norton Company of Worcester, Massachusetts, manufacturer of artificial pulpstones.

Rotational grinding employs a series of grinding wheels so arranged that they impart a rotational movement to the pulp log and propel it forward while grinding off pulp.The grinding wheels and supporting rollers comprising grinding stations are adjusted with a narrowing gap from station to station so that the log is ultimately reduced to pulp.

The arrangement of grinding wheels and supporting rollers is shown in the schematic drawing (Figure 9.15). The wood to be ground is placed upon two rollers; one or both rollers may be driven, or one or both may simply be idler rollers. The grinding wheel, which is positioned above the wood, has a conical grinding face and is set at definite angles in relation to the log. As the grinding wheels turn and because of the angles mentioned, they cause the log to rotate and the log is propelled forward to subsequent grinding stations. In rotating and passing between rollers and the grinding wheel, the log is subjected to compression and decompression which assists in the absorption of fluids. Figure 9.16 shows the fiber separation during the grinding process.

Many working models of machines utilizing the principle have been built and tested

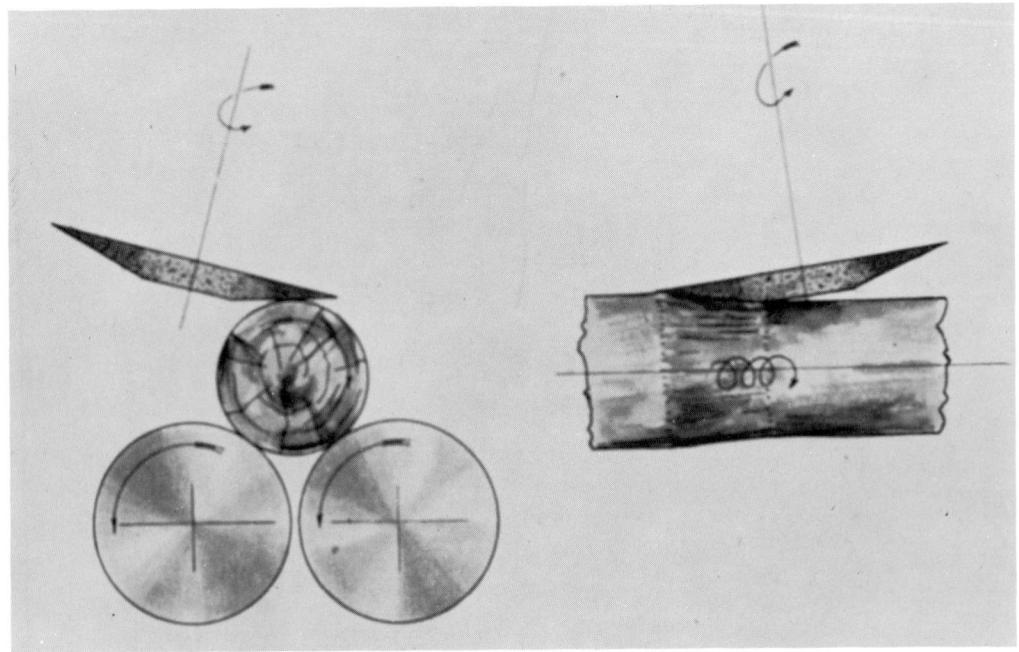

Fig. 9.15. Position of grinding wheels—Bersano process.

Fig. 9.16. Fiber separation in Bersano process.

in the laboratories of Cartiere Burgo. These several models, employing many mechanical designs, have been aimed at simplification and dependability and have enabled the inventor to prove some of the advantages claimed for rotational grinding over the conventional method. Groundwood or mechanical pulp through full commercial ranges has been produced. Power savings of the order of 23% for equivalent quality pulp have been obtained in the laboratory and logs of indefinite lengths can be ground.

Through the compression and decompression action mentioned above, pulps having semichemical characteristics have been produced.

TREATMENT OF PULP AFTER GRINDING

Figure 9.17 illustrates a fairly standard grinding, screening, and thickening flow diagram. Pulp from the grinders passes through a bull, or "sliver" screen, which consists of an inclined plate or series of plates with $5/8$- to $3/4$-inch orifices. This screen removes the coarsest waste. The stock is then usually passed through a "knotter" screen to remove waste the size of match sticks. These screens are of the centrifugal or vibrating type such as the Allis-Chalmers or Jonsson, with $1/4$- to $3/16$-inch perforations. In recent years, the vibrating screen with $1/8$- to $1/4$-inch perforations has become very popular because of its high production and low power consumption. The coarse material screening step and the "knotting" step are sometimes combined.

Accepted stock from the combined bull and knotter screens or the knotter alone passes to the fine screens for the last (usually) of the screening steps. Fine screens are most often of the centrifugal type, with perforations from 0.045 to 0.075 inch or larger depending on the type of stock.

Groundwood fine screening is almost exclusively accomplished today by the use of centrifugal screens (Figure 9.18). Their success is due to the hydraulic action within the screen which aligns the fibers with the screen plate orifices and allows the denser reject material to be discharged through the tailings outlet.

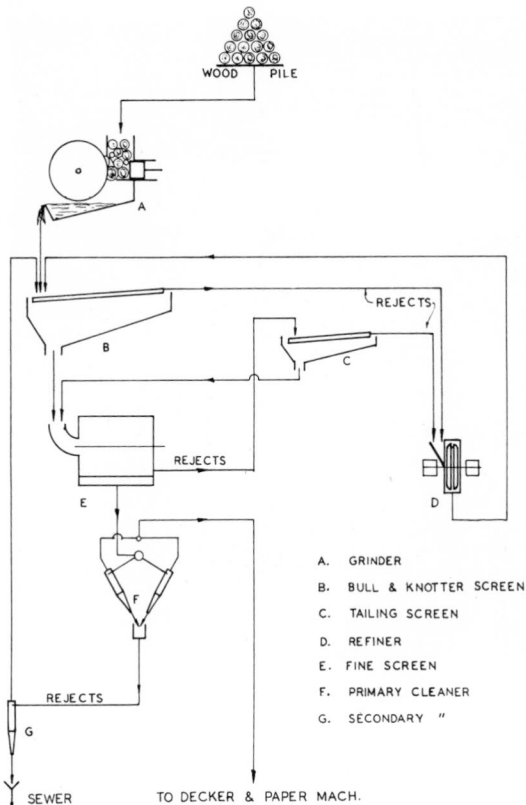

A.   GRINDER

B.   BULL & KNOTTER SCREEN

C.   TAILING SCREEN

D.   REFINER

E.   FINE SCREEN

F.   PRIMARY CLEANER

G.   SECONDARY   "

Fig. 9.17. A simple groundwood mill flow diagram which may be changed to suit individual mill requirements.

This is best expressed by the following quotation from Bulletin C-104 of the Montague Machine Company on the Cowan Centrifugal pulp screen. See Figure 9.19.

"Stock from the coarse screens enters the inlet at a consistency of about 0.75% to 1.50% dependent on nature and type of pulp. The mixture leaves the barrel radially through slots marked 'A.' That portion of the screen body up to the baffle 'B'—may or may not be completely filled, depending on the desired capacity.

"Accepted fiber is forced through the screen plate holes under the action of centrifugal force. The static head on the screen inlet causes axial movement so the rejected fiber travels to the tailings discharge at the end of the screen. As this mixture passes the baffle 'B,' shower water, from slots 'C' in the hollow shaft, dilutes the rapidly thickening pulp suspension and washes the good fiber through the plates. That area of the plate outside the center baffle functions virtually as a second screen. It will be noted that this occurs over about half the screen area.

"Provisions for shower water should be from 20 to 30% of the total volume of discharge. Pressure required is not more than 5 psig. The baffle marked 'D' acts as a dam and increases the centrifugal pressure over this portion of the plate by retaining a volume of mixture.

"The residue drops off the ends of the rotor blades as tailings and leaves through the discharge opening as shown."

The Cowan screen has been widely accepted throughout the industry for fine screening of groundwood. Its construction allows it to perform the duties of both a primary and secondary screen, and since it will screen at high consistencies, it materially reduces the amount of thickening equipment required.

The operation of the Cowan screen is as follows:

"The purpose of centrifugal screening is to remove coarse fiber. In a mixture of pulp and water at rest the fibers lie in all directions. As this mass is rotated in a centrifugal screen the fibers tend to align themselves with the direction of flow. The greater the peripheral speed the closer the alignment, and fibers in closest alignment with flow are those in the outside layer of the mixture, travelling at the speed of the water. These are the fibers in the fluid mixture which is discharged under pressure of centrifugal force through the holes in the screen plate, after penetrating a mat of accumulated coarse fibers and shives which also helps to screen it.

"For all practical purposes these fibers may be assumed to have the specific gravity of water. Not so the tailings. Because shives, coarse fiber and dirt are not thoroughly hydrated, their density is somewhere between that of water and that of wood. With this factor limiting the effect of centrifugal

Fig. 9.18. Cowan centrifugal pulp screen. (*Courtesy Montague Machine Co.*)

force, this material will tend to lag behind the main body of pulp and to barrel axially through the screen for discharge as rejects.

"By controlling variables such as shower water, consistency and screen plate perforation size, it is possible to control screening efficiency."

The most recent Cowan screens, the K and the KX series, have some changes and improvements in the interior portions including baffling and rotor, and this new model will accept stock up to $2\frac{1}{2}\%$ and produce up to 160 tons per day as against 125 to 150 tons on the previous model. These screens are manufactured in the United States by the Montague Machine Company and Appleton Machine Company.

Improved Paper Machinery Company and Koehring-Waterous Company of Canada also manufacture a similar type screen which has proved highly satisfactory in groundwood mills.

Rejected stock from fine screens is either passed directly to a tailing screen or re-screened in a centrifugal screen with smaller perforations, the waste being sent to the tailing screen for final stock separation. The tailing screen is sometimes a flat screen but in modern mills is usually another vibrating

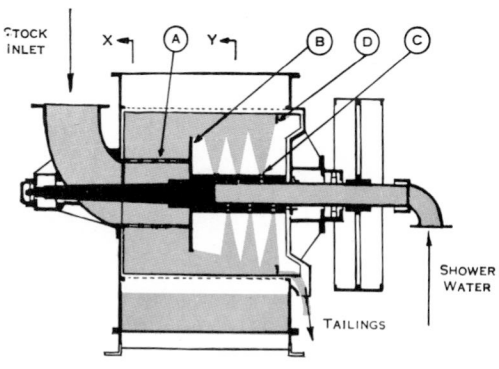

Fig. 9.19. Diagram of Cowan centrifugal screen.

unit, again because of high production and low power cost.

Accepted stock from the rescreen, or secondary screen, is usually sent directly to the machine or stock tank while the accepted stock from the tailings unit is customarily returned to the bull screen for further cleaning.

Disposal of Rejects

Many more mills each year are finding that properly treated groundwood rejects make excellent stock. Considerable power has been spent reducing a log to reject size, and with comparatively little further effort, this waste can be made into fiber of as good, if not better, quality than that from the grinders. With the current high cost of wood and labor this waste recovery becomes attractive economically.

Constant improvements in disk refiners, which are described elsewhere in this book, allow greater horsepower usage with designs, eliminating deflection due to high operating temperatures and make highly practical the refining of grinder tailings. Even bull screen rejects, initially broken up in hammer-mill type equipment, are easily defibered, and all such refined material, if the full potential of the equipment is used, can add very desirable characteristics to the final groundwood quality.

In fact, pulp from the refiner following cleaning becomes an excellent product for many uses. Its high freeness and long fiber plus excellent tear and burst strength make it attractive in hanging, molding and board grade.

PULP CLEANING EQUIPMENT

In the past few years pulp cleaning equipment has taken a definite place in paper production because of its increasing versatility and adaptability to all types of stocks and all types of dirt. Originally the Vortrap was produced as the first of the pressure-drop vortex type cleaners. Pulp was pumped in under pressure tangentially to the side of the conical device, the heavier particles of dirt settling to the bottom and the cleaned stock passing out through the top. Dirt was periodically dumped by hand. Later units of the same type appeared, among them the Dirtec and Hydraclone, which functioned in somewhat the same manner.

The most widely used of the pressure drop cleaners is now the Bauer Cleaner manufactured by the Bauer Brothers Company. A development from research work done by two mills, Hammermill Paper Company of Erie, Pennsylvania, and Howard Smith Paper Mills of Cornwall, Ontario, it is made in different sizes for coarse or fine cleaning requirements and seems to work well on shape of dirt as well as weight. Shives and light bark specks are removed, as well as heavier dirt particles such as grit from pulpstones. A constant bleed permits a secondary and tertiary stage if required. Most widely used size is the #606 with a capacity of 100 gpm.

The use of these cleaners has definitely simplified the woodroom operation by decreasing the need for rigid wood inspection and rejection for residual bark.

THICKENING EQUIPMENT

Mills using a "slush" system or mills using screened stock directly to the paper machine via a storage chest, dewater or thicken the stock to a consistency of about 4% A.D. (air dry) by means of the "decker." A revolving wire-mesh covered cylinder in a vat of screened stock picks up a mat of stock on the wire, removes the water so the consistency increases from about 0.5 to 4% A.D. and transfers it to a felt or rubber covered "couch" roll. A "doctor," or knife, of iron, wood or plastic, is held against the couch and scrapes the stock off the roll to a conveyor from which it is pumped or conveyed to the storage chest.

The water, or "white" water, removed from the stock is returned to the system for re-use if the mill is using a "closed" system, in order to catch all the solids which escape through the wire and to build up the temperature of the grinding system.

While there are other types of thickeners, usually more elaborate, this is by far the most universally used.

If the mill is thickening the pulp for a long term of storage or for shipment, a consistency of 35 to 40% A.D. is reached with ordinary wet machines, or deckers, to which an endless felt with a press section is added. The felt picks up the sheet and transfers it to the top press roll; from here, after reaching the desired thickness, it is cut off by a doctor, or knife, and folded, or lapped, into bundles for storage or shipment.

Modern versions of the wet machine are of the feltless type, the sheet being formed by vacuum to a thickness sufficient to be self-supporting. Press sections are heavier and usually employ a steam-heated dryer section between presses.

CONCLUSION

There are experimental groundwood laboratories in operation today where accurate answers are being sought to what happens when a stick of pulpwood is pressed against a revolving pulpstone. In addition, manufacturers are striving for equipment which will level off the many variables and pinpoint final quality. In the future many, if not all, of the problems will be solved. But what groundwood is today and will be for some time to come is due to the skill and experience of the operators and the ability of each one to cope with his individual requirements and limitations.

REFERENCES

1. Cline, H., and Thickens, J. H., "The Effect of Variable Grinding Conditions," *orig. Comm. 8th Intern. Congr. Appl. Chemistry,* 13, 83 (1912); 27, 110 (1913); *J. Soc. Chem. Ind.,* 31, 869 (1912); *Paper,* 9, No. 2, 20 (1912).

2. Thickens, J. H., "The Grinding of Spruce for Mechanical Pulp," *U.S. Dept. Agr., Forest Service Bull. 127* (1913).

3. Dickson, G. W., "Some Variable Conditions Affecting the Manufacture of Groundwood," *Pulp Paper Mag. Can.,* 14, No. 4, 83 (1916).

4. Gevers, K., "Grinding of Wood," *Paper Trade J.,* 62, No. 15, 54 (1916).

5. Argy, M. J., "The Manufacture of Groundwood," *Pulp Paper Mag. Can.,* 24, No. 8, 14 (1926).

6. Johnston, H. W., "Studies in the Manufacture of Groundwood Pulp," *Pulp Paper Mag. Can.,* 31, No. 6, 221 (1931).

7. Schoengut, J., "The Theory of the Wood Grinder," *Papier-Fabr.,* 33, No. 3, 17 (1935).

8. Schafer, E., and Pew, J. C., "Effect of Temperature and Consistency in Mechanical Pulping," *Tech. Assoc. Papers,* 19, 401 (1936).

9. Andrews, H., "The Effect of Grinding Consistency and Temperature Using a Miniature Grinder," *Pulp Paper Mag. Can.,* 41, No. 2, 87 (1940).

10. Brecht, W., Mueller, W., Schroeter, N., and Luttinger, R., "The Effect of Grinding Temperature in the Manufacture of Mechanical Pulp," *Papier-Fabr.,* 38, Nos. 9-10, 53; No. 11, 61 (1940). *Bull. Inst. Paper Chem.,* 10, 381; *C.A.,* 34, 7601.

11. Brown, J. D., "Studies in Classification and Refining of Groundwood Pulp," presented at Annual Meeting, C.P.P.A., January, 1941.

12. Paper presented at the 4th International Mechanical Pulping Conference at the Edgewater Beach Hotel, Chicago, Sept. 19-21, 1961.

13. W. M. Orchard, Project Manager, Bauer Brothers Co., Springfield, Ohio, 1961.

GENERAL REFERENCES

Daniell, Warren, "Grinders and Grinding," in "University of Maine Lectures on Pulp and Paper Manufacture," Series II, p. 52, New York, Lockwood Trade Journal Co., Inc., 1953.

Graham, Duncan, "Operation and Maintenance of Grinder Load Regulators on Waterous Hydraulic Grinders," *Proc. Tech. Sect. Can. Pulp and Paper Assoc.,* 224 (1952).

Libby, C. Earl, and O'Neil, F. W., "The Manufacture of Chemi-groundwood Pulp from Hardwoods," *Empire State Paper Research Assoc.,* 1950.

Winchester, A. J., and Cuthbertson, A. M., *Proc. Tech. Sect. Can. Pulp and Paper Assoc.,* 103 (1953).

CHAPTER 10

Pulp Bleaching

JOHN L. PARSONS

Consultant, Rye, New Hampshire

The main object of the bleaching process is the removal of coloring materials in the fibers and the production of a white pulp of satisfactory physical and chemical properties. This is accomplished by a bleaching agent which is usually an oxidizing agent but may be a reducing compound. After the bleaching operation, the fibers are thoroughly washed with water to remove solubilized impurities.

Until the discovery of the bleaching action of chlorine, rags for paper making were bleached or decolorized by boiling them in alkali and exposing them to the sun for a long time. With the advent of chlorine bleaching, the processing of raw fibrous materials for the manufacture of paper was speeded up. Colored rags, heretofore unavailable because they could not be satisfactorily whitened, were susceptible to chlorine bleach and became additional raw material for paper.

As early as 1798, the use of chlorine for bleaching rags for paper making was the subject of an American patent granted to Cyrus Austin. In 1804, an agreement was made with the Gilpin Paper Mills, Brandywine, Delaware, to use the Austin patent.[14] This was the first paper mill in the United States in which chlorine was utilized for bleaching purposes. Incidentally, another U.S. "first" for the Gilpin brothers was the mechanical manufacture of paper in 1817 in the form of a continuous web or sheet.

The estimated production of bleached wood pulp in the United States during 1961 is in excess of 8,000,000 tons, divided as follows: 2,008,000 tons of sulfite pulp, 5,452,000 tons of sulfate pulp, and over 500,000 tons of mechanical pulp.[58] The 1961 per capita consumption of paper in the U.S. was 440 pounds of which approximately 92 pounds is made from pulp bleached in the U.S.

Important dates in the development of pulp bleaching, following the use of chloride of lime, are:

(1) 1919, the use of liquid chlorine in the manufacture of calcium hypochlorite bleach solution;

(2) 1920, adoption of multistage bleaching of pulp;

(3) 1924, Richter and Schur in the U.S. and Opfermann in Germany reported that brighter pulps with greater yields and strength properties were obtained when the entire hypochlorite bleaching operation is conducted under alkaline conditions;

(4) 1925, continuous and high density bleaching, with the development of new vertical bleaching equipment;

(5) 1930, use of elemental chlorine in a bleaching stage—continuous chlorination of pulp introduced;

(6) 1930, first sulfate pulp bleached to 70 brightness;

(7) 1940, peroxide process for bleaching mechanical pulp put into operation;

(8) 1946, chlorine dioxide used as a bleaching agent in a multistage bleaching process;

(9) 1960, sulfate pulp bleached to a 90+ brightness.

Pulp bleaching is now regarded as a continuation of the stepwise isolation and purification of wood fibers begun in the chemical pulping process. The lignin materials and colored compounds are converted into a water-soluble form, while fiber degradation is held at a minimum. Thus, the cooking and bleaching operations must be considered in relation to each other, and must be adapted to the raw fibrous material (wood) and to the properties required in the bleached pulp.

Three factors have contributed to the rapid progress made in pulp bleaching over the past twenty years: (1) the availability of liquid chlorine and other bleaching agents, and the reduction in the cost of bleaching; (2) the use of improved equipment and materials of construction; (3) the expanded usage of wood pulps, not only for paper but for cellulose products and derivatives.

In general, two objectives are sought in bleaching chemical wood pulp fibers: (a) removal of residual lignin material, and (b) destruction and solubilization of the coloring matter. Undesirable chemical reactions which proceed simultaneously involve (c) loss of bleaching agent which reacts with the solubilized fibrous materials, and (d) chemical attack on the fiber, impairing its physical properties. Control of the bleaching process should favor reactions (a) and (b), and minimize reactions (c) and (d). The reduction of objectionable dirt particles in the pulp is also an important phase of the bleaching operation.

The visual whiteness of a bleached pulp is usually defined in terms of "brightness." Thus, by means of a reflection meter (TAPPI Standard Method T 217) "brightness" is determined as the numerical value of the reflectance of pulps to light in the blue and violet portions of the spectrum

(457.0 ± 0.5 millimicrons). The measurement is made with an instrument that is in calibration with a master instrument of a specified type and design, described in the official TAPPI method. The spectral reflectivity of pulp, which serves to specify the optical properties responsible for its color, can be determined spectrophotometrically (TAPPI Standard Method T 216). The brightness of unbleached and bleached pulps varies widely, depending on the wood species, the pulping process and the bleaching operation. The use requirement of the pulp is a controlling factor. See Chapter 14.

Bleaching is a continuation of the fiber purification begun in the pulping process. Dry spruce wood, for instance, with the bark removed, contains small amounts of mineral substances, approximately 70% holocellulose, 27 to 28% lignin, and a few per cent of extractives, such as resins and fats. The holocellulose or total carbohydrate portion includes cellulose and hemicellulose, and may be divided into alpha-, beta-, and gamma-cellulose. Bleached sulfite pulp comprises a portion of the holocellulose of the wood, shown in Figure 10.1,[47] which illustrates the changes in the composition of wood fiber as it is progressively purified during the pulping and bleaching operations. The degree to which these operations are carried out depends on the properties desired in the bleached pulp. As far as lignin removal is concerned, the pulping process is more economical for this purpose than the bleaching process.

The pulping process dissolves the hemicelluloses to a considerable extent because of their low resistance to hydrolysis. Most of the lignin is also dissolved. In sulfite pulp, the residual lignin is modified only slightly and is largely removed by the bleaching process. In soda and sulfate pulps, the lignin and hemicellulose residues are modified to a greater extent. These pulps are darker in color and require more bleach to produce a given brightness.

The extractives vary in quantity and

type with the wood species and the nature of the pulping operation employed. For instance, the alcohol- and ether-soluble portion is removed to a greater extent in the alkaline pulping processes than in the sulfite process. Traces of resin present in the bleached pulp may influence the stability of its color as well as its brightness.

Cellulose and the organic compounds associated with it are high polymers. With the removal of the impurities, the internal surface area of the cellulose is enlarged and frequently swelling occurs. This condition increases the reactivity of the cellulose, which is more easily attacked by bleaching agents. The type of bleaching system and the operating conditions, such as time, temperature, pulp consistency, concentration of chemical, pH, etc., must be carefully selected in relation to the properties specified for the bleached product.

An "easy bleaching" pulp is one that contains a minimum amount of residual lignin, depending on the type of pulp. For instance, easy-bleaching sulfite pulp would contain less than 3% of lignin, whereas a hard-bleaching sulfate pulp might contain about 10%. A so-called bleachable semichemical pulp contains about 10% lignin. For a specific pulp, the bleach requirement is closely related to the lignin content of the unbleached pulp. The difference in color between an unbleached sulfite and an unbleached sulfate pulp is not due entirely to the lignin content, however. Other substances of unknown composition are believed to be responsible for the color differences and may account for the difficulty in bleaching the fibers to a high brightness of satisfactory stability.

High-yield pulping has been developed during the past decade. Such bleaching, according to Giertz,[20] is termed "surface bleaching," and its main objective is to decolorize the materials without substantial loss of fibrous constituents.

In recent years much knowledge has been accumulated on multistage bleaching. Except for the production of a relatively low-brightness pulp, a modern bleaching process comprises two or more stages where each is usually concluded with a pulp-washing operation. The determining characteristics of modern pulp bleaching are (1) the number of stages, (2) the combination of stages, and (3) the order or sequence of the stages.

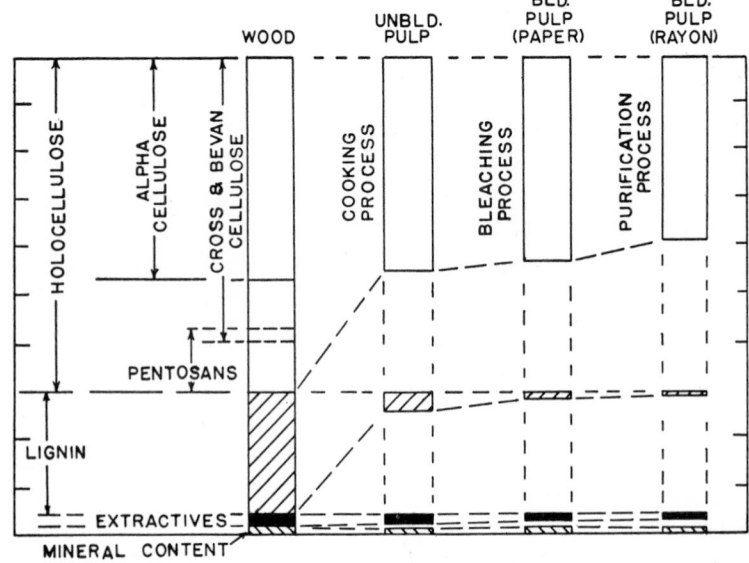

Fig. 10.1. Diagrammatic representation of changes in the composition of wood as it is progressively purified by pulping and bleaching.

CHEMICALS, TERMS, EQUIPMENT AND MATERIALS

Chlorine (Cl_2) and its compounds, such as hypochlorous acid (HOCl), sodium hypochlorite (NaOCl), calcium hypochlorite [$Ca(OCl)_2$], chlorine dioxide (ClO_2), and sodium chlorite ($NaClO_2$), containing "available chlorine," are commonly used for bleaching wood pulp fibers, chiefly because of their low cost. The "available chlorine" content of such a bleaching agent is a measure of its oxidizing capacity to react with the residual lignin and coloring materials in the unbleached fiber. This value is determined volumetrically in the laboratory in terms of the amount of iodine released from an iodide. Thus, one molecular weight of chlorine liberates one molecular weight of iodine, and this represents 100% "available chlorine":

$$Cl_2 + 2KI \longrightarrow I_2 + 2KCl$$
$$Cl_2 \backsimeq I_2 \backsimeq 100\% \text{ available chlorine}$$

Chlorine dioxide is an oxidizing agent which has a much higher "available chlorine" content than chlorine. According to the following equation:

$$2ClO_2 + 10KI + 4H_2SO_4 \longrightarrow$$
$$5I_2 + 2KCl + 4K_2SO_4 + 4H_2O$$
$$2ClO_2 \backsimeq 5I_2 \backsimeq 5Cl_2,$$

or, one molecular weight of chlorine dioxide is equivalent to $2\frac{1}{2}$ times the molecular weights of iodine or chlorine. Thus, the "available chlorine" content of chlorine dioxide on a weight for weight basis is:

$$\frac{71 \times 2.5 \times 100}{67.5} = 263\%$$

Sodium chlorite has an oxidation power equivalent to 156.9% available chlorine, according to the following equation:

$$2NaClO_2 + 4H_2SO_4 + 8KI \longrightarrow$$
$$4I_2 + 2KCl + 3K_2SO_4 + Na_2SO_4 + 4H_2O$$
$$NaClO_2 \backsimeq 2I_2 \backsimeq 2Cl_2,$$

or, one molecular weight of sodium chlorite is equivalent to twice the molecular weight of iodine or chlorine. The "available chlorine" content is calculated thus:

$$\frac{71 \times 2 \times 100}{90.45} = 156.9\%$$

Sometimes the peroxides are defined in terms of their so-called "available chlorine" or oxidizing power. Thus, a molecular weight of sodium peroxide (Na_2O_2) or of hydrogen peroxide (H_2O_2) is equivalent in oxidizing power to a molecular weight of iodine or chlorine, i.e., 1 pound of Na_2O_2 $\backsimeq$ 0.91 pounds of Cl_2 and 1 pound H_2O_2 $\backsimeq$ 2.10 pounds Cl_2.

"Residual chlorine" refers to the amount of available chlorine remaining in the pulp mixture after any point in the bleaching operation where chlorine oxidants are employed.

"Per cent chlorine added" to the pulp is the figure giving the percentage, based on the weight of the pulp, of available chlorine added (but not necessarily consumed) to a bleaching stage. The calculation may be on pulp in the air-dry or moisture-free condition, whatever is the mill practice. The basis of the calculation should always be specified.

"Per cent chlorine consumed" refers to the available chlorine actually consumed in the bleaching stage, based on pulp weight.

The bleach requirement of the pulp is expressed in terms of the per cent of available chlorine or other bleaching agent required to bleach it to a predetermined brightness.

Other bleaching agents of the oxidizing type include peroxides, especially hydrogen peroxide and sodium peroxide, and some work has been done with peracetate. Reducing agents which bring about a whitening of the fiber are sulfur dioxide, sodium bisulfite, sodium hydrosulfite, zinc hydrosulfite, and sodium borohydride. The relative costs per pound of the more important bleaching agents now in use are: chlorine, about 3.5 cents; chlorine dioxide, about 20 cents; hydrogen peroxide (100%), about

50 cents; and sodium peroxide, about 22 cents.

Chemicals other than bleaching agents are also used in this phase of the pulp purification process. Sodium hydroxide, lime, or other alkaline materials are used for pH control, for the preparation of hypochlorites from chlorine, and for solubilizing the chlorinated lignin and other constituents of the fiber, as may be desired. Sodium silicate, magnesium sulfate (Epsom salt), sulfuric acid, calcium chloride, and sodium tripolyphosphate and other sequestering agents are among the chemicals required for special purposes in groundwood bleaching and chemical pulp bleaching.

Chlorine is purchased in tank cars or cylinders as a liquefied gas under pressure, although a few mills produce chlorine, as well as sodium hydroxide, by the electrolysis of sodium chloride brine. Sodium hypochlorite, or calcium hypochlorite is usually produced at the mill. Chlorine dioxide is made at the mill by the reduction of sodium chlorate.

Sodium peroxide (Na_2O_2), sodium hydrosulfite ($Na_2S_2O_4$), and zinc hydrosulfite (ZnS_2O_4) are solids shipped in drums. Hydrogen peroxide (H_2O_2) is a water-white liquid which is commercially available in concentrations of 35, 50 and 70%. It is shipped in aluminum tank cars and drums, and stored in aluminum tanks.

Sulfur dioxide (SO_2) may be available from sulfur burning at the mill or can be purchased as a liquefied gas. Sodium bisulfite ($NaHSO_3$) is available as a solid in drums. Caustic soda (NaOH, sodium hydroxide) is obtainable either as a 50% or 75% water solution in tank cars, in flakes, or solid in drums.

Silicate of soda (Na_2O, SiO_2) is generally a 40° to 41° Baumé (Bé) grade, containing approximately 8.9% Na_2O. This is a solution, shipped in tank cars or drums. Magnesium sulfate ($MgSO_4 \cdot 7H_2O$, Epsom salt) is a white solid readily obtainable on the market.

Calcium hypochlorite [$Ca(OCl)_2$] bleach liquor is prepared by the addition of chlorine to a milk of lime (calcium hydroxide) solution. The present trend is toward continuous manufacture of calcium hypochlorite, rather than by the former batch method. The successful operation of a continuous process depends on an accurate, reliable control of the reaction involved. Oxidation-reduction potential (redox) measurements are suitable for this purpose. The redox controller compensates for changes in the lime slurry and maintains the redox potential of the finished bleach liquor by adjusting the flow of chlorine. With close control of the lime slurry concentration, a uniform bleach liquor is obtained. Sodium hypochlorite may also be produced continuously, utilizing redox control (see Figure 10.2).

Advantages of a continuous hypochlorite system over that of the batch system are (1) lower installation cost and the use of smaller storage tanks, (2) reduced space requirements, (3) reduced operating labor costs, (4) improved stability and uniformity of bleach liquor, and (5) more complete utilization of chlorine and alkali.[27]

Zinc hydrosulfite (ZnS_2O_4), a reducing agent, is a stable white powder containing 86 to 88% of the active ingredient. Sodium hydrosulfite ($Na_2S_2O_4$) is also a white powder with a purity of 94 to 95 per cent. When moistened or heated, the sodium compound may ignite, producing fires which are difficult to extinguish. "Zepar" BP (duPont) is a white granular powder based on sodium hydrosulfite but compounded to give the reducing power of zinc hydrosulfite. It is specifically formulated for bleaching groundwood and has greater heat stability than soduim hydrosulfite even when moist.[15]

Sodium borohydride ($NaBH_4$) is a hygroscopic, white crystalline solid, stable in dry air to 300°C. It ignites from free flame in air, burning quietly; its purity is 98+%. Shipping regulations classify sodium borohydride as a flammable solid.[37]

One of the earliest and simplest bleachers was the Hollander washer, employed in rag mills for washing and bleaching. It was

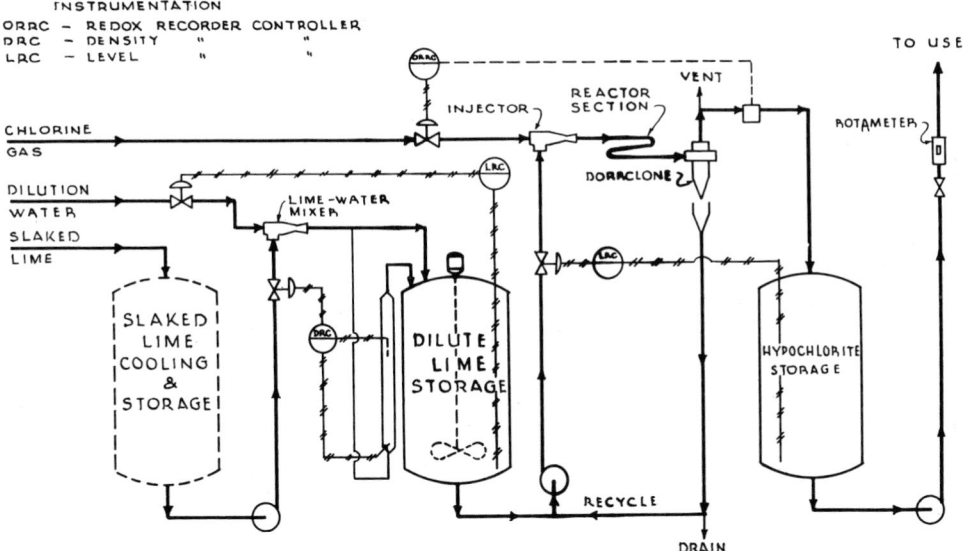

Fig. 10.2. Automatic bleach liquor production calcium hypochlorite. (*Courtesy Hooker Chemical Corp.*)

wasteful of power and altogether very inefficient. Later the Bellmer bleacher was developed and is still in use, especially where single-stage hypochlorite systems are employed. The Bellmer is a beater-shaped tub with one or two midfeathers. Usually it is constructed of tile-lined concrete and the pulp is circulated around the tub by a helicoid screw propeller. This equipment is limited to the handling of low pulp concentrations, up to 7%. The pulp and hypochlorite bleach liquor are added at the same time, and direct steam is allowed to enter as soon as the fiber suspension begins to circulate. Usually the maximum temperature is about 95°F. This single-stage operation requires 4 to 6 hours.

The next development involved equipment which would handle pulp at a pulp concentration up to 20%. First there was a horizontal bleacher, and subsequently a vertical unit was designed. Wolf, Fletcher, and Thorne were foremost in the development of high-density bleachers. At the present time the bleaching operation is a continuous system where chemical and mechanical wood pulps utilize towers for retention vessels. The batch system of bleaching with its many tanks, uncertain control, high horsepower, high capital installation cost, and high manpower requirements has been on the decline. In the modern continuous bleach plant, the equipment is designed and adapted to suit the individual mill requirements. With proper recirculation of process water, the consumption of fresh water has been reduced from up to 80,000 gallons to around 20,000 gallons per ton—a major step in the conservation of water [26].

Materials of construction for a modern bleach plant are summarized below [5,7,32,39,61]:

Dry chlorine:
  Iron

Moist chlorine:
  Rubber-lined steel
  Saran-lined steel
  Saran
  Hastelloy C
  Tantalum

Hypochlorite:
  Rubber-lined steel
  Saran-lined steel
  Saran

Caustic soda (sodium hydroxide):
  Iron pipe

Sulfuric acid (66° Bé):
  Mild steel
  Carpenter 20

Sodium chlorite:
  Saran-lined steel
  Stainless steel

Chlorine dioxide:
  Hastelloy C-lined mixers
  Lead-lined steel
  Glass-lined steel
  Saran-lined steel or glass piping for solution piping
  Durachlor for pumps
  Bisphenol A polyester spray coat
  Titanium and Hastelloy C or glass piping for reactor piping, instrument inserts, and nozzles
  Durachlor for pumps

Hypochlorite supply tank:
  Lead-lined steel
  Tile or brick-lined steel
  Plastic-base painted
  Concrete

Caustic soda supply tank:
  Iron

Sodium peroxide solution:
  Stainless steel

Chlorine dioxide storage tank:
  Brick- or tile-lined, with membrane behind brick.
  Glass-lined
  Fiber glass reinforced polyester resin

Sodium chlorate storage tank:
  Gunnite lining
  Polyester fiber glass lining
  304 stainless steel
  316 stainless steel clad
  Glass-lined steel

Towers and chests:
  Same as stock lines

Tile linings:
  Dense, highly vitrified, salt-glazed
  Semi-stoneware
  Ceramic

Cements:
  Portland cement
  Phenolformaldehyde or furane resin

Stock piping:
  Unbleached stock
    Iron
    Wood-lined
    Stainless steel
    Transite

Stock piping, with chlorine present:
  Rubber-lined steel
  Saran-lined steel

Stock piping, with hypochlorite present:
  Rubber-lined steel
  Saran-lined steel
  Wood-lined steel
  Transite
  Cement, alkali-resistant

Ventilation:
  "Transite"
  Fiber glass polyester resin

Hoods:
  Transite
  Glass-reinforced polyester material
  Wood
  Laminated sheet plastic

Face wires for washer:
  317 Stainless steel
  316 Stainless steel.

Good maintenance of the bleach plant begins with: (1) adequate plant planning, (2) careful selection of equipment, (3) well kept operating records and history card files, (4) operator responsibility for equipment care and attention, (5) periodic inspection by mechanical department, and (6) immediate attention and repairs to trouble spots.

BLEACHING METHODS

The availability of liquid chlorine at low cost is perhaps the chief factor which has contributed to the rapid development of modern pulp-bleaching processes. Chlorine is injected in the gaseous form into the water suspension of pulp fibers. It also finds application in the production of hypochorites from calcium hydroxide or sodium hydroxide solutions. Used as elemental chlorine, however, it is the cheapest chemical containing "available chlorine" to satisfy the bleach demand of the fibers, although by itself it has no whitening action on wood pulp.

When chlorine gas is dissolved in water, a molecule each of hypochlorous and hydrochloric acid is formed. The composition of a chlorine solution depends on its pH (degree of acidity or alkalinity). For instance,

Below pH 2　Chlorine is present predominantly as elemental chlorine;

pH 2-3　Elemental chlorine with hypochlorous acid;

pH 4-6　Hypochlorous acid predominates;

pH 7-9　Hypochlorous acid with hypochlorite;

Above pH 9　Chlorine is present predominantly as hypochlorite.

Below a pH of 7, hydrochloric acid is present, but this plays no direct part in bleaching except to remove mineral impurities and to control the amount of hypochlorous acid present. Prolonged exposure of the fibers to hydrochloric acid will result in degradation and loss of strength. Above a pH of 7, hydrochloric acid will react with the alkali present to form a chloride which has no part in bleaching. Thus, the pH of the system is an important factor because it controls the proportions of chlorine, hypochlorous acid, and hypochlorite ions in the bleaching solution.

The chemical reactions taking place during the chlorination of wood fibers are not well defined, except that lignin is partially chlorinated and partially oxidized. These products are to a great extent soluble in alkaline solution or in water. The amount of bleaching agent required depends on the quantities of reactive materials in the fibers. The use of an excessive amount of chlorine is of doubtful value because undesirable secondary reactions occur, leading to degradation of the fibers. The entire operation should be under strict laboratory control for most efficient operation.

Few bleaching systems are exactly similar in design and operation, although the basic principles involved are the same. The bleaching system in a mill is the result of research, planning and engineering toward a specific objective.

Bleaching procedures involve the use of oxidizing agents other than chlorine compounds, such as peroxides. Also reducing compounds, such as hydrosulfites, find application as bleaching agents. Table 10.1 summarizes a list of bleaching processes frequently employed for the various types of pulps. Other processes may also be used. The gain in brightness points and the range of brightness are to be considered only approximate; much depends on the bleaching conditions, type of wood, concentration of bleaching agent, etc.

Single-Stage Hypochlorite Bleaching

Hypochlorites react readily with unbleached pulps to whiten or bleach them. The simplest bleaching process comprises a single stage operation, using either calcium or sodium hypochlorite on a chemical pulp, sulfite, soda, or sulfate. Many pulps, especially those produced by the sulfite or soda process, can be bleached to a brightness of 78 to 80 with a single stage hypochlorite treatment but with serious loss of fiber strength.

In bleaching with unbuffered hypochlorite, the pH of the mixture decreases during the reaction, owing to the formation of carbon dioxide and organic acids. Starting with a pH of about 11.0, the terminal pH is usually between 6.0 and 7.0. Unde-

TABLE 10.1. CLASSIFICATION OF PULP BLEACHING PROCESSES

		Brightness	
Type of Pulp	*Bleaching Process* *	*Points Gain*	*Range*
Mechanical, groundwood	Hydrogen and/or sodium peroxide	6-12	65-75
	Zinc or sodium hydrosulfite	6-12	65-75
	Sodium bisulfite	2-4	62-64
	Multistage: peroxide-hydrosulfite	20+	Over 80
Hardwoods	Hypochlorite	10-20	70-75
Mixture of mechanical and sulfite pulps	Peroxide	15	69-72
Chemigroundwood	Peroxide	7-15	60-65
	Hypochlorite	7-15	60-65
Semichemical—NSSC	Multistage: C-E-H	About 40	80-87
Hardwood neutral sulfite	Hypochlorite	25-30	70-75
Cold soda	Hypochlorite	25	65-70
	Tower method: peroxide	25-30	65-75
	Multistage: peroxide-hydrosulfite	35	80
	Refiner method: peroxide	15-25	55-65
Chemical			
Sulfite	Hypochlorite	20	75-80
	Peroxide	10-15	70-75
	Multistage: C-H	20+	Up to 82
	C-E-H	25+	Up to 87
	C-E-H-P⎫ C-E-D-P⎬	30	87-90
	C-E-D-H	30+	88-92
	C-E-H-D-H	30+	92
	C-E-D-E-D	32+	92-94
	C-E-D	30	90
Soda	Hypochlorite	30+	70-75
	Multistage: C-H	20-30	60-70
	C-E-H	40+	82
	C-E-H-H	45+	87
	C-E-H-D	50	88
Sulfate, kraft	Hypochlorite	10-20	40-50
	Multistage: C-H	30-40	60-70
	C-E-H	35-40+	65-70+
	C-E-D	50	Up to 80
	C-E-D-D	60+	88-91
	C-E-H-E-D	60+	86-88
	C-E-H-D	60+	86-88
	C-E-H-H-H-D	62+	86-88
	C-E-D-E-D	60+	88-91
	C-H-D-P-D	65	88-92
	C-E-D-P-D	62	90-92
Deinked paper stock	Hypochlorite	10+	70+
	Peroxide	10	70
	Hydrosulfite	5-10	65-70
	Multistage: C-H⎫ C-E-H⎬	15+	85

* NSSC = neutral sulfite semichemical pulp.   H = hypochlorite stage.
C = Chlorination stage.   D = chlorine dioxide stage.
E = caustic extraction stage.   P = peroxide stage.

sirable reactions, resulting in a weakening of the fibers, occur near the neutral point, pH 7. This may be caused by the great activity of hypochlorous acid in this pH range.

Hypochlorite bleaching should be carried out at a pH where the active bleaching agent is mostly the hypochlorite ion and not hypochlorous acid. In commercial hypochlorite bleaching, it is customary to use buffered hypochlorite containing an excess of alkali to neutralize the acidic substances formed during the operation. The recommended final pH range is 9.0-10.0.

Pulp consistency in single stage bleaching may vary between about 4 and 15%. At a consistency of approximately 5%, a temperature much above 100°F (38°C) should be avoided; otherwise oxidation of the cellulose may occur, with loss of fiber strength.

Temperature is an important factor in controlling the rate of bleaching. Adequate temperature regulation is a necessity for the efficient use of the bleaching agent and the production of a uniform product. Conditions of temperature, pulp consistency, pH and concentration of bleaching agent must be controlled to give the desired degree of purification and brightness, with a minimum attack on the fiber constituents. Typical of commercial practice for the single stage bleaching of sulfite pulp with hypochlorite are the conditions shown in Table 10.2.

TABLE 10.2. CONSISTENCY, TEMPERATURE, AND TIME RELATIONS FOR BLEACHING SULFITE PULP

Consistency of Pulp (%)	Temperature (°C)	(°F)	Hours
3-4	40-50	104-122	5-6
5-7	40-45	104-113	4-6
8-10	35-40	95-104	4-6
12-16	25-35	77-95	2-4

According to Russell[49], a single stage bleach gives the following results: (1) a minimum of purification, (2) a maximum chemical cost per unit of brightness obtained, (3) a minimum investment per unit of brightness for sulfite and soda pulps, and

(4) a maximum strength loss per unit of brightness.

Usually a single hypochlorite stage is not applicable to sulfate or high yield pulps, unless a low brightness is desired.

TABLE 10.3. BLEACH REQUIREMENTS OF DIFFERENT PULPS FOR SINGLE STAGE HYPOCHLORITE PROCESS [10]

Type of Pulp	Bleach Requirement (% available chlorine as hypochlorite)
Easy bleaching sulfite	3-5
Average bleaching sulfite	5-7
Hard bleaching sulfite	Up to 10-13
Hardwood soda	4-6
Bleachable sulfate	5-8
Hard bleaching sulfate	Up to 12-15

Multistage Bleaching

Multistage bleaching with chlorine compounds is an operation involving pulp purification as well as the whitening of the fibers. By this procedure, the purifying and bleaching chemicals are added in stages, separated usually by intermediate washing operations with water or an alkaline solution to remove the products of the reaction. Thus, the impurities are gradually removed in steps, and chemical attack on the fibers is reduced to the minimum in any one stage. Bleaching chemicals are used more efficiently in this type of operation.

In the bleaching of wood pulp in stages, three definite phases may be distinguished[17]. (1) There is a consumption of chlorine up to about 20% of the requirement. The lignin is chlorinated; oxidation and substitution occur; opacity and tear strength of the pulp increase, while brightness and bursting strength decrease. (2) Chlorination of the lignin has practically ceased but oxidation and solubilization continue; tear strength decreases and burst increases, and the brightness of the pulp improves in proportion to the amount of bleaching agent consumed. (3) There is chemical attack on the fibers; physical degradation, with loss of strength properties, begins to appear. This phase, which shows little lignin removal or increase in brightness, should be minimized by adequate control of all the operations.

The advantages of multistage bleaching are [49]: (1) a lower chemical cost per unit of brightness, (2) a higher brightness ceiling, (3) a larger capital investment, (4) higher pulp strength at equivalent brightness, and (5) less color reversion in the bleached pulp. By means of successively applied chemical reactions, the fiber impurities are removed with a high degree of selectivity. Typical of such reactions are (a) reaction of chlorine with lignin (chlorination stage), (b) solution of the chlorinated lignin and other impurities in sodium hydroxide solution (caustic extraction stage), (c) destruction of the coloring materials in the fibers by means of a bleaching chemical, such as hypochlorite, and/or chlorine dioxide (whitening stage), and (d) use of sulfur dioxide to neutralize traces of bleaching chemical, to remove iron and other mineral constituents of the fibers and to give color stability to the pulp (acid stage).

A properly designed multistage bleaching process will meet the following requirements: (1) removal of decomposition products and residual chemicals from the pulp following each stage, (2) equipment for the precise control of chemicals, time, consistency and temperature which influence the degree of bleaching, and (3) thorough and rapid mixing of the chemicals with the fibers.

Chlorination Stage. The availability of low-cost liquid chlorine and of suitable equipment for handling this corrosive chemical has revolutionized pulp bleaching. By itself, chlorine is more of a pulp purification chemical than a bleaching agent. Three types of chemical reaction occur in the chlorination stage: (1) addition of chlorine to form chlorinated compounds, (2) substitution, whereby a chlorine atom replaces a hydrogen atom and hydrochloric acid is formed, and (3) oxidation by means of the hypochlorous acid present. It is important to convert the residual lignin in the unbleached pulp to a form soluble in water and in an alkaline solution.

Grangaard [21] states that 40 to 70 per cent of the total chlorine consumed is by oxidation. In pulps of low permanganate number, the chlorine consumption may be entirely by oxidation. Solubilization of lignin by chlorination may be the result of oxidation rather than substitution. The importance of removing the chlorinated products from the pulp is emphasized. The relative amounts of chlorine reacting with the fiber components to form substitution and oxidation products depends on the amount of chlorine added, time and temperature of the reactions, type of pulp, lignin content, etc.

The chlorination stage is usually carried out at low pulp consistencies of 3 to 4%, in a continuous operation. Although the chlorination reactions are rapid, 30 minutes to about 1 hour may be required for 90 to 95% consumption, depending on the conditions and type of pulp being treated. The pH of the solution drops to about 2 which facilitates the reaction:

$$Cl_2 + H_2O \rightleftharpoons HCl + HOCl$$

Chlorination of pulp proceeds rapidly over a wide range of temperature. For instance, in a 500 ton sulfate mill bleaching operation, the temperature of the chlorination stage is 70°F. This stage tends to eliminate inequalities in the chlorine demand of the pulp. These inequalities inevitably occur in the pulping operation, and if they can be reduced by chlorination, the subsequent bleaching stages can be more accurately controlled. Depending on conditions such as pulp cleanliness, desired brightness, and other bleached pulp properties, the amount of chlorine added to the chlorination stage is usually related to the permanganate number of the unbleached pulp or other bleachability test. From 40 to 80% of the total bleach requirement may be added in the chlorination stage.

Duncan and Rapson [12] point out three major factors indicating the need for improvement of the pulp chlorination stage:

(1) loss in pulp strength is traceable to the chlorination procedure, (2) oxidation reduction potential measurement (redox) now makes available a dependable means for the automatic control of chlorine addition, and (3) a redesign of chlorinating equipment to permit optimum mixing and variable retention times to compensate for variation in temperature is necessary. To maintain optimum conditions, the chlorination time should approximate the following:

Temperature		Time (min.)
(°C)	(°F)	
5	41	120
10	59	80
20	77	40
30	95	20
40	113	10

Mixing of pulp and chlorine should be accomplished within 5 minutes.

Alkali Extraction Stage. Following the removal of the solubilized chlorination products from the chlorination stage by washing, the bleachability of the pulp is further lowered by subjecting it to a hot caustic soda extraction stage, using 1 to 2% or more of alkali. The temperature is generally between 110 and 160°F, depending on the nature of the pulp and the degree of purification desired. The time is usually from 60 to 90 minutes, at 10 to 16% pulp consistency.

Thus far, the two stages in the multistage bleaching operation have removed fiber constituents rendered soluble by chlorination in acid solution, and chlorinated lignin residues and other materials solubilized by alkali.

Meller [36] states that the alkaline extraction of chlorinated pulp is related to (1) the chemical nature of the chlorinated lignin, (2) the physical nature of the chlorinated lignin, (3) the chemical and physical nature of the fibers, and (4) the conditions of the extraction, such as pH, temperature, retention time, and concentration and nature of the extracting chemical. Rate of extraction depends more upon temperature than time.

The permanganate number of the chlorinated and extracted pulp is frequently employed as a control test in relation to subsequent stage treatments. A figure of about 4 has been mentioned for high brightness pulps.

Hypochlorite Stage. The development of brightness, the actual whitening of the pulp, occurs after the chlorination and caustic extraction stages by the application of a bleaching agent, such as hypochlorite or chlorine dioxide. In the chlorination and extraction of pulp fibers there has been purification but no bleaching. A chlorine demand in the range of 0.6 to 0.8% is considered about maximum for this stage. Calcium or sodium hypochlorite is the bleaching agent. To minimize chemical and physical degradation of the fibers, the pH range of this stage should be preferably between 9 and about 11. Pulp strength decreases as the pH drops below 9; below 10, the stability of the final color of the pulp is affected [42]. Starting pH is by far the most important variable in the hypochlorite bleaching stage. Other variables fall in the following order: temperature, per cent available chlorine, and time [54].

For paper grade pulps, the hypochlorite stage is most used for controlling brightness, while for dissolving pulps, it controls viscosity. Compared to single stage bleaching, multistage procedure, with its stepwise removal of fiber impurities, offers an economy in total available chlorine consumed for a pulp of specified brightness. This economy in bleach is reflected in improved pulp properties, such as strength and brightness.

Russell [49] comes to the following general conclusions concerning the multistage bleaching of sulfite, soda and sulfate pulps: (1) chemical cost is reduced, (2) brightness ceiling is raised, (3) investment per ton of pulp is increased, (4) cost per ton per brightness unit is reduced when the proper sequence of stages is employed, (5) purification is the chief function of both the chlorine and caustic extraction stages, and (6) temperature and pH must be controlled in the hypochlorite stage to protect pulp strength.

Chlorine Dioxide Stage. Within the last decade increasing interest has been shown by the pulp and paper industry in the use of chlorine dioxide as a bleaching agent [2,41]. It is a gas with an odor resembling chlorine and is highly toxic. At high concentrations it is spontaneously explosive. When diluted with an inert gas to a concentration of 10% or less, the explosive hazard is eliminated. For these reasons chlorine dioxide is generated at the pulp mill.

For bleaching fibers chlorine dioxide possesses two unique properties: (1) one pound is equivalent to 2.63 pounds of chlorine in oxidizing value, and (2) lignin and other colored compounds in the fibers are oxidized to water-soluble, colorless materials, without appreciably affecting the cellulose. The gas is absorbed in water to yield a solution for bleaching purposes.

One source of chlorine dioxide is sodium chlorite, which under operating conditions is "activated" by [9,48]:

(1) *Chlorine:*

$$2NaClO_2 + Cl_2 \longrightarrow 2ClO_2 + 2NaCl$$

(2) *Acid:*

$$5NaClO_2 + 2H_2SO_4 \longrightarrow \\ 4ClO_2 + 2Na_2SO_4 + NaCl + 2H_2O$$

(3) *Hypochlorite:*

$$2NaClO_2 + NaOCl + H_2O \longrightarrow \\ 2ClO_2 + 2NaOH + NaCl$$

These methods are too expensive for general use.

There are upwards of seven processes for the production of chlorine dioxide by the reduction of sodium chlorate. In three of them, gaseous sulfur dioxide is the reducing agent (Holst, Mathieson, and Canadian International Paper Company):

$$2NaClO_3 + SO_2 + H_2SO_4 \longrightarrow 2ClO_2 + 2NaHSO_4$$

Two processes use hydrochloric acid or sodium chloride as the reducing agent (Kesting-Brown, Hooker R-2):

$$2NaClO_3 + 4HCl \longrightarrow \\ 2ClO_2 + Cl_2 + 2NaCl + 2H_2O$$

also

$$NaClO_3 + NaCl + H_2SO_4 \longrightarrow \\ ClO_2 + \tfrac{1}{2}Cl_2 + Na_2SO_4 + H_2O$$
$$NaClO_3 + 5NaCl + 3H_2SO_4 \longrightarrow \\ 3Cl_2 + 3Na_2SO_4 + 3H_2O$$

Two processes based on sulfur dioxide as the secondary reducing agent depend on the reduction of chlorate to chlorine dioxide by the use of chromic sulfate (Persson).

In another process methyl alcohol is the reducing agent (Solvay):

$$2NaClO_3 + H_2SO_4 \longrightarrow 2HClO_3 + Na_2SO_4$$
$$4HClO_3 + CH_3OH \longrightarrow 4ClO_2 + HCOOH + 3H_2O$$

Serafin and Scribner [50] reported recently on the comparative costs of the R-2 and the Mathieson processes for the production of chlorine dioxide. When the latter is rated at a 90% yield and the former at 95%, the cost of chlorine by the R-2 method is about 1.3 cents per pound higher than by the Mathieson process. Excluding credit for sulfuric acid, chlorine dioxide costs 17.25 cents per pound by the R-2 method and 15.91 cents per pound by the Mathieson operation. Many mills operate the latter method at less than 90% efficiency. In such mills the R-2 process may be economically attractive, and especially so where the effluent acid may be credited for some additional use in the sulfate pulp mill. The initial capital cost is lower for the R-2 process and it should be possible to automate it with fewer problems.

The cost of producing chlorine dioxide closely approximates that of a hypochlorite, when compared on the available chlorine basis. It is now possible to bleach sulfate pulps to a brightness in excess of 90 by using the following stage sequence: chlorination, caustic extraction, chlorine dioxide, chlorine dioxide. This four stage sequence is shown in Figure 10.3. A more popular arrangement at the present time for bleaching sulfate pulp is the five stage sequence: C-E-D-E-D. Several mills, however, have adopted the 4 stage sequence as being the best for their purpose. Other con-

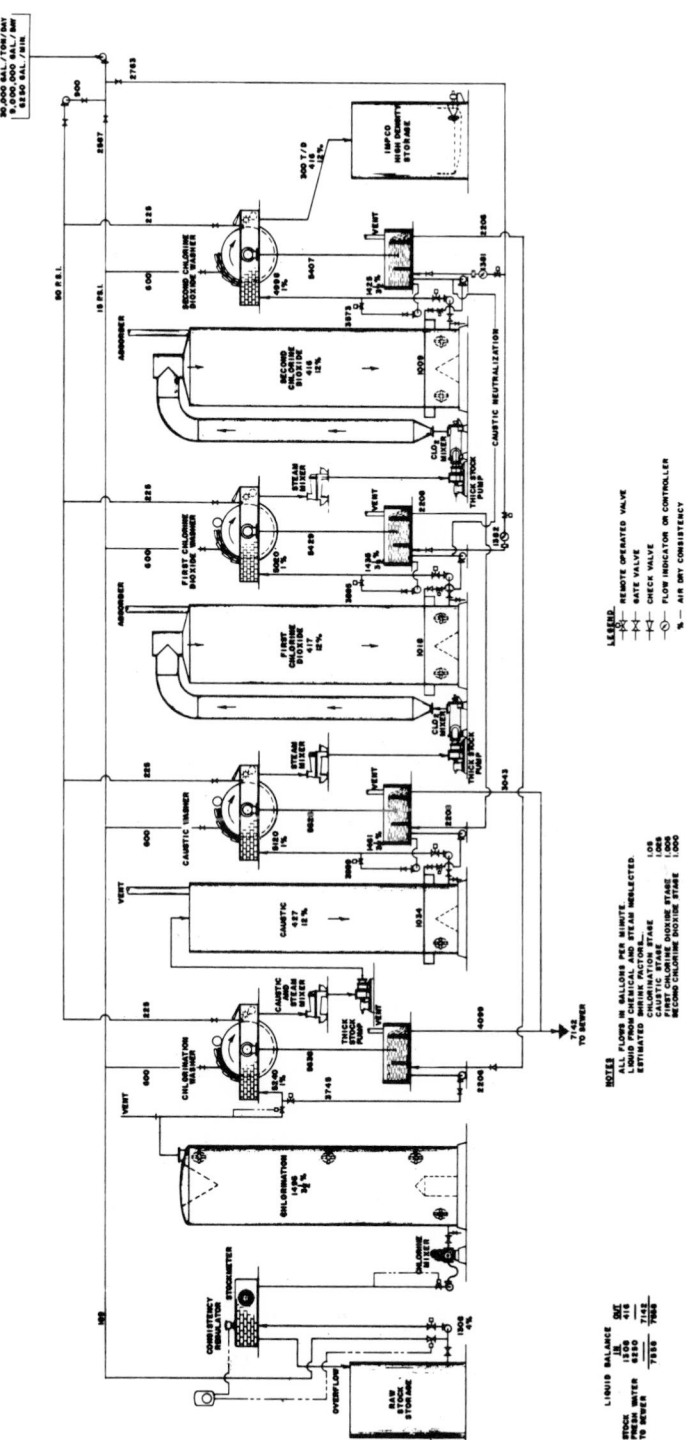

Fig. 10.3. Flow sheet of four-stage (C-E-D-D) bleach plant, 300 tons per day. Designed for 90+ brightness, sulfite or sulfate pulp. (*Courtesy Improved Machinery Inc.*)

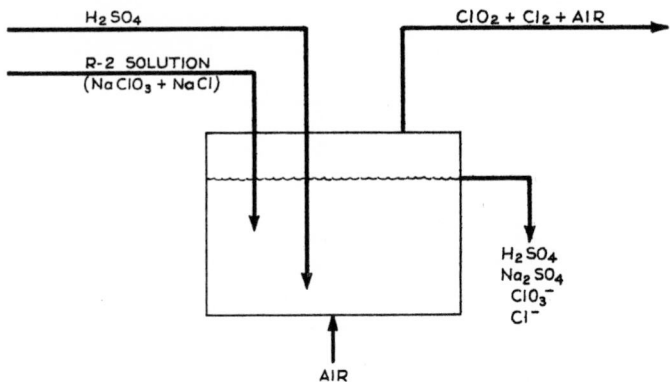

Fig. 10.4.   Schematic diagram of R-2 generator for chlorine dioxide.
(*Courtesy Hooker Chemical Corp.*)

ditions being equal, the C-E-D-E-D sequence will yield a pulp about 2 points
brighter than C-E-D-D, although the latter
has given pulps in excess of 90 brightness.

In the bleaching of western sulfate pulp[25]
by a five stage process, C-E-D-E-D, the
total chlorine dioxide usage was 0.9%. The
permanganate number of the pulp at the
end of the first extraction stage should be
about 4.0. The optimum conditions for the
final chlorine dioxide stage were found to
be: temperature, 160°F; time, 5 hours; pulp
consistency, 12%; final pH of 3.0, adding
sodium hydroxide as necessary to maintain
it. Better dirt removal was observed with
this sequence than by adding hypochlorite.

The R-2 process for the continuous production of chlorine dioxide is described by
Rapson and others[40,43]. In this process, sodium chloride (or hydrochloric acid) acts
as the reducing agent in the reaction between sodium chlorate and sulfuric acid.
The general plan of an R-2 generator is
shown schematically in Figure 10.4.

A 95% yield of chlorine dioxide is claimed
for the R-2 process, compared to about 90%
for the sulfur dioxide and methyl alcohol
processes. The savings in chemical costs depend not only on the higher yield of chlorine dioxide but also on the use of the by-
products: chlorine, salt cake and sulfuric
acid. Optimum savings are claimed for sulfate mills which (1) cook southern pine,

(2) bleach about 50% of the production
with both hypochlorite and chlorine dioxide, and (3) have a tall oil soap splitting
operation.

A recent development[4] in the multistage
bleaching process involves changes in the
stages of the chlorine dioxide five stage
process for chemical pulps. The conventional chlorine, caustic extraction, chlorine
dioxide, caustic extraction, chlorine dioxide
five stage process, which yields a pulp
brightness of about 90, is replaced by (1)
chlorine, alkaline hypochlorite, chlorine dioxide, hydrogen peroxide, chlorine dioxide, to
give a brightness up to 94, or (2) chlorine,
alkaline hypochlorite, chlorine dioxide, caustic extraction, chlorine dioxide, to give up
to 92 brightness. The first process is claimed
to produce a bleached pulp at a slightly
higher cost but with minimum color reversion and without fiber degradation. In the
second modification, the cost is stated to be
the same as for the conventional five stage
process but the pulp has a higher brightness and shows no loss of strength properties.

Peroxide. Following the successful use of
peroxide in the bleaching of groundwood, it
was natural to investigate its application
for the bleaching of chemical pulps. For
this purpose it is usually applied as a last
bleaching stage to give a high brightness
pulp with good color permanence and high

strength properties. Recently there has been a trend towards reducing the number of bleaching stages because of the large capital expenditure involved in multistage bleaching. The objective has been the production of a satisfactorily bleached pulp with the minimum of stages. The advent of chlorine dioxide has made possible a reduction in the number of stages to four or five in the bleaching of sulfate pulp.

Rapson and Anderson [44] have proposed a three stage sequence for bleaching sulfate pulp to 85 to 87 brightness, with excellent strength properties and moderate color reversion. This sequence comprises the addition of a small amount of chlorine dioxide (0.1-0.2%) to the chlorination stage and the addition of hypochlorite (1 to 2% available chlorine) to the caustic extraction stage, plus a chlorine dioxide third stage. The addition of a peroxide stage lifted the brightness to about 89 while maintaining good strength and improving its brightness stability.

On the basis of a laboratory study, Chadwick, Fennell and Wagoner [11] recommend the following sequence for bleaching sulfate pulp: chlorination, alkali extraction, hypochlorite, chlorine dioxide, and peroxide. This arrangement yields a bleached pulp of high brightness stability.

In Table 10.4 are given data from a southern mill employing these five stages.

TABLE 10.4 FIVE STAGE SEQUENCE USED FOR BLEACHING SOUTHERN PINE SULFATE PULP [16]

Stage	% Chemical Used	Brightness
1. Chlorination	5.0-5.5	26
2. Caustic extraction	1.75	29
3. Calcium hypochlorite	0.75-1.0	65-70
4. Chlorine dioxide	0.35-0.45	82-84
5. Hydrogen peroxide	0.10-0.15	86-88

The major objectives in the production of a bleached sulfate (kraft) pulp of high brightness are (1) no significant loss of its strength properties, and (2) good brightness stability.

Laboratory results with peroxide in the bleaching of sulfite pulp have been shown to improve brightness and brightness stability. Single stage bleaching with peroxide raises the level of pulp brightness to 70-80. For values above 80, examples of multistage bleaching are given in Table 10.5.

TABLE 10.5. MULTISTAGE BLEACHING OF SULFITE PULP WITH PEROXIDE

		Brightness			
Stage Sequence *	% H_2O_2 (100%)	Un-bleached	Before Peroxide	After Peroxide	After Aging 1 hour at 105°C
C-E-H	—	60.8	85.9	—	80.8
C-EH-P	0.125	60.8	83.9	87.2	84.6
C-E-H	—	59.8	84.8	—	80.2
C-E-H-P	0.125	59.8	84.8	88.2	87.3
H-P	0.50	58.5	—	87.3	79.5

* C—Chlorination, E—caustic extraction, H—hypochlorite, EH—high pH hypochlorite, P—peroxide.

Neutral Sulfite Semichemical, and Cold Soda Pulps

The high chemical demand in the bleaching of neutral sulfite semichemical pulps is usually satisfied with chlorine. Thereafter follows a caustic extraction stage, hypochlorite stage, or peroxide stage, or a sequence of these stages. The data in Table 10.6 show how peroxide can be utilized in the multistage bleaching of neutral sulfite pulp. Peroxide is well suited for the bleaching of high-yield pulps, but its higher cost cannot always be justified for use with chemical pulps, except for sulfate pulps requiring a brightness above 91. Hypochlorite has been used for cold soda pulps but the bleached pulp has a pale yellow color, and a peroxide or sequence of peroxide-hydrosulfite stages yields a pulp of improved brightness.

Two types of application of peroxide have been developed: (1) refiner bleaching yielding brightnesses of 55-65, and (2) tower bleaching for brightnesses of 65-75. Jahne and Price [28] report the bleaching of a mixture of beech, birch and maple pulp, with an unbleached brightness of 40 to 42, to a brightness of about 60 with peroxide. The

TABLE 10.6 LABORATORY BLEACHING OF NEUTRAL
SULFITE SEMICHEMICAL PULP

Bleaching Sequence *	% Cl_2	% NaOH	% Average Cl_2	% H_2O_2 (as 100%)	Brightness Bleached	Brightness 1 hour 105°C	Viscosity
Unbleached	—	—	—	—	49.2	—	8.2
H-P	—	—	19.0	0.37	89.2	85.5	10.0
C-E-P	17.5	4.0	—	1.0	87.6	83.1	10.2
C-H-P	16.0	—	2.0	0.83	88.2	85.2	10.4
Unbleached	—	—	—	—	44.1	—	5.6
H-P	—	—	11.0	0.38	82.2	78.4	12.6
C-E-H	10.5	2.0	4.5	—	83.7	74.9	9.6
"	11.5	3.0	1.0	—	88.4	81.0	9.7
C-E-H-P	11.5	3.0	1.0	0.125	91.5	89.4	7.8
C-EH-P	10.0	1.5	4.0	0.25	82.8	78.4	12.1

* C—chlorination; E—caustic extraction; H—hypochlorite; P—peroxide; EH—high pH hypochlorite.

bleaching chemicals (1.25% H_2O_2, 100% basis) were added to the chips as they entered the primary double-disk refiner. After passing through two refiners and remaining a maximum of 4 hours in a chest after the secondary refiner, the pulp had a brightness of 60. The wood was stored in the yard less than 3 months. Older wood, stored more than 12 months, yielded a bleached pulp with a brightness of about 10 points lower, although the unbleached brightness of the new and old wood was about the same. Jahne and Price claim that refiner type bleaching of cold soda pulp gives better results than batch type bleaching.

Using a two-stage peroxide-hydrosulfite bleaching sequence, cold soda pulp from beech, birch and maple hardwoods is being bleached commercially from 40 or 45 to about 80 brightness. This can also be accomplished by means of a single-stage high density peroxide operation [29]. A pretreatment of the unbleached pulp with acid, reducing agents or chelating agents, before the peroxide is added, is advantageous in obtaining maximum brightness. For instance, unbleached, screened cold soda pulp when acidified to pH 2 with sulfuric acid, washed with warm water and then bleached with 0.75% hydrogen peroxide (100%), at 12% consistency for 2 hours at 170°F yielded a brightness of 73 to 75. An additional hydrosulfite stage (1 hour at 140°F)

increased the brightness to 78 to 80. Peroxide yields an increase of 25 to 30 units of brightness, while hydrosulfite adds another 5 units, as a second stage.

Reducing Agents

The use of reducing agents, such as bisulfites, hydrosulfites, and sulfurous acid, for bleaching groundwood, and as antichlors and color stabilizers for chemical pulps, has been practiced for some time. The usual brightness increase for groundwood, however, has been only a few points, but following recent research in this field, color reversion has been reduced and other disadvantages overcome. Already several hydrosulfite bleaching installations are in operation in Canada and the United States.

(1) Bisulfite Bleaching. Bleaching with sodium bisulfite is the oldest known method of bleaching groundwood, having been known, according to Klemm [31] since about 1877. In the form of a 10% freshly-made solution, an amount is sprayed or applied by a roll to the lap or sheet of pulp to the extent of 1 or 2%, based on the pulp weight (oven-dry basis). The bleaching time involves 12 to 24 hours, at room temperature, and an increase in brightness of 2 to 4 units may be expected. An intimate mixing or saturation of the groundwood by the bisulfite solution is necessary for optimum re-

sults. Color reversion takes place slowly on storage.

(2) Hydrosulfite Bleaching. The use of zinc hydrosulfite for bleaching groundwood is chiefly a West Coast development. Andrews [1] reported that two factors brought about the use of hydrosulfite for bleaching: (1) the necessity of increasing the brightness of groundwood made of western hemlock and balsam fir to be competitive with the brightness of eastern spruce groundwood, and (2) reduction of process discoloration resulting from a combination of groundwood acidity and bacterial action. Hydrosulfite bleaching aided this situation considerably. Initially, a brightness gain of about five units was desired, but with the development of the use of groundwood in the printing field, brighter pulps were required.

With a better understanding of the behavior of hydrosulfites in solution and improved techniques of application, the hydrosulfites will yield a brightness gain of 10 to 12 points with spruce groundwood [6]. The use of hydrosulfites is generally restricted to the bleaching of groundwood, however. This subject will be discussed more extensively under that subject.

Where a higher brightness level is desired than can be obtained with a single-stage hydrosulfite bleaching process, a combination two-stage peroxide-hydrosulfite process is available. With this sequence, brightness gains of 12 to 18 or 20 units are possible. The sequence of bleaching consists of a peroxide stage, followed by a sulfur dioxide treatment between the stages, and then a hydrosulfite bleach. Reversing the sequence is reportedly not effective on groundwood [6]. This two-stage sequence is shown in Figure 10.5.

(3) Borohydride Bleaching. Attention is being given to the use of borohydrides as a reducing agent for bleaching fibers and as a color stabilizing compound for bleached pulps. The borohydrides function by reducing the carbonyl groups, formed by the action of oxidizing bleaching agents on wood fibers. The presence of carbonyl groups has been correlated with the color reversion of bleached pulps.

Mayer and Donofrio [35] reported that sodium borohydride produces a bleaching effect on coniferous groundwood comparable to an equal amount of sodium peroxide. In Table 10.7 a comparison is made between three groundwood bleaching agents.

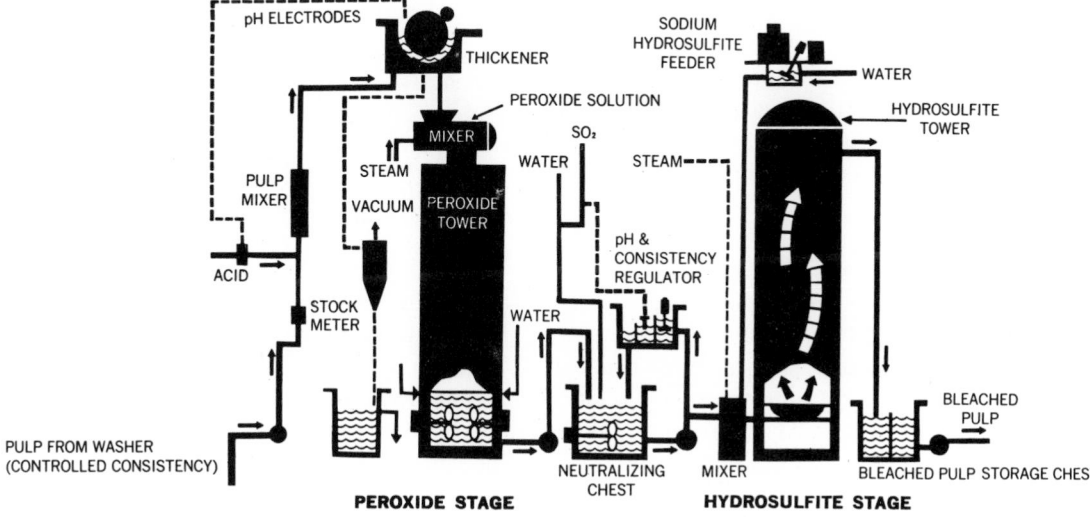

Fig. 10.5. Two-stage peroxide-hydrosulfite bleaching process. (*Courtesy Du Pont-Electrochemicals Department*)

TABLE 10.7. BRIGHTNESS INCREMENTS ON
GROUNDWOOD WITH PEROXIDE, HYDROSULFITE,
AND BOROHYDRIDE BLEACHING AGENTS

Bleaching Agent	% Used	Brightness Increment
Sodium peroxide	2	10.4
Zinc hydrosulfite	2	4.9
Sodium borohydride	1	7.9
Sodium borohydride	2	10.4

Spectral analysis of the bleached pulps revealed that borohydride improves reflectance over a wider range than either peroxide or hydrosulfite. Also, the action of borohydride is different from that of zinc hydrosulfite as a bleaching agent. Owing to the fact that borohydride decomposes readily in solution with the production of hydrogen, conditions should be chosen to permit the minimum of decomposition and maximum of bleaching. Unbuffered systems, in which the pH level is around 10, appear to be more satisfactory. A lower pH results in increasing the rates of both decomposition and bleaching. Stability is improved at a higher pH but the bleaching time is increased markedly.

Much of the color formation in cold soda pulp can be prevented by adding 1 to 2% sodium borohydride to the caustic soda during the soaking process [59]. Giertz first showed that reduction of carbonyl groups in the pulp decreases its tendency to color reversion by heat. Investigators in this field generally agree that the higher the carbonyl content of pulp, the greater is its tendency to yellow by heat aging. Reduction with sodium borohydride or oxidation with sodium chlorite reduces the degree of color reversion.

The chief reason why borohydride bleaching is not used is due to the cost of the material. The figure of $7.50 a pound must be reduced before the chemical finds commercial application. A substantial reduction in price to the range of $2.50 to $3.00 per pound is anticipated in a short time.

Optical or Fluorescent Brighteners, or Bleaches

A recent development for increasing the visual brightness of paper is the addition of an optical brightener, bleach or white dye. These unique chemical compounds possess the property of converting invisible ultraviolet light, present in most light sources, to visible light. Recently optical brighteners have been added to market pulps to enhance their brightness.[18] The demand is still great for ultrawhite papers and this can be met, in general, by the following methods: (1) the use of bleaching agents, on the pulp fibers, (2) the addition of a blue dye to the paper stock to compensate for the yellowish hue of its components, actually producing a gray tint, (3) the addition of a white pigment, and (4) the use of an optical bleaching agent to increase the total visible light reflectance, improving the visual whiteness.

The claim is made that by incorporating the optical brightener at the pulp mill, many variables are eliminated. The brighteners have no effect on the physical properties of the pulps. When added to sulfite pulp, the brightness gain in one mill was as much as 3.5 units, and for soda pulp the brightness increase was up to 2.5 units. These differences were maintained through accelerated reversion tests. The following Table 10.8 shows the reversion of two pulps, treated with an optical brightener, after natural aging in a bale.

TABLE 10.8 REVERSION OF PULPS TREATED WITH
0.2% OF AN OPTICAL BRIGHTENER, AFTER
NATURAL AGING

Pulp	Initial Brightness	Days in Bale	Final Brightness
"Glo-White" soda	91.1	54	89.9
"Glo-White" sulfite	94.1	34	92.1

The higher the bleached brightness of the pulp, the more effective is the optical bleaching agent or fluorescent brightener. These materials have a negligible effect on unbleached pulps. The amount to be added depends on numerous conditions, such as the color of the sizing materials, quality of the process water, and brightness of the pulp.

A recent development in this field is the improved stability or color yield resulting from using EDTA or DTPA * with optical brighteners. Less optical dye is required when a chelating agent is added to the pulp prior to the application of the dye.

BLEACHING OF HIGH YIELD PULPS

Mechanical Pulp (Groundwood)

With the bleaching of mechanical pulp to a brightness range of that of some chemical pulps, the type of papers in which this high yield pulp can be used has been considerably broadened. The appearance and desirable printing characteristics are generally improved by bleaching, and the yield and strength properties are not greatly affected.

New pulping processes have been developed for producing mechanical pulps from wood chips by treatment with chemicals and then defibering the chips in refiners. Eberhardt's summary of the characteristics and bleachability of high yield pulps are given in Table 10.9.

The application of reducing agents, such as bisulfites, hydrosulfites, and sulfurous acid for bleaching mechanical pulp and as an antichlor or brightness stabilizer has been practiced for some time. Formerly, the action of hydrosulfite on mechanical pulp

* EDTA is ethylenediaminetetraacetic acid; DTPA is diethylenediaminetetraacetic acid.

only yielded a brightness gain of about 5 points and considerable color reversion occurred. After recent investigations in this field,[6, 55] however, these disadvantages have been overcome to a degree. The use of hydrosulfites is expanding as an economical process for bleaching mechanical pulp.

(1) Bisulfite Bleaching. This subject has already been discussed under reducing compounds.

(2) Hypochlorite Bleaching.[30] Mechanical pulp prepared from hardwoods is amenable to hypochlorite bleaching, but softwood mechanical pulp is yellowed rather than whitened by the conventional hypochlorite treatment. The success of mechanical pulp bleaching with this bleaching agent depends on slowing the reaction rate initially by the proper choice of pulp consistency, temperature, and alkalinity.

With 10% of available chlorine, using calcium hypochlorite, the brightness of hardwood groundwood pulps is increased to the range of 70 to 79 units. Yields are 98 to 100% of the unbleached groundwood. In general, consistency should not exceed 6% and the temperature need not go above 30°C. Alkalinity at the beginning should be equivalent to the pH range 11 to 12, with a final pH of not less than 8. Depending on the pulp, the use of sodium silicate as a part of the buffer system will give an improved brightness up to 5 units.

TABLE 10.9. CHARACTERISTICS OF HIGH YIELD PULPS [13]

Pulp	Wood Types	Burst	Tear	Unbleached Brightness	Bleach-ability
(1) Mechanical pulp	Mostly softwood; some hardwood	Poor	Poor	Fair	Peroxide, and hydrosulfite
(2) Neutral sulfite, semi-chemical	Hardwood	Excellent	Fair	Fair	Good
(3) Cold soda, very high yield	Mostly hardwood	Fair	Fair	Poor	Peroxide, and hydrosulfite
(4) Cold soda, yield below 85%	Mostly hardwood	Good	Fair	Poor	Peroxide, and hydrosulfite
(5) Cold soda	Softwood	Good	Fair	Poor	Very poor
(6) High-yield acid sulfite	Softwood	Excellent	Good	Good	Fair
(7) Ultrahigh-yield sulfite	Softwood	Good	Good	Good	Excellent
(8) Chemigroundwood	Hardwood	Fair	Fair	Fair	Fair
(9) Chemigroundwood	Softwood	Fair	Good	Fair	Poor
(10) High-yield sulfate	Softwood	Excellent	Excellent	Poor	Very poor

(3) Peroxide Bleaching. Progress in the application of peroxides to the bleaching of mechanical pulp, as well as chemical pulps, has been rapid since 1941. Data developed from early studies in this field by the duPont Company lead to the conclusion that peroxide bleaching increases the brightness of wood pulps with little or no change in the chemical or physical properties of the fibers.[46] Strength is not impaired and there is practically no loss in weight due to the bleaching operation. Peroxide is used in about 35 mechanical pulp mills in the United States.

Bleaching with peroxide does upgrade mechanical pulp, permitting the manufacture of a wider range of papers. Although not much is known concerning the chemical reactions involved in peroxide bleaching, it is generally accepted that the HO_2^- ion, shown in the following equation, is the active bleaching agent:

$$H_2O_2 \longrightarrow H^+ + HO_2^-$$

The formation of HO_2^- ions is promoted by the neutralization of the H^+ ions. This occurs when an alkali is added.

Under improper storage conditions, hydrogen peroxide decomposes into oxygen gas and water. This decomposition is promoted by metal catalysts, such as iron, copper, and manganese, and by certain enzymes. For this reason, stabilizing agents, such as sodium silicate and magnesium sulfate are added in the preparation of peroxide bleaching solutions.

The peroxide bleaching process comprises five basic steps: (1) preparation of the alkaline bleach solution from sodium peroxide and/or hydrogen peroxide (35, 50 or 70% solution), (2) dewatering of the pulp to the desired consistency, (3) rapid and thorough mixing of the bleach solution with the pulp in controlled proportions, (4) retention of the peroxide-treated pulp for sufficient time at a given temperature to complete the bleaching, and (5) neutralization of the residual bleaching chemicals to the proper pH, usually with sulfur dioxide.

For the production of many groundwood specialty papers a brightness range of about 65 to 72 is desired, although brightnesses up to 80 can be obtained. Brightness depends on many factors, such as the type and time of storage of the pulpwood, concentration of peroxide, pulp consistency, time of bleaching, temperature, and alkalinity. Improved bleach response is obtained from

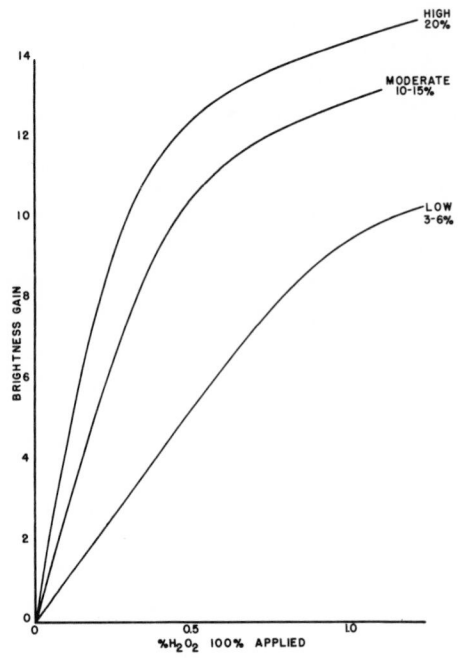

Fig. 10.6. Effect of pulp density on bleached brightness. (*Courtesy Becco Chemical Division, FMC Corp.*)

freshly cut wood, with a resultant increase in bleached brightness.[62]

To help in the bleaching efficiency, the pulp is often given a pretreatment, which subject will be discussed later in this chapter. The effect of pulp density on bleached brightness is shown in Figure 10.6. Because of the reduced bleach solution to fiber ratio, the efficiency of the system is increased by employing a high density system. The most suitable bleaching installation for a pulp mill must be determined by a consideration of its requirements. The widely accepted pulp consistency range is 12 to 15% because of better peroxide efficiency. Usually such a bleaching operation is carried out for 1 to 3 hours at 110° to 115°F, compared to 4 to 5 hours at 4 to 6% consistency.

The availability of the screw press and the disk press has made possible high density (25%) bleaching of groundwood. By means of these dewatering devices, pulp can be brought from consistencies of 10 to 15% to above 30%. The high density pulp is

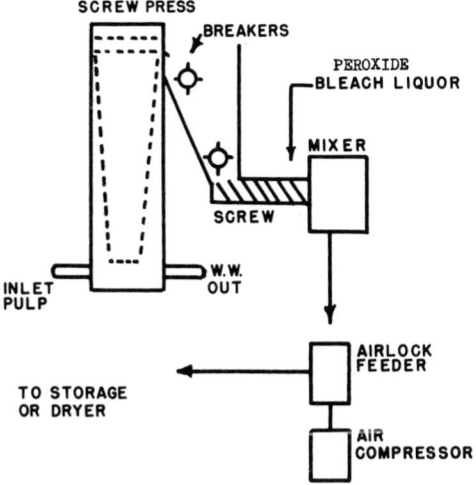

Fig. 10.7. Steep bleaching of pulp crumbs. (*Courtesy Becco Chemical Division, FMC Corp.*)

mixed with the bleach solution by a disk-type mixer, the minimum volume of solution necessary for adequate mixing being 100 gallons per ton of pulp. Retention systems may be (1) a continuous tower with a flared-type design to permit the free flowing of the pulp which is kept for 2 to 4 hours at 110° to 120°F or (2) the steep bleaching of pulp crumbs at ambient temperature for several hours to several days depending on the conditions. Neutralization is carried out as the pulp discharges from the tower system, but is not usually necessary with the steep bleaching operation because it is carried out at a lower alkalinity level.[29] This arrangement is shown in Figure 10.7.

The high density steep bleaching system can also be applied to sheets from feltless type wet machines. The alkaline peroxide bleach solution is applied by spray or applicator rolls to one or both sides of the pulp sheet. The bleaching takes place during storage of the pulp for 1 to 5 days. No neutralization of the residual bleach is necessary.

(4) Hydrosulfite Bleaching. Mention has already been made of the use of sodium and zinc hydrosulfites for bleaching mechanical pulp. These compounds are now available in the form of a stable, dry powder and it has been found that for most purposes, sodium and zinc hydrosulfite can be used interchangeably. Improvements in conditions and methods of application of hydrosulfite, together with the proper temperature and the use of sequestering agents, have resulted in a bleaching system which will give up to a 12 point increase in brightness with spruce groundwood.[6]

Owing to the rapidity with which dissolved hydrosulfite reacts with oxygen and the decomposition of the compound by auto-oxidation, there is severe competition between these reactions and the pulp fibers for the bleaching agent. The equations for the undesirable reactions are:

$$(1)\ Na_2S_2O_4 + O_2 + H_2O \longrightarrow NaHSO_3 + NaHSO_4$$
$$(2)\ 2Na_2S_2O_4 + H_2O \longrightarrow Na_2S_2O_3 + 2NaHSO_3$$

For effective use of hydrosulfites for bleaching purposes, the following rules have been developed: (1) all possible air should be removed from the pulp mixture before the hydrosulfite is added, (2) the chemical should be rapidly and thoroughly mixed with the stock in the absence of air, and (3) the fiber mixture should not be exposed to air until the retention time is completed.

The important variables in hydrosulfite bleaching are: concentration of reducing agent, concentration of additive (sequestering agent), temperature, time, pulp consistency, pH, and type and time of storage of wood. A suggested range relating to these variables is listed below:

	Range	Average
Zinc or sodium hydro-sulfite concentration	0.1-1.5% *	1.0%
Additive or sequestering agent	0-0.5%	0.5% **
Temperature	above 100°F	140°F
Time	0.5-3.0 hours	1-2 hours
Pulp consistency	4-14%	4-5%
pH with zinc hydrosulfite	4.5-6.0	5.6
pH with sodium hydrosulfite	6.0-7.5	7.0

* Based on oven-dry weight of pulp.
** 0.5% sodium tripolyphosphate ($Na_5P_3O_{10}$).

It has been stated that the pH of the pulp mixture has a bearing on the most economical hydrosulfite to use. If the pH is 4.5 to 5.5, zinc hydrosulfite is usually the more effective material to employ. If the pH of the pulp is above 6.0, the sodium salt is preferred. Between pH 5.5 and 6.0 either compound may prove the better one to use. The selection is usually made after mill trials are carried out at various hydrosulfite concentrations.

Small amounts of iron in the pulp and/or process water have harmful effects on the brightness of both the unbleached and the hydrosulfite bleached pulp. To control the effect of the iron content, sequestering or chelating agents are added, such as sodium tripolyphosphate or ethylenediaminetetraacetic acid (EDTA). Usually 0.5% of the tripolyphosphate or 0.1% of EDTA, based on the dry weight of the pulp, is the quantity applied. The former is most often used, and its value should be established by mill trials. Patents covering the use of sequestering agents and the bleaching of groundwood with hydrosulfite have recently been issued.[57]

Although corrosion of mill equipment was serious with the early use of hydrosulfite, with a better understanding of its use and the availability of both the zinc and sodium salts in powder form and of higher purity, there is practically no corrosion problem at the present time.

The quality of the wood affects the response of mechanical pulp to bleaching. The type and geographical location of the wood, its iron content and time of storage before use, and the age of the pulp are important factors. It is known that wood cut and used within 3 months yields a brighter mechanical pulp, whereas a storage period of a year or longer penalizes the efficiency of the bleaching agent.[62]

TABLE 10.10. RESPONSE OF GROUNDWOOD PULPS TO BLEACHING WITH ZINC HYDROSULFITE [60]

Bleaching conditions:
Chemicals: 1.0% ZnS_2O_4, 0.2-0.5% $Na_5P_3O_{10}$
Temperature: 140°F
Time: 1.0 or 2.0 hours
Consistency: 3-5%
Finishing pH: 4.5

Wood Species	U.S. Geographical Location	Pulp Brightness (% MgO)		
		Unbleached	Bleached	Increase
Spruce	Northeast	58.6	70.4	11.8
Spruce	Midwest	61.1	73.1	12.0
Spruce	West Coast	60.5	70.6	10.1
Jack pine	Northeast	54.2	65.4	11.2
Mixed pines	Southeast	59.5	70.0	10.5
White fir	West Coast	58.2	69.3	11.1
Hemlock	West Coast	55.1	66.7	11.6
Aspen	Midwest	61.1	73.1	12.0
Aspen	South Central	65.0	73.3	8.3
Aspen	West Coast	58.8	69.2	10.4

In Table 10.10 are typical variations in brightness response resulting from the action of 1.0% zinc hydrosulfite (based on the oven-dry wood) on a number of woods.

"Zepar" BP is a bleaching agent (du-Pont) based on sodium hydrosulfite but compounded to give the same reducing power as zinc hydrosulfite. It is specifically formulated for bleaching groundwood and chip mechanical pulp.[15] The material is a free flowing white powder which possesses more heat stability than sodium hydrosulfite even when moist.

The conditions recommended for the use of "Zepar" BP are (1) 3 to 6% pulp consistency, (2) 140° to 175°F temperature, (3) pH range, 5.5 to 6.5, (4) 1 to 1.25% concentration of chemical, based on the oven-dry weight of the pulp, and (5) 30 to 60 minutes bleaching time. As with other hydrosulfites, "Zepar" BP should be mixed as rapidly and as efficiently as possible with the pulp out of contact with the air which destroys the bleaching agent rapidly. The entire bleaching operation involving hydrosulfites should be carried out in a closed system free from air.

"Zepar" BP is licensed to sell by its manufacturers for the bleaching of wood pulp according to the methods of U.S. patents 2,707,144 and 2,707,146 and Canadian patents 520,083 and 520,085.[57] Figure 10.8 shows the effect of hydrosulfite concentration on brightness gain.

Chemigroundwood

Chemigroundwood[33] from hardwoods can be bleached generally by the same methods employed for coniferous mechanical pulps. Brightness gains to 15 points are obtainable with 2% sodium peroxide on aspen pulp. Hardwood pulps of the same initial brightness bleach as easily and to the same brightness as coniferous pulps.

Chemigroundwood also responds to the bleaching action of calcium hypochlorite. Brightness gains of 9 to 12 points on aspen chemigroundwood have been reported with

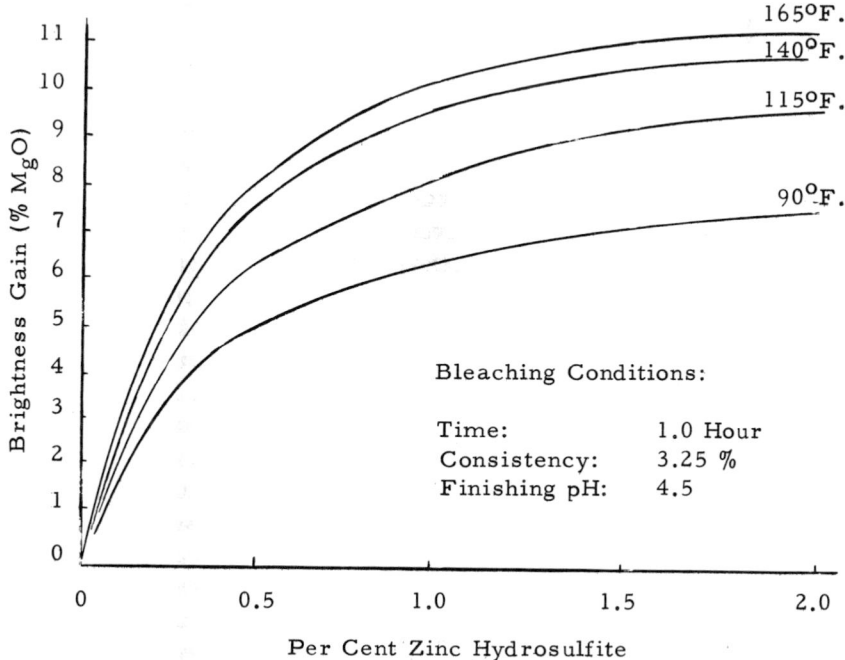

Fig. 10.8. Effect of hydrosulfite concentration on brightness gain. (*Courtesy Virginia Chemicals & Smelting Co.*)

TABLE 10.11. GROUNDWOOD BLEACHING METHODS [63]

(After A. A. Yankowski)

	Peroxide	*Hypochlorite*	*Hydrosulfite*	*Bisulfite*
Bleaching chemicals	Sodium peroxide Hydrogen peroxide Sodium and hydrogen peroxides	Calcium or sodium hypo-chlorite	Zinc or sodium hydrosulfite "Zepar" BP	Sodium bisulfite
Effect of bleach	Good gains up to 3% *	Good gains up to 15%	Good gains to 1-1.25%	2-4 points of brightness with 1-2%
Pretreatment	0.1% DPTA or 0.5% sodium tripolyphos-phate or 1-2% calcium chloride	None	0.5% sodium tripolyphos-phate	—
Effect of increasing consistency	Decreases reac-tion time; increases brightness	Decreases reac-tion; harder to control	Optimum 4-6%	Slight
Temperature increase	Decreases time; range 90-160°F	Decreases time; increases brightness; control more difficult; optimum 38°C	Decreases time; increases brightness; range 90-160°C	Slight
pH	10-10.5	9-11	5-6.5	Below 7
Posttreatment	Neutralization and acidifica-tion with SO_2	Acidification with SO_2; wash	None	None
Brightness gain	6-7 points, with 1% chemical *	12 points with hardwoods and 10% available chlorine; 10 points for softwoods and 15% available chlorine	8-12 points with 1% chemical	2-3 points with 1% chemical; 3-4 points with 2%
Chemical cost	$10.64 with 2% peroxide *	$11.82 with 10% average chlorine	$4.30 with 1% zinc hydro-sulfite	$0.90 with 1% chemical
Cost per point per ton pulp	$0.70-$1.00	$0.80-$1.00	$0.30-$0.60	$0.35

* 50% hydrogen peroxide.

the use of 10% available chlorine as calcium hypochlorite, with 2.5 to 10% calcium hydroxide. The addition of 10% sodium silicate to the mixture containing the hypochlorite and alkali yields an even greater gain in brightness.

Semichemical Pulps

Neutral sulfite semichemical pulp (NSSC) and cold soda pulps, containing substantial amounts of lignin and other fiber incrustants, especially from hardwoods, can be bleached by a single stage or multistage bleaching process to brightness values 75 or above with only a slight loss in yield.[52] An improvement in strength results from single stage bleaching. Higher brightness can be achieved with multistage bleaching, usually chlorination, alkaline extraction, and oxidation. This involves a purification operation and the yield of hardwood pulp is 55 to 60% of the wood. Multistage bleaching, with chlorination, yields a superior pulp not only with improved brightness but with less color reversion and better strength properties.[38]

Sulfate semichemical pulp can be bleached by the same multistage process but, owing to its high lignin content, requires more chlorine.

A disadvantage of cold soda pulp is its low brightness (30 to 40), but by means of conventional single stage bleaching the brightness can be elevated to 60 plus. Its yellow color persists after bleaching. A peroxide or combination peroxide-hydrosulfite treatment yields an improved bleached color. By means of refiner bleaching and with peroxide, it is possible to bleach most cold soda pulps to between 60 and 70 when fresh wood is used.[29] For brightness values up to 80, either a peroxide single-stage high density or two-stage moderate density peroxide-hydrosulfite treatment is required with hardwood cold soda pulps.

Deinked Paper Stock

Deinked pulp from reclaimed paper usually possesses a yellowish color and a brightness of around 60. To obtain a pulp which can be used in the manufacture of papers of satisfactory whiteness, the deinked fibers must be bleached. Most of these processes fall into two groups: (1) single-stage hypochlorite or peroxide treatment, (2) multistage operation, involving chlorination-hypochlorite, chlorination-alkaline extraction-hypochlorite, hypochlorite-peroxide or peroxide-hydrosulfite.[22]

The choice of bleaching method will depend on the type of deinked stock, the brightness desired, and the equipment or capital available for the process. Usually deinked stock is a mixture of mechanical and chemical pulps. These are frequently classified according to the mechanical pulp content: (1) high groundwood content, such as news, coarsebook, etc., (2) moderate groundwood content, such as number 1 book, magazine, etc., and (3) low to no groundwood content, such as tabulating card, bond, ledger, etc.[53]

Harbin and Greene [23] report that a three stage bleaching process (chlorine, caustic extraction, sodium hypochlorite) on deinked stock yields a bleached pulp with better physical properties than with a single stage operation, and with less chemical consumption. The deinked stock comprised waste kraft, ledger, tab cards and magazines.

With moderate to high groundwood content deinked stock, the use of peroxide is claimed to offer an economical solution to the problem. Variations of the continuous tower or steep bleaching methods may be used. Additional brightness can be obtained by the application of a second stage hydrosulfite treatment. The selection of the proper bleaching installation depends on the type of deinked stock, the end use of the fiber, and the equipment available for the bleaching operation.

Pulp Pretreatments

To gain the maximum brightness in the bleaching of mechanical pulp, either with peroxide or hydrosulfite, it is generally beneficial to give the fibers a chemical treatment before the thickener, or at some other place in the bleaching operation. It is claimed that in the bleaching of chemical pulps, the use of chelating compounds prior to the hypochlorite or chlorine dioxide stages improves color stability and increases washing efficiency.[19]

The following pretreatments should be evaluated by a given pulp mill to determine the one best suited for its purpose.

(1) Acidification, in which the pH of the dilute pulp suspension is adjusted to 2.5 to 3.0, with 1 to 2% sulfuric acid.

(2) An inorganic salt, such as calcium chloride, added to the diluted stock to the extent of 1.0 to 2.0%, based on the oven-dry weight of the pulp, may yield beneficial results.

(3) Addition of sodium tripolyphosphate, applied in an amount equal to 0.5 to 1.0%, based on the oven-dry weight of the pulp, is a suggested treatment.

(4) Chelating or organic sequestering agents, applied to the extent of 0.1 to 0.2%, based on the oven-dry pulp, are helpful when pulps and/or process water are contaminated with heavy metal ions, such as manganese, iron and copper, which bring about decomposition of the bleaching agent. The chelating agent best suited for this purpose appears to be diethylenetriaminepentaacetic acid (DTPA), although ethylenediaminetetraacetic acid (EDTA) has also been used.

In hydrosulfite bleaching of mechanical pulp, 0.5 per cent sodium tripolyphosphate added to the bleach solution often yields an additional 1 to 2 points of additional brightness. The amount of tripolyphosphate used is based on the oven-dry weight of the pulp.

Pulp Washing [24]

Emphasis should be given to the importance of pulp washing after the chemical treatments in the bleaching process because it is closely connected with the efficiency of bleaching and the consumption of the bleaching agent. Organic compounds solubilized by the bleaching operation, and bleach residues should be removed, otherwise they may increase consumption of chemicals in the stages to follow. Continuous vacuum filters are employed for this purpose, with a plentiful supply of water for dilution of the fiber suspension.

Multistage bleaching requires large volumes of water for interstage washing and countercurrent practices are employed as far as possible. Highly contaminated filtrates, such as those from the chlorination and caustic extraction stages, are sent to the sewer. Efficient washing in multistage bleach plants requires 30,000 to 40,000 gallons of water per ton of bleached pulp.[3]

A tentative water standard, suggested by TAPPI, for pulp manufacture is given below: [56]

Substance	Maximum Parts per Million
Turbidity as SiO_2	25
Color in platinum units	5
Total hardness as $CaCO_3$	100
Calcium hardness as $CaCO_3$	50
Alkalinity to methyl orange as $CaCO_3$	75
Iron as Fe	0.1
Manganese as Mn	0.05
Silica (soluble) as SiO_2	20
Total dissolved solids	250
Free carbon dioxide	10
Chlorides as Cl	75
Magnesium hardness as $CaCO_3$	50

In some pulp mills, especially after a final hypochlorite bleaching stage, sulfur dioxide or clear cooking acid is added to a pH of 6.0 to 6.5 to lower the ash content of the pulp, reduce its alkalinity and to facilitate its washing, with especial attention to the removal of any iron, as ferrous iron, and the destruction of traces of available chlorine. The use of sulfur dioxide as a final treatment may also improve the color of the pulp slightly and reduce color reversion.

Brightness Stability

With the production of pulps of high brightness (about 90), there has been a tendency for color reversion to occur during the storage period. Consequently within recent years there have been investigations into the causes of yellowing of bleached pulps. Accelerated aging tests have been developed to evaluate pulps with respect to their brightness stability. One such test involves heat aging a bleached pulp for one hour in an oven heated to 105°C.

The major causes of color reversion have been traced to the presence of carbonyl, aldehyde, and carboxyl groups in bleached pulp. The various colored materials formed during the aging process have not been identified but appear to contain carbonyl groups, which seem to contribute more to reversion than carboxyl groups. Rapson [45] and others have noted that hypochlorite at pH 7 introduces carbonyl groups into the cellulose of bleached pulp and color reversion occurs. As the pH is raised, carboxyl groups are formed and the color reversion is reduced. In general, the higher the pH of hypochlorite bleaching over the range 7 to 11, the less is the reversion. This is true both of sulfite and sulfate pulps.

The fact has been established that bleaching should not continue until the bleaching agent is exhausted; a small amount of residual bleach should be present, especially in an alkaline solution, to reduce color reversion. Even the inclusion of a small quantity of bleach in the caustic extraction stage is recommended to prevent a loss in brightness.

The resin present in sulfite pulps and to a lesser extent in sulfate pulps affects reversion. By extracting this material, there is a substantial improvement in the degree of reversion. It is probable that some of the yellowing of bleached pulp is due to color forming groups attached to the hemicellulose constituent of the pulp. Correlation has been established between color reversion and the copper number and also the hemicellulose content of the pulp.

Treatment of pulp with chlorine dioxide to give maximum brightness and then with sodium borohydride to reduce the carbonyl groups to hydroxyl groups yields also maximum color stability.[37]

Control of the Bleaching Process

Adequate control of bleaching systems is available largely through the use of automatic instruments, assuming that the plant has been properly designed and engineered. Whether the pulp is intended for the manufacture of paper or for chemical purposes, the control methods employed are similar. Lyon [34] has divided chemical control into four divisions:

(1) Tests on the unbleached and/or partially bleached pulp, such as permanganate number, consistency, and speck count;

(2) Determination of the strength of the bleaching chemicals;

(3) Metering of chemicals to the system in accordance with the calculated test results;

(4) Control of process variables by means of routine tests, such as temperature, consistency, residual chemicals, brightness, viscosity, pH and other tests as required.

Bleachability Tests. The relative "hardness" or bleachability of pulp is frequently determined by the permanganate (K) number (TAPPI Method T 214) or the Kappa number (TAPPI Method T 236). Other tests employed for this purpose are the following: (1) chlorine consumption of pulp (Roe chlorine number), TAPPI Method T 202, and (2) bleach requirement of pulp, TAPPI Method T 219.

Not only are bleachability tests carried out on the unbleached pulp but also during a multistage bleaching process, especially following the first caustic extraction stage, for control purposes.

Redox (ORP) Control of Continuous Hypochlorite Manufacture and Pulp Chlorination.[51] The measurement of oxidation potential has been developed into an excellent method of controlling (1) the strength of hypochlorite in a continuous process of manufacture and (2) the pulp chlorination stage. In the manufacture of bleach liquor, the redox controller maintains the potential of the finished liquor by adjusting the flow of chlorine into the alkaline solution. Similarly the oxidation potential of a chlorinated pulp depends on the ratio, at a given time, of chlorine to chloride ion. This depends on the pulp demand for chlorine and the reaction or retention time. The chlorine flow valve automatically varies the input of chlorine as the ORP meter holds the oxidation potential constant.

Hypochlorite Analysis. For the analysis of dry hypochlorites, or their solutions, residual chlorine, or other solutions containing available chlorine, reference should be made to Method T 611 in the TAPPI Manual of Standards.

Alkalinity or Acidity. To determine the alkalinity or acidity of pulp mixtures during bleaching, a pH meter, as a recorder, controller, or portable instrument for intermittent testing, is usually employed. Alkalinity or acidity is expressed in pH units. pH is defined as the logarithm of the reciprocal of the hydrogen ion concentration. At pH 7.0, a solution is neutral, the concentrations of the hydrogen (H^+) and the hydroxyl (OH^-) ions being equal. The lower the pH, below 7, the higher the acidity; the higher the pH, above 7, the higher is the alkalinity.

Brightness. The term "brightness," as applied to naturally colored pulps, bleached and unbleached, is associated with the numerical value of the reflectance of those pulps to light in the blue and violet portion (457 millimicrons) of the spectrum. The measurement is made with an instrument in calibration with a master reflection meter of particular type and design, described in TAPPI Standard Method T 217.

Viscosity. For checking pulp quality the disperse viscosity test is often employed. Variations in the viscosity figure reflect changes in the physical properties of the pulp fibers. An over-bleached or degraded pulp has a low viscosity value. TAPPI Suggested Method T 230 is generally preferred to Standard Method 206 because of the convenience and rapidity of the former.

Copper Number. The overbleaching of pulp fibers can be measured by the copper number test, which has also been employed

as an indication of the brightness stability of bleached pulp. TAPPI Standard Method T 215 is recommended for this purpose.

Hot Alkali Solubility. Fiber degradation due to overbleaching is shown in the increase of alkali-soluble material. The TAPPI hot dilute alkali solubility test (T 212) is employed for this purpose.

Other Control Tests. The testing required for the control of the variables in pulp bleaching are more extensively described in "The Bleaching of Pulp," TAPPI Monograph Series—No. 10, pages 327-350.

REFERENCES

1. Andrews I. H. *Pulp Paper Mag. Can.* **46**, 679 (August, 1945); *Tappi*, **32**, 286 (1949).
2. Anon., *Paper Trade J.*, **145**, No. 21, 22 (1961).
3. Anon., *Chemical Week*, **89**, No. 12, 81, 84 (1961).
4. Anon., *Chem. Eng. News*, **40**, No. 4, 54 (Jan. 22, 1962); *Chemical Week*, **90**, No. 3, 98, 100 (Jan. 20, 1962).
5. Baldwin, N., *Paper Trade J.*, **144**, No. 51, 34 (Dec. 19, 1960).
6. Barton, R. W., *Tappi*, **44**, No. 8, 161A (August, 1961); **41**, No. 3, 161A (March, 1958).
7. Bauer, G. W., *Tappi*, **43**, No. 7, 240A (July, 1960).
8. Becco Chemical Division, FMC Corporation, Bulletin 117, "The Bleaching of Groundwood Pulp with Hydrogen Peroxide," 1962.
9. Carr, R. L., and MacLeod, K. S., *Tappi*, **36**, No. 5, 195A (May, 1953).
10. Casciani, F., and Heilborn, A., *Paper Ind.*, **17**, No. 11, 810 (February, 1936).
11. Chadwick, A. F., Fennell, F. L., and Wagoner, H. E., *Tappi*, **42**, No. 4, 308 (April, 1959).
12. Duncan, E. P., and Rapson, W. H., *Pulp & Paper*, **34**, No. 11, 100 (1960).
13. Eberhardt, L. E., *Paper Trade J.*, **145**, No. 15, 50 (April 10, 1961).
14. Edelstein, S. M., *Tappi*, **43**, No. 4, 40A, 42A, 50A, 52A, 54A, 56A, 60A, 62A, 64A (April, 1960).
15. E. I. du Pont de Nemours and Co., "Peroxide Bleaching of Mechanical Pulps," p. 4, "Zepar" BP Reducing Agent Bulletin.
16. Fennell, F. L., Smedberg, G. E., and Stalter, N. J., *Tappi*, **43**, No. 11, 903 (November, 1960).
17. Forni, P. A., *Paper Trade J.*, **119**, Tappi Sect. 108 (1944).

18. Freedman, Herbert, *Paper Trade J.*, 145, No. 12, 26 (May 8, 1961).

19. Gard, Andrew J., *Tappi*, 44, No. 10, 162A (October, 1961).

20. Giertz, H. W., *Tappi*, 44, No. 1, 1 (January, 1961).

21. Grangaard, D. H., *Tappi*, 39, No. 5, 270 (May, 1956).

22. Hansen, Paul B., "Bleaching of Deinked Paper Stock," TAPPI Monograph Series No. 16, 1956.

23. Harbin, A. D. Jr., and Greene, U. T., *Tappi*, 45, No. 2, 171A (February, 1962).

24. Hatch, R. S., "Cellulose and Cellulose Derivatives," Part 2, in "Bleaching and Purification," New York, Interscience Publishers Inc., 1954.

25. Hinrichs, D. D., *Pulp Paper Mag. Can.*, 62, No. 9, T437 (September, 1961).

26. Improved Machinery Inc., "Impco Bleach Plant Equipment," Bulletin C1-2.

27. Jack, Walter Q., and Dowsley, Allan H., *Pulp Paper Mag. Can.*, 61, No. 10, T490, T504 (October, 1960).

28. Jahne, J. F., and Price, C. E., *Tappi*, 43, No. 7, 226A (July, 1960).

29. Kindron, R. R., and Rosebush, F. J., *Tappi*, 44, No. 10, 158A (October, 1961).

30. Kingsbury, R. M., Simmonds, F. A., and Lewis, E. S., *Tappi*, 32, No. 6, 273 (June, 1949).

31. Klemm, K. H., "Modern Methods of Mechanical Pulp Manufacture," New York, Lockwood Trade Journal Company, Inc., 1958.

32. Klouman, G. H., *Paper Trade J.*, 145, No. 31, 22 (July 31, 1961).

33. Libby, C. E., and O'Neil, F. W., *Tappi*, 33, No. 4, 161 (April, 1950).

34. Lyon, M. G., "The Bleaching of Pulp," TAPPI Monograph Series No. 10, 1953.

35. Mayer, W. C., and Donofrio, C. P., *Tappi*, 43, No. 1, 238A (January, 1960).

36. Meller, A., "The Bleaching of Pulp," in Tappi Monograph Series No. 10, 1953.

37. Metal Hydrides Inc., "Sodium Borohydride," p. 25, 1958.

38. Parsons, S. R., and Lausman, H. J., *Tappi*, 34, No. 3, 97-102 (March, 1951).

39. Pascoe, T. A., "The Bleaching of Pulp," Chapter 13, Tappi Monograph Series No. 10 (1953).

40. Partridge, H., and Rapson, W. H., *Tappi*, 44, No. 10, 698 (October, 1961).

41. Price, F. A., *Pulp Paper Mag. Can.*, 62, No. 6 (June, 1961).

42. Rapson, W. H., *Tappi*, 39, No. 5, 281 (May, 1956).

43. Rapson, W. H., *Tappi*, 41, No. 4, 181 (April, 1958).

44. Rapson, W. H., and Anderson, C. B., *Tappi*, 41, No. 9, 486 (September, 1958).

45. Rapson, W. H., and Hakim, K. A., *Tech. Sect. Proc. Canada*, 277 (1957).

46. Reichert, J. S., and Pete, R. H., *Tappi*, 32, No. 3, 97 (March, 1949).

47. Rue, John D., "Pulp Bleaching," p. 5, Hooker Chemical Corp., Bulletin 200, 1957.

48. Russell, L. E., *Paper Ind.*, 28, No. 4, 528, 537 (July, 1946).

49. Russell, L. E., *Paper Trade J.*, 128, No. 12, 23 (March 24, 1949).

50. Serafin, J. F., and Scribner, H. C., *Pulp Paper Mag. Can.*, 62, No. 10, T473 (October, 1961).

51. Seymour, George W., *Tappi*, 40, No. 6, 426 (June, 1957); Bush, W. H., *Pulp Paper Mag. Can.*, Convention Number 197 (1958); Harbin, A. D. Jr., *Tappi*, 43, No. 8, 180A (August, 1960).

52. Simmonds, F. A., and Kingsbury, R. M., "The Bleaching of Pulp," Chapter 9, TAPPI Monograph Series No. 10, 1953.

53. Sixth Deinking Conference Papers, *Tappi*, 45, No. 2, 164A (February, 1962).

54. Smith, J. W., and Thornburg, W. L., *Tappi*, 43, No. 6, 596 (June, 1960).

55. Sparrow, D. B., *Tappi*, 39, No. 7, 486 (July, 1956).

56. TAPPI, Tentative Standard E-603, s-49; "Water Technology in the Pulp and Paper Industry," TAPPI Monograph Series No. 18, 1957.

57. U.S. Patents, 2,707,144; 2,707,145 and 2,707,146 assigned to the Scott Paper Company. Corresponding Canadian Patents are 520,083; 520,084 and 520,085.

58. U.S. Pulp Producers Association, Inc., N.Y.

59. Varshney, M. C., and Luner, Philip, *Tappi*, 44, No. 4, 285 (April, 1961).

60. Virginia Smelting & Chemicals Company, "Hydrosulfite Groundwood Bleaching Variables," Bulletin 407-C.

61. Wheless, R. E., *Tappi*, 44, No. 6, 134A (June, 1961).

62. Whitman, F. A., *Tappi*, 40, No. 1, 20 (January, 1957).

63. Yankowski, A. A., "Mechanical Pulping Manual," p. 94, TAPPI Monograph Series No. 21, 1960.

CHAPTER II

Stock Preparation

JOHN W. SWANSON

The Institute of Paper Chemistry

Paper-making fibers obtained from the pulp mill are not yet satisfactory for manufacture of paper for several reasons. First, even though the fibers are saturated with water, they do not cohere well when the sheet is formed and dried, and paper of low bursting and tensile strengths results. In order to develop good fiber bonding and high paper strength it is necessary to beat or refine the fibers. Untreated fibers also have a marked tendency to entangle and flocculate, which causes uneven fiber formation of the paper. Finally, the natural fibers may produce paper that is lacking in several desirable characteristics such as surface smoothness, sizing, color, etc. Correction of these deficiencies requires numerous additives such as sizing agents, dyes, white and colored pigments, natural and synthetic polymers of various types, and foam and pitch control chemicals. Processing the fibers and incorporating these additives comprises stock preparation.

BEATING AND REFINING

In the earliest days of paper making it was realized that some sort of mechanical treatment of pulp fibers was required before

Grateful acknowledgment is made to Mr. Ralph Kumler, Waste Paper Utilization Council, and Mr. A. J. Felton of The Black Clawson Company for assistance with the sections on Beating and Refining, and to Dr. E. R. Laughlin of The Institute of Paper Chemistry for assistance with the section on Coloring of Paper.

strong, well-formed paper could be made. This often consisted of manually pounding, beating, or otherwise macerating the fibers in water with various objects, such as sticks or stones. The term "beating" is retained even today. Various early methods for the mechanization of this process are exhibited in the Dard Hunter Museum of Papermaking at The Institute of Paper Chemistry.

About 1690, a machine for beating pulp was developed in Holland. This machine, now called the Hollander, consists of a large oval tub, partitioned longitudinally within three to four feet of each end. The partition is called the midfeather. On one side, extending between the midfeather and edge of the tub, is a large cylindrical roll whose axis is perpendicular to the midfeather. The cylindrical surface of the roll is fitted with steel bars or "knives" arranged parallel to the roll axis. As the roll revolves, the pulp-water mixture circulates around the tub. Under the beater roll is a "bedplate" also fitted with steel bars extending the full width of the roll. The roll may be raised from the bedplate several inches, and it can be lowered to contact the bedplate if desired. Suitable adjustment of the roll level permits a rubbing or brushing action on the fibers, or if the roll is lowered into contact with the bedplate a cutting action occurs which decreases fiber length. A modern version of the Hollander beater is shown in Figure 11.1.

Fig. 11.1. External view of Hollander beater. (*Courtesy Black Clawson Co.*)

Beating Equipment

Many improvements in the design of the Hollander beater have been made since the first machines were built, and some modern equipment appears to be quite different from the Hollanders that served the industry for many years. However, the Hollander beater is a versatile machine and is still popular in many mills, although it has been replaced for certain operations by conical refiners. The Hollander will accept pulp in either slush form, dry lap, wet lap, or in the form of waste papers provided the dry lap pulps are not fed to the machine in too large pieces at a time. The entire beating process may be completed in the beater, and this was the practice for many years. However, conical refiners have come to be used for the later stages of refining. Typical of the conical refiner is the Jordan engine which will be described later. At this point, a more detailed description of the Hollander beater and its various parts will permit a better appreciation of its advantages.

The Beater Roll. The roll consists of four cast-iron disks mounted perpendicular to the roll shaft. The edges of these disks have slots spaced at intervals of two to four inches. The beater bars, or knives, are fitted into the slots and are secured at their ends by heat-shrunk rings that fit into notches in the ends of the bars. Hardwood fillets are then driven between the bars to strengthen them. A vacant space about one inch deep is left between the bars. The wood swells when wet and holds the bars firmly in place. In recent years the body of the roll may have consisted of a one-piece drum with mounted slotted rings which receive and hold the bars. Figure 11.2 illustrates a complete beater roll with the knives and wooden fillings. There has also been a trend toward closer spacings of bars and shallower cells between them. The wooden filling is still used.

The Bedplate. The bedplate against which the beater roll rubs the pulp consists of a cast-iron trough fitted with bars similar to those in the roll. These bars are also braced with hardwood fillers. Beaters intended for processing roofing paper and similar crude pulps may have fillers of metal between the bedplate bars. The bedplate bars may be long and oriented parallel to the roll bars, or they may be arranged diagonally, in a zigzag or even a "herringbone" manner. Shorter bars are used in these special designs. The surface of the bars forms a curved pattern to conform to the curvature of the

Fig. 11.2. Hollander beater roll with knives and wooden fillings. (*Courtesy Black Clawson Co.*)

beater roll. As the bars of either the beater roll or bedplate become excessively worn, they must be replaced. When the beater roll is replaced it is necessary to grind the roll and bedplate bar surfaces until all the knives of the roll contact all those of the bedplate evenly as the roll revolves. It is customary to grind the roll surfaces in the presence of water in which fine sand or grinding compound has been suspended.

The Backfall. In order to encourage circulation of the stock, a backfall or dam across the tub on the discharge of the roll is installed. The backfall, constructed of either wood or metal, is built onto the floor of the tub. The face next to the roll is curved to fit the surface of the roll, but the face away from the roll forms a more or less gradual slope. The stock is cast by the beater roll up over the backfall and its circulation is thus assured. The height of the backfall varies from one type of beater to another, depending upon the desired speed of stock circulation. In some beaters the floor of the beater slopes gradually from the bottom of the backfall to the discharge outlet directly in front of the beater roll. In some old beaters, the floor of the tub is level from the base of the backfall around to the bedplate. This type of beater moves the stock rather slowly.

In order to prevent the pulp from being thrown out of the beater as it emerges from the roll, a hood or cover is placed over the roll and backfall. This is shown in Figure 11.1.

Capacity of the Beater Tub. The oval-shaped beater tub varies widely in size from those accommodating 250 pounds of pulp to those of more than 3000 pounds. Capacities of 600 to more than 7500 gallons are therefore required. The type of pulp to be processed often determines the capacity and the type of beater which should be installed. For example, in making rag papers, the mechanical action between the roll and bedplate is very important. The time of treatment may be several hours of slow circulation. In other mills the beaters may be used primarily as mixers and in this instance circulation is a more important factor. Rapid circulation is especially important where chemical additives such as dyes and sizing agents are to be added to the stock at the beaters. In still other cases beaters known as "broke" beaters are used for disintegration of waste papers or processing dry broke from the paper machine.

Continuous Beating. Certain beaters employed for processing waste papers are equipped with perforated backfalls. This device permits disintegrated stock to be drawn off, while stock that has not yet been adequately disintegrated passes to the next stage over the backfall and is given further treatment. The same purpose is accomplished with a perforated revolving drum having a discharge through a hollow journal at the side of the beater. Waste papers, particularly those containing wet-strength materials, vary greatly in their resistance to repulping, and continuous beating avoids overtreatment of susceptible stocks while providing adequate processing of the more refractory portions. These beaters function much like breaker beaters (described later) but are in reality adaptations of conventional Hollanders.

Washers. The Hollander beater may also be used for washing pulp. This is done by a power-driven hexagonal cylinder covered with fine wire screen and partially immersed in the stock. Extending from the corners of the surface toward the axis are boards, or metal plates, called buckets. As water flows through the screen, it is picked up by the buckets and delivered to a trough at the axis, where it flows out through the hollow journal of the cylinder, either going to waste or to storage for re-use. Fresh water is simultaneously added to the stock to maintain a constant level in the beater. This method of washing is quite inefficient and wasteful of water.

Modification of the Beater. One of the major objections to the old-type Hollander beater is that excessive power is required for stock circulation. Circulation is promoted by deep, wide cells between the bars, while the opposite is best for maximum stock treatment per revolution of the beater roll. Furthermore, when the roll is partially immersed in the stock, there is no control of the feed to the roll. These objections have been met in various ways. One method involves multiple bedplates as shown in Figure 11.3 for the Jones-Bertram beater. Three bedplates, instead of one, and closely set roll bars multiply the beating action several times for each pass under the roll.

Another departure is the placement of the roll and bedplate entirely outside the tub, where the stock is fed to the roll at a controlled rate. In this case the tub may be

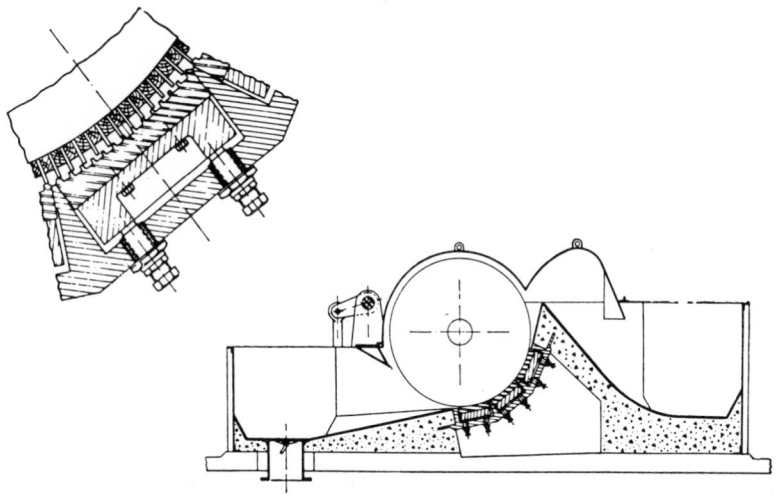

Fig. 11.3. Schematic view of Jones-Bertram beater. (*Courtesy E. D. Jones Co.*)

of quite different design from that of the conventional Hollander. Circulation is secured by a propeller-type agitator revolving in a vertical plane. The shaft of the propeller may be equipped with breaker arms to disintegrate dry pulp furnished to the tub. In this case, disintegration is accomplished batchwise, or an extractor plate may be used, which is a perforated plate that permits only disintegrated stock access to the pump feeding of the roll. Disintegration and beating can thus be carried on simultaneously. Beaters of this type have at least three rolls in series (see Figure 11.4). There are usually three bedplates for each roll so that in one pass, nine times as much treatment is given as in a conventional Hollander having the same bar spacing. The bedplates may be adjustable and the roll bearing stationary, or vice versa. After passing under the rolls, the stock may return to the tub of origin, or it may be delivered to a second tub. The beater charge may be repassed under the roll as many times as necessary for completion of the beating. The advantages claimed for this type of beater are (1) substantial power saving; (2) good control of beating by control of the feed rate to the roll; (3) rapid furnishing of dry paper or pulp to the tub without damage to the roll because the stock is disintegrated before it reaches the roll; and (4) continuous operation.

Various modifications of the Hollander have been used. One is the Umpherston beater, where the stock circulates in a vertical orbit. After passing under the roll, it returns by a channel under the bedplate and backfall. The Miller Duplex beater operates with the roll completely submerged and with a bedplate above the roll as well as below. The midfeather is in a horizontal position at approximately the level of the roll shaft. The stock circulates under the roll and passes over it on the return trip. The upper bedplate, as well as the roll itself, can be adjusted up or down.

The Vortex beater consists of a large enclosed tub containing central screw and plate arrangement which forces the stock downward at the center under a circular baffle and upward along the periphery of the tub. This beater is capable of handling pulps of somewhat higher consistency than others.

Rod Mills. As the name suggests, the rod mill subjects fibers to the action of steel rods tumbling over each other as the pulp suspension flows through. The mill consists of a horizontal, cylindrical shell partially filled with steel rods extending substantially the full length of the shell. Pulp in water suspension is fed into a small axial opening at one end and flows out through a comparatively large axial opening at the other end.

The rod mill is meant to accomplish maximum fiber separation, splitting, and fraying with a minimum of cutting or shortening of the fiber. To a considerable extent this objective is realized, and rod mills can be used advantageously as one stage in stock preparation. However, the power cost is excessive when the entire job of stock preparation is done in rod mills.

Pulpers. With the advent of large, high-capacity paper machines, particularly those using waste papers as raw material, a demand arose for equipment that could be furnished (filled) more rapidly and would have higher capacity. Machinery manufacturers brought out the pulper type of equipment in answer to this demand chiefly to disintegrate dry pulp or paper quickly. While there is some variation in design, the general principle is that of a large tank with a revolving disk in the bottom or side. The disk is equipped with vanes or ribs which cause the charge to circulate. A cutaway view of the Hydrapulper is shown in Figure 11.5. Large bales of raw material may be dumped into this vessel by merely cutting the wire or metal strapping and allowing it to go into the tank. As means are provided for removing junk, wire, rags, and twine, the labor required for furnishing is reduced to a minimum.

Most pulpers do not depend on close

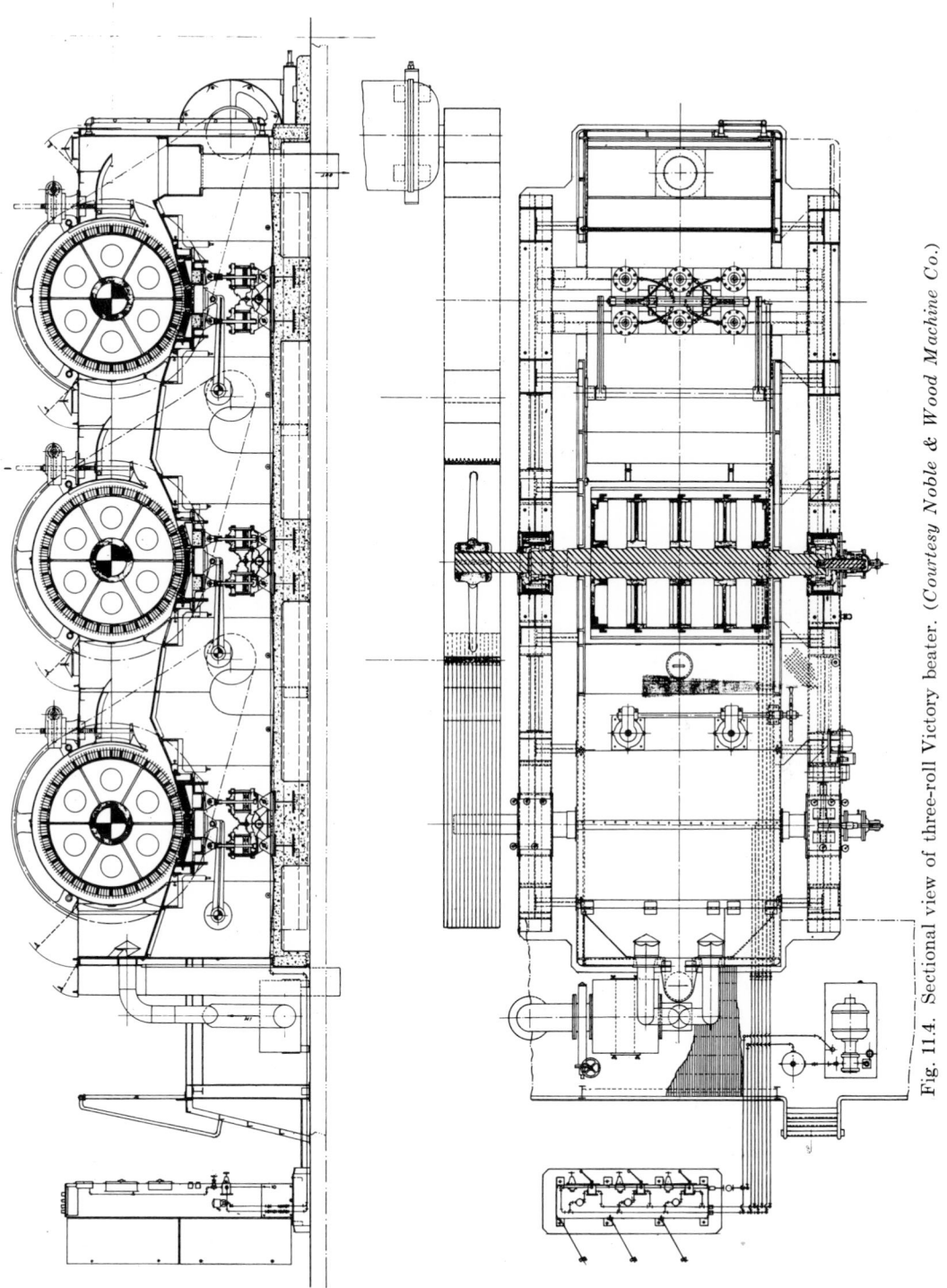

Fig. 11.4. Sectional view of three-roll Victory beater. (*Courtesy Noble & Wood Machine Co.*)

clearances for work on the pulp but operate by means of violent agitation, which causes internal friction and shearing action within the charge. One design of pulper has an agitator in the form of a horizontal, ribbed hourglass. The ends are fitted with knives or bars which bear against a circular bed-plate set in the tank wall. Thus, pulping action is combined with refining treatment.

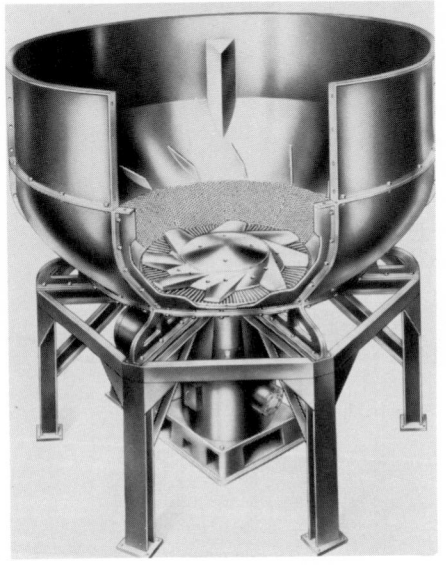

Fig. 11.5. Cutaway view of Hydrapulper showing Vokes rotor. (*Courtesy Black Clawson Co.*)

More recent modifications of this design are said to give improved results. In another design, agitation is provided by rough silicon carbide disks revolving in a vertical plane at high speed, as shown in Figure 11.6. These disks are mounted near the middle of the tank wall in shafts extending through the wall, driven externally. Another design has a tank with a four-leaf clover cross section, and is agitated by a horizontal disk at the bottom of the tank.

It will be noted that, where raw material is received in dry or semidry form, beating equipment must serve two functions: (1) to disintegrate the stock, separating the fibers and (2) to do work on the individual fibers. Obviously, close-clearance rubbing or cutting is unsuitable for stock disintegration.

Violent agitation not only disintegrates the stock, but does some work on the individual fibers by internal shear. The fibers in waste papers have already been through stock preparation at least once, and may require very little treatment beyond that given by the pulper.

Pulpers or beaters are frequently located in the basement beneath the calenders of the paper machine so that dry broke and trim can be repulped near the point where they are produced, and then pumped to the beater room for inclusion in the furnish with fresh pulp. One such pulper is designed with a figure-8 cross section and has rotors in the bottom of each side. Perforated false bottoms permit continuous removal of defibered stock.

Refiners are often attached to pulpers or beaters so that the stock may be given close clearance treatment after disintegration. Stock is recirculated to the pulper until the work is complete.

Breaker Beaters. One of the first machines designed for waste paper disintegration only was the breaker beater. The general design is similar to that of the Hollander, particularly with respect to the tub. The roll, however, consists of paddles for circulating stock at a high rate. The breaker beater has no bedplate. It may operate both continuously or batchwise. Devices for removing junk, cordage, and rags are provided, and furnishing can be accomplished rapidly. Breaker beaters have been replaced by pulpers for new installations.

The Breaker Trap. Another type of pulping equipment known as the breaker trap operates on a close-clearance principle but the clearance is not extremely close. The gap is set and cannot be adjusted.

Mills using waste papers, particularly the low grades, have considerable foreign material to contend with, consisting of strings, rags, cellophane, plastic film, foil, and other pieces of metal. If the fibers can be separated while leaving the unwanted material intact, the foreign material can be removed readily by screening. On the other hand,

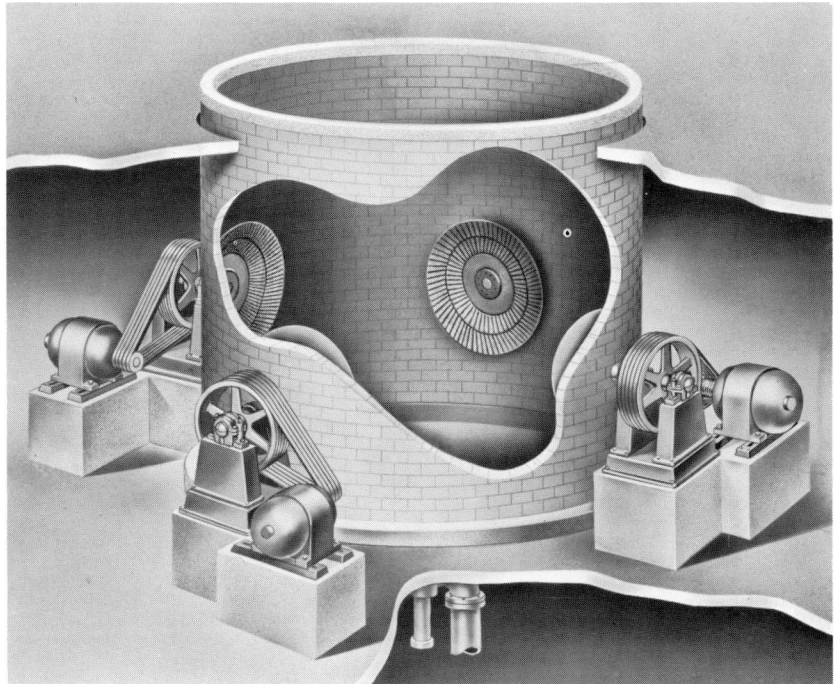

Fig. 11.6. Quatropulper with tile vat. Rotating disks are shown at sides. (*Courtesy Rice Barton Corp.*)

drastic grinding reduces the foreign material to such fine pieces that they pass through screens and show up in the finished product. The breaker trap is designed to provide selective pulping.

It consists of two chambers between which is a revolving plug bearing ridges parallel to the axis. It revolves within a cylindrical shell having a diameter a fraction of an inch larger. Partially pulped stock of flowable consistency is pumped under pressure into the feed chamber. The rotation of the plug sets up a swirl that throws large pieces of metal and heavy objects to the bottom where they are removed without ever getting into the working area. Smaller and lighter trash passes through the space between the plug and the shell. The violent shearing action separates good fibers from each other, but it is claimed that nonpapermaking materials are not disintegrated. Subsequent screening removes trash. The manufacturers recommend the breaker trap for use also in pulp mills, particularly for

breaking up cooked chips of high-yield pulps. The power consumption is said to be low.

Dirt and Junk Removers. Mills using waste papers as raw material encounter much foreign material, which must be removed if clean products and uninterrupted production are desired. These materials consist of string, rope, rags, sand, cinders, metal, and other foreign substances. Gritty materials cause wear of equipment if not removed at the outset. For this purpose, sand traps are installed in the floor of the beater, just ahead of the beater roll. Usually, such traps are troughs covered with a grating or perforated plate which allows small, heavy particles to settle into them and which can be cleaned periodically when the beater is empty.

String and rag catchers are generally prongs arranged along a shaft and extending into the stock. String and rags accumulate on the prongs and may be removed by rotating the shaft, which lifts the accumu-

Fig. 11.7. Continuous ragger shown removing foreign material from adjacent hydrapulper. (*Courtesy Black Clawson Co.*)

lations above the stock, where they can be reached by hand. An ingenious device used in Hydrapulpers winds such debris into a rope that can be continuously drawn from the stock. A few "primer" wires are rotated in the stock, which starts the rope, after which the "debris rope" serves as the catcher. A continuous ragger is shown in Figure 11.7.

For other upright cylindrical types of pulpers, junk may be removed from the stock by means of a power-driven bucket elevator extending downward into a recess in the side of the pulper at the bottom. Heavy objects are thrown into this recess by centrifugal force and perforated buckets haul it up and discharge it outside the pulper. A shower of water washes back any good fibers that may adhere to the junk.

Other types of stock cleaning equipment are described in Chapter 12.

Refining Equipment

Many grades of paper and board can be made from stock which has been disintegrated and processed in a beater, as described previously. However, many stronger, finer, better-formed papers and boards require a further shortening of fiber length, reduction of fiber lumps, and more "hydration." Such stocks are most efficiently treated in a refiner, which subjects the fibers to much more intensive mechanical action under carefully controlled conditions. Refiners are capable of accurate adjustment of the moving parts and operate continuously rather than batchwise. Refiners alone may be used for processing some types of slushed wood pulps. There has been a marked trend in recent years to continuous refiners because their operation fits in well with the continuous paper-making process, labor

Fig. 11.8. Side view of modern Jordan with manual control of plug. (*Courtesy Black Clawson Co.*)

costs are lower, and greater integration of pulp mill and paper mill operations is possible.

In general, refiners may be classified as *conical* or *jordan type* and *disk type*. Rodmills have occasionally been classed as a refiner, but this machine is no longer in extensive use for this purpose.

The Jordan. This refiner was developed by Joseph Jordan at the S. D. Warren Company in 1860. The jordan is one of the most popular refiners in use today (Figure 11.8). The basic jordan consists of a cast-iron tapered shell fitted inside with bars running almost the full length. A conical "plug" fits into the shell and is also equipped with bars lengthwise on its surface. The plug is shown in Figure 11.9. The bars are held in position by wooden fillets driven between them. The plug is rotated inside the shell and may be moved in or out to regulate the clearance of the bar and shell. The pulp slurry at a consistency between 2 and 4% is fed into the small end of the jordan and discharged at the large end. In this manner the jordan pumps the stock through the engine. The fibers are cut or brushed between the jordan bars during passage. Occasionally, stock is fed to the large end of the jordan under pressure and is removed at the small end. This assures that the space between the bars is full at all times.

The extent of stock treatment is varied by regulation of the clearance between the bars, the peripheral speed, the type of bars or tackle, and the stock consistency. Steel bars are standard and maintain better cutting edges, but when brushing only is desired, bronze or brass bars may serve better. The cutting action may be increased by filling the jordan with diagonally or helically placed bars, or bars arranged in zigzag form. These arrangements ensure a contact surface for all possible positions of the plug. Modern practice is toward higher pulp consistencies and higher speeds. Plug speeds range from 300 to about 550 rpm which give peripheral speeds of 2000 to 4500 fpm at the large end. This is about twice the peripheral speed of the usual beater roll. Other types of conical refiners may reach speeds of 12,-000 fpm. Where more extensive refining of the stock is desired, groups of jordans may be operated in series and parallel combinations.

Other Conical Refiners. Various modifications of the jordan have been made during recent years. Among these is the Claflin refiner which is a short, wide-angled jordan used to process rejects and very brash pulps. The Hydrafiner resembles the conventional jordan quite closely but is so constructed that pressure "baffling" concentrates the stock in the zone of mechanical

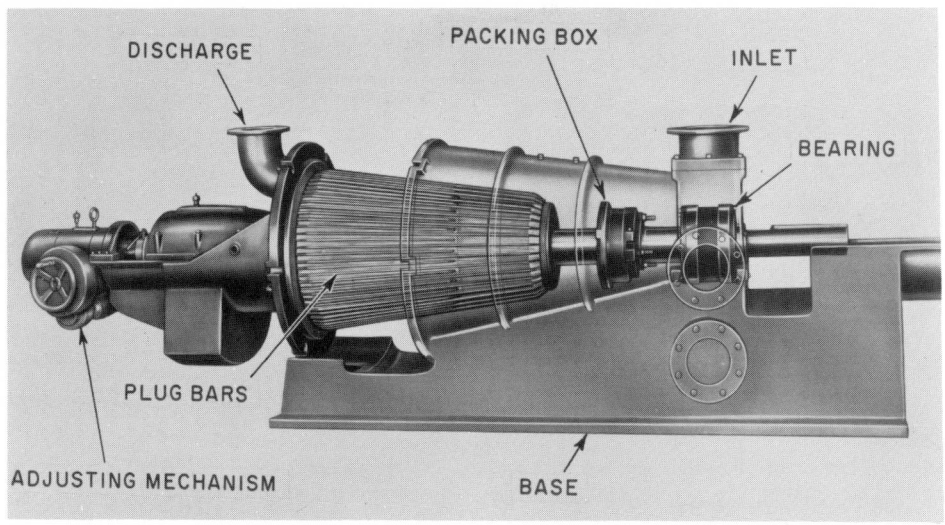

Fig. 11.9. Cutaway view of Jordan showing plug and how packing box moves through opening.

action. The Morden stockmaker features a hollow rotor and a movable bedplate shell and a valve which permits a controlled amount of recirculation of stock within the machine.

Disk Refiners. In recent years, disk refiners have been extensively used to accomplish all fiber treatment in a single machine. In general, there are two types of such refiners, single-disk and double-disk. In both instances there are two disks; in the single refiner one disk is stationary, while in the double-disk refiner both disks rotate, but in opposite directions. The stock is pumped between the faces of the disks while they rotate at high speed. The facing of the disks is capable of wide variation but, generally, the rotating disk carries raised bars, while grooves are cast or cut into the stationary disk. Clearance between the disks is adjustable, so that capacity and extent of treatment may be controlled.

Disk refiners are capable of performing two functions—fiber separation and mechanical work on individual fibers. They were first used for disintegration of steamed wood chips and chips from semichemical pulping where the lignin binder still maintains considerable strength between the fibers. The disk refiner is capable of sep-

arating such partially pulped fibers. In recent years, disk refiners have also been used for the preparation of paper stock. They are said to give maximum brushing and fibrillation, with little cutting and debris formation, and minimum lowering of freeness. Examples of disk refiners are shown in Chapter 8.

Control of Refiner Action. In general, refiners are controlled by the power input to maintain continuous action on the stock. For example, the jordan may be operated at a current of 300 amps at 550 volts. At a constant voltage, the amperage may be used as a measure of the extent of stock treatment. Increasing the pressure on the jordan (decreasing the clearance between the rotor and the shell) will increase the power requirement, whereas backing off on the plug pressure will decrease it.

Power Requirements for Beating and Refining. The internal friction between the fibers in the beater is considerable, particularly if the stock consistency is high. This condition requires high circulating capacity of the beater and substantial amounts of power. The major quantity of power in the beating process, however, is required for the action of the roll against the stock and bedplate. Clark [1] has estimated that the majority of types of paper require between 200 and 2000 kilowatt hours per ton and, in special cases such as glassine manufacture, the figure may be even higher. At best, however, the beating process is very inefficient. Higgins and Harrington [2], for example, have calculated that the efficiency is only about 0.1%. It is often said that "paper is made in the beater" and, if this is so, a better understanding of the fundamentals of the beating process might permit substantial savings in power and better control of the paper-making process. It must be remembered that improvements in paper characteristics resulting from beating are not necessarily related to the duration of the treatment.

The Curlator. The Curlator is a machine which rubs and rolls the pulp between two surfaces, the upper of which is gyrating in a circle about 2.5 inches in diameter. The stock is pumped under low pressure to the inlet at the center part of the machine. It first passes over perforated plates where part of the water drains away and the stock is then pushed over plates by revolving sweeper arms. The consistency of the stock is increased to about 20% as it enters the treating area. The treating surfaces contain small pyramidal projections which roll the pulp into nodules as it moves toward the periphery of the treating plates where the pulp is discharged. It is claimed that this action is radically different from that of beating and refining in that the fibers are curled or crinkled and very little or no cutting occurs. Pulp freeness is unchanged or increased slightly. This defibrating device is intentionally made for gentle, mechanical action required to separate fibers completely.

Water Requirements

An adequate supply of good clean water is necesssary for manufacture of quality pulp and paper. Consumption of 30,000,000 gallons per day is not unusual and a few mills use as much as 100,000,000 gallons per day [102]. Impurities such as hardness, organic extracts, bacteria, and undissolved solids will adversely affect bleaching, sizing, and color of pulp, and water must be treated chemically and mechanically to remove these materials. The majority of this water is used in stock preparation and papermaking. Shotwell and Henderson [103] state that a minimum of 985 gallons per ton to a maximum of 198,000 gallons per ton, or an arithmetical average of 34,000 gallons per ton of air-dried finished product, are required. These figures do not include water used for generation of power. An integrated pulp and paper mill manufacturing bleached alkali, sulfite, and groundwood pulp and paper requires 100,000 gallons per ton of paper, whereas a board plant using only purchased pulp may need about 11,000 gallons of water per ton of product. Wide variations exist between plants, however.

Savealls and Re-use of Water

For many years the paper industry has striven for more economical use of water and remarkable progress has been made. Most paper mills today operate their white water systems in such a way that each gallon of water is re-used several times before it is discarded from the mill. In a typical well-closed white water system 85% of the water is re-used. It is, of course, difficult to run the white water system completely closed because fresh water must be used for make-up purposes and certain types of cleaning equipment where water containing any significant amount of suspended solids would be unsuitable. Such re-use of water permits the paper maker to recover huge quantities of fiber, additives, pigments, and other paper-making chemicals which might otherwise add to the pollution of water sources. Additional quantities of heat would also be lost.

One of the most important installations for the re-use of water and recovery of fiber and pigment is called the saveall system. Savealls are of three general types and each may have advantages for particular purposes. These advantages are as follows:

(1) The sedimentation type of saveall consists of a large concrete or tile tank to which all waste waters are pumped. Suspended solids are allowed to settle to the bottom from which they are removed for further processing. The clarified overflow water is pumped to various parts of the paper-making system and re-used. In general, separation of solids by this method is incomplete, and sedimentation is often used only for secondary treatment of overflow water which otherwise must be directly discharged.

(2) The vacuum filter saveall is a rotary vacuum drum which filters flocculated solids from the processing waters. Often, a small amount of partially beaten pulp (sweetener stock) is added to the white water suspension just ahead of the filter. This pulp forms a better filter mat and gives more complete removal of the finer suspended matter. Often, white water which is to be processed in a filter-type saveall may be given a pre-liminary settling in a sedimentation tank to concentrate the solids. The clarified water is then used for make-up in the beaters or for dilution of stock, while the concentrated solids are pumped to the filter. The efficiency, size of filter needed, and filterability of waste water solids may be determined quite easily on a laboratory scale by making filter leaf tests on representative samples of the water to be processed (see Figure 11.10).

(3) The flotation saveall operates by continuously dispersing and dissolving air in the white water under pressure. The water then passes into a large tank under atmospheric pressure which releases the gases that are no longer soluble. The bubbles carry fibers, fillers, and other suspended additives to the surface where they are collected and removed by a scraper unit. The recovered solids are pumped back to the system and combined with incoming fresh stock near the paper machine and the clarified water

Fig. 11.10. Vacuum filter. (*Courtesy of E. D. Jones Corp.*)

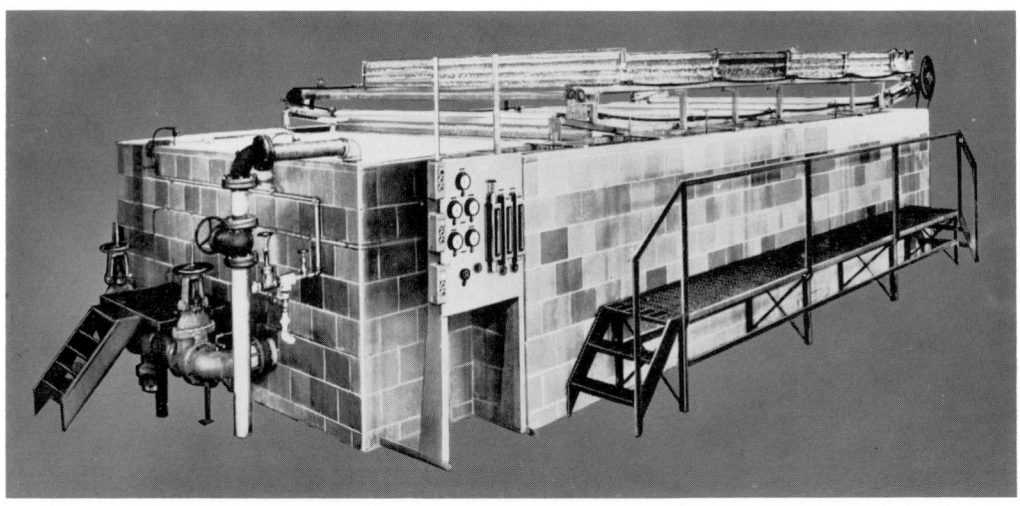

Fig. 11.11. Sveen Pedersen flotation saveall. (*Courtesy of E. D. Jones Corp.*)

is used where needed (see Figure 11.11).

Among the more popular flotation savealls is the Sveen-Pederson unit in which a small amount of a colloidally active glue is added to white water for improving flocculation and collection of the solids by the air bubbles. This process will yield clarified water which has no more than ½ pound per 1000 gallons or 60 ppm of total filterable solids. Sveen glue in amounts of about 2 pounds per ton of pulp may also be added directly to the paper-making furnish to improve retention of fiber fines and additives on the paper machine. Flow diagrams of paper machine white water systems are shown in Chapter 12.

REASONS FOR BEATING

When cellulose fibers are beaten in water and made into paper it is found that sheet characteristics change considerably as the degree of beating is increased. Some of these changes are shown in Figure 11.12. It is observed that bursting and tensile strengths, tearing resistance, and folding endurance rise to maxima and then decrease with further fiber processing. The maxima occur at strikingly different parts of the beat-

ing cycle, however. For example, tearing strength rises very quickly to a maximum with processing and then decreases sharply to a much lower level for the duration of the beating cycle. On the other hand, bursting and tensile strengths rise for a greater part of the mechanical processing and decrease much more slowly. Considerable attention has been given over the years to fundamental reasons for these changes in sheet properties with degree of beating. Although some of the basic factors probably are unrecognized at present, the following properties are known to be important in many types of papers and boards:

(1) Chemical and physical composition of the fiber

(2) Fiber dimensions

(3) Fiber strength

(4) Filtration resistance of fiber suspension in water

    (a) Hydrodynamic surface area of fibers

    (b) Swollen specific volume of fiber

(5) Fiber flocculation

(6) Bonded surface area between fibers in paper

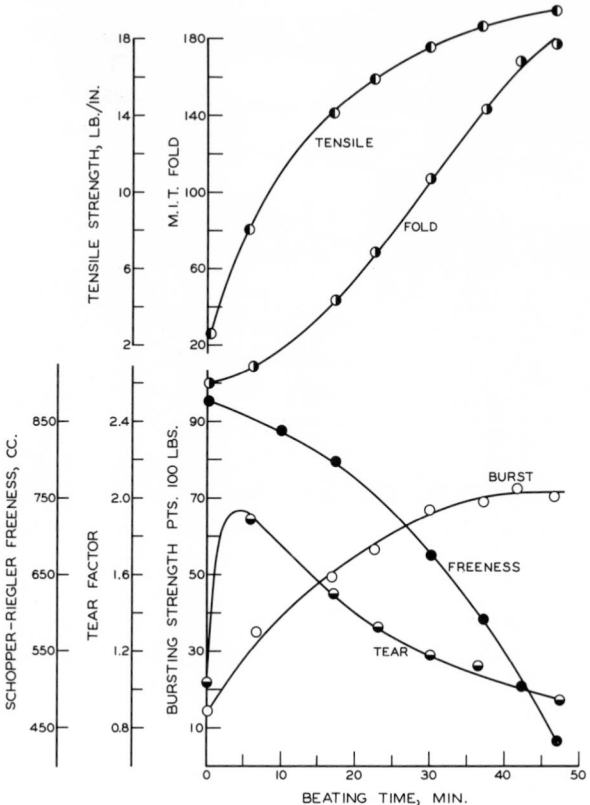

Fig. 11.12. Changes in paper properties with beating of the pulp.

(7) Unbonded surface area of fibers in paper

(8) Bonding strength per unit bonded area in paper

(9) Distribution of fiber bonds (sheet formation) in paper

(10) Stress distribution in paper

(11) Fiber flexibility or conformability in the wet condition.

Although each of these factors is important, it is beyond the scope of this chapter to consider them individually. It is apparent, however, that many of these properties are interrelated and the majority of them govern either fiber-to-fiber bonding or individual fiber strength. The beating process alters these properties so strongly that they deserve special consideration. A more detailed discussion is given by Swanson and Jones [3].

Adhesion and Fiber-to-Fiber Bonding

In the field of adhesion it is well established that secondary intermolecular forces determine the strength of the bond between contiguous solids. This situation explains the bonding of cellulose fibers. Much scientific evidence supports the theory that the strength of paper and board depends primarily upon hydrogen bonding and other intermolecular bonds between fibers, and not upon mechanical entanglement and frictional effects between fibers [4,5,6]. The strength of intermolecular bonds is concentrated largely in the surface region of the solid fiber and the associated attractive forces have an unusually short range. That is to say, very close contact on a *molecular scale* must occur between two solid surfaces before strong bonding can exist. The extent of the area of molecular contact, the so-called bonded area, will obviously be important also.

It is clear that one of the most important aspects of paper making is to prepare the fibrous material in a form that will promote intimate contact between the surfaces of fibers and fibrils on a molecular scale. This is one of the primary reasons for beating and refining paper-making pulps. As we shall note later on, it is also one of the basic reasons for the use of beater or wet-end adhesives in paper-making systems. The latter materials, when fixed to the fiber surfaces permit the surfaces to bridge distances between fibers and fibrils and to establish molecular bonds that would not have otherwise formed. Wet pressing of the fibrous web also promotes better molecular contact and greater contact area between fibers [101].

There is abundant evidence that swelling of the fibers and marked plasticization are important in the promotion of fiber-to-fiber bonding. The fact that unbeaten, unplasticized cellulose fibers in water do not form strong paper is a good indication of the necessity for swelling which promotes better molecular contact. Before discussing fiber swelling in greater detail, let us examine the elements of fiber morphology or structure.

Fiber Morphology. The ability of cellulose fibers to bond to one another and to respond to beating and refining depends to a large degree upon the origin of the fibers, their morphology, and their history. Before pulp fibers have received mechanical treatment they consist largely of undamaged cells which vary in average length from about 20 mm for cotton to 3.5 mm for softwood fibers and to about 1.5 mm for hardwood fibers. Cotton linters fibers are approximately 5 mm long on the average. The diameter of cotton fibers is approximately 1000 times less than their length, whereas the diameters of softwood and hardwood fibers are roughly $\frac{1}{200}$ and $\frac{1}{100}$ of their lengths, respectively.

All these fibers contain a center opening called the lumen. The portion of the fiber between the outer surface and the lumen is composed of several layers which for purposes of simplification are called the primary and secondary walls. The walls of fibers grown in the spring are, in general, thinner than those of fibers grown in the summer, and these differences may cause the fibers to respond differently to beating. Where these fibers have been separated, it is found that springwood fibers beat more rapidly and form denser, more transparent paper than summerwood fibers [7]. Climatic conditions, position in the tree, tension, etc., may also affect the nature of the fibers. Thus, considerable variability exists among the fibers even of a single species. (See Chapter 2.)

The primary and secondary walls of fibers are comprised of layers of cellulose fibrils or strands which, after pulping and some mechanical treatment, may be observed under the light and electron microscopes by means of appropriate techniques. The fibrillar structure is not fully established for all pulp fibers, but for many fibers it is known that the fibrils are oriented at different angles from one layer to the next, as shown schematically in Figure 11.13. The primary wall is usually very thin and in some species appears to differ chemically from the secondary wall [8]. During beating the primary wall is quickly damaged and removed and the layers of the secondary wall are unwound and become highly fibrillated. Under these circumstances the specific surface of the fiber increases, the degree of swelling increases, the fiber becomes more flexible, and the quantity of water closely associated with the fibrous mass becomes greater. The water drains from the beaten pulp more slowly than from the unbeaten, and it is said that the freeness decreases. The rate of drainage of water from the pulp forms one method of characterizing the degree of beating of the pulp.

Fiber Swelling and Moisture Relationships. Experience has shown that numerous factors influence the amount of fiber swelling

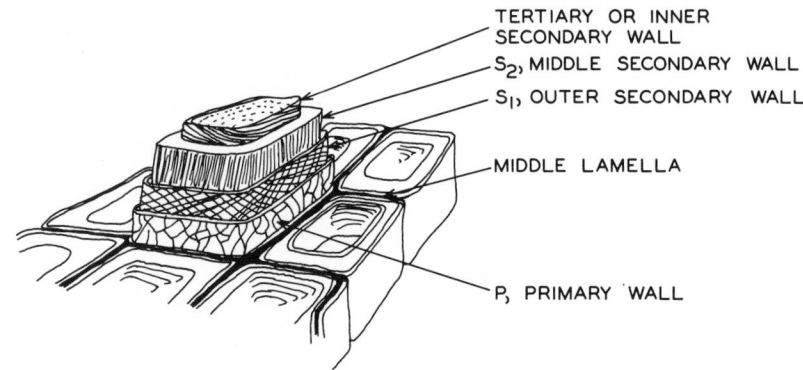

Fig. 11.13. Schematic drawing of wall structure of cellulose fiber as suggested by Emerton.

and the strength of fiber bonding. It is clear, however, that the greater the degree of swelling, the stronger are the fiber bonds in paper. Cellulose fibers which have been treated in various ways to alter the degree of swelling also exhibit changes in their ability to bond to one another in the form of paper. It is found, for example, that fibers that have been previously dried below 20 to 25% solids before processing do not absorb as much water as fibers that have never been dried. Neither do previously dried fibers make as strong paper. Lyne and Gallay [9] have shown that previous drying of pulp fibers may cause a loss of as much as 85% of the bursting strength as compared with similarly processed never-dried fibers. Part of this loss in strength may be recovered by further beating and refining. This effect of drying has an important commercial significance, because the paper maker who buys market pulp must decide whether it is better to purchase dry lap pulp and accept the lower strength potential or to purchase stronger wet lap pulp and pay the additional freight costs on significant quantities of water.

The effect of previous drying of cellulose fibers is evident from equilibrium moisture content-relative humidity curves, shown schematically in Figure 11.14. The first isotherm is obtained by allowing samples of wet fiber to come to equilibrium at the des-ignated relative humidity. Curve 2 is obtained by allowing thoroughly dried fibers to gradually resorb moisture at higher relative humidity. It is observed that Curve 2 falls below Curve 1 at all relative humidities which means that the previously dried fibers were unable to resorb as much water as they held formerly. The hysteresis loop formed by the desorption isotherm (Curve 1) and the absorption isotherm (Curve 2) does not close at the high relative humidity end unless the fibers are saturated with liquid water. Even then, however, the second desorption isotherm (Curve 3) does not follow the first curve, but falls below it for a substantial part of the curve. If the fibers are not fully dried before being subjected to a higher relative humidity, intermediate curves such as 4 and 5 may be obtained. Thus, any point (any equilibrium moisture content) within the hysteresis loop may be attained by suitable preconditioning of the fiber sample or paper.

The moisture content of paper has a marked effect on many strength properties. Hence, previous drying and conditioning of paper may have an important effect upon measured strength properties because of differences in equilibrium moisture content. The effects of preconditioning on the strength of papers have been studied extensively by Wink [10].

The volumetric swelling of cellulose fibers

also follows curves similar to those of Figure 11.14, and the effects of other factors on moisture sorption and swelling may thus be determined by means of such isotherms. It is found, for example, that pulps containing higher quantities of hemicellulose absorb larger quantities of water at a given relative humidity and swell to a greater degree than pulps containing less hemicellulose. Similarly, extensive multistage bleaching of pulp fibers may remove hemicellulosic materials and decrease the degree of swelling.

The presence of lignin residues in the pulp may, under some circumstances, decrease the moisture sorption capacity and interfere with fiber-to-fiber bonding. Natural resinous materials in wood pulps may produce sizing effects which make the pulp more difficult to wet with water and may thereby retard repulping and beating operations. Such resins do not affect the final equilibrium moisture content, however. Synthetic resins such as those used for wet strength (see later discussion of these materials) may also restrict fiber swelling and give weaker paper from reprocessed pulp.

When dry cellulose fibers are brought into contact with water, heat is evolved. This exothermic behavior of cellulose fibers and water may be predicted from the following thermodynamic equation:

$$\triangle H = \triangle F + T \triangle S$$

where $\triangle H$ is the exothermic heat of absorption, F is the change in free energy, and S is the change in entropy occurring during the sorption process. Under equilibrium conditions this equation and Le Chatelier's principle of equilibrium indicate that cellulose fibers should sorb less water and swell to a lesser degree at higher temperatures than at lower temperatures. This is found to be the case. In the intermediate relative humidity ranges, each 10°C rise in temperature causes the fibers to sorb approximately 1% less water than they do at the lower temperature. Cellulose fibers beat and refine more slowly at higher temperatures

than at lower temperatures [11]. Furthermore, if a pulp is beaten at one temperature and then its temperature is increased substantially before it is made into paper, that paper will generally possess lower strength properties than paper made from the pulp at a lower temperature. The Schopper-Riegler freeness value (see p. 344) of a pulp beaten to approximately 200 cc will increase to that of a lightly beaten pulp, 700 to 800 cc after bringing the pulp near the

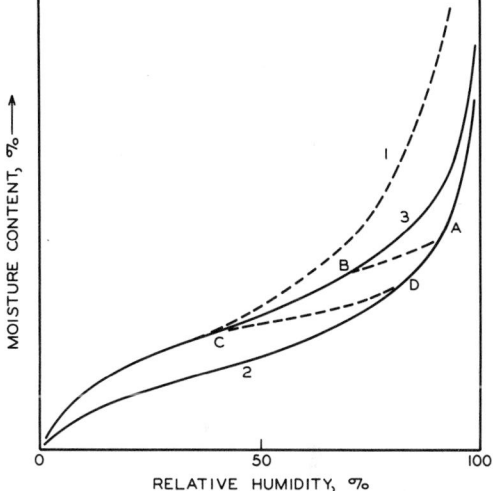

Fig. 11.14. Hysteresis effects in sorption of water vapor by cellulose fibers.

boiling point for a brief time before cooling and repeating the freeness determination. (See also Nakano [12] on the effect of heating). The thermodynamic equation indicates that the higher temperature decreases the degree of fiber swelling and produces weaker fiber-to-fiber bonding when the fibers are made into paper.

The importance of swelling in the beating and bonding of cellulose fibers is attested by the work of Kress and Bialkowsky [13], Bletzinger [14], Aiken [15], Harrison [16], and more recently by McKenzie and Higgins [17]. Kress and Bialkowsky [13] showed that strong, well-bonded paper could be formed by beating cellulose fibers in liquids which swell cellulose (formamide, glycerol, ethylene glycol) to an equal or greater degree than water. On the other hand, liquids such as butanol and fuel oil, in which fibers do not swell appreciably, do not permit fibrillation during beating and the papers made therefrom possess negligible strength. Bletzinger [14], and Aiken [15] showed that extensively acetylated fibers neither swell appreciably in water nor fibrillate when processing is done in water. Paper made from such fiber is weak and practically unbonded. However, acetylated fibers swell extensively in acetone, or benzene-water emulsion, and in these liquids the fibers can be beaten and formed into papers having strengths equivalent to the nonacetylated fibers beaten in water. Walecka [18], Talwar [19], and Ward [20] have also shown that judicious introduction of hydrophilic chemical groups, such as carboxymethyl and hydroxyethyl into cellulose fibers, increases swelling in water and improves the beating and bonding properties of fibers. This latter process has led to a commercial cotton linters product which is beaten and refined much more easily and forms paper having strength equivalent to rag paper.

Early Theories of Beating. At one time it was proposed that the beating of cellulose fibers in water involved a chemical process which caused water to combine with cellulose fibers in much the same way that the pentahydrate of copper sulfate is formed. According to this theory, the increases in paper strength produced by beating resulted from hydrate formation on the surface layers of the fibers; the hydrate became gelatinous and acted as an adhesive to bond the fibers together. Later work by Strachan [21], and Campbell [22] showed that although cellulose itself may be hydrated, beating of the fibers produces little, if any, change in the true water of hydration of the cellulose fiber.

True hydrates of cellulose appear to exist but they are not formed to a significant degree by the beating process. Rather, more water appears to be held physically within the fibrillar structure as beating proceeds.

It is this physical association of water with the fibrils that accounts for the change in drainage rate with increased beating and refining. Well-beaten stock is said to become slow, slow-draining, or "hydrated," and the term "wet beating" is sometimes applied to the phenomenon involved. Thus it is found that the beating of cellulose fibers produces only a negligible change in the moisture sorption-relative humidity curves of paper-making fibers, as shown in Figure 11.14. It must be remembered, however, that water is very strongly held by cellulosic surfaces, as indicated by the substantial heat of adsorption involved. It is extremely difficult to remove the last traces of moisture from any cellulosic material.

Strachan proposed that the strength of paper was due to mechanical entanglement of the fibrils produced on the surface of fibers by the beating process. This theory, too, fails to explain some of the observed effects of beating on fiber bonding and the present theory of beating involves a combination of theories.

Current Theory of Beating. Modern theory of polymer behavior indicates that the cellulose-water relationship is not unique but is similar to many other polymer-solvent interacting systems. According to this theory, swelling is considered to be a limited solubility. Polymer chains in the solid state may be attached to neighbors by secondary valence bonds. Such bonds are characterized by low energies, and so-called swelling agents are able to rupture many of these bonds. If the action is carried far enough, the polymer may disperse or dissolve. However, where linkages of somewhat higher energy exist, swelling is limited and only partial solubility of chain ends may occur. This concept was developed by Campbell [22, 23, 24, 25], who suggested that cellulose molecules are partially dissolved by water and in this form the fibrils are more easily loosened and unraveled from the parent fiber by the beating action. Such plasticized fibrils then become more readily available for bonding to neighboring fibrils and fibers with which they come into contact during formation and drying of paper.

Fiber Flocculation. Pulp fibers suspended in water show a marked tendency to flocculate or "clot" together. This phenomenon may be observed by stirring a very dilute (0.01%) pulp slurry in a glass cylinder, removing the agitator, and then watching the fiber behavior. As the fibers move they gradually form flocs, which are easily recognized. If paper is made from flocculated pulp, poor fiber and bond distribution exist in the sheet, and it is said to have poor formation.

The time required for flocs to form depends upon many factors such as the type of pulp, fiber length, degree of beating, fiber consistency, agitation, pH, presence of additives, and many others [26, 27, 28]. Generally speaking, formation of paper improves with beating in commercial practice, but in the laboratory it is observed that more highly beaten pulps flocculate more rapidly and yield poorer sheets than lightly beaten pulps. Turk [29] attributed this difference to mechanical effects of machine shake and the dandy roll which are not simulated in the usual laboratory handsheet mold. Whatever the cause, there is little doubt that shortening the fiber length and increasing the amount of water associated with the fiber by beating and refining will improve formation and numerous other properties of commercial papers. As we shall see later, polymer additives may also substantially alter formation of paper.

Mechanism of Fiber-to-Fiber Bonding. The foregoing discussion presents evidence that surface molecular forces will form strong adhesive bonds between adjacent fiber surfaces, provided the fibers and fibrils are sufficiently swollen and plasticized to provide a significant area of molecular contact between the gel-like surfaces. However, it is well known that a wet sheet of paper made from even highly swollen and beaten fibers is still weak after substantial wet-pressing. This behavior indicates that few fiber bonds

form during the pressing operation or the fibers spring back when the pressure is released, thereby breaking the bonds. There must be, then, some mechanism which brings the fibers back into contact during the drying operation. Campbell [23, 24, 25] developed the required theory for this action in 1934, and Van den Akker [30] and others [31, 32] have published data more recently which support it. This is now known as the Campbell effect.

Campbell proposed that in the early stages of dewatering the fibrous web, that is, in the range of 8 to 20% fiber solids, a compacting pressure develops because of the surface tension of the water and the menisci which form between the fibers as the water layer recedes into the structure. This compacting pressure increases as long as the total length of line contact between fiber-water-air increases. As Campbell showed [24], this pressure attains values of the order of magnitude of 6 psi. Although this pressure is not large, it is sufficient to impart considerable wet-web strength in that region of dewatering characteristic of the couch and press sections of the paper machine. In the later stages of drying, however, there is sufficient water to form thin films only between near fiber surfaces, and the differential pressure, $\triangle P$, upon the fibrous mat then becomes inversely proportional to the thickness of water film, X, as shown in the following equation,

$$\triangle P = \frac{2\gamma}{X}$$

where γ is the surface tension of water. If, during the later stages of drying, water films of the order of 70 A (7.0 × 10^{-7} cm) exist, pressures of the order of 200 atmospheres are attained. Campbell suggests that such pressures force plastic fiber surfaces sufficiently close together for molecular bonds to form between the surfaces. Of course, at a particular moisture content and degree of beating, the rigidity of the fibers and the Campbell effect balance one another. Beating and refining increase the degree of fibrillation; the average fiber diameter becomes smaller, and the fiber and fibrils become more plastic and deformable. The rigidity of a beam supported at the ends varies as the fourth power of the cross-sectional diameter. Thus, as beating proceeds, the Campbell pressure becomes more effective in promoting fiber bonds and greater bonded area.

Van den Akker[30] has shown that paper made under conditions which restrict the surface tension forces (by freeze-drying) is very weakly bonded.

The wet-web drying studies of Lyne and Gallay[33, 34, 35] with cellulose fibers and with glass fibers which do not form hydrogen bonds illustrate and confirm quite clearly the role of surface tension forces during the several stages of drying paper.

NONFIBROUS ADDITIVES

Modern papers and boards serve such a multitude of purposes that it is now difficult to find a product that is manufactured from pulp fibers alone. Most papers and boards contain supplementary materials which improve one or more properties that would otherwise be deficient. For example, sizing agents are employed to make papers resistant to penetration of certain liquids; clays and other pigments improve brightness, opacity, and printing properties; starches and gums improve fiber bonding and fiber distribution; various synthetic polymers impart wet strength; dyes and colored pigments give desired color; surface-active agents may be employed to improve absorbency, combat self-sizing, and decrease foam and pitch troubles. The majority of these nonfibrous materials are added to the stock system before the sheet is formed. Various specific terms, such as beater additive, wet-end adhesive, fan pump additive, or headbox additive, are used when a preferred point of addition to the stock exists. In addition to stock additives, numerous materials are also added to the more or less finished paper as surface-sizing

agents, coatings, impregnants, etc. These materials and their associated equipment are considered in Chapter 12. The present chapter is concerned only with stock additives.

Large quantities of many additives are consumed each year by the paper industry. Table 11.1 lists a few of these materials and their annual consumption in tons.

It is evident that paper and paperboard are desirable markets for many natural and synthetic products of the chemical and processing industries. The paper industry consumes more white clays than any other, and it is second only to the food industry in its use of starches. Moreover, it is the third largest user of all industrial chemicals. Even small percentages of additives, if broadly used in an industry producing approximately 39 million tons of paper and board, represent a large market. From another point of view, attempts to make new and more versatile paper products by incorporation of additives to an already complex papermaking system often lead to unpredictable behavior and further problems. In general, retention of additives in the fibrous web is incomplete and circulation of the nonretained components in the white water may lead to agglomeration and deposition problems which require further additives for their elimination. The chemical industry, therefore, finds the paper industry an attractive market for new chemical additives which improve processing and quality of product.

Beater Adhesives

The foregoing discussion pointed out that beating and refining of pulp fibers is done to improve swelling, flexibility, and distribution of the fibers in order to attain better molecular contact between fiber surfaces and stronger fiber-to-fiber bonding. Although beaten pulp yields stronger and somewhat better formed paper, it is clear that mechanical beating and refining is detrimental to many other desirable properties. For example, paper made from mechanically beaten

TABLE 11.1. ESTIMATED CONSUMPTION OF SEVERAL STOCK ADDITIVES BY THE PAPER INDUSTRY

Chemical Additive	Uses	Annual Amount Used (tons)
Starches [a] (includes corn, potato, tapioca, wheat)	Improved paper strength, surface sizing, coating, laminating, corrugating	580,000
Starches (part of above)	Stock additive for internal strength	200,000
Natural gums [b] (guar and locust bean)	Improved paper strength, fiber deflocculation, retention aid	9,000
Rosin [c]	Internal sizing	150,000
Urea-formaldehyde resin [d]	Wet strength	13,000
Melamine-formaldehyde resin [d]	Wet strength	5,000
Polyamide resin [b]	Wet strength, filler retention	3,000
Waxes [d]	Internal sizing, coating	95,000
Antifoams [d]	Combating foam	8,000
Clay (kaolin) [e]	Filling and coating	1,255,000
Clay (kaolin) [e]	Filling	500,000
Titanium dioxide [d]	Filling and coating	53,000
Calcium carbonate [f]	Filling and coating	134,000
Dyes and colored pigments [d]	Coloring	7,800
Slimacides [d]	Prevention of slime	5,800
Surface-active agents [d]	Wetting, absorbency, felt washing	17,500
Alum [d]	Sizing, pH control	422,000
Sodium aluminate [d]	Sizing, pH control	3,200

[a] Estimated U.S. Tariff Commission Reports, March, 1960.
[b] Estimated by supplier.
[c] U.S. Dept. Agriculture, See *Chemical Week*, 112 (Nov. 25, 1961).
[d] Paper Trade Journal report, "Market for Chemicals in the Pulp and Paper Industry, 1960," 1959.
[e] Estimated composite from several sources.
[f] Paper Coating Pigments. TAPPI Monograph Series, No. 20, p. 104.

pulp forms more slowly on the wire, shrinks more upon drying, becomes more dense, more translucent, less opaque, less compressible, and less oil-receptive. Greater hygroexpansivity and greater tendency to curl and cockle are also evident in papers made from more highly beaten pulps. Although certain of these properties may be desired for special papers, there are vast tonnages of other papers—for example, those employed for printing purposes—where they are undesirable. Thus, although beating and refining are necessary in many paper-making operations, they have associated disadvantages and are costly in terms of power required. For these reasons, paper makers have long sought greater versatility in stock preparation and paper-machine operations by the use of starches, natural gums and synthetic polymers which impart to the surfaces of relatively unbeaten paper-making fibers bonding properties similar to those of mechanically beaten fibers. These materials are often called "beater adhesives," although the beater is often not one of the better points of addition. The terms fan pump- and headbox adhesives are now more commonly used.

Uses of Beater Adhesives. Beater adhesives are used primarily to improve fiber-to-fiber bonding, and paper makers have found that this property may be used advantageously in several ways. The primary use, of course, is improvement of bursting and tensile strengths of papers and boards by direct addition of a small percentage of prepared adhesive directly to the refined pulp. This effect is illustrated in Figure 11.15 for laboratory handsheets. It is also possible to decrease power requirements for beating and refining and maintain strength at a desired level. Alternatively, a mill may increase refiner capacity by increasing the stock throughout and add sufficient adhesive to attain the desired strength. Higher percentages of short-fibered, low-strength pulps and pigments also may be employed at constant strength levels.

The tearing strength of normally well-beaten softwood pulps may be increased substantially by reducing mechanical refining and improving fiber bonding strength with a suitable adhesive. This technique not

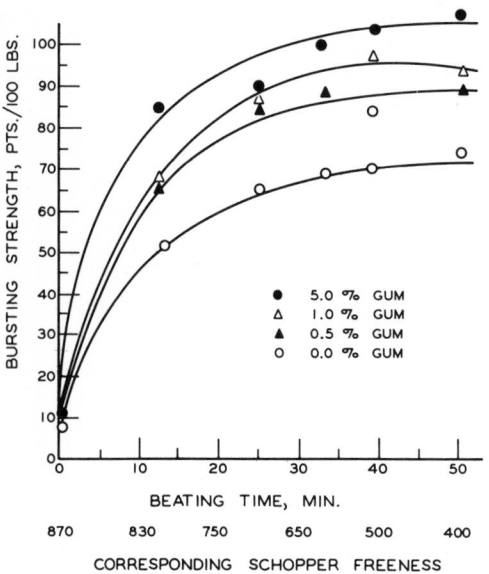

Fig. 11.15. The effect of beating and locust bean gum on bursting strength of coniferous sulfite pulp handsheets.

only improves tear but will also yield a faster-draining pulp, which permits higher machine speeds and greater production. Similarly, papers of high strength, better opacity and improved porosity and hygroexpansivity may be obtained by this method.[36]

Certain adhesives will improve fiber distribution and sheet formation substantially. This property is particularly important where long-fiber pulps are required for extraordinary strength.

Other polymers, called wet-strength resins, will substantially increase wet strength of the final paper. The term "wet strength" refers to the strength of once-dried paper

which has been rewetted, and should not be confused with the term wet-web strength which denotes the strength of a never-dried sheet.

Materials Used as Beater Adhesives. Many natural and synthetic polymers are used as beater adhesives by the paper industry both in the United States and abroad. Perhaps foremost among these, in terms of tonnage consumed, are the starches from corn, tapioca, potato, and wheat. Next are the natural gum products based upon the reserve polysaccharides of guar gum and locust bean gum, and upon tamarind kernel powder, and okra and karaya gums. Various commercial products bear the names Lycoid, Jaguar, Mannogal, Stargum, Guartec, Burtonite, and Keygum. Mixtures of gum and starches are also used. Karaya gum, which is used primarily for fiber deflocculation, must be deacetylated before use.[37, 38]

Modified celluloses such as methylcellulose, carboxymethylcellulose[39] and hydroxyethylcellulose have been employed periodically, but economics has precluded their widespread use. Mixtures of carboxymethylcellulose with potato and cornstarches have been suggested recently.

Urea-formaldehyde and melamine-formaldehyde polymers and copolymers are employed primarily for imparting wet strength to paper. Many of these materials also improve dry-strength properties. Starch which has been oxidized with periodic acid has aroused considerable interest as a wet-strength polymer for specialty uses.[40] Other synthetic polymers, such as certain polyamides,[41] polyethyleneimine,[42] and phenol-formaldehyde polymers,[43] are also used for this purpose. Polyacrylamides[44] are used for improvement of dry-strength properties (at medium molecular weight ranges) and as retention aids (at high molecular weight ranges) for filler pigments and fiber fines.[45] Numerous other synthetic polymers such as butadiene styrene copolymers, polyvinyl acetate emulsions, polyvinylpyrollidone, and polyvinyl pyridines and copolymers, have been suggested, but because of either economic or technical difficulties, these have not been widely adopted as beater adhesives.

Hemicellulosic materials from agricultural as well as pulp wastes have also been studied as beater adhesives,[46, 47] but industrial processors have not become sufficiently interested to market such materials in substantial quantities. It is interesting to note that recent pulping research indicates that hemicellulose polymers existing in pulps may have been dissolved and readsorbed upon the fiber surfaces during pulping.[48] This action may be particularly important in alkaline pulping of mixed woods.

Numerous other polymers are under development in various industrial laboratories and it may be expected that improved quality and efficiency will lead to more widespread use of these materials because of the much greater processing versatility which they afford.

The Use of Beater Starches in Paper Making. Various starches have been used in paper making almost from the time that paper was invented. Today, starch is one of the more important nonfibrous raw materials for making many grades of paper. Until the important supplies were cut off during World War II, tapioca was the dominant starch in the United States. During the war, however, paper makers learned how to use other starches, principally corn, with equal effectiveness. Although tapioca has returned to the market and presently has an economic advantage, it has never regained its former market.

Starch is the reserve polysaccharide found in many species of seeds and tuberous roots of plants. The common starches used as internal additives in paper making are obtained from corn, tapioca, potato, and wheat. As purchased from the starch supplier, the air-dried product consists of small particles of polysaccharide varying in size from 2 to 100 microns in diameter. The particles of each species are easily recognizable under a microscope.[106] When a starch suspension in water is gradually heated, the particles retain their characteristic shape until a certain temperature range, called the gel point, is attained. At this temperature the particles suddenly expand like balloons and the viscosity of the starch suspensions increases substantially. The sudden swelling of these common starches occurs in the temperature ranges between 65 and 80°C. As the temperature is further raised toward the boiling point, the swollen starch breaks up, particularly under agitation, and the polysaccharide disperses to smaller fragments in the hot water. If a cooked dispersion of such starch is allowed to cool back to room temperature at a solids concentration of 5% or greater, it will set to a gel which is not completely redispersible in hot water. The chemistry and manufacture of various starches are considered in detail by Kerr.[106]

The polysaccharide comprising the major part of the starch granule consists of two glucose polymers called amylose and amylopectin. Amylose is a linear polymer of anhydroglucose units connected by a-1,4 linkages. The average number of anhydroglucose units per molecule is about 250. This polymer gives a deep blue-black color with iodine and this test may often be employed on paper to determine if starch has been added to paper stock. The amylopectin polymer also consists of anhydroglucose chains joined predominantly by a-1,4 linkages, but these chains are occasionally branched at the a-1,6 positions of the anhydroglucose units involved. Thus, the amylopectin is quite ramified and highly branched in structure. The average number of glucose units between branching points is approximately 25 and the total number of glucose units per molecule may average 2500. This polymer gives a reddish color with iodine. The common starches mentioned above are comprised of approximately 28% amylose polymer and 72% amylopectin polymer. So-called waxy or glutinous varieties of cornstarch are available which consist of very nearly 100% amylopectin. Other varieties of corn which yield starches having up to 65% amylose have also been produced recently. Neither of these special starches has found extensive use in paper making because of their greater cost.

Starch is used in paper making primarily for two reasons which are more or less interrelated: (1) to improve strength properties, such as bursting and tensile strengths, and folding endurance; (2) to supplement the beating operation. There are also several other reasons for use which are more difficult to measure but nevertheless are quite real. These are improvement of erasure, decreasing surface fuzz, prevention of filler dusting, increased rattle, and with some oxidized starches betterment of sizing.

The easiest method of adding starch to paper is at the beater or prior to sheet formation. Starch added here builds more internal strength than chemically modified starches applied at the size press, where penetration of the adhesive is limited. Usually, unmodified pearl starch is used; for this purpose, it is cooked and added to the pulp after the rosin size but preferably before the alum.

The cooking of starch is done in several ways. Often the simplest method consists of suspending the starch in water with stirring at 5 to 8% concentration and injecting live steam until the temperature reaches 87 to 95°C, depending upon the kind of starch used. More recently, several kinds of continuous cookers for starch have been introduced.[49] These consist of a steam injector through which a 10 to 20% starch dispersion is passed simultaneously with steam into a dilution and holding tank. The cooked starch is then continuously added to the stock at a prescribed rate. This cooking system lends itself well to automatic control.

The cooking temperature is important where optimum benefits from starch are desired. Inadequate benefits from starch are obtained most often from improper cooking and dispersion. If the temperature is not high enough the starch granules swell but do not burst, and subsequent dilution with relatively cold stock causes shrinkage and toughening of the granule. Such starch gives minimum improvements in strength properties. However, too high a cooking temperature for too long a time may disperse and degrade the starch excessively and lead to poor retention and effectiveness. Houtz[50] has studied the proper cooking conditions for various starches with a cooking viscometer and the soap-starch complex. According to his results, cornstarch should be cooked at 95°C (205°F) for 5 minutes for best results. Tapioca and potato starches which have lower gel temperatures may be cooked at somewhat lower temperatures. Casey[51] has shown that optimum cooking conditions vary somewhat with the density of the paper being made; higher-density papers require thoroughly cooked starch, whereas low-density papers should be made with somewhat undercooked starch. Cushing and Schuman[107] have made an extensive study of various starches and other additives in paper making.

Occasionally, unmodified, uncooked starch is added to the pulp, and the paper maker depends upon the heat in the dryer section and the residual moisture in the sheet for cooking of the starch. The desired result is obtained only in heavier weight papers and boards, and even here prior cooking of the starch would yield much better results. Where such addition is required, an oxidized starch will give better results.

Addition of starch to the stock ahead of the refiners does not give as satisfactory results as adding it after refining. Wheat starch and chemically treated cornstarches which are more resistant to mechanical degradation are suggested where it is necessary to add starch before refining.

The nuisance of cooking starch in the paper mill has been recognized by the starch manufacturers, who have marketed pregelatinized, cold-water dispersible products to be added as dry powders directly to the stock. This must be done at a point which gives sufficient time for swelling and dispersion prior to formation of the sheet on the machine. Caution should be exercised in the use of such products because some of them gradually retrograde and become partially nondispersible during storage. Such aged products are not only inefficient adhesives but they may cause "fish eyes" (transparent spots) in the paper.

Gums and Mucilages. Certain natural gums and mucilages are steadily finding greater use in paper manufacture. Prominent among these materials are the mannogalactans (sometimes called galactomannans)—the endosperm reserve polysaccharides of the legumes, of locust beans (*Ceratonia siliqua*) and guar seed (*Cyamopsis tetragonoloba*). These polysaccharides apparently have similar chemical structures and are composed of long chains of anhydromannose units attached by α-1,4 linkages and galactose units attached to the side of the polymer chain by means of an α-1,6 linkage. Locust bean polysaccharide has a somewhat higher mannan-to-galactan ratio (70:30) than guar polysaccharide (60:40). Both gums swell strongly upon contact with water and when heated they form viscous colloidal dispersions at concentrations as low as 0.5 to 1.0% solids. Guar gum is cold water-dispersible if ground to a sufficiently fine powder, but locust bean gum requires heating to 195 to 200°F for adequate dispersion. Commercial products are compounded with small amounts of alkaline chemicals such as borax to promote smooth wetting and dispersion of finely powdered gums. Without such chemicals, lumps of the gum may form on contact with water, and these lumps may produce transparent spots in the paper. The cooked gums should be added to the stock at the fan pump, headbox, or regulator box in amounts between 2 to 25 pounds per ton of fiber. Good agitation at the point of addition is important. Certain dry guar gums may be added at the beaters.

The mannogalactan gum products are superior adhesives for improving strength properties of paper, and at addition levels of 0.5 to 1.0% or more based on the fiber they improve fiber distribution and sheet formation.[36] The majority of starches lack the latter property. The better adhesion and fiber distribution obtained with such gums permit the paper maker to exercise considerably greater latitude in stock preparation and machine operation than is possible with starches. This greater effectiveness is evident from the data presented in Figure 11.16.

The gums have also found interesting applications in cylinder machine operations. Small additions (5 to 10 pounds per ton) to the stock improve liner formation, ply adhesion, stiffness, and pick strength. Karna and Nordman[108] and Swanson[36] have made extensive studies of the effects of mannogalactan gums on paper and paperboard furnishes.

In some instances a synergistic effect has been obtained when gum and starch (in a ratio of 40 to 60 by weight) are cooked together before being added to the pulp. This effect has been studied by both Goldstein[52] and Cushing[53].

Where the guar and locust bean gums are employed for supplementing the refining operation or improving drainage on the wire, the average fiber length remains longer. In the absence of gum, the pulp would be expected to flocculate to a greater degree, but in the presence of gum, flocculation is slowed and better formation may be attained. This effect of locust bean gum is illustrated in Figure 11.17. However, where extraordinarily long-fibered pulps are employed such as manila, hemp, or old rope fibers, these gums appear to be inadequate to prevent flocculation. For such pulps, deacetylated karaya gum, or the mucilages obtained from okra pod (*Hibiscus esculentus*) or the root of *Hibiscus manihot* are required. The latter product is widely used in the orient for deflocculation of mitsumata and gampi fibers. Karaya gum is imported to the United States from India and Pakistan and must be deacetylated in the paper mill with dilute alkali[38]. Okra pod mucilage is now manufactured in the United States. The mucilages and karaya gum are much more complex polysaccharides than locust bean and guar gums and greater care

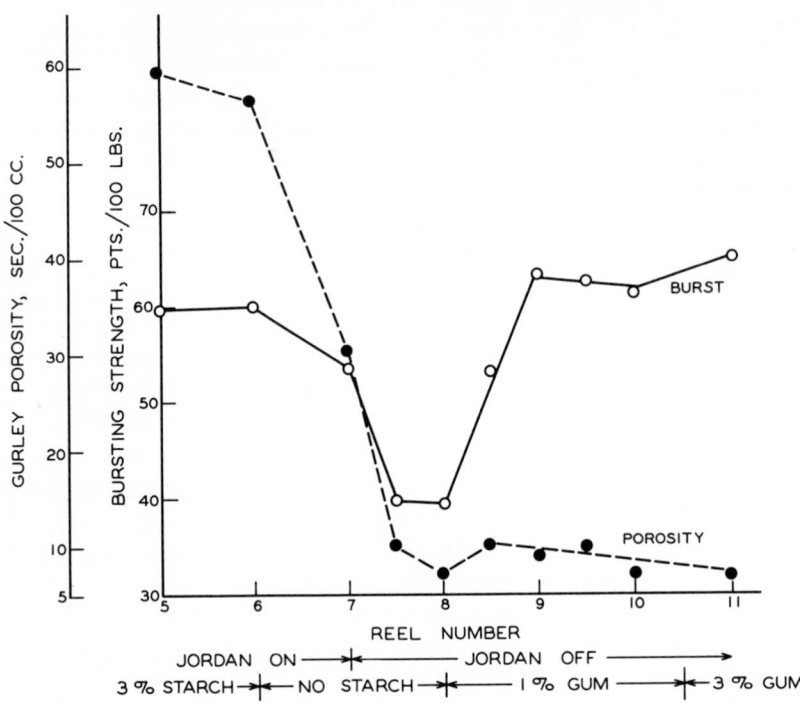

Fig. 11.16. The effect of locust beam gum on bursting strength and gurley porosity of an unrefined sulfite-soda furnish.

in both preparation and use must be exercised [37,38]. The effectiveness of these products for fiber deflocculation appears to be related to a peculiar rheological condition which is referred to as stringy or pituitous. The more pituitous preparations are more effective. Ion sensitivity is also important. For example, if alum is not carefully avoided in the paper-making system, fiber flocculation may be worse than if no mucilage were employed. Locust bean and guar gums are much less sensitive to multivalent ions such as aluminum.

Wet-Strength Resins. When most ordinary papers are saturated with water or other aqueous liquids, the fibers swell and fiber-to-fiber bonding is essentially destroyed. Thus, many papers which are subjected to rain, wet snow or many other hot or cold liquids may fail in tensile or other strength properties unless treated to develop wet strength. A wet-strength paper may be defined as one which has substantially greater than 10% wet over dry tensile strength when saturated with water. This property should not be confused with temporary water repellency due to sizing effects (see TAPPI Standard T 456 m-49 for methods of testing wet strength).

During the past 20 years production of wet-strength papers and boards has grown tremendously as a result of the development of synthetic resins for the purpose. Prior to 1942, wet strength was imparted by tub sizing or otherwise impregnating already formed paper with glue-formaldehyde dispersions or with acidic solutions of urea-formaldehyde (dimethylolurea). The glue-formaldehyde treatment is suitable for higher-cost papers, but adversely affects absorbency and folding endurance at desired wet-strength levels. Urea-formaldehyde treatments gave fugitive wet strength, that is, aging the paper, particularly at elevated temperatures and humidities, caused the wet strength to disappear. Dry tearing strength and folding endurance were also impaired.

In 1942, melamine-formaldehyde and partially condensed anionic urea-formaldehyde resins were introduced to the paper industry. These resins can be added to the papermaking stock and are retained by the fibers when the paper is formed. If the sheet is then dried at a pH value of approximately 4.5 and at machine dryer temperatures, significant wet strength develops. The melamine-formaldehyde product is made by partially polymerizing trimethylol melamine in dilute hydrochloric acid. The resulting colloidal polymer is cationic (positively charged) in solution and is attracted and retained by the negatively charged pulp fiber surfaces.

The urea-formaldehyde product is obtained by polymerizing dimethylolurea under mildly acidic conditions in the presence of sodium bisulfite. This produces an anionic (negatively charged) water-dispersible polymer which is substantive to cellulose fibers when alum is added in sufficient amounts. More recently it has been found that copolymerizing the dimethylolurea with smaller amounts of strong organic nitro-

gen-containing bases produced positively charged polymers that are substantive to the fiber without alum. These resins are also more efficient and less subject to pulp variability than the anionic products. The melamine- and urea-formaldehyde resins appear to be strictly competitive; while the former resin is somewhat more efficient on a weight basis, it is also higher-priced.

It should be pointed out that, although alum is unnecessary for retention of the modern resins, a pH of 4.5 in the white water system and wet sheet is required for cure of resin and final development of wet strength. Therefore, alum is usually employed. Typical wet-strength data for a cationic urea-formaldehyde resin are presented in Table 11.2.

TABLE 11.2. WET STRENGTH OF RESIN-TREATED PAPERS *

Resin Added (% based on pulp)	Wet Tensile (lb/in.)		Dry Tensile (lb/in.)		Wet Strength (%)	
	M.D.	C.M.D.	M.D.	C.M.D.	M.D.	C.M.D.
0.0	1.9	0.9	25.5	11.2	7.4	8.0
0.5	4.5	2.8	25.3	14.2	17.7	19.7
1.0	8.5	4.8	26.7	14.5	31.8	33.1

* 45 lb basis weight papers (25x40/500) made from a coniferous unbleached kraft pulp, sized with 2% rosin and 4% alum to pH 4.5.

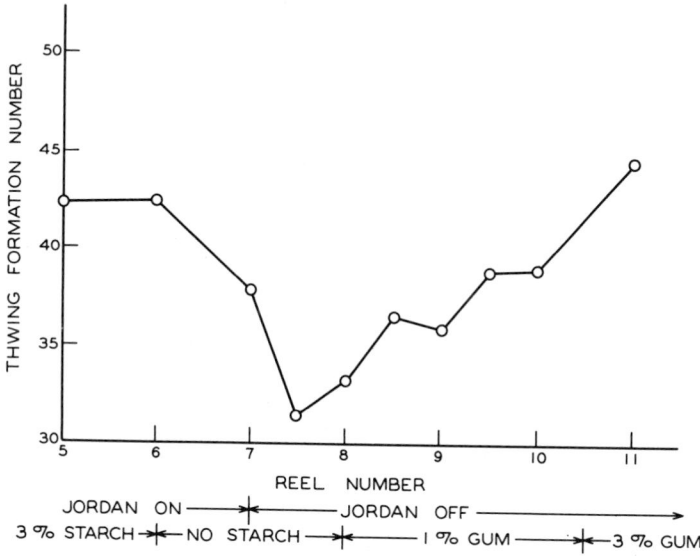

Fig. 11.17. The effect of locust bean gum on thwing formation number of an unrefined sulfite-soda furnish.

Although wide differences exist between various pulps used in paper making, modern cationic resins successfully produce wet strength in all of them. However, pulp variables and processing conditions have marked effects on retention and efficiency of wet-strength resins. Generally, well-beaten pulps respond better to the resins and it is important that the resin be added after completion of refining for best results. The electrical charge on resin particles is subject to influence from other ions, particularly multivalent anions, in the system. Apparently, chloride ion improves resin efficiency at concentrations normally existing in the paper-making system, but sulfate ion improves efficiency up to about 75 ppm, and higher concentrations are detrimental[54]. The action of trivalent ferricyanide ion is similar to that of sulfate but is more pronounced.

Kinetic studies of melamine resin[55] and cationic urea-formaldehyde resin[56] have shown the sorption of the polymer by the fiber surface is extremely rapid even at low pulp (0.01%) and resin concentrations. The rate of retention appears to be controlled by the rate at which the polymer can diffuse to the fiber surface[57]. Thus, good agitation of the pulp should exist at the point of resin addition.

Curing of the resin is important for development of efficient wet strength; pH, temperature, and time are the more important variables. Rate of cure increases at higher temperatures and lower pH values, but practical limits are determined by conditions which decompose the cellulose fiber. Usual operating conditions involve pH values between 4.0 and 5.0 and temperatures of approximately 220°F on the final dryer cans of the paper machine. Few paper machines reach sufficiently high temperatures for a long enough time to effect complete cure of the resin. However, both types of resins will continue to cure for one to two weeks during storage, at which time a plateau value of wet strength occurs. Melamine resins cure somewhat faster than urea resins.

Delayed cure off the paper machine is often a distinct advantage where the "broke," or waste paper, is recovered and reprocessed within the mill. However, fully cured wet-strength paper may be repulped under conditions which hydrolyze the wet-strength resin. This usually involves loading the wet-strength paper in a breaker beater or other pulper along with live steam and sufficient acid or an acid salt to lower the pH to 4. Such recovered fiber does not product wet-strength paper unless it is again treated with fresh resin.

Recently, polyamide-type wet-strength resins which also cure under alkaline conditions have reached the market. These resins permit manufacture of wet-strength papers under alkaline conditions (pH 8 to 10) and are reported to favor increased absorbency and less corrosion of machinery. They present special conditions of broke recovery because they are not acid-sensitive[41]. Numerous other materials have been suggested and tried as wet-strength additives. Among these are neoprene and acrylonitrile latices, polyethyleneimine[58,42] and other polyamines, but in general these materials have not been widely adopted because of either technical or economic difficulties. The mannogalactan gums also induce wet strength if the gum-treated paper is subsequently treated with an alkaline borate. The wet strength produced thereby is destroyed if the paper is leached with water. The difficulty in applying the borate to the gum-treated paper has discouraged wide use of this process.

Qualitative tests for the presence of wet-strength resins in papers have been developed by Stafford and co-workers[59].

The Sizing of Paper

As the term "sizing" has several meanings in the industry, a few words of explanation are in order. In general, it refers to treatment of either the pulp fibers or the already formed paper with materials which control wettability and surface properties of the final paper. Sizing agents may be placed in two categories—internal and surface. Internal sizing agents are added to the paper-making pulp and are used primarily for making papers and boards resistant to the penetration of water and other aqueous liquids. Other terms sometimes used for this process are "engine sizing" and "beater sizing." The paper industry is the largest consumer of rosin and waxes for this purpose. Large quantities of many other materials such as chemically modified rosins, hydrocarbon resins, asphalt emulsions, fatty acids, silicones, alkyl ketene dimers, perfluorocarbons, polyethylene emulsions, and other synthetics are also used.

Surface sizing agents are applied to paper or board for the purpose of augmenting internal sizing or for improving such properties as porosity, feathering resistance to writing inks, abrasion resistance (erasure), fuzz, abrasiveness, surface bonding strength (pick resistance), and printing properties. Typical of the materials used for this purpose are chemically and physically modified starches, gums, glues, alginates, methyl- and carboxymethylcellulose, and polyvinyl alcohol. When solutions or dispersions of these materials are applied to paper as a separate operation, the process is called tub sizing. Tub sizing will also improve bursting and tensile strengths, and folding endurance of fine papers if adhesives of low viscosity and good film strength are employed. A paper not treated in this way may be called a "waterleaf" sheet. When the application is made to paper or board by means of a pair of rolls part way through the dryer section, the operation is called size pressing; if done at the calender stack it is called calender sizing. These sizing operations are discussed further in Chapter 12. The present section will be concerned with internal sizing.

The Process of Internal Sizing. Internal sizing involves reacting a sizing agent—such as partially saponified rosin size, modified rosin, or a mixed emulsion of rosin and wax —with aluminum sulfate (paper makers' alum) in the presence of the paper-making pulp. The usual procedure is to add the rosin size to the pulp and, after thorough mixing, follow with the alum. Although certain theories of sizing predict that this order of addition should yield better sizing, many have tried reverse order of addition with equally good results. The reaction product of size and alum, the so-called size precipitate, is a voluminous floc whose composition varies with conditions of precipitation. For best sizing with rosin, sufficient alum must be added to lower the pH to 4.5 or 5.0. The ionic conditions of the white water and type of pulp also have marked effects on the sizing efficiency. More will be said of this later.

The size precipitate is not attached and distributed evenly over the fiber surface in the final sheet, but rather it is retained in the form of more or less small particles or islands on and within the structure. The dimensions of the particles and their retention and distribution on the unbonded cellulosic surfaces cause variations in sizing efficiency which are sometimes baffling. Some pulps are sized more easily than others. Some mills encounter poor or "slack" sizing during the summer months or when higher stock temperatures exist. In others, extreme variations in degree of sizing may occur from day to day or even from one shift to another. Sometimes sizing is "fugitive," that is, it is satisfactory immediately off the paper machine, but becomes unsatisfactory when the customer has received the product. There are also manufacturers of intentionally absorbent papers who find that their products gradually become sized even though no sizing agent is added to the pulp.

Much research has been done to solve such problems, and although a better fundamental understanding of the process exists today, there is still a great deal to be learned about the relationship between theory and practice.

Among the materials already mentioned as internal sizing agents, the more important are rosin and chemically modified (fortified) rosins and waxes. Certain special sizing agents will be discussed later. It is usual to consider a hydrophobic (water-hating) material such as rosin acid as the sizing agent and aluminum sulfate as the "fixing" or mordanting agent which attaches the rosin to the fiber surfaces. It will be seen, however, that both play an important part. Other aluminum compounds, such as aluminum chloride, sodium aluminate, and sodium phosphoaluminate, are sometimes used in place of part of the alum to control the pH and to decrease build-up of total acidity and sulfate ion concentrations in recirculating white water systems.

Rosin and Rosin Sizes. Rosin is derived in the United States from pine trees, principally the long leaf and slash pines, grown in the southeastern region. Three general types of rosin are produced, each in a different manner. Gum rosin is obtained from living trees by cutting the bark on one side each week during the growing season and collecting the oleoresin at the base of the tree. The oleoresin is largely a mixture of rosin acids and turpentine which are cleaned and then separated by steam distillation.

A grading system for gum rosin has been set up by the United States Government consisting of designations with letters of the alphabet, B, D, E, F, G, H, I, K, M, N, WG (water glass), WW (water white), and X. The first letters designate darkest color, and X is the lightest grade recognized. With modern processing methods, gum rosin grades lower than K are no longer marketed. Cleanliness is also important in grading.

Wood rosin is obtained from the stumps of pine trees. The stump must be from a mature tree and it must have aged eight years or more after the tree was felled. During this time, the sapwood rots, leaving only the resin-rich heartwood. The stumps are removed from the ground with machinery and are then taken to the rosin plant where they are splintered and extracted with solvent (naphtha or benzene). This removes

rosin, turpentine, pine oil, and many other products which are separated by fractional distillation. Crude rosin is much darker in color than gum rosin and it is designated "FF Wood Rosin." Rosin size may be prepared from this product and used in unbleached papers and board where dark color is unobjectionable. Further processing of the FF grade yields light-colored (pale) and very dark grades. The dark fraction is designated "B Wood Rosin" and is used for making size, although its sizing efficiency is somewhat lower than either FF or pale grades. The pale wood rosins are marketed in grades varying from I to X for manufacture of size.

Tall oil rosin is derived from the paper industry itself. When the spent liquor from alkaline kraft cooking of pinewood is allowed to stand for a time, a scum collects on the surface which is comprised chiefly of the sodium salts of rosin and fatty acids in about equal proportions. The skimmed soaps are acidified with sulfuric acid and separated into two layers. The lower layer, consisting mainly of a solution of sodium sulfate, is returned to the pulp mill. The upper layer, called crude tall oil, is a viscous liquid composed of rosin acids, fatty acids, and numerous unsaponifiable materials. The rosin and fatty materials can be separated by fractional distillation which yields a pure light-colored rosin that is excellent for paper sizing. Despite rumors that the supply of rosin is dwindling, it appears that the sources will be adequate for many years to come [60].

Rosin is composed of approximately 90% resin acids and 10% nonacidic material made up of fatty and resin esters, various sterols, terpenes, and complex hydrocarbons. The resin acids are monocarboxylic acids of alkylated hydrophenanthrene nuclei and may be classified into two types—abietic and pimaric—on the basis of position of double bonds and chemical reactions. Some of the double bonds are subject to oxidation which may cause darkening of color. Rosin acid has a molecular weight of approximately 300 and a softening range of 158 to 177°F. It is insoluble in water but soluble in methyl and ethyl alcohol, acetone, chloroform and various oils. It has an acid number of 155 to 175 and dissolves in alkalies to form soaps.

Rosin size is prepared by cooking rosin with alkali, usually soda ash or caustic soda, in water. The process is carried out in a steel tank equipped with steam coils. Good agitation and means for handling foam should be provided especially if soda ash is used. The amount of alkali used depends upon several factors, such as the acid number of the rosin and the degree of saponification desired. Generally, about 12 pounds of caustic soda are required to neutralize 100 pounds of rosin. Sizes prepared in the mill usually contain 40 to 50% total solids as prepared.

Most rosin sizes are not completely saponified but contain a certain percentage of free rosin depending upon the wishes of the user. In some mills high percentages of free rosin give better sizing results while in others the free rosin content makes little difference. It is common practice today to buy prepared rosin size in the form of 70 to 80% solids pastes or as dry powders. The pastes are diluted with warm water and vigorous agitation in the paper mill. This usually involves a combination of steam, water, and a series of ejectors where hot rosin size is introduced through the suction intake. The high solids content paste is a water-in-oil (rosin) emulsion and upon dilution to 10 to 15% solids the paste inverts to a fine particle size oil-in-water type emulsion. Cold water is then added to dilute the size to 2 to 6% solids in the storage tank. Automatic dilution and metering equipment is used in many mills today.

Dry sizes are usually readily water-soluble and may be added to the paper stock without predissolving. This property should be checked, however, for if immediate solution does not occur, specks and poor sizing may result.

Several specially prepared rosin sizes are worthy of mention. The Delthirna process for making size, originally developed in France, consists of trickling a 0.3 to 0.5% caustic soda solution over crushed rosin in a V-shaped pipe. The dissolved rosin flows out the top of the opposite leg of pipe and into a storage tank. Such size is fully saponified and has a solids content of 3.5 to 6.0%.

Bewoid size, also first developed in Europe, is prepared by melting rosin in a kettle equipped with an agitator and then introducing an alkaline solution of casein protein slowly at a controlled rate. A water-in-oil (rosin) emulsion first forms which later inverts to an oil-in-water emulsion when sufficient casein has been added. Very little saponification occurs and the rosin is nearly 100% in the free state. This type of size has not proved to be as widely applicable as more highly saponified sizes.

Prosize is obtained by adding approximately 15% (based on size) of dry soy bean protein to a dilute solution of conventional, saponified rosin and then treating the mixture with about 15% of boric acid. The protein forces hydrolysis of the sodium rosinate to free rosin. The free rosin particles are very finely divided and protected by the protein in such a way that better distribution of size is obtained on the fiber.

When refined rosin is heated at 150°C with maleic anhydride, the levopimaric acid in the mixture forms an adduct which now contains three carboxyl (acid) groups per molecule instead of one. Continuation of the heating furnishes further levopimaric acid at the expense of the abietic-type acids present until the reaction is complete. Fumaric acid will react similarly with rosin to yield adducts of higher softening temperatures. When the synthesized product is saponified it resembles rosin size, but it is generally a more efficient sizing material. Commercial manufacturers offer such products under various trade names as "Mersize," "Pexol," and "Cyfor."

Wax Sizes. Various wax emulsions are used as internal sizes, sometimes as the sole sizing agent but more often as a supplement to rosin size. Two types of waxes, paraffin, or macrocrystalline, and microcrystalline are used almost exclusively. Although both are composed of paraffinic hydrocarbons, they differ in chemical structure and physical properties. The melting point of the paraffin waxes ranges from 120 to 145°F, and that of the microcrystalline ranges from 140 to 180°F.

Such waxes are emulsified in various ways to form acid-precipitable and acid-stable emulsions depending upon the type and nature of the emulsifying agent used. Today, most of the wax emulsions used are of the acid-stable type, and the acid- or alum-precipitable types are used only in special instances. Although the precipitable types produce good water repellency they must be used with great care to avoid agglomeration of wax particles, fouling of paper machinery, and wax spots in the paper.

Acid-stable emulsions do not coagulate in the presence of alum, although they are retained on the fiber in the presence of alum. They are generally trouble-free. Where rosin and wax sizes are employed in the same furnish it is good practice to add the rosin size, followed by the alum, and finally the acid-stable wax size. Acid-precipitable waxes and wax-rosin mixtures of this type are added after the rosin size but before the alum.

Commercial wax sizes are free flowing liquids at 30 to 50% solids. It is good practice to dilute them to 5% solids before addition to the stock.

Waxes develop excellent water repellency in papers and boards, but where used in amounts greater than 0.5% (based on fiber), fiber-to-fiber bonding and sheet strength will be reduced, wax may accumulate on the presses, and the final sheet will become slippery.

Asphalt Emulsions. Asphalt emulsions are employed for sizing of many paperboard and structural insulation board products where color is of no importance. The diluted size is added in amounts of 1 to 2% size solids for light sizing to as high as 10% for

hard sized grades. Alum is used to precipitate and retain the size.

Special Sizes. A great many special sizing materials have been used in paper making during recent years. Foremost among these is "Aquapel," an alkyl ketene dimer which reacts chemically with the cellulose fiber to produce extremely efficient sizing. The chemical structure of the material and its reaction with cellulose are shown below:

$$R-CH=C-CH-R$$
$$\underset{O-C=O}{\big|\qquad\big|} + \text{Cellulose} \longrightarrow$$

Alkyl ketene dimer

$$\underset{H_2C-C-CH}{R\qquad\quad R}$$
$$\underset{O\quad C=O}{\big\|\quad\big|}$$
$$\underset{OH\ OH\ OH\ O\ OH\ OH\ OH}{\big|}$$

cellulose fiber surface

where R is a hydrocarbon chain of 16 to 18 carbon atoms.

The alkyl ketene dimer will also react with other hydroxyl-containing compounds such as water, and it is therefore desirable to encourage retention of as much of the product as possible by the fibers before the reaction with water has occurred. In order to obtain satisfactory retention the "Aquapel" is emulsified along with a retention aid such as cationic (positively charged) starch or a polyamide resin. About 0.05 to 0.15% "Aquapel" is needed for unbleached kraft pulp and up to 0.3% for bleached pulps. The presence of alum in the system is detrimental to development of efficient sizing with "Aquapel." One of the interesting applications of this material is development of good sizing under alkaline paper-making conditions (pH 7.0 to 8.5), which is impossible with rosin sizes.

Fatty acid soaps have long been used for sizing specialty products such as photographic papers, but because of their relatively greater cost they have not been adopted widely for other papers. The technology of their use is similar to that of rosin sizes. Certain fatty amines have also been used for sizing.

Two further products deserve mention as sizing agents. "Quilon" is a stearato chromic chloride which is soluble in dilute isopropyl alcohol and may be applied as a solution to surfaces of paper or board to develop water repellency. "Scotchban" is a similar chromium complexed compound but instead of stearic acid, a fluorinated long-chain fatty acid is used. This product will develop oil and grease resistance in addition to water repellency on surfaces of papers and boards to which it is applied [61].

The Chemistry of Aluminum Sulfate. When paper maker's alum $[Al_2(SO_4)_3 \cdot 14H_2O]$ is dissolved in water the aluminum ion becomes solvated with six molecules of water and hydrolysis occurs according to the following mechanism:

$$\begin{bmatrix} H_2O & & H_2O \\ & \diagdown & \diagup \\ H_2O & Al & H_2O \\ & \diagup & \diagdown \\ H_2O & & H_2O \end{bmatrix}^{+++} \quad \underset{\longleftarrow}{\overset{H_2O}{\rightleftharpoons}}$$

$$\begin{bmatrix} H_2O & & OH \\ & \diagdown & \diagup \\ H_2O & Al & H_2O \\ & \diagup & \diagdown \\ H_2O & & H_2O \end{bmatrix}^{++} + H_3O^{+1}$$

$$[Al(OH)(H_2O)_5]^{+2} \quad \underset{\longleftarrow}{\overset{H_2O}{\rightleftharpoons}}$$
$$[Al(OH)_2(H_2O)_4]^{+1} + H_3O^{+1}$$

$$[Al(OH)_2(H_2O)_4]^{+1} \quad \underset{\longleftarrow}{\overset{H_2O}{\rightleftharpoons}}$$
$$[Al(OH)_3(H_2O)_3] + H_3O^{+1}$$

The predominant species in ordinary alum solutions is the hexahydrated tripositive aluminum ion, but sufficient hydrolysis occurs to give a pH of 2 to 5, depending upon concentration. As the pH is increased by addition of alkali, basic aluminum ion begins to appear in greater concentration and under mildly alkaline conditions aluminum hydroxide precipitates. Further addition of alkali will dissolve aluminum hy-

droxide to form a basic aluminum ion known as aluminate,

$$[Al(OH)_3(H_2O)_3] + Na^+OH^- \rightleftharpoons$$
$$[Al(OH)_4(H_2O)_2]^{-1} + Na^+ + H_2O$$
$$\text{sodium aluminate}$$

The equilibrium above may be driven to the left by neutralization of hydroxyl ion and therefore aluminate solutions must be stabilized with excess alkali such as caustic soda.

The hydroxyl groups on hydrolyzed aluminum ion may be replaced by anions, provided their coordination ability is stronger than that of hydroxyl ion or if their concentration is sufficiently higher. Thus, in the presence of rosin acid anion, various aluminum rosin salts may form depending upon the molar ratios of the reactants. The following reactions may occur:

$$[Al(H_2O)_6]^{+3} + H^+R^- \rightleftharpoons$$
$$[Al(H_2O)_5R]^{+2} + H_3O^{+1}$$
$$[Al(OH)(H_2O)_5]^{+2} + H^+R^- \rightleftharpoons$$
$$[Al(H_2O)_5R]^{+2} + H_2O$$
$$[Al(OH)_2(H_2O)_4]^{+1} + 2[H^+R^-] \rightleftharpoons$$
$$[Al(H_2O)_4R_2]^{+1} + 2H_2O$$
$$[Al(OH)_3(H_2O)_3] + 3[H^+R^-] \rightleftharpoons$$
$$[Al(H_2O)_3R_3] + 3H_2O$$

where R^- represents the rosin acid anion. Similarly, an aluminum rosinate may, in turn, form a coordinate bond with anions present on the surfaces of cellulose. For example,

$$[Al(H_2O)_5R]^{+2} + (\text{Cellulose-COO})^{-1} \overset{H_2O}{\rightleftharpoons}$$
$$[Al(H_2O)_4R(\text{Cellulose-COO})]^{+1}.$$

Guide [64] has suggested that the various aluminum rosinates may, during drying, further react with one another through formation of hydroxyl bonds—a process termed olation. This process anchors the rosin in such a position that a high, stable contact angle is achieved when an aqueous liquid contacts the sized surface.

If other anions having higher coordinating ability than rosin or the cellulosic surface anions exist in the system, they preferentially occupy the coordination sites and the aluminum rosinate is either not formed or not properly held by the fiber surface to produce a high contact angle. Organic ions such as oxalate, citrate, tartrate and the inorganic ions, sulfate and phosphate may become detrimental at sufficient concentrations [67].

Important Factors in Rosin Sizing. Measurement of the degree of sizing of papers and boards usually involves determination of the rate at which the test liquid penetrates into the porous structure. The rate of penetration, R, may be expressed by where γ is the surface tension of the liquid, r is the radius of the capillary involved, η is the viscosity of the liquids, l is the length

$$R = \frac{\gamma r \cos \theta}{4 \eta l}$$

of the capillary, and θ is the cosine of the contact angle which forms between the solid fiber surface and the liquid involved. The surface tension and viscosity of the liquid and the caliper of the sheet are usually constant for a given set of conditions and the equation indicates that the penetration and the degree of sizing are therefore dependent primarily upon the value of the contact angle θ and the pore radius, r. It should be pointed out that the relationship expressed in this equation is qualitative in nature. However, it is useful in considering the variables involved in a sizing problem. For example, it indicates that decreasing the value of r by beating and refining the paper-making pulp and thereby making a denser paper should improve sizing. It is often found that well-beaten stocks are easier to size than lightly beaten pulps. However, for a given beaten pulp which should yield a paper of given average pore size, it becomes clear that the degree of sizing of the paper depends to a large extent upon the contact angle, θ.

Basically, sizing of a porous structure such as paper depends upon the development of a condition which makes the fiber surfaces nonwettable by water or other aqueous liquids. One of the measures of wettability is the contact angle, θ, which forms between the solid surface and the liquid involved. When the liquid forms a low contact angle with the pores of a solid structure, capillary attraction causes spontaneous entrance of the liquid into the capillaries. However, if the contact angle is greater than 90°, the value of cosine θ becomes negative, and a resisting pressure develops which prevents entrance of the liquid into the capillaries. This latter condition develops if a wettable solid surface is coated or otherwise covered with a hydrophobic substance which resists wetting, such as rosin size precipitate.

Fundamentally, good rosin sizing depends upon attaining the following conditions: (1) preparation of rosin size-alum precipitate which has the potential ability to develop a maximum contact angle with water; (2) retention of the size precipitate as uniformly as possible upon the fiber surface; (3) conversion of the wet sizing compound on the fiber surface to a substance which develops a high (preferably obtuse) contact angle against water and aqueous liquids. Furthermore, it is preferred that the high contact angle remain stable with time.

Studies of the composition of rosin-alum size precipitates have led to the conclusion that under ideal sizing conditions the precipitate consists of a mixture of rosin acid, aluminum dirosinate, and aluminum monorosinate. Ekwall and Bruun [62,63], studied the reaction product between rosin acids and aluminum sulfate by a very sensitive method involving use of the surface balance. They concluded that under ideal conditions the sizing material is dibasic aluminum monorosinate. They further showed that films of this compound give contact angles of approximately 100°, whereas films of rosin acid give angles of 70° in contact with water. Guide [64] also studied the reaction products of pure sodium aluminate and sodium abietate under acidic and alkaline conditions and found that the size precipitates were not stoichiometric compounds but co-precipitates of several compounds. The compositions of the size precipitates were independent of the pH of precipitation, but dependent upon the initial abietate-to-aluminum ratio prior to acidification.

Many years ago it was observed that paper-making pulps vary in the ease with which they can be sized with rosin and alum. For example, rag, alpha, and certain other high-purity pulps are difficult to size even with relatively large amounts of rosin size, but unbleached sulfite and other less pure pulps are comparatively easy to size. It is now known that the acidic impurities in various pulps interact with both rosin size and alum to form exchange compounds which under proper conditions of pH and ionic composition, improve the retention of the rosin size precipitate because of differences in electrical charge.

Cellulose fibers suspended in water normally bear a negative electrical charge, the origin of which is not completely understood. However, it appears that the electrical double layer system on the fiber surfaces plays an important role in the retention of the size precipitate. Thode and co-workers [65,66] have examined this relationship for sized and unsized cellulose fibers. They concluded that cellulose fibers dispersed in water have a negative electrical charge, the sign of which is difficult to reverse. They suggest that the size precipitates are attracted to the fiber surfaces because, under the conditions of rosin sizing, the precipitate has a positive electrical charge whereas that on the fiber is negative. This difference in electrical charge causes a mutual coalescence of the sizing material and the fiber.

Guide [64] studied these effects further and showed that a high positive electrical charge on the size precipitate is favored by a high aluminum-to-rosin acid ratio, a low pH of sizing (approximately 5.0) and a low concentration of easily sorbed anions in the sizing suspension. The latter point emphasizes the importance of eliminating the build-up of high concentrations of anions such as sulfate, oxalate, tartrate, and citrate. It has been suggested that summer sizing troubles may be related to the presence of the later organic ions during the summer months when organism growth is favored by higher temperatures [67].

If the size precipitate has the desired composition and is retained well by cellulose fibers, it must then be converted during drying to a material which causes a large contact angle to develop between the fiber surface and aqueous liquids. It has been shown [63,64] that considerably larger contact angles (90 to 105°) are obtained between water and aluminum rosinate than between water and rosin acid (60 to 70°). The probable reason for the smaller contact angle for the rosin acid-water system lies in the amphipathic (polar-nonpolar) nature of the rosin acid. In the absence of aluminum ion, rosin acid should orient its molecules during drying in such a position that a large temporary contact angle is produced against water. However, such molecules are not fixed in position, and soon after contact with water they may overturn and promote better wetting, as indicated by a change in the contact angle with time. However, where such rosin molecules have reacted with aluminum ion which, in turn, is chemically bound to the fiber surface through acidic carboxyl groups or similar exchange sites, the rosin molecule is unable to overturn and a stable and large contact angle is obtained. It is believed that this mechanism explains one of the important functions of aluminum ion in the rosin sizing system. It is well known that acid alone will cause precipitation of rosin in the fiber system, but neither good retention nor fixation of a large and stable contact angle precipitate is assured under these conditions. The work of Yiannos [68] on fatty acid monolayers and further work in The Institute of Paper Chemistry laboratories on rosin acid monolayers [69] have confirmed these hypotheses.

Effect of Drying and Calendering. It has been reasonably well established by at least two independent studies [70,71] that the moisture content of the paper should be in the range of 40 to 50% at the time it reaches the sintering temperature (80°C) of the rosin size precipitate in the sheet if maximum sizing is to be obtained. The optimum moisture content is about 5% higher for high free rosin sizes such as Bewoid.

It is also well known in industry that machine calendering of rosin-sized papers will substantially lower the degree of sizing. The mechanism of these effects is unknown.

Pitch Control

Pitch trouble in one of its various forms is an ever-present threat in most paper mills. The trouble may appear in the form of pitch balls which vary in average size up to $\frac{1}{4}$ inch in diameter. Smaller pitch balls may pass through the screens and cause dark spots in paper and board, picking, sheet breaks, plugging of the fourdrinier wire and dandy roll, and poor sheet formation. Pitch may also aggravate foam troubles in the mill system. In other instances, the pitch may be invisible within the pulp, but it apparently assumes a very tacky condition and deposits on various parts of the machine which the pulp or sheet contacts. Felts may fill up rapidly and become nonabsorbent, and pitch may deposit upon the walls of pulpers, beaters, pumps, and various other kinds of tanks. Pitch may also collect upon dryer rolls and breaker and calender stacks. Such deposits not only lower the quality of the printing surface, but often actually tear the sheet and lower production. The presence of pitch within a pulp system may also cause loss of absorbency and development of self-sizing in products which are intended to be absorbent. Lastly, the presence of even small quantities of pitch in high-purity pulps intended for dissolving purposes (cellophane and rayon manufacture) may cause discol-

oration, slow the rate of filtration of the viscose solution, and produce cratering of the spinnerettes during the spinning operation.

It is reasonably well established that pitch trouble stems from the resin and fatty acids which exist in all wood pulps. Occasionally, rosin size may cause a similar trouble, particularly in the summer months when warm, hard water or excess rosin and alum are used to establish better sizing. High free rosin sizes may cause more trouble than fully saponified sizes in this respect. The natural resin present in the original wood is contained in the ray cells and in the resin canals. During the pulping operation, particularly under alkaline conditions, a considerable part of this resinous material is removed, especially if pulp is washed with warm, soft water. However, even under the best processing conditions, a typical coniferous sulfite pulp will contain approximately 1% of such pitchy material.

Various components in the pitch may be extracted with petroleum ether or alcohol-benzene, but no relationship between the amounts of these extractions and pitch troubles has ever been established. It is apparently impossible to tell by chemical analysis or solvent extraction of the pulp whether pitch trouble will occur when that pulp is run on the machine. However, chemical analysis may be useful for identifying a particular troublesome pulp in a mixed furnish, or an additive such as an antifoam which may be aggravating the trouble. Pitch particles in a pulp may be identified by staining with a solution of "Sudan III" dissolved in three parts of alcohol and one part of water.

Chemical companies supply numerous dispersants, protective colloids, pigments, etc., as pitch-control agents. It is well known, however, that pitch troubles are quite unpredictable and often, when the trouble is most acute, none of the control agents is effective. On the other hand, certain materials sometimes decrease the severity of the trouble. These are discussed later.

The Effect of Various Factors on Severity of Pitch Trouble. Many factors influence the severity of pitch trouble. Among these are wood species, seasoning, pulping method, washing, water conditions, bleaching, refining, and foam and dissolved gases. Generally speaking, pinewoods are higher in natural pitch (3 to 5% or more) and give more pitch trouble than sprucewood, which has approximately 2 to 4% of natural resin. Though hardwoods contain little or no resin acid, they do contain substantial quantities of fatty acids and unsaponifiable material, which may be just as troublesome as the resin acid-containing material. Seasoning the wood, especially in chip form, often decreases or even eliminates the pitch trouble. The reason for this is not clear but it has been suggested that the seasoning process oxidizes and polymerizes the unsaturated fatty compounds. These reactions decrease the tackiness and reduce the possibility of coalescence between pitch particles.

On the other hand, seasoning of wood under water appears to be definitely detrimental for pitch difficulties. Also, some manufacturers of groundwood from southern pines and hardwoods have found that green wood often gives less pitch trouble than seasoned wood in southern climates. Back [72] has shown that the viscosity of the pitch determines to a large extent its rate of deposition on shear surfaces such as pump impellers, piping, and tanks. Chemical reactions or added materials which increase the tackiness may increase pitch deposition because the pitch is better able to withstand shearing conditions. On the other hand, addition of materials which markedly reduce the viscosity of pitchy substances may be beneficial.

Perhaps more important than the type of wood is the type of cook used. Unbleached sulfite pulp appears to be among the most troublesome from the standpoint of pitch trouble. Soda and well-washed sulfate pulps rarely cause pitch trouble. Apparently, a significant part of the resin is removed by saponification and subsequent washing in the alkaline pulping processes.

Efficient washing of the pulp with hot, soft water will often largely eliminate the troublesome pitch from the system. Such washing operations reduce the pitch content of a pulp by more than 50%. Hard water apparently increases pitch trouble, particularly at pH values above 6.0, because of the formation of calcium, magnesium, and iron soaps with the resin and fatty acids of the pitch. These compounds adhere more strongly to various metallic surfaces and are also more tacky and viscous.

Generally speaking, multistage bleaching of pulps is usually beneficial to pitch difficulties. Probably, the several washing steps, the alkali treatment, etc., remove further quantities of pitch from the pulp which, in turn, decreases the amount of trouble. It is, of course, quite important to remove any residual calcium ion from pulps which are bleached with calcium hypochlorite. Gustafsson and co-workers [73, 74] showed that low pH, the presence of alum, high temperature, and complex phosphates decrease the tendency of pitch to adhere to metal surfaces.

Beating and refining of pulps which tend to give pitch trouble will only add to the problem. Possibly, the beating and refining damages the ray cells and loosens and frees pitch from various surfaces. It is best to separate those pulps which tend to have the most pitch and refine them separately in the presence of a good pitch-control agent. Sodium hexametaphosphate has been suggested for this purpose. Experience indicates that this chemical will decrease severity of pitch trouble in groundwood systems and in paper-making systems which do not contain high concentrations of alum or other multivalent cations.

Back [75] has developed a pitch control method involving the addition of 0.3 to 0.5% excess sodium hydroxide followed by 0.2 to 0.5% excess alum to a pH of 5.5 to

6.0 in the system. Too much alum is undesirable in this treatment because it apparently increases the depositable pitch content of the pulp. Back [75] has suggested that this treatment produces a negative electrical charge on the cellulose fibers and a positive charge on the pitch particles, which are then attracted to the fiber surfaces and held there. The pitch is thereby carried out of the paper-making system continuously and is not permitted to build up in the form of tacky particles nor to deposit on various other solid surfaces. Somewhat similar methods involving the addition of 1 to 4% of bentonite or talc to the pulp have been suggested for controlling pitch troubles.

Deaeration of Stock and Foam Problems

The modern trend of increasing machine speeds and the numerous surface-active materials added to the furnish, coupled with the demand for higher-quality papers, are making the paper maker more cognizant of foam problems. Significant quantities of foam in the stock may cause beater overflow, reduced beater circulation, stock pump binding, uneven pulp consistency, and poor internal sizing. Foam in stock may consist of large bubbles which cause thin areas in the sheet, and in extreme cases, significant fiber losses. In other instances, foam may consist of very small bubbles that are not readily apparent in the stock but that interfere seriously with drainage on the wire and cause fine pinholes and poor sheet formation. The latter type of foam is often unsuspected by the machine operator, but it may limit production and seriously lower sheet quality.

Foam consists of small bubbles of gas dispersed in water either by vigorous agitation or liberation of dissolved gases. The process of dispersion or formation of the bubble surfaces requires the expenditure of energy, part of which is stored in the surface of the gas bubbles as surface energy. Thermodynamic law predicts that such systems tend to acquire a state of minimum energy by coalescence and collapse of the bubbles. This natural tendency of foam results in a competition between two rate processes, namely, the rate of foam generation and the rate of destruction or collapse of the foam. A pure liquid does not form a stable foam because there is no opportunity for the formation of stabilizing films of surface-active materials or finally divided solids at the gas-liquid interface. The usual paper-making system, however, contains a multitude of materials which tend to stabilize the foam, among which are the alkali metal salts of rosin and fatty acids and various pulping liquor components which have not been thoroughly washed out of pulps. A further source of contamination of the mill water supply arises from the many synthetic detergents and soaps used and discarded by communities upstream from the mill. Synthetic detergents are scientifically designed for high surface activity and chemical stability, and many are good foam stabilizers. These substances often pass through sewage disposal plants and remain in the water supply up to the time it is taken into the mill. In addition to the surface-active substances, the usual mill system may contain fiber fines, dyes, various fillers, and colored pigments which may be adsorbed at the bubble interface and promote foam stability.

Many stock systems in older mills were not adequately designed for removal of foam and dissolved gases. Numerous places are commonly observed where air is incorporated into the stock and recirculated with the white water. With increased volumes of stock and greater production, this recirculation has been speeded up to the point where little opportunity exists for foam to escape from the system before the sheet is formed. The many possible areas where air is incorporated into the stock in a typical system have been discussed by Tester.[76] He mentions that a typical 500-ton per day mill may spend $80,000 per year for additives which assist in the destruction of the foam. Where foam problems exist in a mill it is more economical first to eliminate as nearly as possible leaky pumps, cascading of stock, suction of air into refiners, and release of dissolved gases arising from increase in temperature of water. Only then should antifoams be added to the system.

Antifoams, sometimes called defoamers, are surface-active materials which replace the stabilizing film in the bubble interface with a material which lacks the properties that cause foam stability. Among these materials are higher alcohols, kerosene, silicones, and complex mixtures of hydrocarbons, fats, and fatty glycerides. The quantity of such material employed is about 0.01 to 1.0% based on the fiber weight. Antifoams should be added to the stock as close as possible to where the trouble occurs. Where restricted drainage exists on the paper machine wire, a very dilute dispersion of the antifoam is often sprayed onto the stock immediately after the slice. Effective antifoams will produce dramatic results, but it is often found that some antifoams are successful in combating one foam problem and are unsuccessful with another. The reasons for this variability are unknown, and it is often necessary to try several antifoams in order to find one that works efficiently. Considerable research on the mechanism of destruction of foam remains to be done.

A composite theory of antifoam action has been suggested by Ross.[77, 78] This theory suggests that a good antifoam possesses sufficient surface activity to replace the elastic, shock resistant, stable film surrounding each bubble with a film which is fragile and inelastic. Under these conditions, mechanical forces such as water sprays easily rupture the bubbles and cause rapid collapse of the foam.

In recent years, several mechanical devices for removing gas from paper stock have been developed. Boadway[79, 80] has developed a modified Vortrap, called the "Vorvac." This is a centrifugal device which displaces the gas from the stock. Another device called the "Deculator" consists of a vacuum tank through which the screened and diluted stock is passed on its way to the paper machine.[81] The diluted stock is introduced through nozzles which spray the stock against a baffle or side of the tank. The vacuum within the large tank causes the bubbles to enlarge many times and collapse at a faster rate.

Determination of Foam in Paper Stock. Determination of the amount of foam in paper stock permits estimation of the problem and locates the difficulty if tests are performed on stock taken from various parts of the system. Such determinations also are useful for estimating the effectiveness of antifoam treatments. Several tests have been devised for this purpose. TAPPI Routine Control Method 173 involves weighing a given volume of stock before and after deaeration of the stock by boiling for a given time. Reduced pressure may also be employed for deaeration at room temperature. Holland[82] has proposed a combination measurement of the degree of flotation of the stock and the volumetric determination of the amount of air present. Procedures for the study of relative effectiveness of antifoams in stock systems have also been outlined.[82, 83] Gavelin[84] suggests that foam arising from supersaturated systems is much more detrimental than entrained air to formation and drainage of stock. He proposes the use of a drainage tester for evaluating this behavior.

Slime Control

Pulp and paper systems offer a fertile field for growth and propagation of many types of bacteria and fungi. Accumulations of such organisms may degrade and stain pulps, decrease drainage of the sheet on the wire, form deposits on suction boxes and other solid surfaces, cause transparent slime spots in the paper, and decrease felt life by plugging the pores and by chemical degradation of the wool fiber. In addition to the biological slimes, increasing recognition is being given to so-called non-microbiological slimes. These materials often consist largely of alumina ($Al_2O_3 \cdot xH_2O$), but in other instances may be composed of cellulose fines, degraded cellulose, resinous particles, and various colloidal materials which may have been added to the system. It is said that nonbiological slime can be eliminated by replacing alum with sulfuric acid.[104] However, rosin-sized papers and boards require a certain minimum quantity of alum for development of sizing. Furthermore, modern paper making involves so many noncellulosic additives which are incompletely retained in the sheet that the solution of these problems is not easily obtained.

Control of microbiological slimes requires good housekeeping and the addition of chemicals that are toxic to the organisms involved. Appling [105] discusses the use of five different categories of such chemical toxicants.

(1) Chlorine with or without ammonia.

(2) Organomercurials.

(3) Phenols, chlorinated phenols and their salts.

(4) Mixtures of toxicants.

(5) Miscellaneous toxicants.

Best results with these materials are obtained through periodic peaks of concentration commonly known as the intermittent or slug treatment. The detailed use of toxicants depends upon the nature of the organisms present and mill conditions, and becomes quite involved. The subject is thoroughly treated in the TAPPI Monograph "Microbiology of Pulp and Paper." [104]

Filler and Loading Pigments

Mineral pigments are used in the manufacture of many grades of paper and paperboard, and the terms "filling" and "loading" refer to this process of incorporating pigments into the pulp during the manufacturing process. Filling and loading should be distinguished from pigment coating of paper products, which involves the application of a layer of pigment and adhesive to the surface of the sheet after it is formed.

When mineral pigments were first used in paper making they were considered as adulterants, but printers soon discovered that the filled sheet had better printing properties. This created a demand for pigment-filled papers and a search for brighter and better pigments. A wide variety of such filler pigments are presently used for making many grades of papers and boards, e.g., kaolin clays, calcium carbonate, titanium dioxide, talc, calcium sulfate, barium sulfate, calcium silicates, zinc sulfide, diatomaceous earth, and luminescent pigments. The estimated consumption for some of these pigments is given in Table 11.1.

Effects of Pigments on Paper Properties. Pigments are used in amounts varying from 2 to 40% of sheet weight, and the majority of papers contain between 4 and 15%. Suitable pigments improve brightness and opacity, basis weight, sheet density, softness, smoothness, finish, and ink absorption (printing) properties. Less pitch trouble is often encountered in paper stocks containing appreciable amounts of filler. Talc and other clays are particularly good for this purpose. On the other hand, mineral fillers lower internal sizing and invariably reduce those strength properties which depend primarily upon fiber-to-fiber bonding. The reduction of sheet strength and retention difficulties are perhaps the two greatest problems encountered in the use of fillers.

Optical Properties of Pigments and Papers. Several important properties of the major filler pigments are listed in Table 11.3.

The Kubelka-Munk theory relates light reflectance to the transmittance of translucent media. This theory has been applied to paper by Steel,[85] Judd,[86] and Van den Akker.[87] It suggests that the ability of a white pigment to improve the brightness of paper depends upon its surface area available for scattering light (the scattering coefficient) and upon its refractive index. Because the specific surface area increases with decreasing particle size, it is important that white pigments have a small average particle size. However, Sawyer [88] has shown that pigments have an optimum particle size of approximately 0.3 micron (μ) for scattering and reflecting light. The best pigment par-

TABLE 11.3. SOME TYPICAL PROPERTIES OF SEVERAL FILLER PIGMENTS

	Clay	Calcium Carbonate (precipitated)	Titanium Dioxide	Zinc Sulfide
Brightness, %	75-85	95	98	98
Refractive index	1.56	1.56	2.55-2.70	2.37
Average particle size, μ	0.5-1	0.2-0.5	0.3-0.35	0.3
Valley abrasion, mg wire loss	15-20	0.6-4	20-30	Low
Specific gravity	2.5-2.8	2.7-3.0	3.9-4.2	4.0
Solubility, gm/100 gm,				
in H_2O	Negligible	0.0014	Negligible	Negligible
in diluted acid	Negligible	Soluble	Negligible	Soluble
Cost, cents/lb	0.6-1	3-4	25-28	25-26

ticle size occurs at approximately one-half of the wavelength of light used for observation. For this reason many manufactured pigments have particle sizes in the 0.25 μ range. When two pigments have the same particle size, the one of higher refractive index will scatter more light.

White pigments which have brightness values greater than that of the pulp will increase the brightness of paper for two reasons: (1) the pigment in the sheet increases the surface area available for scattering light, and (2) the pigment decreases fiber-to-fiber bonding, which increases the external fiber surface area capable of scattering light.

The opacity of paper is determined in the following two ways:

$$R_0/R_\infty = \text{printing opacity}$$
$$R_0/R_{0.89} = \text{TAPPI opacity}$$

where $R_{0.89}$ is the light reflectance of a single layer of paper over a white body which has an absolute reflectance of 0.89 when the paper is in place, R_∞ is the reflectance of a pile of many layers of paper so thick that no change in reflectance occurs if the backing material is changed from black to white, and R_0 is the reflectance of a single layer of paper over a black cavity. Both expressions for opacity are related to the fundamental light scattering and absorption coefficients through the Kubelka-Munk equations. These relationships between light scattering and absorption coefficients indicate that the filler pigment of inferior

brightness can improve the opacity of paper by increasing the light absorption of the sheet. The more ideal situation is obtained when opacity is improved through larger light-scattering power and this is attained with high brightness small particle size pigments.

When paper is impregnated with waxes, oils, greases, etc., which make optical contact with fibers and fillers, much less of the incident light is scattered and the paper becomes transparent because of the similarity in refractive index of all components in the sheet. Under such conditions, fillers with low refractive indices, such as clay, calcium carbonate, talc, and calcium silicates, impart no improvement in opacity. However, higher refractive index pigments, such as titanium dioxide and zinc sulfide, do impart opacity to impregnated papers.

Pigment Retention. Retention of filler pigments presents several problems in paper making. Where circulating white water systems exist and lower levels of addition of inexpensive pigments are employed, filler retention may not be economically important. However, poor retention often coincides with marked two-sidedness of papers (a condition wherein the wire side of paper contains less pigment than the felt side). Where expensive pigments are used, poor retention is costly.

Many pigment properties affect retention; among them are solubility, specific gravity, particle shape and size, and degree of dispersion. Other additives in the system also markedly affect retention. Many of these properties have the obvious effects. The solubility of most pigments is negligible, but calcium sulfate is appreciably soluble and it has a negative solubility coefficient with temperature. Therefore, increases in temperature of the machine system may cause deposition of calcium sulfate in pipe lines. Calcium carbonate is soluble in acidic furnishes and should not be used under these conditions. The high specific gravity of barium sulfate (about 4.5) is said to cause poor retention of this pigment.

The addition of rosin size in itself has no effect on retention, but when alum is added the combination generally improves retention, probably by flocculation of the pigment.

Starches and gums used as beater adhesives have various effects on pigment retention. Starches which have been oxidized with sodium hypochlorite (the so-called starch gums) are particularly harmful to retention. This type of starch is seldom used as a beater adhesive, but it frequently gets into the stock preparation system because of its wide use as a size press adhesive and the recovery of broke containing such starch. The retention problem becomes particularly acute with titanium dioxide pigment, which is many times more expensive than clays and other pigments. Brill [89] studied various retention aids for titanium dioxide filler in the presence of oxidized cornstarch. He found that as little as 0.1 to 0.25% of such starch lowered retention markedly. Willets [90] has suggested that the effect of starch is due to its protective colloid action on the pigment dispersion. On the other hand, cationic starch improves retention of titanium dioxide even in the presence of 2% of oxidized starch. Brill and Hecklau [91] studied the effects of various processing factors on retention and optical efficiency of titanium dioxide. Severe agitation such as refining was found to reduce the retention of titanium dioxide substantially if starch is present, but not in the absence of starch. They also found that

starch has a greater detrimental effect on retention of titanium dioxide than of clay. The optical efficiency of titanium dioxide was seriously impaired by excessive flocculation such as obtained with acrylic acid-type flocculating agents. However, a slightly flocculated pigment was optically more efficient than a dispersed pigment.

The high cost of titanium dioxide and zinc sulfide pigments has led to the development of several polymer retention aids. Chemically, these materials are based on high molecular weight acrylamides. [92] In using such materials it is important that the filler and sufficient alum be added to the desired pH before the highly diluted acrylamide polymer solution (0.05%) is incorporated. Best retention is often obtained with 2 to 3% of alum based on the fiber and a pH of approximately 6. Earlier materials of this type based on sodium salts of polyacrylic acid were said to flocculate the cellulose fibers rather badly but the non-ionic acrylamides are claimed not to flocculate the cellulose fibers. [92]

Mechanisms of Pigment Retention. Three mechanisms of retention of fillers in paper have been described: (1) the filtration theory, whereby filler particles which are larger than the opening in the forming web are simply filtered out of the slurry; (2) the colloidal or coflocculation theory, wherein the filler particles and fibers coflocculate under the influence of long-range surface forces and the particles are then held to the fiber surface by similar forces; (3) the mechanical theory, wherein the filler particles are embedded within the fibers during beating or refining or are trapped in the fiber lumen. The last mechanism is believed to be relatively unimportant.

The nature of the paper-making process leads to the conclusion that filtration is probably an important part of the retention mechanism for any pigment. Relatively coarse pigments may be retained almost entirely by filtration. However, well-dispersed pigments are often poorly retained in the absence of flocculating agents. It is well known that such pigments may easily pass through the pores of filter papers. It is believed that the theories of stability of various colloids are directly applicable to filler retention. The application of these theories to the dispersion and coagulation of kaolin clays has been studied by Hemstock and Swanson [93] and by Holtzman.[94] Johnson [95] studied retention of titanium dioxide in nylon fiber mats and has concluded that the electric charge of both fiber and pigment particle is very important to retention of the pigment by the fiber surfaces. He also concluded that the factor which controls retention under the conditions of zero electrical charge on fiber and pigment is the rate at which the pigment particles can diffuse to the fiber surface. This work should have some interesting implications to retention of pigments in cellulosic fiber systems. It is clear, however, that the latter system is much more complex and involves other phenomena than the model fiber-pigment system studied by Johnson.

Filler Clay. Filler clay (china clay, kaolin) is a naturally occurring hydrated aluminum silicate mined from various deposits throughout the world. However, most of the filler clay used in the United States comes from the southeastern United States and England. Its chemical composition varies according to source but, in general, clay is comprised of about 45% SiO_2, 40% Al_2O_3, 13% bound water, and fractional percentages of Fe_2O_3, CaO, and MgO. The bound water is not removed at 110°C, but is removed on ignition at 800°C. In addition to the water of composition, clay may contain various small amounts of free moisture which normally does not amount to more than a few per cent.

The most important properties of filler clays are brightness and particle size. Typical values are presented in Table 11.3. The amount of grit depends upon the nature of the original deposit and the method of refining the clay.

There are three general methods of processing filler clays—air flotation, water washing, and centrifuging. Briefly, the raw clay as taken from the ground is dried, ground to small particles, and passed through a blast of air which separates the fine from the coarse particles. Water-washed clays are produced by suspending the ground clay in water, preferably with a good dispersing agent, and allowing it to settle slowly which removes the coarse, larger particles. The slurry of finer particle clay is then decanted to another basin where it is allowed to settle and the water is drawn off. The beneficiated clay is then removed and dried, ground, and shipped. This method is more expensive than air flotation, but it produces a better quality product. Centrifuging of the dispersed clay-water suspension permits more precise separation of the various particle sizes present in the natural clay. The finer particle size products made by this technique sell at a premium price.

The higher brightness kaolin clays have usually been subjected to a bleaching action consisting of treatment with sodium or zinc hydrosulfite and sulfuric acid or alum before the final settling and water removal. The finer particle size bleached clays are more frequently used as paper-coating pigments than as filler pigments.

Calcium Carbonate. Calcium carbonate filler pigment is produced either as a by-product in the causticization of spent cooking liquor in alkaline pulping processes or by treatment of milk of lime with carbon dioxide under controlled conditions of temperature and agitation. Smaller amounts of calcium carbonate are made by grinding pure limestone or chalk, or occasionally, oyster shells. Calcium carbonate is generally brighter than clay and when carefully prepared is an outstanding opacifying agent. This pigment has an alkaline reaction in water and when added in appreciable quantities to paper-making stock it makes the furnish alkaline. It is impossible to obtain rosin sizing in the presence of calcium carbonate filler. However, "Aquapel" or paraffin wax emulsions may be used under these circumstances. High water resistance is rarely obtained when calcium carbonate filler is used in paper.

Titanium Dioxide. Titanium dioxide is made principally from ilmenite ore, a black mineral containing 30 to 60% of titanium dioxide and several oxides of iron, and from titanium slags which contain 70 to 75% titanium dioxide and various oxides of iron, magnesium, and aluminum. Some titanium dioxide has been manufactured from rutile ore which contains 80 to 90% rutile titanium dioxide. The ilmenite is dried and milled to a fine powder and then dissolved in concentrated sulfuric acid. The iron and heavy metal compounds are removed by crystallization and titania crystals of either the anatase or rutile form are added to the evaporated concentrate and the solution is boiled to hydrolyze and precipitate hydrous titanium dioxide. The precipitate is thoroughly washed to remove the liquors, treated with various conditioning agents, and calcined to the desired pigment. The calcined product is classified by centrifugal means to remove oversized particles, then treated with surface-active agents and washed to remove water-soluble salts. The final product is then dried and milled to insure maximum dispersion of the pigment. The dried product is usually shipped in 50-pound bags.

Composite pigments containing barium or calcium sulfate and titanium dioxide were popular several years ago, but pure titanium dioxide pigments are now preferred.

The refractive index of the rutile form is higher (2.70) than that of the anatase form (2.55), but this difference is important only in papers that are to be impregnated with resins or waxes. The brightness of titanium dioxide is better than 98% and the particle size averages 0.3 μ. To ensure maximum dispersion and effectiveness of titanium dioxide, the pigment should be added to the pulp as early as possible in the beating cycle. Rosin size may also be added along with the pigment. However, if wet lap pulps are used and the defibering and beating cycle is short, the pigment should be slurried in water before addition to the pulp. It is also recommended that pigment be introduced before dyestuffs or coloring pigments are added. This facilitates better color matching. Alum should be added to the system only after thorough dispersion of the pigment is attained.

Titanium dioxide is expensive but it imparts high brightness and opacity at low percentages additions. The pigment is therefore often used in high-grade printing and writing papers where the usual addition is 1 to 5% based on the pulp. Opaque waxing papers require approximately 5% of pigment, air mail papers 9 to 10%, and very light-weight printing papers such as Bible paper require as high as 15% pigment based on the fiber.

Zinc Pigments. Several zinc compounds are also used as fillers, for example, zinc sulfide, lithopone, and composite zinc sulfide compounds. Lithopone is produced by the interaction of barium sulfide and zinc sulfate, coprecipitating zinc sulfide and barium sulfate in approximately a 30 to 70 ratio. The zinc sulfide pigments have excellent brightness and small particle size. Care must be exercised under low pH conditions to avoid the formation of black copper sulfide which lowers brightness of the paper. This reaction does not usually occur in the part of the pH range normally employed in rosin sizing of paper. Zinc pigments also have fungistatic properties and tend to keep the machine systems free of slime.

Miscellaneous Fillers. Numerous other fillers are used in smaller quantities than those mentioned above. Among these are calcium sulfite, which is somewhat soluble under low pH conditions, and calcium sulfate which is sold under various names such as crown filler, pearl hardening, pearl white, pearl finish, annaline, "Alabastine," and tissue filler. Magnesium silicates of various forms, such as talc, asbestine, and agalite, are also used. Most of these materials impart good brightness but they are not especially good for increasing opacity. The magnesium silicates are soft pigments which impart a soft, silky feel to papers in which they are used.

Asbestine is fibrous in nature and well retained in the sheet. Barium sulfate is also used as a filler, particularly in photographic papers. This pigment has a high brightness but also a high specific gravity (4.2 to 4.5) and it tends to settle to the bottom of the sheet as it is formed, making the paper two-sided. Diatomaceous earth, nearly pure silicon dioxide, is comprised of the skeletons of microscopic organisms. It is used for preventing the agglomeration of pitch particles and improving bulk and drainage properties of board furnishes. This pigment tends to be quite abrasive.

Calcium silicates of various kinds have been introduced recently for use as fillers in paper making. These may be purchased either in dry powdered form having a very small particle size (0.07μ) and high brightness $(+95\%)$, or the pigment may be produced in the paper stock by the addition of calcium chloride and sodium silicate. The latter method is called the fibrous filler process.

Sodium silicate has been used along with alum and/or lime for many years for generating a filler-type material within the paper stock. Addition of the sodium silicate early in the beating cycle will increase the rate of beating and refining, and it is claimed that paper so treated shows better printing and writing properties and improved retention of short fibers and fines. Probably, the increase in beating rate is produced by the alkaline nature of the usual sodium silicate employed for this purpose.

Luminescent pigments composed of zinc oxide-zinc sulfide-cadmium sulfide mixtures are used in the manufacture of certain map papers and marking tapes. In general, these pigments have rather large particle sizes and are expensive. Retention is therefore a major problem and there appears to be a trend to apply such pigments by coating processes.

Coloring of Paper Stock

It is not always appreciated that almost all papers are colored in some way during their manufacture. This is as true of so-called white papers as it is of those having more obvious tints and deeper colors. As a matter of fact, the production of white papers is often a more difficult problem of controlling the shade than the deeper colored products, because a small error in the measurement of one of the dyes is much more noticeable than an error of similar magnitude in a more deeply tinted or dyed paper.

In coloring of paper it is usually required that a submitted sample be matched not only with regard to color and shade but also with regard to fastness to light, acid and alkali stability, and bleaching materials with which the paper may come into contact. Fastness to light is often a particularly critical problem because the fastness of the colors may be masked by the changes in the fibers themselves. Several hundred dyes and colored pigments are used for the purpose and often mixtures of these materials must be employed to obtain the proper shade and meet use requirements. Thus, the coloring of paper is quite complex. It requires extensive knowledge about the coloring materials as well as their behavior with various kinds of fibers, the effects of mechanical refining on color development, water conditions, effects of rosin size and alum, various fillers and other non-fibrous additives, the stock preparation systems and paper machine conditions. Needless to say, the color man in any mill must have extensive knowledge and a keen sense of color perception and judgment.

The coloring materials may be classified into two general groups: (1) pigments, which are insoluble in water, and (2) dyes, which are generally soluble in water. It is said that over 90% of paper is dyed in the beater where good mixing and distribution can be obtained, but in recent years continuous stock preparation methods in some of the larger mills have eliminated beaters, necessitating color addition to stock chests and continuous coloring of the furnish at some point before the sheet-forming process. There are also considerable tonnages of paper which are surface stained by suitable methods of application, such as size press or calender coloring on the paper machine, or by other surface coloring as dipping of the dried sheet as a separate converting operation. This section of the chapter will be concerned with beater coloring of papers and boards.

Colored Pigments. Insoluble pigments used for coloring by the paper industry may be divided into five broad classifications:

(1) Mineral earths such as oxides (ferric oxide, red hematite, calcined ferric oxide clay mixtures), ocher (hydrated ferric oxide in various shades from yellow to brown, sometimes mixed with chrome yellow for more brilliant shades), and umbers (burnt ferric hydroxide, brown manganese silicate);

(2) Carbon black;

(3) Synthetic inorganic pigments such as chrome yellow, Prussian blue, and ultramarines;

(4) Synthetic organic pigments and lakes such as the anthraquinone and phthalocyanine pigments and azo dyes as pigments which have been precipitated on mineral materials such as barium, aluminum, lead, or calcium salts, or phosphotungstate or phosphomolybdate salts and basic dyes such as methyl and ethyl violet and the Victoria blues;

(5) Vegetable colors, which are little used today.

The oxidation-reduction dyes such as the vat and sulfur colors which are water-insoluble in the oxidized form but are soluble and substantive to cellulose in their reduced "leuco" form and are employed extensively in textile dyeing, but are little used for paper because of their greater expense and the trouble involved. However, some of the vat color pigments, particularly the anthroquinone blues and violets in highly dispersed form are used for tinting certain white papers where maximum light fastness is required. Other vat dye pigments and also the phthalocyanine pigments, the basic

color phosphotungstates and selected azo pigments and lakes, all in highly dispersed form, are employed for pastel and deeper shades of paper where fastness to light and other color-destroying influences are a major consideration.

Colored pigments in general behave as typical fillers and are affected by the same variables. The pigment should be added to the beater as early in the beating cycle as possible to ensure good dispersion and retention. Retention is improved by increasing the degree of refining of the stock and by the addition of alum. The white water from heavily pigmented papers is always highly colored. Generally speaking, pigments are very fast to light but duller in shade than many of the soluble dyes. They are also resistant to other chemicals and exhibit maximum fastness to bleeding. However, if used in excess, they do have a tendency to rub off or crock. The majority of pigments are not bleached by hypochlorite and where a bleachable waste stock is desired, such pigments should be avoided. When used in excessive quantities, colored pigments weaken the strength properties of papers just as mineral fillers do.

Dyes. The water-soluble dyes used for coloring paper are classified as acid dyes, basic dyes, and direct dyes. Each of the products in these groups has its own specific place in the paper industry. Chemically, there is considerable similarity between acid and direct dyes. They are compatible with each other under most operating conditions. Basic dyes, however, are chemically different from either of the other groups. While they may be employed in conjunction with acid and direct dyes to color paper, they are chemically incompatible in solution and should not be mixed together in this state.

Acid dyes are the sodium salts of color acids and have little or no affinity for cellulose fibers. Such dyes are available in practically all desired colors, and are characterized by high solubility in water and a wide range of fastness properties between individual members, some, for example, being quite fast to light while others are extremely fugitive. Because of the low affinity for cellulose fibers acid-dyed paper has minimum fastness to water bleeding and it is necessary to use rosin size and alum along with such dyes in order to obtain retention. The preferred order of addition is fiber, dye, rosin size, and alum, although occasionally the rosin size may be added prior to the addition of the dye. Because of their high water solubility the acid dyes are generally preferred for surface staining applications.

Basic dyes are the salts of color bases, and generally appear as the chlorides, hydrochlorides, sulfates, or oxalates. They are characterized by brilliance of shade, extremely high tinctorial value, considerably lower solubility in water than other water-soluble dyes, and poor fastness to light. Because of their pronounced affinity for highly lignified furnishes, such as groundwood and unbleached wood pulps, particular care must be exercised in their use to avoid graniting, or uneven dyeing of fibers. Whereas acid or direct dyes are generally added dry to the beater (but from solution for chest addition or continuous stock coloring), basic dyes should always be dissolved (in warm, not hot water) and added from fairly dilute solution. In the tinting of newsprint and other groundwood papers, the diluted basic dye solution should be added to the groundwood portion of the furnish and thoroughly mixed before blending in the unbleached sulfite or semibleached kraft, as otherwise basic dyes would be preferentially adsorbed by the latter, resulting in graniting.

There are some ten different chemical classes of basic dyes; hence considerable variation in both physical and dyeing properties among individual members may be expected. The foregoing remarks apply generally to dye types most widely employed in paper dyeing such as ethyl, methyl, and crystal violets, fuchsine and the Victoria blues (triphenylmethane or related types),

safranine (azine), and methylene blue (thiazine). These also show affinity for clay. The last two are perhaps unique in that they may be used on fully bleached pulps, even without rosin size or alum, whereas the others are not generally recommended and some, like the basic browns and chrysoidine (azo types), show no affinity whatever for purified cellulose. The rhodamines (xanthene types), which give the most brilliant pinks obtainable, in contrast to all other basic dyes exhibit fair fastness to light and Rhodamine B, containing a free carboxyl group, is the only basic dye which is compatible in solution with acid and direct dyes.

Direct dyes, like the acid dyes, are the sodium salts of colored acids. The distinguishing feature of direct dyes is that they will color cellulose fibers without the addition of dyeing assistants or mordants. They are probably the most versatile of the paper dyes and may be used on all types of fibers in both sized and unsized papers. Many such dyes are available and, in general, they possess desirable fastness properties. By proper selection the paper maker can achieve most required color properties. For example, color formulas may be developed which have either a high degree of sensitivity or excellent resistance to many chemicals. Direct dyes may be added to the beater, pulpers, mixing chests, or even at the headbox on the paper machine. The dye may be added to the beater in dry form but should be dissolved for other points of addition. However, because of the high affinity of these dyes for cellulosic fibers, good mixing must be obtained and hot concentrated solutions avoided to minimize graniting.

Where deeper shades are desired with direct dyes in unsized papers, it is a frequent practice to use common salt ($NaCl$) as a dyeing assistant. Such salt should be free of calcium and magnesium compounds as well as dirt and other insoluble material in order to prevent formation of compounds having lower brilliancy and color intensity.

The optimum temperature for dyeing with direct dyes on unsized paper is 140°F. The pH should be neutral or slightly alkaline, but if the pH is allowed to drift too far on the alkaline side, there may be a loss of color in the white water. Small amounts of alum may be used to adjust the pH and improve retention under these circumstances.

Recently, fluorescent dyes have been introduced rather widely in the paper industry. These compounds are also called optical whiteners, and optical bleaching agents. They have the property of absorbing light in the ultraviolet range and re-emitting it in the blue portion of the visible range, thereby making the paper appear whiter. Some reflectometers used in brightness testing may not indicate an increase in brightness where these fluorescent compounds are present but the Standard Brightness tester, properly adjusted, will register this property. The most convenient point of addition of fluorescent dyes is at the beater or wet end of the machine and the general practice is to dissolve the dye in water or use the solution form now being supplied and add it to the stock before the alum. Many such dyes are substantive and behave like direct dyes.

It should be remembered that dyes are specific chemical compounds whose colors are affected by a great many processing factors during the manufacture of paper. Changes in raw materials, degree of refining, wet pressing, or chemical control may cause substantial changes in the color of the paper. The accumulation of data on the individual characteristics of dyes and pigments and their performance in various grades of paper under a variety of conditions is a tremendous task, and new circumstances often require consultation with a specialist in the field. The paper mill technician may, however, by active participation in coloring problems, generally acquire the necessary experience to become proficient in handling those grades which his mill regularly manufactures.

CONTROL OF STOCK PREPARATION

It has often been said that "paper is made in the beater." Many years ago the beater man was one of the most important members of the paper-making team because only he, through long years of practice and experience, could determine by feeling, squeezing, and otherwise handling the pulp, when it had been beaten and refined to the desired degree for making a specific grade of paper. Today, the industry is more inclined to depend upon various mechanical devices and chemical analyses for such control. In some instances this represents an improvement and in others, the older methods may be superior.

For many years the degree of beating or refining of the pulp has been determined from the rate at which water drains through a given weight or volume of the pulp held on a screen. This may be done, for example, with the Williams instrument by timing the flow of a definite quantity of pulp suspension through a screen of fixed character at a given temperature. The Schopper-Riegler freeness tester and the Canadian freeness tester measure the drainage of the beaten pulp from the number of milliliters of water which are collected as the pulp drains. The freeness tester consists of a chamber of slightly more than one-liter capacity with a bottom screen and metal support. Below this chamber a funnel is attached which has a small bottom outlet of precise size and a side outlet which is considerably larger. If the water from the pulp sample held on the screen drains slowly, the level of water never reaches the side outlet and all passes through the bottom outlet and is discarded. However, less beating causes the stock to drain more rapidly, and a part of the water reaches the side outlet and is collected and measured in a graduated cylinder. The number of milliliters so collected under standard temperature conditions is termed the "freeness" of the pulp. The apparatus and test are described in detail in TAPPI Standard T 27 m-58.

One of the weaknesses of the freeness test as described above is the difficulty of interpreting and applying the results. A low freeness value may result either from splitting and fraying long fibers, which still essentially retain their length, or from cutting and formation of much fines and debris. Fiber fines and debris have a major effect on decreasing the freeness test but a comparatively minor effect on strength properties of papers. Therefore, it must be concluded that the freeness test is only useful for control purposes of the refining of a given type of pulp over a comparatively narrow range of beating or refining conditions.

Another method for estimation of the effect of beating on stock involves determination of "drainage time" with a standard British handsheet machine. These tests and the calculations are covered in TAPPI Standard T 221 m-51.

A much better characterization of pulps may be obtained from a drainage test performed under conditions of better control of the variables. Work on such an instrument has been carried out in the laboratories of The Institute of Paper Chemistry and a suitable commercial instrument is available.

A number of other methods for obtaining information on the effects of beating have been suggested. Determination of changes in fiber length distribution by a pulp classifier of either the type recommended by Clark [96,97] or the Bauer-McNett classifier [98] is useful for this purpose. Both of these instruments subject a sample of the beaten and refined pulp to a screening operation and collect the fiber fractions on various screens between 14 and 100 mesh. The fractions are collected, dried, and weighed. The details of the method are presented in TAPPI suggested method T 233 sm-53. Direct measurement of average fiber length and fiber length distribution may also be made by projection of the magnified image of a pulp sample onto a suitable screen followed by direct measurement of

fiber dimensions. This technique is, of course, much more tedious but yields reliable information about a given pulp sample. The equipment and method are described in TAPPI suggested method T 244 sm-60. The coarseness of pulp fibers, defined as the weight per unit length, has also been suggested for estimation of the effect of beating and refining on fiber splitting. (See TAPPI suggested method T 234 sm-60.)

Much more elaborate characterization of pulps for the intelligent direction of pulping research and the genetic production of tree species having better fiber properties, requires many more tests [3]. A great deal remains to be learned in this field of paper making.

Handsheets, of course, can be made rather quickly from a batch of beaten pulp and often this gives a meaningful indication of the quality of paper that will come from the paper machine. It is, of course, not possible to duplicate machine conditions with handsheet equipment. Some of the operations of recirculation of white water, forming and pressing, and drying of the paper can be simulated, but these operations are much different from those carried out on a complex paper machine. For these and other reasons, handsheet preparation is not a complete answer to control of stock preparation. In many mills controlled tests in the beater room are kept to a minimum. Three of the more common variables determined are color, acidity, and freeness.

Color Control

The specifications for many papers require close adherence to a given color standard. Even though raw materials are uniform, variations creep in which call for constant vigilance. Comparison of stock being colored with stock known to give the proper shade serves as a fair guide, particularly when carried out by an experienced color man. However, allowance must be made for the amount of water present, the degree of beating and refining of the stock, the amount of alum present, and the degree of acidity. More precise comparisons may be made by drying a handsheet made from the stock in question and comparing it with a standard handsheet prepared from previous stock which was satisfactorily colored.

Control of Acidity (pH)

The considerable amount of alum used in the majority of paper-making operations and the recirculation of white water systems requires that control of acidity and pH be maintained as carefully as possible. The amount of alum, of course, is one of the most important factors in sizing, filler retention, color, and stock freeness. Control of alum addition is generally approached through measurement of the pH value which is defined as the reciprocal of the logarithm of the hydrogen ion concentration. Modern mills use potentiometers for determining the stock pH at various points and it is becoming common practice to employ recording pH meters. However, colorimetric methods for determination of pH are useful when a potentiometer is not available. They are sufficiently accurate for control work in the absence of bleaching chemicals. Wooding [99] has written a good discussion of the principles of pH determination and control. In most mill systems the most important point at which to measure pH is immediately before, or in, the headbox of the paper machine. It is here that automatic controls are usually installed.

It should be emphasized that determination of pH does not tell the complete story about the acidity and alum in the paper-making system. At low pH ranges in the neighborhood of 4.0 to 4.5 considerable buffering capacity may exist and it may become desirable to determine total acidity by an alkaline titration method. Where the total acidity is found to be excessively high, sodium aluminate or sodium phosphoaluminate may be used along with alum to decrease total acidity to a more favorable range.

Instrumentation of the stock preparation system is described in Chapter 15.

REFERENCES

1. Clark, J. d'A., *in* Ott, E., and Spurlin, H. M., "Cellulose and Cellulose Derivatives," Vol. II, p. 634, New York, Interscience Publishers, Inc., 1954.
2. Higgins, H. G., and Harrington, J. K., "The Structure and Properties of Paper. V. The Problem of More Efficient Beating," *Australian Pulp and Paper Ind., Tech. Assoc. Proc.*, **9**, 71, 88 (1955).
3. Swanson, J. W., and Jones, E. J., "Factors which Affect Strength Properties of Paper," *Pulp Paper Mag. Can.*, **63**, No. 5, T251 (May, 1962).
4. Van den Akker, J. A., "The Elastic and Rheological Properties of Paper-making Pulps. Some Problems to be Met in Developing an Analytical Approach to the Subject," *Tappi*, **33**, No. 8, 398 (August, 1950).
5. Nissan, A. H., "Fundamentals of Adhesion from Molecular Forces in Cellulose," *Tappi*, **42**, No. 12, 928 (December, 1959).
6. Swanson, J. W., "Beater Adhesives and Fiber to Fiber Bonding—the Need for Further Research," *Tappi*, **39**, No. 5, 257 (May, 1956).
7. Van den Akker, J. A., "Structural Aspects of Bonding," *Tappi*, **42**, No. 12, 940 (December, 1959).
8. Kallmes, O., "Distribution of the Constituents across the Wall of Unbleached Spruce Sulfite Fibers," *Tappi*, **43**, No. 2, 143 (February, 1960); Lange, P. W., "The Distribution of the Chemical Constituents throughout the Cell Wall," *in* Bolam's "Fundamentals of Papermaking Fibers," Transactions of the symposium held at Cambridge, September, 1957, p. 147, Kenley, England, Brit. Paper and Board Makers' Assoc., Inc., 1958.
9. Lyne, L. M., and Gallay, W., "The Effect of Drying and Heating on the Swelling of Cellulose Fibers and Paper Strength," *Tappi*, **33**, No. 9, 429 (September, 1950).
10. Wink, W., "The Effect of Relative Humidity and Temperature on Paper Properties," *Tappi*, **44**, No. 6, 171, 178 (June, 1961).
11. Lewis, H. F., and Gilbertson, L. A., "The Effect of Temperature on the Beating of Rag Stock." *Paper Trade J.*, **100**, No. 15, 37 (April 11, 1935).
12. Nakano, N., "Studies on Beating," *Papier-Fabr.*, **30**, No. 22, 337 (May 29, 1932).
13. Kress, O., and Bialkowsky, H., "Some Chemical and Physical Observations on Hydration," *Paper Trade J.*, **93**, No. 20, 35 (Nov. 12, 1931).
14. Bletzinger, J. C., "Effect of Acetylation on Water-binding Properties of Cellulose," *Ind. Eng. Chem.*, **35**, 474 (April, 1943).

15. Aiken, W., "Effect of Acetylation on Water-binding Properties of Cellulose," *Ind. Eng. Chem.*, **35**, 1206 (November, 1943).

16. Harrison, J. J., "Effect of Esterification of Pulp Fibers upon Strength Properties, Hygroscopicity and Hygroexpansivity of Paper," *Paper Trade J.*, **119**, No. 5, 28 (Aug. 3, 1944).

17. McKenzie, A. W., and Higgins, H. G., "The Structure and Properties of Paper. III. Significance of Swelling and Hydrogen Bonding in Interfibre Adhesion," *Australian J. Appl. Sci.*, **6**, No. 2, 208 (June, 1955).

18. Walecka, J. A., "An Investigation of Low Degree of Substitution Carboxymethylcelluloses," *Tappi*, **39**, No. 7, 458 (July, 1956).

19. Talwar, K. K., "A Study of Improved Strength in Paper Made from Low-substituted Carboxymethylcellulose Pulps," *Tappi*, **41**, No. 5, 207 (May, 1958).

20. Ward, K., "Chemical Modification of Papermaking Pulps," *Tappi*, **43**, No. 1, 54 (January, 1960).

21. Strachan, J., "Hydration of Cellulose in Paper Making," *Brit. Paper and Board Makers' Assoc. Proc. Tech. Sect.*, **6**, No. 2, 139, 170 (1926); **7**, No. 1, 48 (1926).

22. Campbell, W. B., and Pidgeon, Lloyd M., "Hydration of Cellulose by Beating," *Pulp Paper Mag. Can.*, **29**, No. 6, 185 (February 6, 1930).

23. Campbell, W. B., "A Physical Theory of the Beating Process," *Paper Trade J.*, **95**, No. 8, 29 (Aug. 25, 1932).

24. Campbell, W. B., "The Cellulose-water Relationship," Bulletin 84, Forest Service, Dept. Int. Canada, 1933.

25. Campbell, W. B., "Hydration and Beating of Cellulose Pulps," *Ind. Eng. Chem.*, **26**, No. 2, 218 (February, 1934).

26. Wollwage, J. C., "The Flocculation of Papermaking Fibers," *Paper Trade J.*, **108**, No. 12, 41 (March 23, 1939); No. 13, 25 (March 30, 1939); *Tech. Assoc., Papers*, **22**, 578 (1939).

27. Erspamer, A., "The Flocculation and Dispersion of Paper-making Fibers," *Paper Trade J.*, **110**, No. 24, 33 (June 13, 1940); *Tech. Assoc. Papers*, **23**, 132 (1940).

28. Mason, S. G., "The Flocculation of Pulp Suspensions and the Formation of Paper," *Tappi*, **33**, No. 9, 440 (September, 1950); *Tappi*, **37**, No. 11, 494 (November, 1954).

29. Turk, John, "Variables Affecting Sheet Formation," Master's Dissertation, Appleton, Wis., The Institute of Paper Chemistry, 1941.

30. Van den Akker, J. A., "A Note on the Theory of Fiber-Fiber Bonding in Paper; the Influence on Paper Strength of Drying by Sublimation," *Tappi*, **35**, No. 1, 13 (January, 1952).

31. Marchessault, R. H., "The Effect of Freeze-drying on the Physical Properties of Cellulose Fibres and Paper," Doctor's Dissertation, Montreal, Quebec, McGill University, 1954; *Svensk Papperstid.*, **59**, No. 24, 859 (Dec. 31, 1956).

32. Broughton, G., and Wang, J. P., "The Mechanical Properties of Paper. III," *Tappi*, **38**, No. 7, 412 (July, 1955).

33. Lyne, L. M., and Gallay, W., "Studies in the Fundamentals of Wet-rub Strength," *Tappi*, **37**, No. 12, 698 (December, 1954); *Pulp Paper Mag. Can.*, **55**, No. 11, 128 (October, 1954).

34. Lyne, L. M., and Gallay, W., "Measurement of Wet-web Strength," *Tappi*, **37**, No. 12, 694 (December, 1954); *Pulp Paper Mag. Can.*, **55**, No. 11, 135 (October, 1954).

35. Lyne, L. M., and Gallay, W., "Fiber Properties and Fiber-Water Relationships in Relation to the Strength and Rheology of Wet Webs," *Tappi*, **37**, No. 12, 581, 661 (December, 1954); *Pulp Paper Mag. Can.*, **55**, No. 13, 158 (December, 1954).

36. Swanson, J. W., "The Effects of Natural Beater Additives on Paper-making Fibers," *Tappi*, **33**, No. 9, 451 (September, 1950).

37. LeCompte, T. R., U.S. patent 2,069,766 (Feb. 9, 1937); U.S. patent 2,088,479 (July 27, 1937).

38. Swanson, J. W., "Karaya Gum," *Tappi*, **40**, No. 8, 164A (August, 1957).

39. Barber, E. J., "CMC as a Paper Machine Additive," *Tappi*, **44**, No. 2, 179A (February, 1961).

40. Hamerstrand, G. E., Hofreiter, B. T., Mehltretter, C. L., Schulze, W. E., and Kay, D. J., "Dialdehyde Starch Retention by Use of Cationic Starch for High Wet-strength Paper," *Tappi*, **44**, No. 6, 430 (June, 1961).

41. Schmalz, A. C., Handling of Polyamide-type Wet-strength Brokes," *Tappi*, **44**, No. 4, 275 (April, 1961).

42. Trout, P. E., "The Mechanism of the Improvement of the Wet Strength of Paper by Polyethylenimine," *Tappi*, **34**, No. 12, 539 (December, 1951).

43. Nagel, S. C., "Paper Products Containing Phenolic Resins Added at the Wet End," *Tappi*, **40**, No. 4, 189A (April, 1957).

44. Reynolds, W. F., "Some Recent Research on 'Accostrength' Resin 2386," *Tappi*, **44**, No. 2, 177A (February, 1961).

45. Linke, W. F., "Polyacrylamide as a Stock Additive," *Tappi*, **45**, No. 4, 326 (April, 1962).

46. Thompson, J. O., Swanson, J. W., and Wise, L. E., "Hemicelluloses and Arabogalactans as Beater Adhesives," *Tappi*, **36**, No. 12, 534 (December, 1953).

47. Russell, C. R., Buchanan, R. A., Rist, C. E., Hofreiter, B. T., and Ernst, A. J., "Cereal

Pulps. I. Preparation and Application of Cross-linked Cereal Xanthates in Paper Products," *Tappi*, **45**, No. 7, 557 (July, 1962).

48. Yllner, S., and Enstrom, B., *Svensk Papperstid.*, **59**, No. 6, 229 (March 31, 1956); **60**, No. 15, 549 (August 15, 1957).

49. Farin, W. G., "How to Prepare and Proportion Starch to the Paper Machine Furnish," *Paper Trade J.*, **145**, No. 11, 36 (December 18, 1961).

50. Houtz, H. H., "Colloidal Differentiation of Starches," Doctor's Dissertation, Appleton, Wis., The Institute of Paper Chemistry, 1941; *Paper Trade J.*, **113**, No. 6, 32 Aug. 7, 1941); *Tech. Assoc. Papers*, **24**, 131 (1941).

51. Casey, J. P., "Beater Sizing with Starch," *Paper Ind.*, **26**, No. 10, 1277 (January, 1945).

52. Goldstein, A. M., "Gums as Wet-end Additives in Paper," *Tappi*, **40**, No. 9, 180A (September, 1957).

53. Cushing, M. L., "An Evaluation of Combinations of Starches and Natural Gums as Papermaking Aids," *Tappi*, **41**, No. 7, 155A (July, 1958).

54. "Wet Strength in Paper and Paperboard," TAPPI Monograph Series No. 13, p. 38, New York, Technical Association of the Pulp and Paper Industry, 1954. See also Maxwell, C. S., and Reynolds, W. F., *Tech. Assoc. Papers*, **31**, 112 (1948).

55. Thode, E. F., Swanson, J. W., Kurath, S. F., and Hoffman, G. R., "Mechanism of Retention of Wet-strength Resins. I. Kinetic Studies of Melamine Resin Adsorption," *Tappi*, **42**, No. 3, 170 (March, 1959).

56. Kurath, S. F., Chu, C. Y., and Swanson, J. W., "Mechanism of Retention of Wet-strength Resins. II. Rate Studies on the Adsorption of Urea-formaldehyde Resin," *Tappi*, **42**, No. 3, 175 (March, 1959).

57. Becher, J. J., Hoffman G. R. and Swanson, J. W., "Mechanism of Retention of Wet-strength Resins. III. The Rate-controlling Step in the Retention Process," *Tappi*, **44**, No. 4, 296 (April, 1961).

58. Wilfinger, H., "Manufacture of Wet-strength Papers by Means of Beater Additives with Special Reference to the Effects of Polyethylenimine," *Papier*, **2**, No. 15/16, 265 (August, 1948).

59. Stafford, R. W., Thomas, W. M., Williams, E. F., and Woodbury, N. T., "Identification of Melamine and Urea Resins in Wet-strength Paper," *Paper Trade J.*, **120**, No. 16, 51 (April 19, 1945).

60. McClane, J. H., "Future of Rosin Size in Paper," *Paper Trade J.*, **145**, No. 4, 24 (Jan. 23, 1961); *Paper Mill News*, **84**, No. 3, 12 (Jan. 16, 1961).

61. Ernlund, J. H., "A New Concept in Paper Sizing—Oil-Repellent Size," *Tappi*, **40**, No. 3, 90A (March, 1957).

62. Ekwall, Per, and Bruun, H. H., "Surface Chemical Studies on the Formation of Alumium Soaps. I. The Interaction between Aluminum Ions and Rosin Acid Monolayers," *Chem. Scand.*, **9**, 412 (1955); "II. The Product of the Reaction between Aluminum Ions and Monolayers of Tall Oil Rosin Acid," *Chem. Scand.*, **9**, 424 (1955).

63. Ekwall, Per, and Bruun, H. H., "Surface Chemical Studies of the Conditions of Rosin Sizing," *Tappi*, **37**, No. 7, 303 (July, 1954).

64. Guide, R. G., "A Study of the Sodium Aluminate-Sodium Abietate Size Precipitates. I. The Composition of the Size Precipitates," *Tappi*, **42**, No. 9, 734 (September, 1959). "II. The Relationship between the Physicochemical Properties of the Size Precipitate and Sizing," *Tappi*, **42**, No. 9, 740 (September, 1959).

65. Thode, E. F., and Htoo, Shwe, "Surface Properties of Rosin Size Precipitate. III. Electrokinetic Properties of Rosin-sized Wood Pulp Fibers," *Tappi*, **38**, No. 12, 705 (December, 1955).

66. Thode, E. F., Gorham, J. F., Kumler, R. W., and Woodberry, N. T., "Surface Properties of Rosin Size Precipitate. IV. Influence of the Electrokinetic Potential of Rosin Size Precipitate on Sizing Efficiency," *Tappi*, **38**, No. 12, 710 (December, 1955).

67. Cobb, R. M. K., and Lowe, D., "The Coordinate Role of Alum in the Sizing of Paper," *Tappi*, **38**, No. 2, 49 (February, 1955).

68. Yiannos, P. N., "Molecular Reorientation of Some Fatty Acids when in Contact with Water," *J. Colloid Sci.*, **17**, No. 4, 334 (April, 1962).

69. Unpublished work. The Institute of Paper Chemistry, 1962.

70. Samuelson, S., and Ellefsen, G., "Sizing of Paper. The Dependence of Size Resistance on the Temperature and Moisture Relationships of the Paper Sheet during Drying," *Papir J.*, **31**, 23 (1943).

71. Glover, G. F., "Some Experiments on Sizing," *Brit. Paper and Board Makers' Assoc., Proc. Tech. Sect.*, **38**, No. 3, 515, 528 (December, 1957).

72. Back, E., "The Mechanism of Pulp Resin Accumulation at Solid Surfaces," *Svensk Papperstid.*, **63**, No. 17, 556 (1960).

73. Gustafsson, C., Tammela, V., and Kahila, S., "On Pitch Troubles Caused by Sulfite Pulp," *Paper Timber* (Finland), **34**, 121 (Special number **4a**, 1952).

74. Gustafsson, C., Tammela, V., and Lindh, T., "Pitch Troubles Caused by Sulfite Pulp. II," *Paper Timber* (Finland), **36**, No. 6, 269 (1954); "III. Effect of Wood Storage on the Amounts of Pitch Deposited on a Copper Surface," *ibid.*, **38**, No. 4, 179 (1956); "IV. The Influence of Barking and Storage on Land and in Water on Depositable Pitch," *ibid.*, **39**, No. 5, 277 (1957); "V. The Influence of Cooking Conditions and Cooking Degree of the Pulp on Depositable Pitch from Sulfite Pulp, *ibid.*, **40**, No. 4, 239 (1958).

75. Back, E., "Pitch Control by Combined Alkali and Aluminum Sulfate Addition. Some Principles in Controlling Pitch Troubles," *Svensk Papperstid.*, **59**, No. 9, 319 (1956).

76. Tester, J. W., "Stock Aeration Effects," *Tappi*, **44**, No. 4, 148A (April, 1961).

77. Ross, S., "The Inhibition of Foaming," Troy, New York, Rensselaer Polytechnic Institute, May, 1950.

78. Swanson, J. W., "The Science of Chemical Additives in Paper Making," *Tappi*, **44**, No. 1, 142A (January, 1961).

79. Boadway, J. D., "Gas in Paper-making Stock," *Pulp Paper Mag. Can.*, **57**, No. 3, 185, 194 (Convention issue, 1956).

80. "How the Vorvac System Works," *Pulp Paper Mag. Can.*, **57**, No. 2, 81 (February, 1956).

81. Smith, J. A., and Stewart, J. C., "The Deculator-Cleaner Process," *Tappi*, **39**, No. 3, 198A (March, 1956).

82. Holland, H. T., "Foam Measurement," *Tappi*, **37**, No. 10, 172 (October, 1954).

83. Hollaender, H., "Simplified Test Method for Foam-suppressing Agents in the Paper Industry," *Das Papier*, **9**, No. 9/10, 220 (May, 1955).

84. Gavelin, G., "Some Effects of Gases on Properties of Fibre Suspensions," *Pulp Paper Mag. Can.*, **55**, No. 3, 191 (Convention issue, 1954).

85. Steele, F. A., "The Optical Characteristics of Paper. I. The Mathematical Relationships between Basis Weight, Reflectance, Contrast Ratio, and Other Optical Properties," *Paper Trade J.*, **100**, No. 12, 37 (March 1, 1935); *Paper Trade J.*, **104**, No. 8, 157 (Feb. 25, 1937).

86. Judd, Deane B., "The Dependence of Reflectance and Opacity on Thickness. Relation between Ratio and Printing Opacity," *Paper Trade J.*, **101**, No. 5, 40 (Aug. 1, 1935); *J. Res. Nat. Bur. Std.*, **19**, 287 (1937).

87. Van den Akker, J. A., "Scattering and Absorption of Light in Paper and Other Diffusing Media," *Tappi*, **32**, No. 11, 498 (November, 1949).

88. Sawyer, R. H., "The Basic Principles Involved in the Preparation of Pigments," *J. Appl. Phys.*, **13**, No. 10, 596 (October, 1942).

89. Brill, H. C., "An Evaluation of Various Beater Retention Aids for Titanium Dioxide Filler in the Presence of Chlorinated Starch," *Tappi*, **38**, No. 9, 522 (September, 1955).

90. Willets, W. R., "Factors Affecting Retention," *Paper Trade J.*, **101**, No. 13, 81 (Sept. 26, 1955); "Effect of Beating and Pigmentation on Sheet Properties," *Paper Trade J.*, **102**, No. 3, 36 (Jan. 16, 1936).

91. Brill, H. C., and Hecklau, F. L., "Titanium Dioxide Retention," *Tappi*, **43**, No. 4, 229A (April, 1960).

92. Reynolds, J. F., and Ryan, R. F., "A New Polyacrylamide-type Flocculant for Improved Filler Retention," *Tappi*, **40**, No. 11, 918 (November, 1957).

93. Hemstock, G. A., and Swanson, J. W., "Clay Deflocculation and Its Effect on the Flow Properties of Clay Slips," *Tappi*, **39**, No. 1, 35 (January, 1956).

94. Holtzman, W., "The Application of the Verwey-Overbeek Theory to the Stability of Kaolinite-water Systems," Doctor's Dissertation, Appleton, Wis., The Institute of Paper Chemistry, 1959; *J. Colloid Sci.*, **17**, 363 (1962).

95. Johnson, R. C., "A Study of Particle Retention in Relation to the Structure of a Fibrous Mat," Doctor's Dissertation, Appleton, Wis., The Institute of Paper Chemistry, 1962.

96. Clark, J. d'A., "Fiber Length and Beating Control by Classification," *Tappi*, **38**, No. 11, 702 (November, 1955).

97. Reed, Arthur E., and Clark, J. d'A., "An Instrument for the Rapid Fractionation of Pulp," *Tappi*, **33**, No. 6, 294 (June, 1950).

98. Butler, W. T., "The Use of the Bauer-McNett Fiber Classifier," *Pulp Paper Mag. Can.*, **49**, No. 3, 133 (February, 1948).

99. Wooding, W., "pH Measurement and Control," *Paper Trade J.*, **135**, No. 13, 19 (Sept. 26, 1952).

100. Emerton, H. W., "Fundamentals of the Beating Process," Kenley, The British Paper and Board Industry Research Association, 1957.

101. MacLaurin, D. J., and Whalen, J. F., "Effects of Wet Pressing on Sheet Properties," *Tappi*, **37**, No. 12, 608 (December, 1954).

102. Waters, V. F., "Characteristics of Water," *in* "Water Technology in the Pulp and Paper Industry," TAPPI Monograph Series, No. 18, p. 4, 1957.

103. Shotwell, J. S. G., and Henderson, A. D., "Water Technology in the Pulp and Paper Industry," TAPPI Monograph Series, No. 18, p. 16, 1957.

104. Appling, J. W., "Slimes in Mill Systems and Their Control," *in* "Microbiology of Pulp and Paper," TAPPI Monograph Series, No. 15, p. 100, 1955.

105. *See* Reference 104, p. 112.

106. Kerr, R. W., "Chemistry and Industry of Starch," 2nd ed., p. 18, New York, Academic Press, 1950.

107. Cushing, M. L., and Schuman, K. R., "Fiber Attraction and Interfiber Bonding—the Role of Polysaccharide Additives," *Tappi*, **42**, No. 12, 1006 (December, 1959).

108. Karna, A., and Nordman, Lars, "The Use of Mannogalactan Vegetable Gums in the Paper Industry," *Paperi Puu*, **40**, No. 2, 45 (February, 1958).

109. Klinger, L. L., "What You Should Know about Flotation Saveall Design and Operation," *Paper Trade J.*, **142**, No. 35, 26 (Sept. 1, 1958); A.B.I.P.C., **29**, 736.

CHAPTER 12

The Paper Machine

Sherwood G. Holt

Consolidated Papers, Inc.

The "paper machine" includes the paper-making machine itself and various auxiliary equipment located in the immediate area. This includes the paper-machine drives, heat-recovery equipment, winders, coaters and some portions of the stock system. Descriptions are given of the more general forms of machines and equipment, together with the principles of operation and some information on methods of operation. It has been found impractical to include more than passing mention of some special production equipment. References are given at the end of the chapter to more detailed sources of information on various topics.

TYPES OF PAPER MACHINES

Paper machines are generally divided into two main types, (1) cylinder machines and (2) Fourdrinier machines. As several variations of these basic types have been worked out, further classification is necessary. Fourdrinier machines are characterized at the wet end by a headbox which delivers stock to a moving woven-wire belt which is in turn supported by table rolls, suction boxes, and other special equipment designed to control the rate and method of drainage through the wire. Cylinder machines, in general, make use of a cylindrical structure which supports the forming wire mesh. Stock is applied to the outside of the roll by means of a vat, nozzle, or headbox and the rate of drainage through the wire is governed by the pressure of the applied stock and vacuum applied inside the roll and gravity forces. It can generally be assumed that the basic difference between the Fourdrinier and cylinder type of machine is in the method of supporting the forming mesh and the methods used to control drainage through the forming medium.

Fourdrinier Machines

A Fourdrinier machine is characterized by the use of a wire mesh belt of web which is supported by a series of rolls and other drainage control devices in a horizonal position during the draining process. A typical Fourdrinier paper machine is shown in Figure 12.1.

The essential parts are these:

(1) A flowspreader system for spreading the flow of stock from its delivery pipe into a stream equal to the width of the machine;

(2) A headbox or flow control system to improve the uniformity of stock flow, control the level of stock turbulence and to level out variations in consistency over a short time period, while flowing the stock onto the Fourdrinier table at the proper spouting velocity;

(3) The Fourdrinier table section consisting of the hardware necessary to support and run the Fourdrinier wire, and pro-

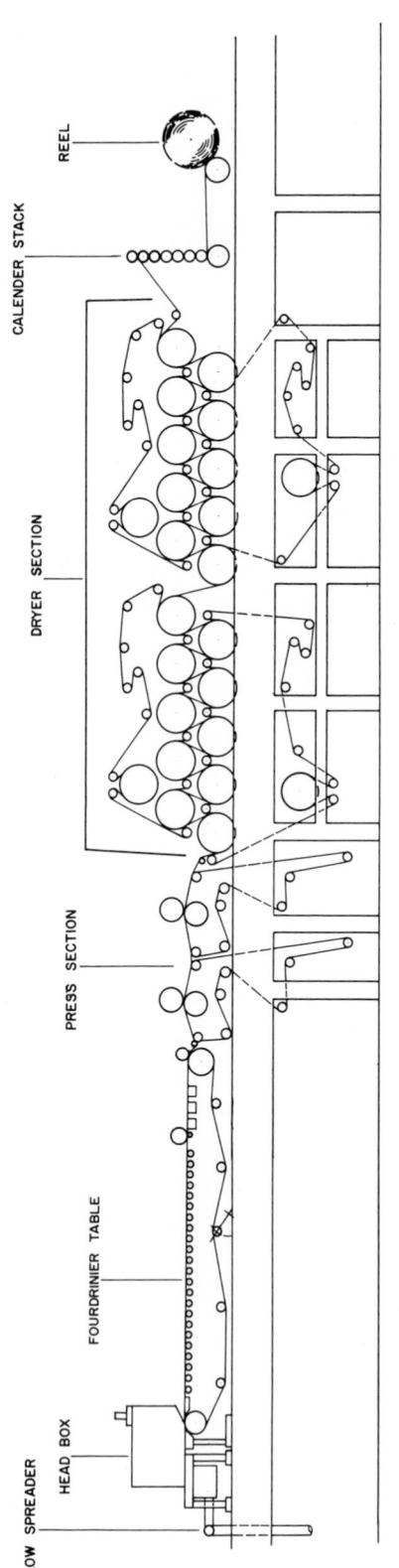

Fig. 12.1. Fourdrinier paper machine. (*Courtesy Beloit Corp.*)

vide drainage through it by means of table rolls, foils, deflectors, suction boxes, suction rolls, and other associated equipment;

(4) A press section to receive the wet web of paper removed from the Fourdrinier wire onto felts which carry it through the press rolls and reduce its moisture content by mechanical pressure and air flow;

(5) The dryer section consisting of a series of heated cylinders or dryers with associated air handling system, felts, etc. to remove the remaining moisture in the sheet by means of heat and vapor transfer;

(6) Calender stack—a series of rolls which is used to apply very high ironing pressures to the dry sheet of paper, and which has the effect of controlling the sheet bulk (or caliper), smoothness, and other characteristics;

(7) Reel—a winder for winding up a dry paper into large rolls which are usually rewound in further converting operations.

The Fourdrinier machine described above may be considered a typical machine which could be used for making a wide range of products ranging from heavy food board to light tissue. Many variations have been worked out which are particularly adapted to special grades and types of paper. A few of these will be described; however, it should be recognized that there is a noticeable trend toward specialized types of paper-making devices for various purposes.

Yankee Machines

A specialized type of paper machine has been developed for making light-weight sanitary paper such as toilet and facial tissue, toweling, and "wadding" (see Figure 12.2). These machines have relatively short Fourdrinier wires because of the low basis weight of the product and the free draining properties of the stock. As a result of this they also operate at relatively high speeds in order to turn out reasonable tonnages of product.

The sheet is pressed in the normal manner. The dryer section, although it may contain some conventional dryers, is different

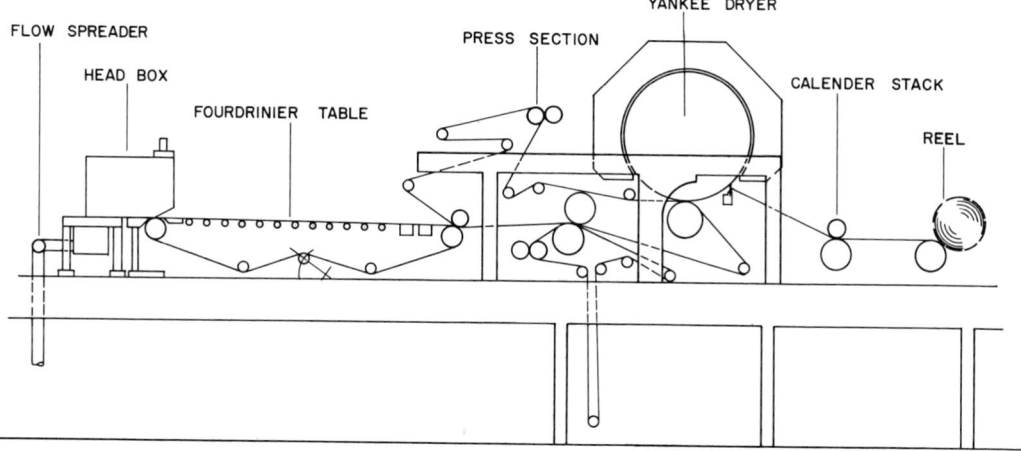

Fig. 12.2. Yankee paper machine.

in that it makes use of a "Yankee" or creping dryer. A Yankee dryer is a large cylinder, 10 to 16 feet in diameter, to which the sheet is applied by a special "pressure roll." The pressure roll serves in effect as the last roll in the press section and is particularly effective because it is working against the hot surface of the Yankee. The intimate contact achieved by the sheet against the Yankee dryer also increases the rate of drying. Yankee dryers with suitable high-velocity air hoods achieve drying rates 10 to 15 times as high per square foot of area as those obtainable in conventional dryers.

The sheet is removed from the dryer by a doctor blade which performs the special operation of creping the sheet, which is highly desirable in sanitary paper products. A creped sheet, in general, has high absorbency, a soft pliable feel and a high bulk. Although the sheet is usually creped at a relatively low moisture content (approximately 4%) it may be creped off at a higher moisture level and subsequently dried over a series of conventional dryers. This method is particularly applicable to toweling where extreme crepe is not necessary and where drying would be severely limited if it had to be accomplished on a single Yankee dryer. The size of Yankee dryers is limited by fabricating methods and shipping facilities from the point of manufacture to the mill.

A similar machine arrangement is used in the manufacture of "MG finish" papers. This refers to the "machine gloss" finish achieved by drying the paper to the point where it can be removed from the Yankee cylinder without creping. A high level of smoothness and gloss is achieved on the side of the paper dried in contact with the dryer surface. Such a sheet has this gloss on one side only but is applicable to many specialized purposes.

Cylinder Machines

Cylinder machines are those in which the forming wire mesh is supported by a porous cylindrical structure. The drainage of the stock through the cylinder is controlled by the pressures applied to the outside and various means utilized within the forming roll. Cylinder machines are frequently made with a multiplicity of forming cylinders. In the average cylinder machine, stock is applied to the outside of each roll by means of a "vat," and the entire center of the roll is carried at a reduced pressure to promote the rate of drainage and sheet formation. The sheet is "couched" or removed from the rolls by a common pick-up felt which combines the individual webs into a single composite mat. Figure 12.3 is a typical cylinder type machine used for forming heavyweight boards. The press and dryer sections

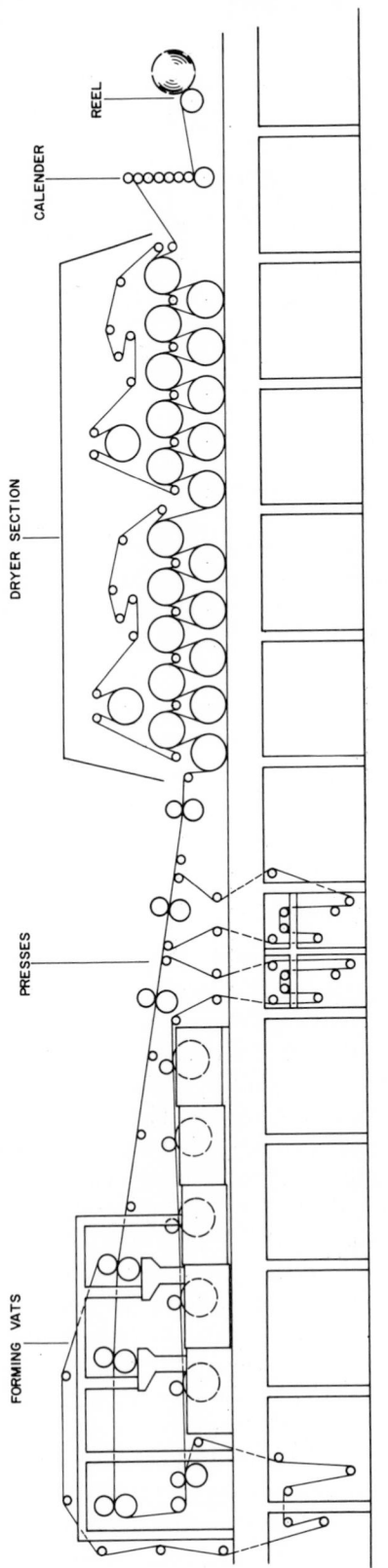

Fig. 12.3. The cylinder paper machine. (*Courtesy Beloit Corp.*)

of cylinder machines are quite similar to those utilized in the normal Fourdrinier machine.

Formers

A series of paper machines has been developed recently which can be classified under the general heading of "formers." These machines make use of a cylindrical forming roll which supports the forming wire mesh. In this respect they are similar to the cylinder machine. They differ from the cylinder machine in that the stock is admitted to the wire surface by means of a nozzle or specially shaped inlet. In general, this forming zone amounts to only a relatively small part of the wire circumference. The second general characteristic, to which there are a few exceptions, is that the vacuum applied to the interior of the roll to promote drainage is restricted to a specific zone by means of a suction box, which is frequently compartmented so that the vacuum levels can be adjusted to the optimum level for the various stages in the formation of the sheet.

The "Rotoformer" forming equipment is shown in Figure 12.4. This device has been constructed in several different forms. It is characterized by a large stock nozzle or inlet and the compartmented internal suction box. The Stevens Former (Figure 12.5), has a different type of inlet nozzle and, in its most usual form, does not have a compartmented suction box, but is equipped with a cylinder mold much like a conventional cylinder machine. It is obvious that this Former could be used with a compartmented suction box. The development of new formers and forming devices is the result of attempts to overcome the cost and complexity of Fourdrinier machines and to avoid the speed limitations and some of the quality deficiencies of conventional cylinder machines.

Multiple Forming Methods

Combinations of various forming methods are often used to obtain desired product qualities. The most obvious of these, of

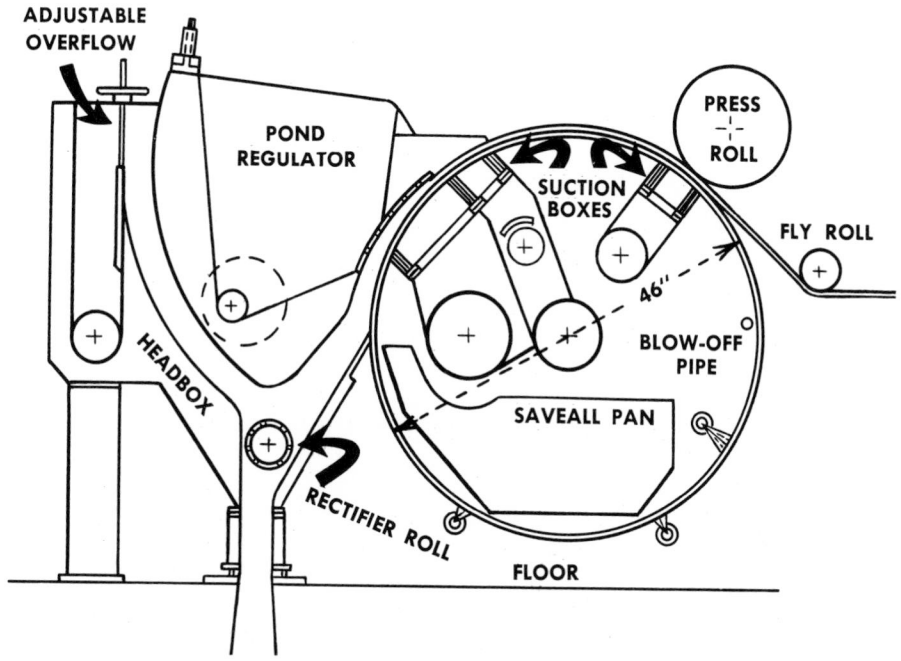

Fig. 12.4. The "Rotoformer." (*Courtesy Sandy Hill Iron and Brass Works*)

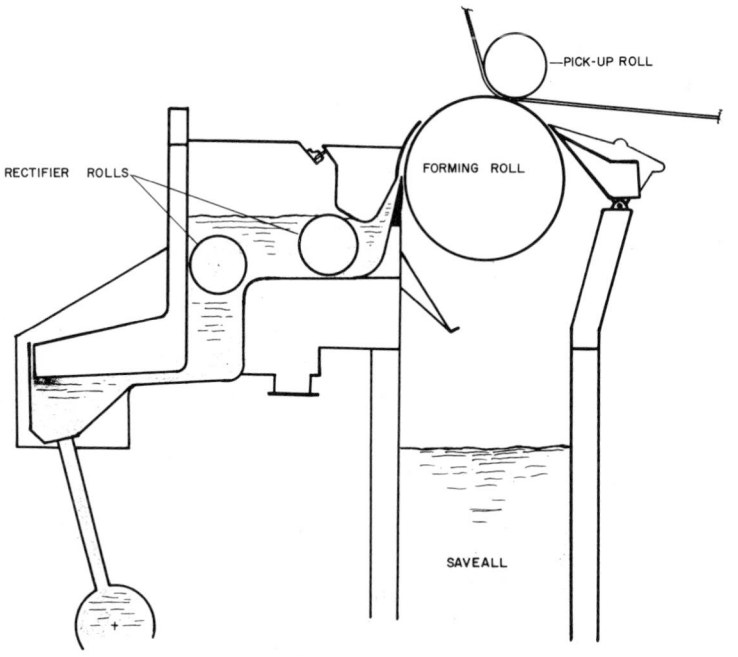

Fig. 12.5. The Stevens Former. (*Courtesy Beloit Corp.*)

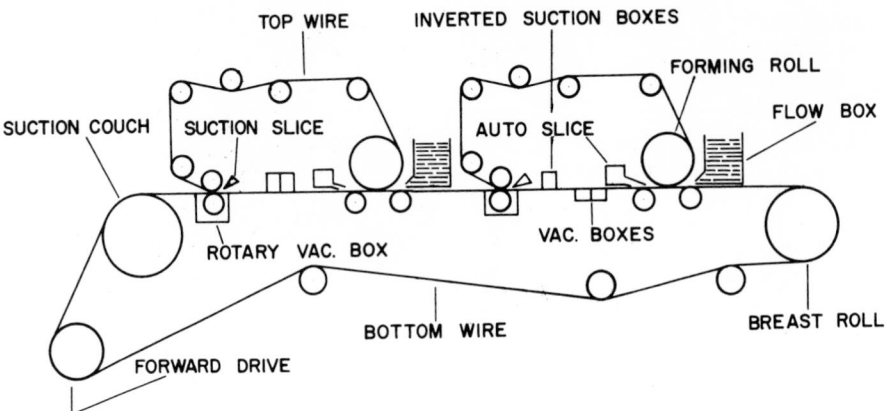

Fig. 12.6. The "Inverformer." (*Courtesy Beloit Corp.*)

course, is the multiple cylinder machine which is used for forming heavy board, roofing felt and similar heavy, slow draining grades.

Combination cylinder and Fourdrinier machines have been constructed which combine a cylinder-formed web with that made on a Fourdrinier to produce a sheet having the large bulk and mass of a cylinder board as well as the higher quality obtained on a Fourdrinier former. In a similar manner, machines have also been constructed for combining two Fourdrinier webs into a single sheet. It is possible to press two relatively wet, newly formed, webs together so that they become, in effect, a single sheet.

Another general type of multiple formation involves forming a new layer over an already formed paper mat. So-called secondary headboxes are frequently used on Fourdrinier machines which will lay down a second layer of stock after the first layer has been sufficiently dewatered.

A recent innovation in this field is a machine using secondary type headboxes and a "top wire" which permits drainage of white water from the top as well as the bottom of the forming sheet. This machine is particularly adaptable for forming heavier weight grades. Figure 12.6 illustrates a typical arrangement of an "Inverformer."

It is well known that a large portion of the non-uniformity and lack of control in conventional paper forming methods is due to the fact that the stock has a "free" surface during the forming operation. Spouting, jumping, and stock waves can frequently be observed on high-speed Fourdrinier machines. The control of stock during the forming operation is a long-pursued and desirable goal. In some cases this has been practically achieved in forming very lightweight grades such as tissue, as well as in some of the cylinder type "formers," by draining or "setting" the stock while it is relatively enclosed or controlled by the forming inlet or a top wire.

STOCK SCREENING AND CLEANING

Before being allowed to flow onto the forming wire of a paper machine, the headbox stock is given a final screening or cleaning treatment to remove traces of dirt, slivers, pitch and other solid foreign materials. In its simplest form the stock screen consists of a flat metal plate perforated with narrow slits ranging in width from about .008 to .018 inch depending on the type of paper being made. These plates form the top of a shallow box or vat, the bottom of which is made up of movable diaphragms, which serve to draw the stock through the screens.

In most modern paper machines, the stock is cleaned just before entering the headbox by centrifugal or "vortex" cleaners and/or vertical, totally enclosed pressure type screens, an example of which is shown in Figure 12.7. Pulp enters the inlet compartment of the screen in a tangential manner. In order to flow into the screening chamber, the stock spirals upward out of the inlet compartment and into the annular screening chamber bounded on the sides by two concentric screen cylinders and on the bottom by the tailings gutter. The acceptable fiber flows radially inward and outward through the screen plates. The rejectable fraction is continuously purged through an opening in the lower portion of the screening chamber which is manually controlled by a valve. The accepted stock from the inner and outer compartments is joined at the outlet flange. The rotating assembly consists of multiple "hydrofoils," which rotate between and act on both screen plates. The pressure pulses produced by the rotating streamlined members tend to improve the rate of screening and maintain the holes unplugged. The reject rate for such a screen is about 5 to 7% in most instances. These rejects usually go to a secondary screen for salvage, or they are treated and further cleaned before returning to another portion of the system.[1]

Centrifugal or vortex type cleaners operate on the principle of separating out material having specific gravity different from that of the pulp fibers.[2] In the case of these cleaners, better separation is achieved by increasing the gravitational effect on the foreign particles by subjecting the pulp suspension to intense centrifugal action. A centrifugal cleaner consists essentially of a hollow truncated cone with a gradual taper from top diminishing toward the bottom. The cone is provided with a tangentially situated stock inlet at the top and a clean stock outlet located centrally at the top, while rejects are discharged at the truncated bottom of the cone.

When the pulp suspension is introduced tangentially at the top, the liquid commences to spin rapidly; while spinning, it moves down the cone, forming a free vortex. The particles of high specific gravity material migrate to the outer periphery of the vortex as a result of the centrifugal force generated, where they tend to form a heavier outer layer. As the liquid moves down the cone, this heavier layer becomes smaller and smaller in cross-sectional area, until it is small enough to be discharged through the orifice at the bottom. It is apparent that efficient operation dictates that the fraction

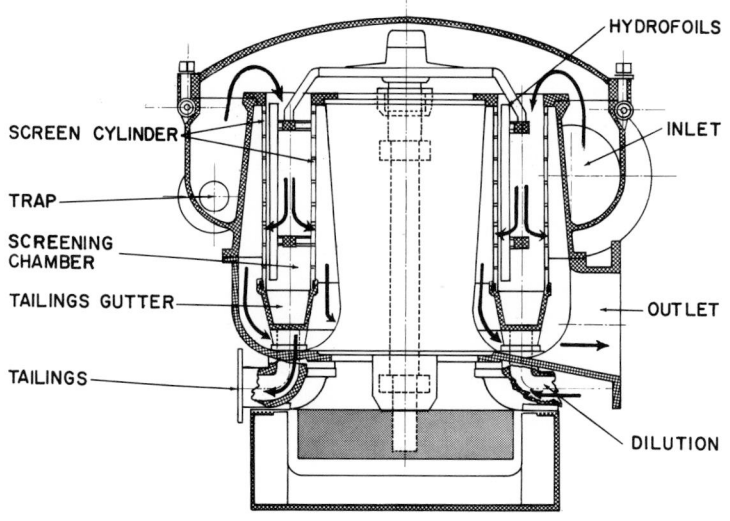

Fig. 12.7. Enclosed pressure-type screen showing flow pattern.
(*Courtesy Bird Machine Co.*)

removed at the bottom must be a reasonable percentage of the input volume; it therefore contains usable fiber which can be reclaimed by secondary, tertiary and sometimes quaternary stages. The clean stock in the suspension, unable to escape at the bottom, forms a centrally ascending column which is removed through the central opening at the top. Figure 12.8 shows the flow pattern in a typical vortex cleaner.

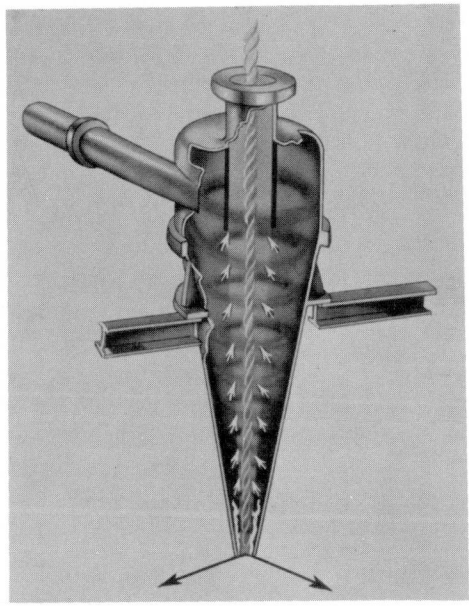

Fig. 12.8. Vortex stock cleaner. (*Courtesy Bauer Brothers Co.*)

The screening system is frequently combined with a receiving chamber held at less than atmospheric pressure. By this means entrained and dissolved air in the headbox stock can be removed, which helps to eliminate troublesome foam and improves machine cleanliness and performance.

FLOWSPREADERS AND HEADBOXES

The purpose of a paper machine inlet system is to convert the flow of "stock," as it is delivered from the fan pump, into a relatively thin flat ribbon equal in width to the trim of the machine, with uniform velocity in the machine direction, ideal turbulence

conditions, and uniformity of flow across the machine. It is generally considered desirable to have a uniformly deflocculated stock flow onto the wire. In view of the fact that so many systems have been built utilizing widely different theories and methods of operation, it can be concluded that no completely satisfactory arrangement has yet been achieved. Some of these systems are better suited to certain grades than others, and it has also been found that an inlet system suitable for one speed will be unsuitable for another. It is only natural that systems have been more highly perfected for slow-speed machines because of the simpler designs which can be employed and the greater amount of experience available. The inlet system consists of a "flowspreader" and a headbox.

Flowspreaders

For the purpose of analysis, the flow-spreading action is considered separately from headboxes in general. It should be recognized that in some machines these two functions are carried out in the same piece of equipment. "Flowspreading" describes the hydraulic process of converting the flowing stream of stock, carried in a pipe, into a flat thin stream having as uniform velocity as possible across the width of the machine. This stream is then fed into the "headbox element" which further "rectifies" or smoothes out the velocity variations in the incoming stream and is designed to control turbulence level in the stock before it reaches the wire. Flowspreaders can be divided into several general types and many examples can be found for each.

Diffuser Types. A diffuser flowspreader is essentially a single open channel which changes in shape from a round pipe cross section to a long thin rectangular flow of suitable depth for delivery to the headbox. Although this is in many ways the simplest concept, the solution of the hydraulic problem of this type of flowspreader is not an easy one. Perhaps the best example of a diffuser type of flowspreader now in use is

FLOW

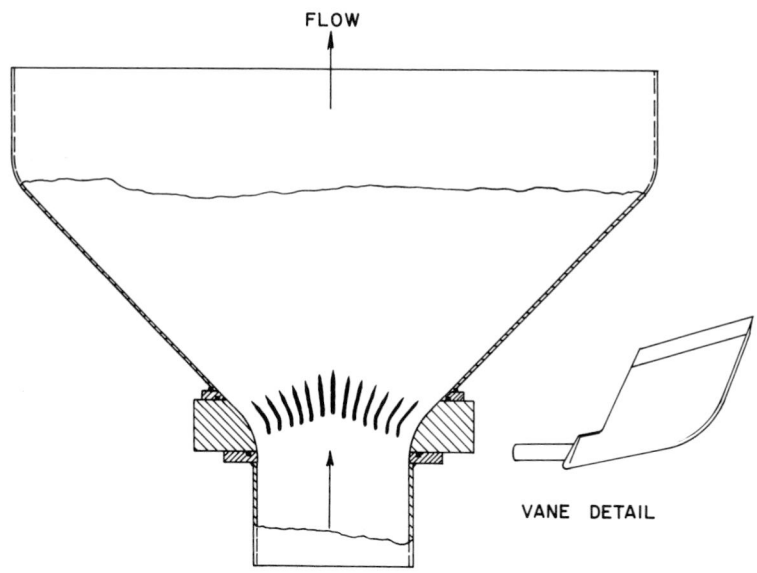

VANE DETAIL

Fig. 12.9. Diffuser-type flowspreader (after C. A. Lee).

that developed by Lee [3] (Figure 12.9). This diffuser makes use of a series of small vanes which permit some degree of adjustment during operation. Other diffuser types of flowspreaders have been developed, some of which are rather simple and capable of good uniformity.

Header Types. The simplest type of header flowspreader is a fairly large pipe placed in a cross machine direction ahead of the headbox (see Figure 12.10). This pipe is fed by the supply pipe, and several smaller pipes connect the header to the headbox at regular intervals across the machine. The header serves as a source of constant pressure which feeds the various supply pipes to the headbox. This device has proved quite satisfactory in many installations. There are certain to be some pressure drops and unstable flows within the system giving rise to small fluctuations which may or may not be objectionable. One further improvement in this general system is to taper the header from the point of supply to the point of discharge so that the velocity is more or less constant in all parts.

A second type of header is fed from one end and tapers in cross-sectional area so that the stock velocity is fairly constant across the width of a machine. This tapered header feeds a series of smaller pipes which lead into the headbox at regular intervals across the width of the machine. In most systems, the header cross-sectional area is reduced to about 30% of the incoming area and a portion of the stock is recirculated through the primary system by means of a special recirculation line (see Figure 12.11). An analysis of this type of header has shown that the ideal area relationship is quite complex, and consequently the straight taper has been modified in some machines to produce more uniform velocity. In an effort to compensate for some of the deficiencies, two headers are sometimes used with the tapers in opposite directions so that first-order cross machine variables will be canceled out. A double header arrangement is shown in Figure 12.12. The two tapered headers feed into a single slot instead of making use of a series of pipes. This type of stock spreader is used to feed a headbox or, in some cases, a short nozzle section going directly to the wire.

A third general type can be described as the branched flow type of flow distributor

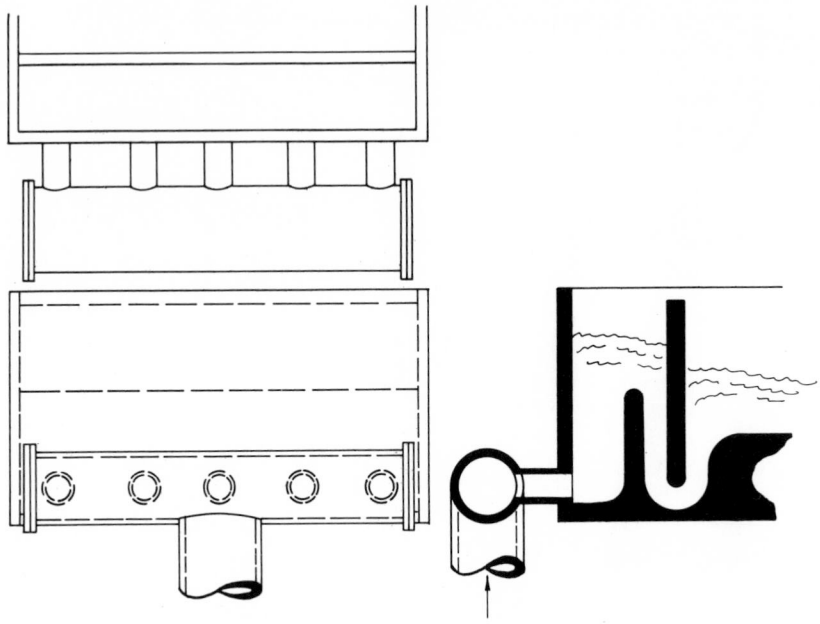

Fig. 12.10. Simple flowspreader. (*Courtesy Beloit Corp.*)

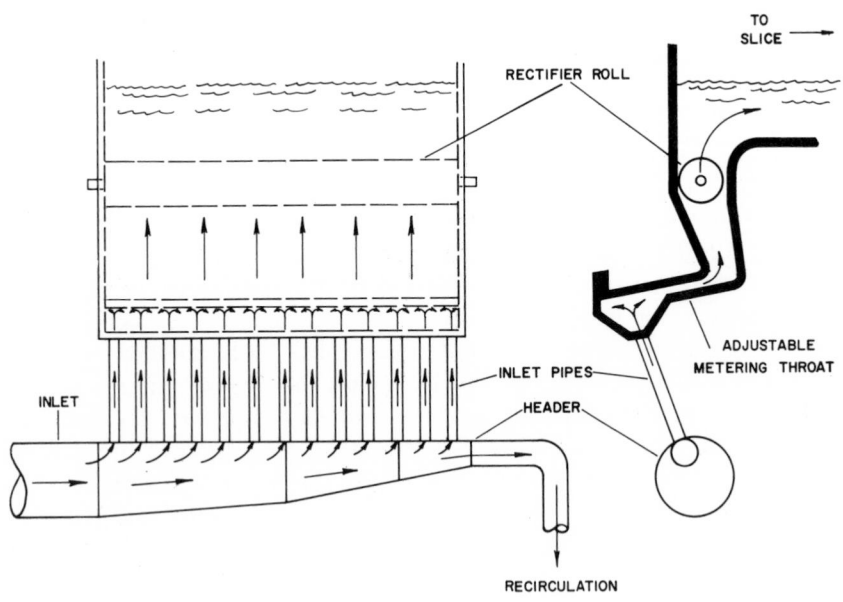

Fig. 12.11. Tapered flowspreader. (*Courtesy Beloit Corp.*)

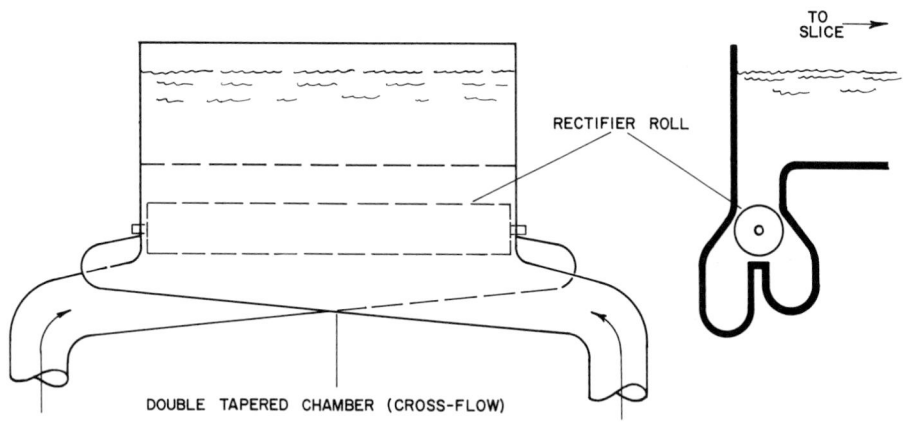

Fig. 12.12. Double tapered flowspreader. (*Courtesy Beloit Corp.*)

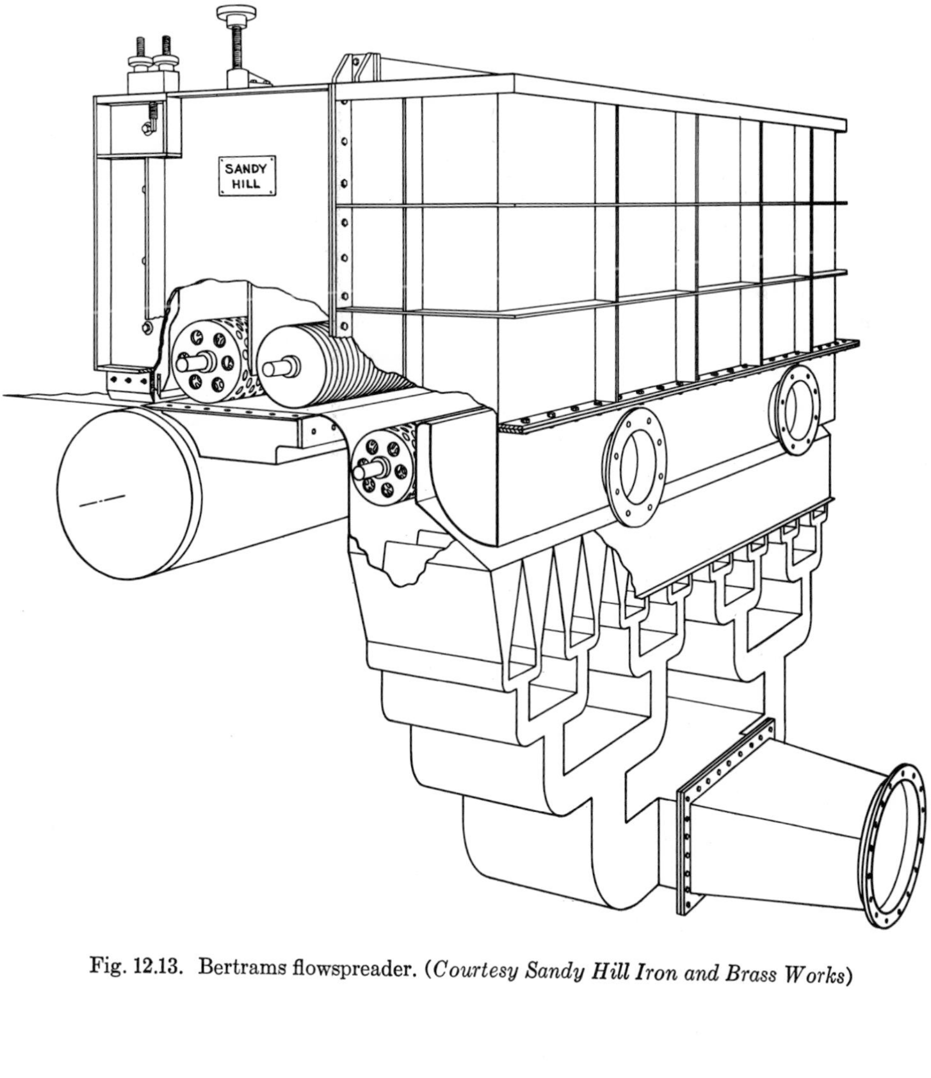

Fig. 12.13. Bertrams flowspreader. (*Courtesy Sandy Hill Iron and Brass Works*)

frequently called a Bertrams flowspreader. A single pipe is divided into two pipes, these two divided into four, four into sixteen, etc. (see Figure 12.13). In this type of flowspreader it is claimed that each particle of stock travels the same distance and undergoes a similar pressure drop. Such flowspreaders have good balance and uniformity across the machine. Care must be taken to see that the velocity variation across a single pipe is not objectionable.

Headboxes

The headbox is that portion of the flow channel which receives the discharge of the flowspreader and, after acting on the stock, discharges it at the slice onto the forming wire or surface. The action of the headbox is to level out any cross machine variations remaining after the flowspreading system, to control and regulate the turbulence of the stock mixture, and to discharge the stock in a uniform manner at a controlled turbulence level to the forming section of the wire. Compensation for any non-uniformities in the incoming flow of the flowspreading system is frequently by means of a series of baffles or "explosion chambers."

An explosion chamber is a rapid enlargement of cross-section area giving rise to hydraulic losses which tend to even out the non-uniformities. Baffles have much the same effect on the flow.

The basic headbox is simply a wooden or metal container approximately the width of the machine, four to eight feet long in the machine direction and of a height sufficient to give the stock issuing from the jet a velocity equal to the wire speed. The jet or slice is frequently a sharp-edged orifice with some adjustment to make cross machine compensations. The box will usually contain one or more devices to improve a flow uniformity such as rectifiers or "holey" rolls and/or baffles. Figure 12.14 is a drawing of a simple headbox equipped with rectifier rolls and having a simple type of explosion chamber.

Rectifier or holey rolls are flow-controlling devices which provide a source of uniform hydraulic friction and tend to generate turbulence of a desirable size and intensity. Similar results could be obtained with simple perforated plates or bars across the interior of the headbox. The slowly rotating rectifier has the virtue of being practically

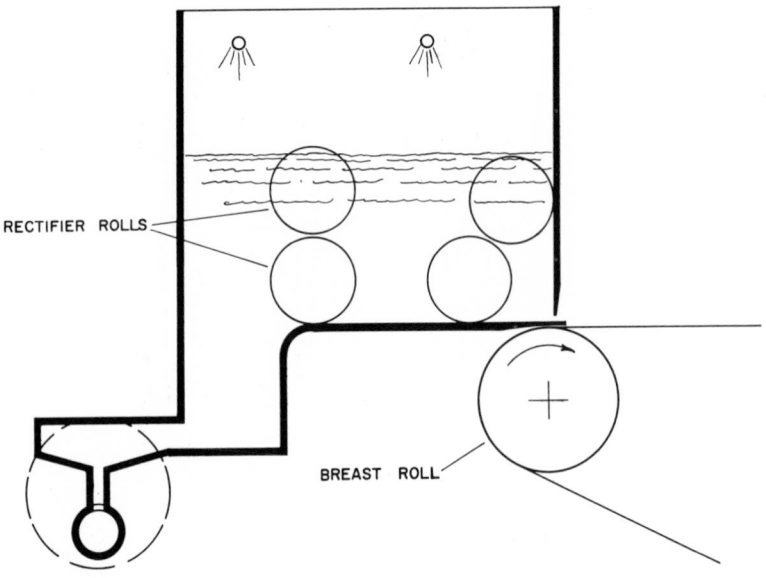

Fig. 12.14. Paper machine headbox.

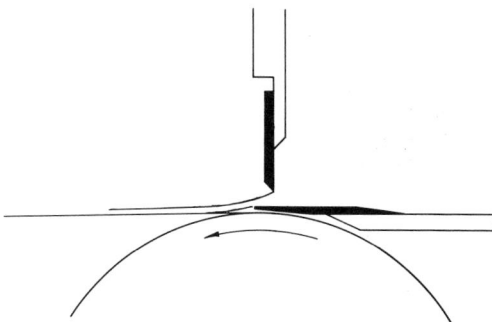

Fig. 12.15. Paper machine slice.

self-cleaning and has proved over many years to be a workable if not ideal device.

The slice, or jet nozzle, where the stock issues from the headbox and flows onto the wire, in its simplest form consists of a flat horizontal blade and a vertical slicing bar (see Figure 12.15). This type of slice is frequently used on both slow and high-speed machines. In one variation of this the top slice lip is slanted to form a nozzle at the discharge point (see Figure 12.16). In other designs the top and bottom lip issuing from the headbox are arranged like nozzles which project streams of stock onto the forming material as fire hoses project streams of water into the air.

The original headbox was conceived with the idea of performing the role of flow-spreader, turbulence control, and jet or nozzle combined in one simple piece of equipment. The demands of high speed and better uniformity have brought about many vari-

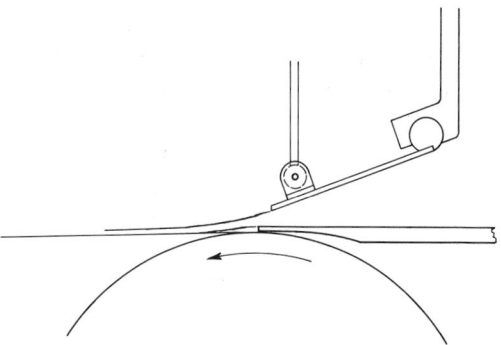

Fig. 12.16. Slice with top lip slanted to form a nozzle.

ations in design. Figure 12.17 illustrates a headbox which is hardly recognizable as a box form and much closer to a nozzle. Figure 12.18 is another example showing a "headbox" which consists of a short inlet spreader section feeding directly into a nozzle.

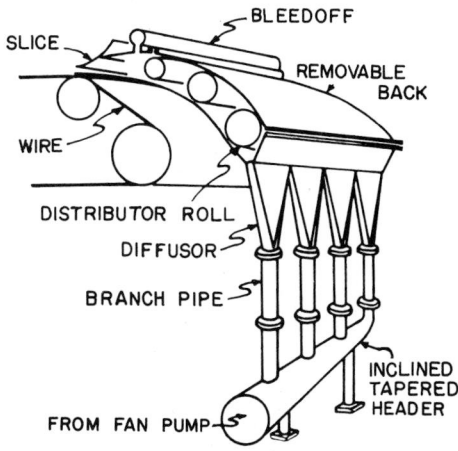

Fig. 12.17. Nozzle type of headbox (after Reitzel). (*Courtesy Rice Barton Corp.*)

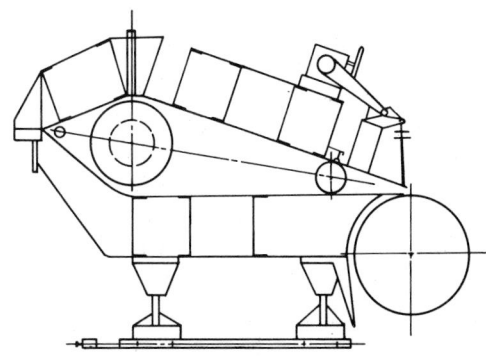

Fig. 12.18. Nozzle-type stock inlet.

As paper machine speeds have increased, it has been necessary to go to higher and higher headboxes to obtain the necessary jet velocity. The large volumes of water and stock contained in such headboxes have made difficult the control of turbulence, uniformity, and cleanliness. This problem has been overcome by building small volume enclosed headboxes through which the stock is pumped under pressure (sometimes called

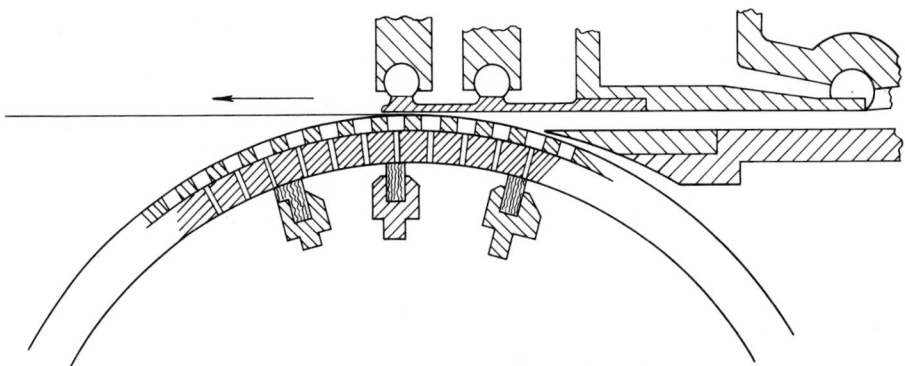

Fig. 12.19. Pressure inlet (after Ostertag and Boylan).

a "pump box"). Other designs use an "air cushion" at the top of the box, which is sealed, and the upper surface of the stock is acted upon by a blanket or cushion of compressed air. The latter applies the necessary loading to increase the stock velocity to the desired speed. The fan pump generates sufficient pressure to force the stock into the headbox inlet. The air cushion serves as an upper retaining member much as a solid wall would serve.

Enclosed Nozzle Inlets.

There is a certain type of paper machine inlet employed on high-speed machines which can in no sense be considered a headbox. It is rather an enclosed nozzle system being fed by a suitable type of flowspreader. Such a flow system and nozzle is illustrated in Figure 12.19. This particular inlet is used on a high-speed tissue machine equipped with a suction or "open" type of breast roll. A considerable portion of the formation takes place on the wire while it is supported by the open breast roll structure. As speeds increase, there is less and less justification for the use of a large open headbox. Friction losses go up rapidly with speed, and the inertia of high-velocity flow becomes almost unmanageable in large open chambers. Figure 12.20 illustrates a similar type of nozzle arrangement with a special forming element located near the discharge point. This element has the effect of controlling flow and turbulence level near the

point of discharge. Light tissue grades are formed with a device of this type at speeds in excess of 3,000 fpm.

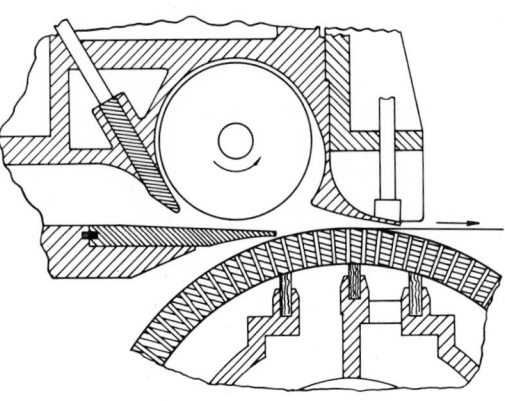

Fig. 12.20. Pressure inlet with forming element (after C. A. Lee).

BREAST ROLL

The breast roll is a large turning roll in a Fourdrinier machine which is located near the wet end or headbox. The Fourdrinier wire makes a slightly less than 180° turn around this roll and is supported by it in the initial part of the forming zone. In its simplest form the breast roll is a large metal or rubber-covered metal roll of sufficient stiffness to avoid deflection under the wire load which supports the wire immediately adjacent to the slice. It has been found that the settings of the slice lip and apron relative to the breast roll are critical and that the proper relationships must be worked out for good performance. It has also been found that the breast roll has a strong "pumping action" tending to remove water from the under side of the Fourdrinier wire under certain settings of the slice lips.

"Open" or suction rolls are used where the pumping action of the roll is undesirable or the slice arrangement is such that a certain amount of drainage is desired while the Fourdrinier wire is supported on the breast roll circumference. Open breast rolls are of several types of construction but are generally composed of drilled or fabricated structures which permit water to flow inward with negligible resistance.

When a certain amount of drainage is required through the wire while it is supported on the open type breast roll, a suction box is sometimes fitted internally in the breast roll to control the formation rate and govern the "throw-off" of water from the breast roll structure. In high-speed operations, where these rolls are most frequently used, it is difficult and undesirable to pull the white water into the center of the suction roll. Instead the water is held within the roll structure by means of suitably adjusted vacuum and is then discharged under the Fourdrinier wire.[4]

FOURDRINIER TABLE SECTION

The Fourdrinier table section of a paper machine is a large framework usually covered with stainless steel. This framework supports the table rolls, breast roll, couch roll, suction boxes, wire rolls, and other Fourdrinier parts.

In the older and simpler machines, the Fourdrinier table is usually of the type known as "fixed." When replacing the Fourdrinier wire which is joined together in an endless form before installation, it is necessary to remove the table rolls, suction boxes, wire rolls, etc., from the Fourdrinier frame. The wire is then draped over the breast and couch rolls, which are specially supported during this operation, and the table parts

are then reassembled inside the wire loop.

New machines, and all large ones, are built with "cantilevered" or "roll out" Fourdrinier tables. In the cantilever arrangement the Fourdrinier frame is so constructed that the supports can be removed from the front side and it will remain cantilevered or overhung, being supported by special beams designed to take the weight of this assembly during the wire-changing operation. It is possible with such a frame to slip a new Fourdrinier wire over the suspended assembly without dismantling the component parts. The wire is usually "strung" on a special frame in the aisle and is then passed back over the Fourdrinier assembly (see Figure 12.21). In the roll-out type of Fourdrinier, the table is rolled out into the aisle, the wire is strung in place in the machine over the couch roll, and the assembly is rolled back in place.

Fourdrinier Wires

The most important functional part of the Fourdrinier is the wire itself, a finely woven metal or synthetic fiber cloth which allows drainage of the white water but retains fibers. Fundamentally, its action may be described as follows:

(1) As the stock issues from the slice, the larger fibers in the furnish quickly form a skeleton or fiber mat upon which the shorter fibers, filler, and additional long fibers are deposited. When the stock first contacts the Fourdrinier wire near the breast roll, a relatively small percentage of it is retained on the top surface, the rest passing through into the save-all system.

(2) As a fiber mat is built up the percentage of retention of fiber goes up rapidly. The over-all retention of fibers is surprisingly small, being in the neighborhood of 40 to 60% for most grades of paper.

The strands of the Fourdrinier wire are usually made of specially annealed bronze and brass, very finely drawn and woven into a web usually from 55 to 85 mesh. Even finer wires are used for some special purposes such as making cigarette and con-

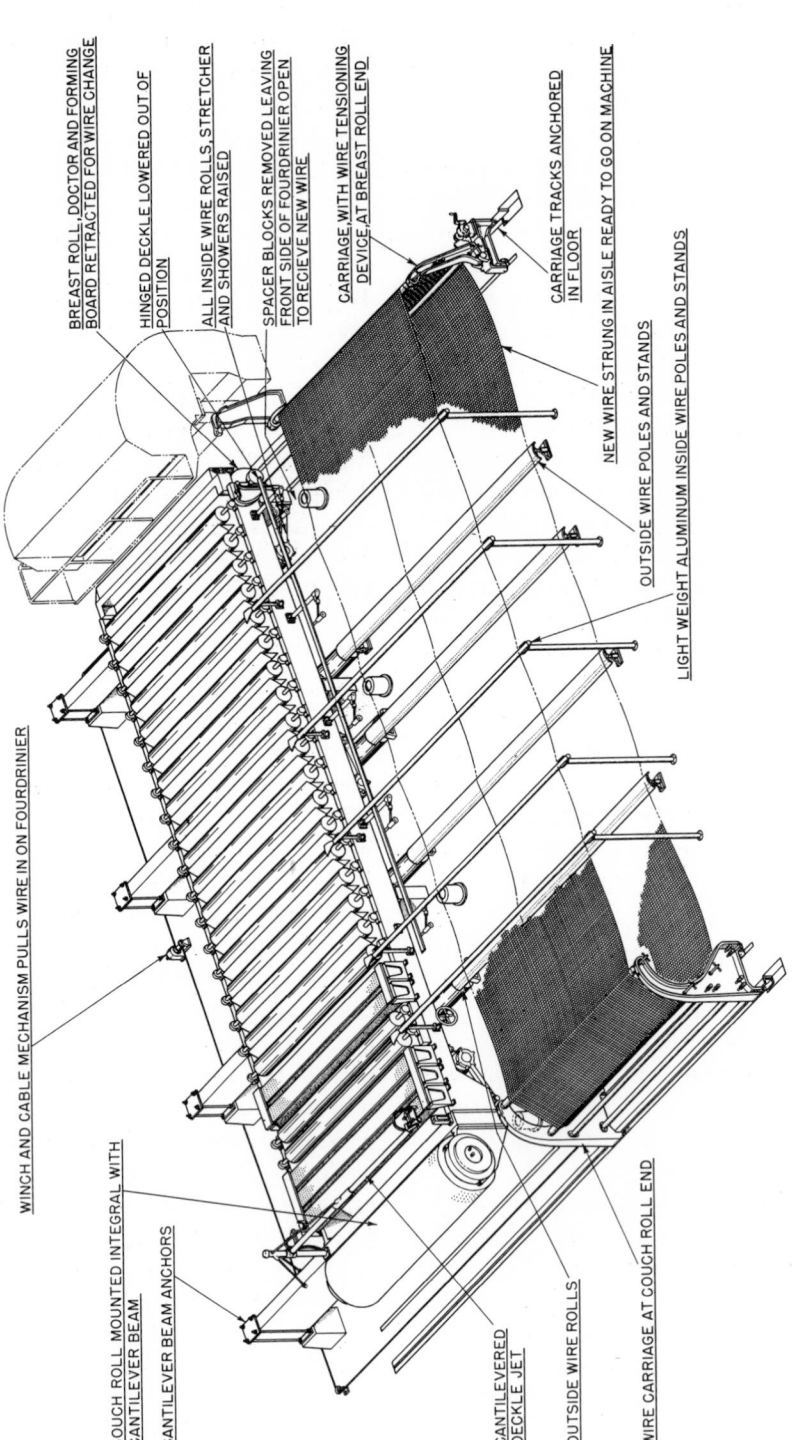

Fig. 12.21. Wire stringing method for non-removable cantilever Fourdrinier. (*Courtesy Black-Clawson Co.*)

denser paper. Coarser wires are used for making heavy paperboard and pulp sheets. Various types of weave are used to obtain maximum wire life and minimize "wire marking" in the final sheet.

The wire is not a permanent part of the Fourdrinier. It is so delicate that its life is often less than a month and sometimes only a few days. Wire life from 5 to 50 days is quite common. Wire wear is due to two principal causes—corrosion and abrasion. Corrosion is principally due to materials in the white water system which are corrosive to the brass, bronze, and other materials used in construction of the wire. Abrasive-type wear is due to the presence of hard materials such as clay, sand and other contaminants in the pulp system. A microscopic examination of the wire surface when removed will frequently indicate the type of wire wear predominating. Abrasive wear is characterized by flattening of the wire strands on the inner surface where they contact suction box covers, rolls, scrapers, etc. Detailed studies of wear and corrosion factors are available in the literature.[5, 6] Various types of corrosion inhibitors are produced which may be of some value in specific cases.

Fourdrinier "wires" are also being made of synthetic fibers which are proving to be applicable for many types of paper and board. They are woven in an endless manner from synthetic fibers and treated to retain their structural properties and dimensions over a long period of time.

Wire Shake

It is extremely desirable to have a uniform, homogeneous mass of fibers with a random arrangement of fibers so that strength is obtained in both the machine and cross direction. This orientation is largely governed by the relative speeds of the stock and Fourdrinier wire as well as the hydraulics of the headbox preceding the slice. It has been traditional on certain grades of paper to apply a "shake" or cross-wise vibration to the Fourdrinier wire while the sheet is forming. Although the shake is believed to have some beneficial effects on slow-speed machines, its contribution to high-speed machines is questionable. Nevertheless, most machines are equipped with shake mechanisms.

Table Rolls

As the name implies, the function of table rolls is to support the wire as a flat surface or table allowing uniform drainage. These rolls also carry off water by a pumping action from the under surface of the wire. For this reason they are a much more important element of the Fourdrinier than has been generally appreciated.

The pumping action produced by a rotating table roll or a fixed foil in contact with the Fourdrinier wire has been analyzed theoretically, and measured under operating conditions. It was found that the effect of a table roll was to produce a moderate upward pulse or pressure wave followed by a stronger downward or suction pulse which produced the pumping effect long noticed in table rolls.[8] The magnitude of the decrease in pressure produced by a table roll or foil was determined theoretically by G. I. Taylor.[9] He found that the suction value cannot exceed one half ρU^2 where ρ is the water density and U is the speed of the wire. The total amount of water drained is proportional to the square of the wire speed and also directly proportional to the roll diameter. As the maximum suction obtained at a table roll is atmospheric pressure, no increase in drainage capacity can be anticipated above approximately 2,500 fpm, the positive-pressure pulse (see Figure 12.22) is thought by many to have a disturbing effect on the sheet. Others believe that this upward thrust has the effect of loosening the sheet and improving drainage. There is considerable evidence to indicate that this has an undesirable effect on the retention of fine pulp particles.

Water Removal Equipment. Other methods are frequently employed to remove water from the forming mat in the Fourdrinier

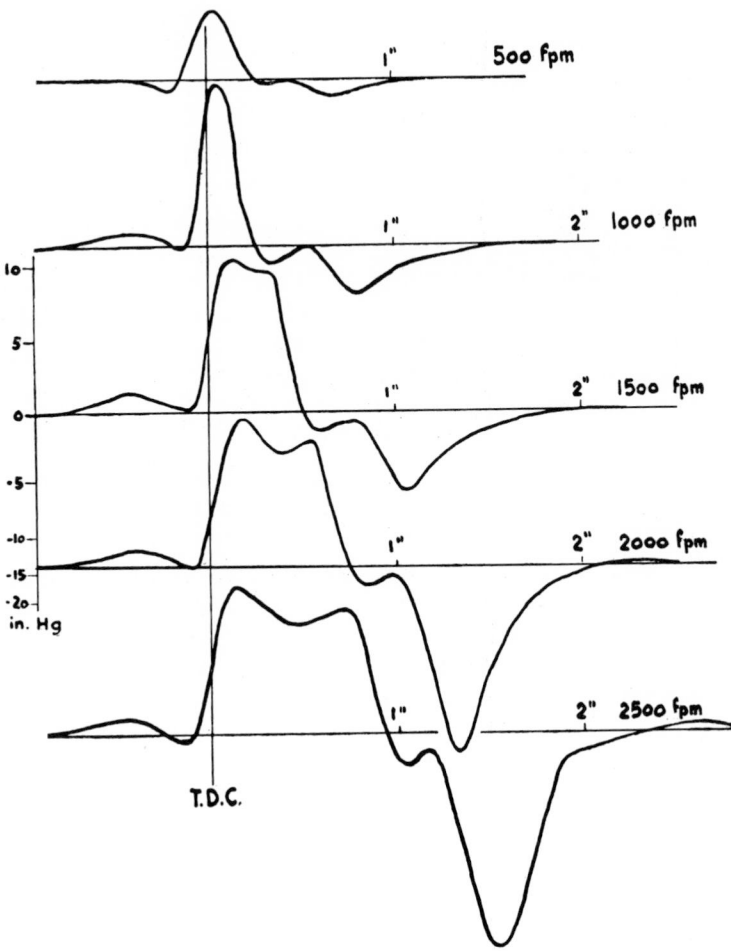

Fig. 12.22. Pressure profiles through nip of a table roll for increasing machine speeds. (After Burkhart and Wrist)

section. Foils or deflectors may be used. They are believed to have the advantage of not producing the upward pressure pulse which is inherent in the table roll action. They do, however, necessitate a rubbing contact with the bottom of the Fourdrinier which increases wire and foil wear. This problem has been partially solved, at least, by the employment of special wear-resistant materials which are also effective in prolonging Fourdrinier wire life. Figure 12.23 is an example of an adjustable type of foil for water removal near the wet end of the Fourdrinier table.

After a considerable fiber mat has built up on the Fourdrinier table, the suction or pumping action produced by table rolls and foils is less and less effective. Suction boxes are employed near the end of the Fourdrinier table to complete water drainage and dewater the mat so that it can be self-supporting at the couch. Suction boxes are airtight trays or troughs located in a transverse direction under the Fourdrinier wire and covered with perforated "tops" of special low friction material. The classic top material is end-grained maple wood. Various new materials such as ureaformaldehyde laminates, polyurethane rubber, "Teflon," and even silicon carbide are being employed. The vacuum used on flat boxes is generally the minimum which will dewater the sheet

Fig. 12.23. Water removal foils for Fourdrinier paper machines. (*Courtesy Lodding Engineering Co.*)

to the desired level in the available space.

Suction boxes may be either oscillating or nonoscillating. If the former, they are carried on oscillating units mounted on links which are driven from a single shaft. The boxes are oscillated across the wire with a slight angular rotation. The purpose of this oscillation is to prevent the wire from wearing grooves in the box tops and "freezing" in place, which is thought to accelerate wire wear.

The back end of each suction box is piped to the vacuum pump in a manner which allows the water to flow down into a seal tank and the air to pass upward into the vacuum pump system. Regulating valves are used to control the level of suction in each box. There is usually an adjustment on the box so that the suction area may be adjusted to suit the width of the sheet.

Wire Cleaning

It is essential that Fourdrinier wire be kept clean and free of all foreign materials. Any spot of foreign material adhering to the wire will produce a corresponding hole in the formed sheet. Pulp or other material

sticking to the inside of the wire will emboss the wire outward, producing a lump or "pimple." Wear will be rapid around any of these non-uniformities in a wire surface, leading to greatly shortened wire life and interference with paper uniformity. Similarly wrinkles, slack spots, ridges, etc., are most harmful in the effects on the final product.

The Fourdrinier wire used on paper machines is probably one of the most fragile components found in commercial production machinery and every effort should be made to care for it properly. Wire cleaning, in general, consists of using showers to remove all stock and other adhering material from the wire on its return run. It is particularly important that stock be removed from the wire before it contacts an outside roll on the return run. Several types of high-pressure showers, sometimes known as "knock-off" showers, are used immediately after the couch roll for this purpose. It has also been found desirable in some cases to wet the sheet with a low-pressure shower before using a high-pressure knock-off or needle shower. The shower should also be properly located to wash the roll surface and

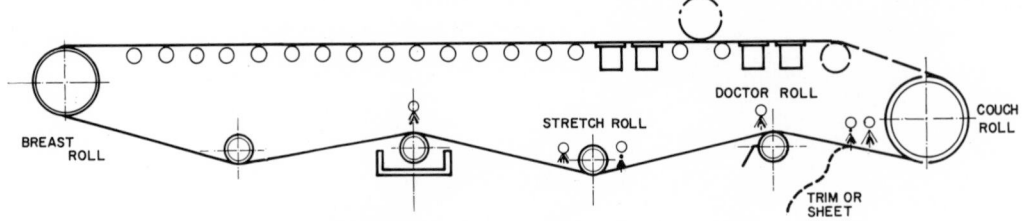

Fig. 12.24. Diagram showing location of showers on a Fourdrinier wire. (*Courtesy Eastwood-Nealley Co.*)

also to lubricate the edge of the roll doctor. Good doctors are considered essential on all outside rolls to complete the removal of stock from the surface of these rolls. When inside rolls are doctored, arrangements should be made to flow the shower water and stock to the ends of the doctor in order to prevent the stock from falling onto the wire from the "inside." Figure 12.24 shows typical locations of showers on a Fourdrinier wire.

Fresh-water showers can be used, without dilution of the stock in the pit, by arranging troughs or save-alls under the rolls to separate shower water from white water drained from the stock. This arrangement will permit the use of fresh water at a minimum cost, minimizing the use of white water, and eliminate overburdening of the filter system in handling the white water.

Wire Guiding

The wire guide roll on a Fourdrinier machine may be located anywhere along the wire run depending on the design of the machine. It is usually placed somewhere in the return run. Activated by an automatic device sensing the position of the Fourdrinier wire, one end of the guide roll is pivoted and the other moved forward and backward a short distance in the machine direction. The wire run is arranged so there is approximately a 10° to 15° wrap around the guide roll. The Fourdrinier wire tends to run to the side of the guide roll which it meets first. In effect, the guide roll acts to displace the wire in a cross machine direction by a very small amount, de-

pending upon the angle of wrap and the angle of displacement of the roll (see Figure 12.25).

Wires should never be too tight when started, as they are thoroughly stretched before leaving the factory and any undue strain on them shortens their service. It should be remembered that the strands of a Fourdrinier wire have a limited amount of elasticity, and when elongated by stretch, they will remain deformed. For this reason, the wire should never be stretched when not in motion. Suction-box covers should be thoroughly dressed so that they are smooth and level. Also they should be properly cleaned, the wire guide properly adjusted, and all particles of hard material brushed and rinsed off before the wire is started. Great care should be exercised to see that all Fourdrinier parts are thoroughly in line and level. If the wire does not guide properly when started, there is sure to be some good reason for it and the Fourdrinier part should be very carefully examined.

Dandy Rolls

The dandy roll on a Fourdrinier is a light, open-structured roll covered with wire cloth. It is placed on the wire between the suction boxes, and rests lightly on the wire. The roll is mainly supported and guided by a system of trunnion bearings. A dandy roll runs freely on the surface of the paper with relatively little pressure. Its purpose is to flatten out the top surface of the sheet, giving it a closer finish. When the dandy roll creates a pattern on the top of the sheet similar to that left by the wire on the bot-

Fig. 12.25. Fourdrinier wire guide. (*Courtesy Rice Barton Corp.*)

tom, the paper is known as "woven"; when it leaves parallel lines that appear translucent when held to the light, the paper is termed "laid." When names, insignia, or designs are formed on the sheet, the paper is said to be "watermarked."

Dandy rolls are usually driven by contact with the wire through the web of fiber, and for this reason, a delicate adjustment is required at the trunnions or journals supporting the roll to control the weight of the roll resting on the sheet.

Some years ago the operation of the dandy roll was improved by use of a positive drive. This gives better sheet formation if there is no watermark, and a much improved watermark if there is one. A dandy roll drive will prevent slippage between the sheet on top of the wire and the dandy, thus improving watermark at faster speeds. With higher-speed machines, washing with a shower pipe during operation outside the dandy roll has been found effective. Many dandy rolls use an internal shower pipe and occasionally a steam shower to achieve cleanliness.

Wire Return Run. The wire returns to the breast roll position on rolls of brass- or rubber-covered steel tubes. The run incorporates wash rolls, stretch rolls, and usually guides. A stretch roll is designed to take up the slack that develops in a wire as it is used. Stretch rolls in modern high-speed machines are frequently of the constant-tension type so that any stretch in the wire will be compensated for automatically. Wire tension should be adjusted to suit the wire weave being used and conditions on the machine. A tight wire will generally result in better sheet formation and more uniformity. The slack wire tends to increase drainage but also promotes stock "jump" and disturbance on the wire. Wire tension must be high enough so that a minimum of slippage occurs at the couch roll, which drives the wire run.

Fig. 12.26. Sheet transfer from wire on "open" machine. (*Courtesy Consolidated Papers, Inc. and Beloit Corp.*)

COUCH ROLL

Couch Arrangements

The last roll over which the formed sheet passes before being removed from the Fourdrinier wire is called the couch roll. (The word "couch" comes from the French *coucher*, to lay, and is pronounced "cooch"). When paper was made by hand, the act of transferring the sheet from the mold to the felt was called couching or laying. Immediately before the transferring operation the couch roll must remove water from and consolidate the sheet so that it can be as strong as possible for the transfer. In modern machines, the couch roll is almost always a suction roll.

The forerunner of the modern suction couch roll was a couch press. The couch press consisted of a brass, rubber-covered bottom roll and a felt-covered top roll. The nip between the two rolls acted as a wringer, but the pressure tended to crush and curl the sheet, interrupting the formation of the sheet, causing breaks and greatly shortening wire life. The suction couch is now almost universally applied for many reasons, its ability to remove great amounts of water safely being the most important.

In most "open draw" machines, the formed web is picked from the wire and must be self-supporting (see Figure 12.26). In suction pick-up machines, the Fourdrinier wire frequently passes around a

Fig. 12.27. Sheet transfer from wire on "pick-up" machine. (*Courtesy Bowaters Southern Paper Corp. and Beloit Corp.*)

wire-turning secondary couch roll and the sheet is picked up from the unsupported wire run between the couch roll and the secondary roll (see Figure 12.27).

Fourdrinier machines are classified into two general categories:

(1) The open machine where the web is self-supporting from its point of leaving the couch roll over to the press felt.

(2) Suction pick-up machines where the sheet is removed from the Fourdrinier wire by means of a suction roll acting through the pickup felts.

Suction pickups or vacuum transfer arrangements are used on almost all high-speed machines.

Suction Couch Roll

The tremendous water-removal capacity of the suction couch roll has made possible the fast modern paper machine employed today. Suction rolls, with their great versatility at the couch and press positions, are essential parts of still more productive paper machines of the future. The suction roll is not, as many people think, a recent innovation. In 1828 George Dickenson, a paper maker in Dover, England, invented and built the first suction couch roll. Drawings and descriptions of this roll show them to be much the same as the suction rolls of today. The roll did not enjoy widespread popularity until almost 100 years later, chiefly because the vacuum pump had not

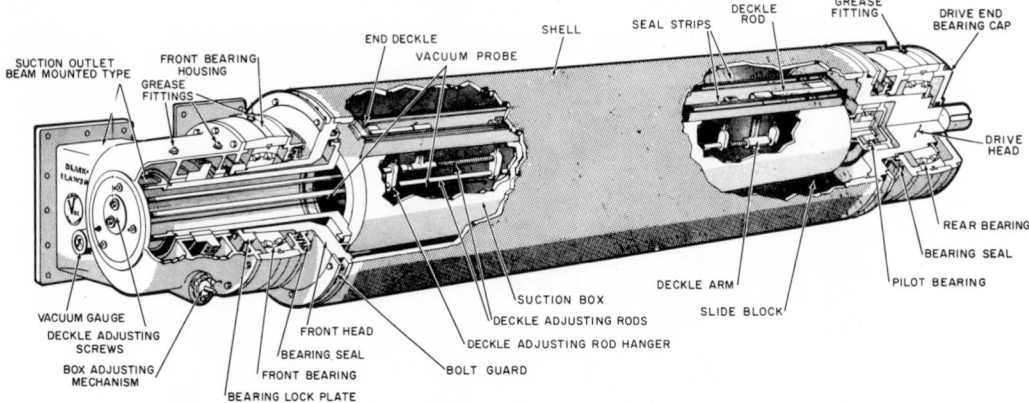

Fig. 12.28. Cutaway of a suction couch roll. (*Courtesy of Black-Clawson Co.*)

been invented, and the plunger pump designed for use with the roll had proved unsatisfactory for water removal. The modern suction roll was invented by William Millspaugh of Sandusky, Ohio, and was first placed in operation at the couch position at the Hammersly Manufacturing Company, Garfield, New Jersey, in 1908.

Suction rolls are made from strong, non-corrosive materials, usually centrifugally cast bronze alloys or stainless steel (see Figure 12.28). The entire face of the shell is drilled and the holes are arranged to present as large a vacuum area as possible. The stationary suction box, located inside, is usually made of cast iron or stainless steel and is supported by roller bearings. The bearings are held by the front and rear heads, which are bolted to the shell. In operation, the suction box is held against the inner radius while the shell rotates about it. The suction area is sealed by longitudinal packing strips mounted on the suction box. These packings are held against the shell by springs or pneumatic loading. End packings or deckles are adjustable to sheet width.

The noise of suction rolls of high-speed paper machines is no longer the serious problem that it was a number of years ago. The noise is generated mainly by the flow of air back into the evacuated holes after the vacuum seal is broken. By restricting the flow of air returning to the holes, a significant reduction in noise has been achieved. The choice of the proper drilling pattern will also do much to cancel out the hole noise and almost all modern shells are provided with such drillings.

Grooved Couch Rolls

Many tissue machines, employing a pick-up felt, use no suction couch. The sheet is substantially dewatered by the action of the table rolls and flat boxes and the couch roll is a plain roll with grooves cut in its surface to facilitate water removal and eliminate ridging of the wire.

Lump Breaker Roll

Sometimes a roll is mounted over the suction area of the couch roll. This roll, which is called the "lump breaker roll," seals the sheet to the couch, raises the vacuum, and keeps the vacuum more constant thus achieving greater water removal. The lump breaker also consolidates the sheet. Such a roll is seldom used on fine papers as its action might affect the desired texture of the sheet.

PICK-UP

Couching Process

At the end of the Fourdrinier table the wet formed sheet is removed from the forming wire. In the open type of Fourdrinier the web is transferred across an open draw to a moving press felt which carries the sheet into the press section. The sheet is transferred at start-up by cutting a narrow tail which is thrown or blown onto the press felt and the strip is widened by moving the trim squirt across the sheet. In machines with a suction pick-up, or direct pick-up as used for tissue, the sheet is transferred directly from the Fourdrinier wire to the bottom surface of the top or pick-up felt.

The picking-up process is aided by the fact that the wet mat of fibers is attracted to the fine capillary structure of the felt in preference to that of the wire. Rewetting the sheet slightly by means of a shower under the wire is frequently employed to improve pick-up. Tissue type pick-up machines usually make use of capillary forces alone to effect sheet transfer.

Pick-up Roll

In a paper machine with a suction or direct pick-up, the sheet is transferred directly from the Fourdrinier wire to a top or pick-up felt, and the pick-up roll must be located accurately relative to the wire or couch roll. Means are also provided for raising the pick-up roll so that the sheet will not be transferred when this is desired by the operator. Because of the light contact between the pick-up roll and the wire or couch roll, loading by means of air cylinders, springs, etc. is usually unsatisfactory. The most common arrangement consists of hydraulic or air cylinders, and a positive stop used to locate the pick-up roll in its operating position. The adjustment of the pick-up roll is quite critical in many operations and requires considerable experience in adjustment. It is most important that it not be loaded too heavily against the Fourdrinier wire or couch roll which would lead to damage of the fragile wire.

Pick-up Felts

The pick-up felt, which removes or receives the sheet directly from the Fourdrinier wire, handles the sheet in its most fragile condition. It is important, therefore, that these felts be smooth, uniform, and of a fine structure. In tissue machines where the sheet is lifted from the Fourdrinier by the capillary attraction of the pick-up felt, it is, of course, essential that the felt have a smooth surface and an extremely fine capillary structure to be presented to the wet sheet. This is usually obtained by weaving a fine felt which is subsequently felted or "fulled" to approximately one half of its original dimensions. This shrinking operation has the effect of densifying and refining the structure so that close to the ultimate in smoothness and small pore size is obtained.

Felts for suction pick-up machines have the further requirement that the felt should be sufficiently porous to permit a reasonable amount of air flow which effects the sheet transfer. As a general rule, it can be said that the resistance to air flow of the felt must be equal to or less than the resistance of the wet sheet to air flow.

It is obviously important that the pick-up and felts be kept cleaned for proper operation. The direct pick-up type of capillary felt must also be properly wetted to perform its operation, which is usually done by means of a shower and "guard board" arrangement.

STOCK AND WHITE WATER SYSTEM

Water is the medium used to convey the pulp and its various additives in the basic sheet-forming process. Because relatively large quantities of water are used (approximately 200 times as much as fiber) and because not all the fiber in suspension is removed at the forming wire, a rather elaborate system is used to minimize losses of fiber and water. Figure 12.29 is a simplified diagram of the stock and white water system. There are actually several circulating systems or "loops" within the diagram. The principal one of these is the "white water" loop which collects all the white water drained from the Fourdrinier section and recirculates the major portion of it to which

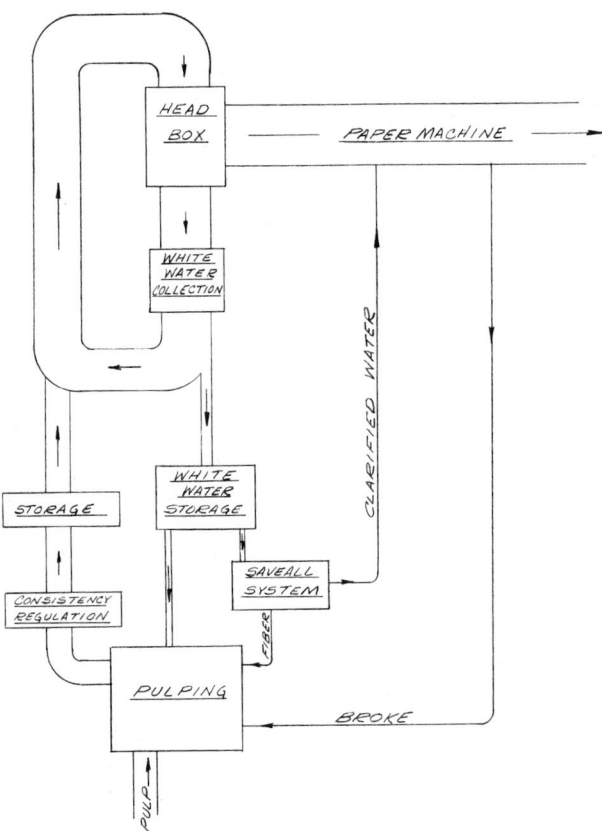

Fig. 12.29. Stock and white water system.

the heavy stock is added. The heavy stock system involves a means for supplying pulp at high consistency, which is mixed with the circulating white water system, after being properly controlled for consistency. The "save-all" system is a means of taking the excess white water and separating fiber from water. The retained fiber goes back into the pulping system and the clarified water has many uses on the paper machine and in the paper mill.

Figure 12.30 is a more detailed stock and white water flow diagram which is somewhat simplified for purposes of explanation. Indicated are many of the typical features found in most stock and white water flow systems. Starting with the pulp mixing chest in the lower left hand corner, a suitable blend of pulp and broke is made up. Each component may receive a certain amount of beating or refining treatment before being pumped over to the beater chest. In the beater chest, a final pulp blend is made up, except that the consistency is usually higher than that desired at the stuff gate. Some recovered fiber and other material from the save-all system may also be added directly to the beater chest without any refining treatment.

Pulp from the beater chest is pumped to the machine chest through a consistency regulator. These regulators, of which there are several types, measure and control the consistency of the pulp by adding water so that the discharge is at a uniform level of consistency. The machine chest is essentially a storage chest which has the further effect of leveling out small swings in consistency. From the machine chest, stock is pumped to the "stuff gate," which is a metering device for controlling flow of heavy stock to the circulating white water system.

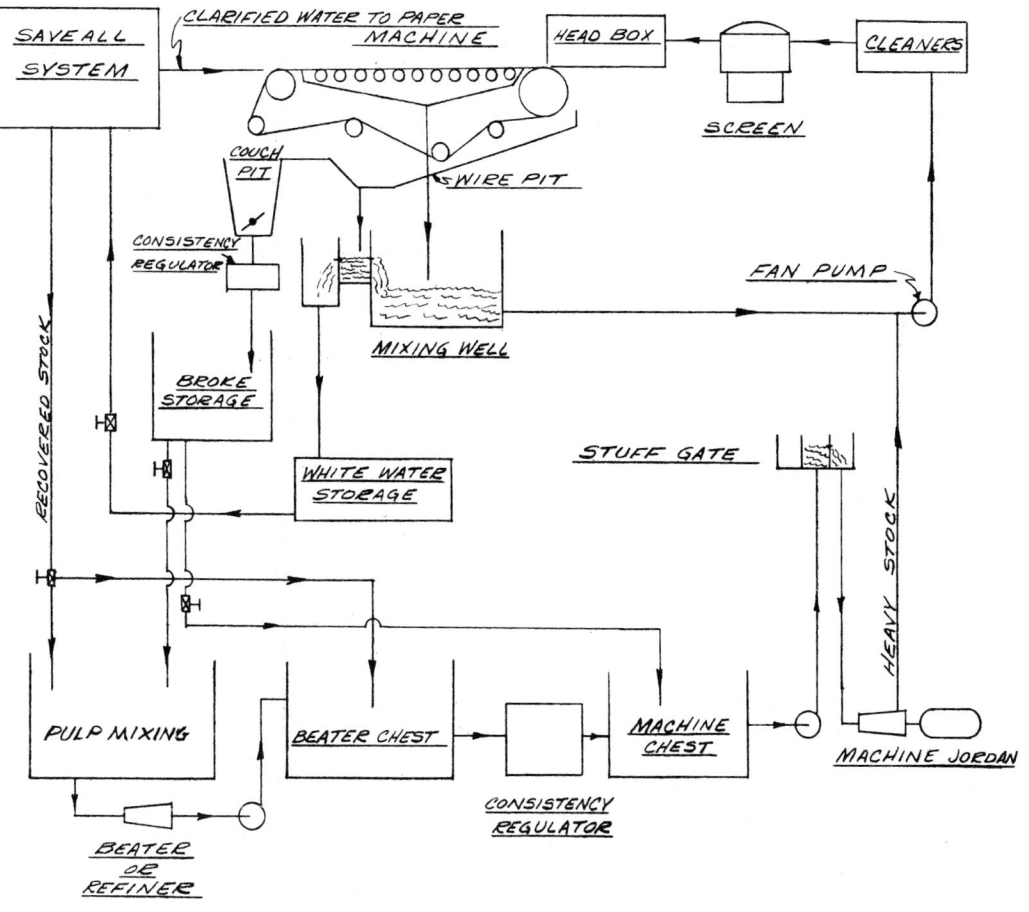

Fig. 12.30. Typical stock and white water system of a paper machine.

All stock admitted by the stuff gate to the circulating white water system goes through the machine "Jordan," where some additional refining may be done on the heavy stock as a whole. The heavy stock is then added to the circulating white water either at the suction of the "fan pump" or in the mixing well. A uniform homogeneous mixture of stock and white water is desired.

The fan pump develops sufficient pressure, or head, to pump the headbox furnish, as it is now called, through the cleaners and screening system to the headbox. Centrifugal type cleaners are used on some machines to remove various foreign materials from the headbox furnish. Mechanical screens are also employed to remove particles exceeding a certain physical size. Such screens are also said to have the effect of breaking up stock "flocks" before the stock enters the headbox.

The headbox stock, which is approximately 0.5 to 1% concentration (one half to one pound of fiber per 100 pounds of water) flows from the headbox out onto the wire. Almost all the water and approximately one half of the fiber goes on through the Fourdrinier wire and is caught by the wire tray or falls into the wire pit. Water from the wire tray, which is the "richest" white water, flows into the mixing well. Water from the mixing well is mixed with heavy stock coming from the machine Jordan and is pumped by the fan pump back into the headbox system. Some of the water which falls into the wire pit is used to maintain the level in the mixing well and the remainder of it overflows and is returned to the save-all system. There is usually an excess of water in the white water system because the fiber leaving the system at the couch carries away less water than comes in with the heavy stock.

The excess water, containing some fiber, flows back from various points in the system to the save-all for reclaiming. The save-all is a filtering operation for separating fiber and various loading materials from the water portion. Both the retained fibers and the clarified water are useful and are routed back to other parts of the system. The retained fiber, fillers and other materials usually go directly back into the beater chest or breaker chest. The clarified water is frequently used for showers, felt washing, and other applications where warm and relatively fiber-free water is needed.

Save-alls generally operate on one of three principles, namely, screening, settling or precipitation, and flotation. In the screening type of save-all, the fibers and solids from the water are separated by catching them mechanically on a fine wire mesh screen which may be precoated with a layer of fibers to improve filtering operation. Settling or precipitation save-alls are large tanks where the velocity of flow is so small that the fibers settle by force of gravity to the bottom. Flotation save-alls make use of a reagent (usually glue) which is added to the inflow, and the injection of air bubbles, which become attached to the suspended solids. Fibers and other solids are removed from the surface of the large flotation chamber by a scraper arrangement. Flotation save-alls are quite popular and widely used; however, they have the disadvantage of introducing one more chemical compound into the machine system.

During normal operation, the water which falls into the couch pit may be treated in the same manner as that falling into the wire pit. If, however, there is heavy trim ribbon dropping into the couch pit, there is usually a consistency regulator to return this material to the broke chest. When the sheet is not being transferred at the couch, fiber is deposited in the couch pit at a rapid rate. White water showers are then provided to dilute this stock to the proper level and recycle it to the beater chest or machine chest.

Although economics and anti-pollution laws make it extremely important that the fiber loss be reduced to a minimum, the importance of obtaining uniform and stable rates of stock flow should not be underestimated. The quality and basis weight of the paper produced on the paper machine is strongly dependent upon uniformity of the headbox stock. This in turn is affected by the heavy stock added through the stuff gate and the circulating fines in the white water system. Every effort should be made to see that all consistency regulators are working properly and that the system is not exposed to any unnecessary upsets of cyclic changes. Proper mixing of the heavy stock with the white water is usually accomplished by means of a mixing well or introduction of the stock into the suction of the fan pump. Improper or inadequate mixing can give rise to serious weight disturbances. Variations in the headbox stock consistency at the time it flows out to the Fourdrinier wire result in corresponding weight fluctuations.

PRESS OPERATION

Principles of Press Operation

After the fibers have been matted or formed on the wire, as much water as possible is removed by table roll action, suction boxes, and the suction couch. The sheet at this point is approximately five parts water to one part fiber, but is sufficiently well formed to be transferred into the press section by the couch operation. In the press section, water is removed from the mat of fibers by both mechanical pressure and vacuum. It is generally cheaper to remove ex-

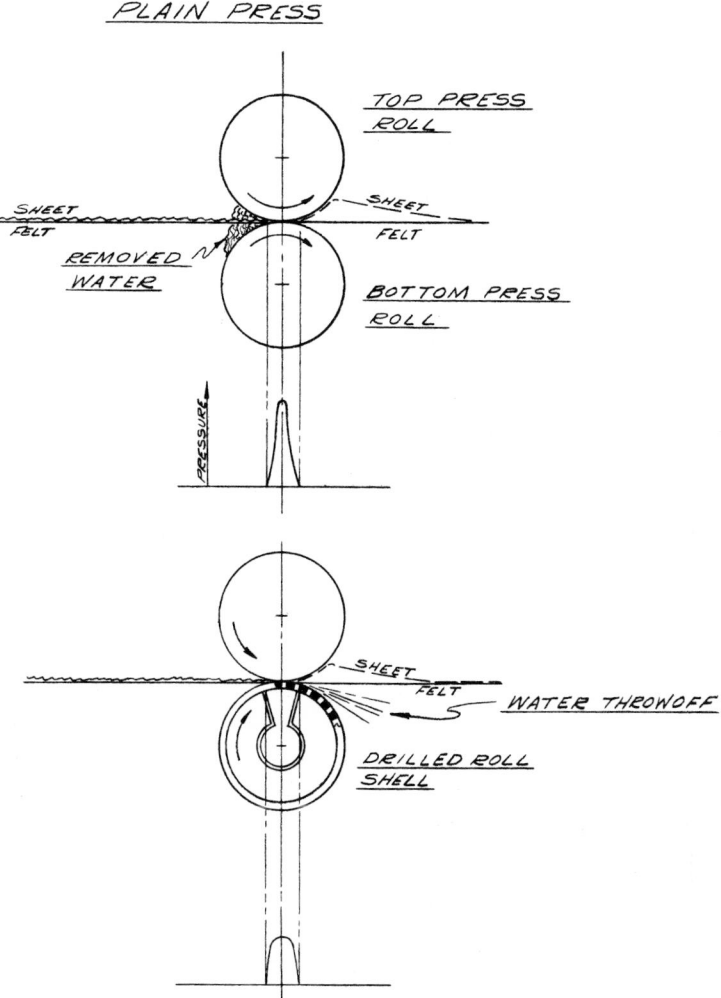

Fig. 12.31. Paper machine press.

cess water from the sheet by mechanical means than by evaporation in the dryer section. The practical limit of mechanical water removal is about 35 to 40% dryness (one part fiber to three parts of water). Drynesses much higher than this cannot be obtained economically. There is a theoretical limit to pressing, dependent largely upon the capillary structure of the sheet, the press felts, and the mechanical pressure employed [10,11].

The sheet is carried through the press section by one or more press felts. These blanket-like webs, made of wool and synthetic fibers, act as conveyors and porous mats to facilitate the pressing or squeezing of water from the wet sheet. When the felt and sheet sandwich passes through the loaded press rolls it undergoes a rapid application of mechanical pressure. With plain "undrilled" press rolls the pressure rise at the ingoing side of the nip causes a reverse flow of water through the felt and sheet. Most of the flow passes through the felt because of its greater thickness and porosity. Figure 12.31 illustrates a plain press and the approximate pressure profile in the nip.

It has been found that plain presses have definite speed and water removal limitations. Many of these shortcomings have

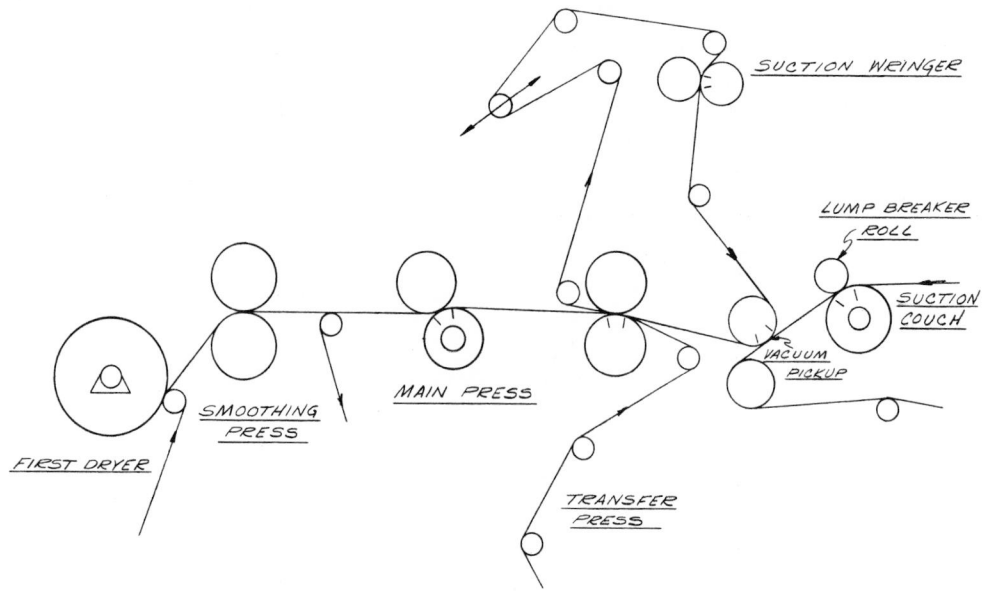

Fig. 12.32. Paper machine press section.

been overcome by drilling one of the press rolls and installing a vacuum box within the roll which applies vacuum in the nip area (Figure 12.32). Pressure is relieved by the closely spaced holes, about $\frac{3}{16}$ inch in diameter, in the shell of the roll which contacts the felt. There will be a felt in contact with the side of the sheet toward the drilled roll in order to avoid marking. One may be used on the other side also.

Although the use of a drilled press roll will improve water removal, vacuum is applied to a sector of the roll by means of a vacuum box to retain the water which is forced into the holes until it can be thrown off where it will not rewet the felt. A special type of suction press applies a vacuum to the felt wrapping the roll before it enters the nip. This so-called "air bleed" type of press dewaters the felt by pulling air through it before the sheet and felt enter the press nip. It has been found that the final press moisture is closely related to the outgoing felt moisture. Consequently where high levels of dryness are desired, every effort is made to dewater the press felt.

In general, most paper machines operate with top press roll doctors. It is the func-

tion of the doctors to keep the surface of the roll clean and free from fiber particles. If the sheet wraps around the press roll, the felt is likely to be ruined. Should a break occur in the sheet anywhere between the first press and the second section of dryers, the web is usually broken down at the first press and the paper is then accumulated at the first press roll location until it can be rethreaded.

Straight-through Press

The most common type of press is a straight-through press (Figure 12.31). In this type, the sheet passes straight through the nip of rolls, the wire side of the sheet contacting the press felt. The straight-through press may use a suction roll in the bottom position in one or more of the presses. In Figure 12.32, the main press would be considered a suction straight-through press.

Reversed Press

In some press arrangements, one of the presses may be reversed. This allows the wire side of the sheet to come in contact with the bare roll of the reverse press. Certain grades of paper require that the compression or felt marks be minimized. The reverse press tends to minimize these effects and the "two sidedness" of the sheet. Figure 12.33 illustrates a typical reverse press arrangement.

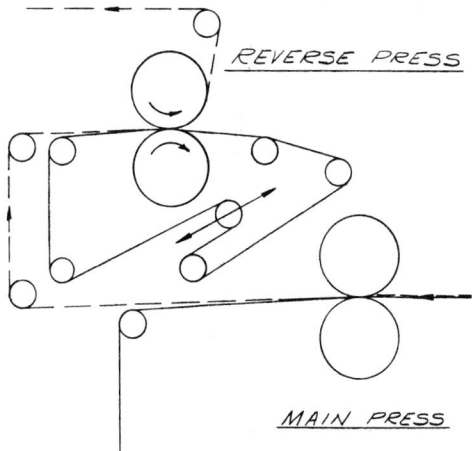

Fig. 12.33. Reverse press arrangement.

Dual Presses

The dual press is composed of three rolls, usually set in approximately the same horizontal plane, which have two pressing nips. The center roll rotates on a fixed center line while the first and third rolls on either side are pivoted and held in position by pneumatic or hydraulic loading. The first roll is usually driven by a positive drive connection and is generally a rubber-covered suction roll. The center roll is a hard-surface roll corresponding to the top press roll in a conventional press. The third is a rubber-covered plain roll or rubber-covered suction roll and is driven by a helper drive. In operation the sheet passes through the first press nip, adheres to the bare center roll and passes on through the second press nip. The advantages of such a press are savings in space, savings in rolls, and the fact that there is no open draw between the two presses.

Various other types of multiple press arrangements are currently in use. Their advantages are somewhat balanced by the more complex drive arrangements necessary, possible difficulty in changing felts, and less space available for maintenance work.

Transfer Press

A suction pick-up arrangement is frequently utilized for light-weight sheets. The suction pick-up roll is similar to a suction press roll and is used to pick the sheet off the wire and hold it on a transfer felt. The sheet is carried by the felt to the first press position. The first press consists of a bottom suction press roll and a plain top press roll. The sheet is transferred to the bottom felt by the suction at the roll nip and is carried on through the pressing operation in the usual manner. This sequence of events is illustrated in Figure 12.32.

Smoothing Press

A smoothing press, as the name implies, is used to smooth the sheet and iron out any small irregularities in it before it enters the dryer section. At this point the sheet is still plastic and can be gently worked. The sheet contacts both rolls, as no felts are used in this type of press. This press is used only for smoothing and is not intended to remove any moisture from the sheet. Such a press is also illustrated in Figure 12.32.

In sheets making crepe, tissue, or machine glazed paper with a Yankee dryer the sheet is pressed against the Yankee surface with a pressure roll. The pressures used are usually quite high, and this press nip constitutes an efficient water removal operation. Water removal is augmented by the fact that the Yankee dryer is hot and aids in transferring water from the sheet to the press felt. Figure 12.34 is a sheet run for a typical Yankee machine in which a dual pressure roll is being used. It has been found that improved press dryness is obtained by using a double pressure roll.

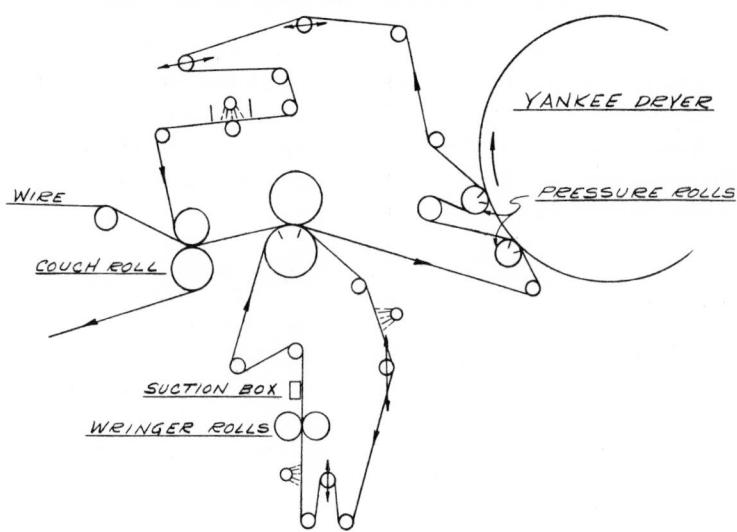

Fig. 12.34. Yankee dryer with dual press rolls.

Felt Types and Their Manufacture

The claim is made that nearly 2,000 years ago Chinese paper makers used woolen fabric to couch or remove a wet web of paper formed in a hand mold. Thus, wool fibers in fabric form have always played an important part in the production of paper. Because of wool's unusual properties of wettability and resilience, wool-synthetic blends continue to be considered the best available for paper machine press or wet felts. Paper machine press felts are woven fabrics, endless in form, designed specifically for the purpose and requiring for their manufacture specialized equipment and skills. Such a felt serves many purposes—that of a conveyor belt, a filter, and a power-transmission device. It must withstand all the difficult conditions encountered on a paper machine and still provide a smooth, soft, yet resilient cushion for conveying a wet web of paper too weak to support itself.

After weaving, paper machine felts are felted or "fulled." In this process, the wool yarns are worked together under the influence of moisture and heat to give a cushion-like surface, the individual yarns interlocking with each other. The construction is sufficiently open to permit the passage of water, but the web of paper can be carried without marking. A wide variety of felt surfaces, porosities, weights, capillary sizes and strengths can be produced to meet the needs of the paper maker. Most felts, particularly for the finer grade, have a nap to prevent the wet web from being pressed against the strength members of the felt and thus receiving an impression. A method of "needling" a protective surface over the felt fabric has also been perfected.

Wool felts with their wettable fibers have the ability to absorb large amounts of water and release it under pressure. They also have a sufficiently fine capillary structure to pick up a wet sheet of paper from another carrying medium, such as the Fourdrinier wire, and deliver it to another point without injuring the sheet and with no particles of paper stock adhering to it.

Certain synthetic fibers such as nylon, "Dacron," "Terylene," and others, are very strong and show increased resistance to-abrasion when properly used in paper-making felts. Felts made of all synthetic fibers have not been particularly successful; however, when properly used in combination with wool, some synthetics tend to improve the over-all product. Increased felt life with lighter weight and greater openness is frequently possible with synthetic fiber content in a properly engineered felt.

Care of Felts

Under a given set of operating conditions, the life of a felt depends largely upon the type of felt employed, the hardness and loading of the rolls, and the speed of the machine. In making up a felt for any position (they are usually custom-made), the felt supplier must compromise between the strength and durability of the felt and the fineness and openness required to prevent sheet damage. In general, the heaviest and coarsest felts used on any position will give the best life. Water removal is improved by more openness in the felt, finer wools, and lighter weight. Higher loading and harder rolls will also increase the amount of water removal but will decrease felt life proportionately. Once a good felt design is found, it should give uniform performance as long as it is properly maintained. Assuming that the felts have been properly stored and installed on the machine which is in good operating condition, felt life depends largely upon good operating conditions and proper cleaning of the felt.

Felt Cleaning and Conditioning

The felts must be cleaned frequently in order to open them up and to enable them to remove water efficiently. Dirty felts have a tendency to mark the sheet and cause crushing and blowing in the press nips. The purpose of washing felts is primarily to remove the dirt, which consists of grease, pitch, sizing, silt, mineral particles, fillers, and pulp fiber particles. This dirt becomes entangled in the nap of the felt and is beaten into the felt body fibers by continuous working through the press rolls and around the felt rolls over the suction boxes.

It is virtually standard practice today to keep press felts in uniform condition by means of some continuous cleaning device which removes foreign matter from the felt. One of the simplest of these is a shower and wringer arrangement which applies an excess of water to the felt which is removed at a wringer roll. Another type of conditioner consists of a box which is oscillated across the width of the felt. As the conditioning box travels across the working face of the felt, warm water is forced through the felt and pulled back again by vacuum, thus cleaning it and treating the yarns so that the felt does not become matted and hardened.

Felts may be washed on the machine by loosening the felt, roping it up a little and letting it run for 30 to 60 minutes under a strong shower of clear water. When clean, the felt may be turned over (if double-napped) to ensure uniform wear on both sides. Sometimes soap and soda ash may be poured onto the felt to aid in cleaning. Felts are sometimes removed from the machines altogether and put in regular washers.

The most popular felt conditioner at present is the Vickery. This device consists of a number of shoes which travel back and forth in contact with the felt. It moves across the machine by means of a screw drive and automatically reverses at the end of its travel. Warm water is forced up through the felt and the suction opening immediately draws it back through the felt along with the removed dirt.

Whippers are rotating spiders which carry rounded blades of wood or brass pipes. They strike the felt, beating and loosening the dirt. They are rotated at low speeds so that the nap of the felt is not destroyed. In general, whippers are found only on older, slow-speed machines and their only action is to work the felt which tends to break loose caked particles.

Causes of Felt Failures

Abnormal felt wear may be due to:

(1) Slippage of felt on roll surfaces due to bad bearing or improperly synchronized driven roll;

(2) Sharp, rough, and worn surface condition of rolls, suction boxes, conditioner shoes, whipper bars, worming strips, etc.;

(3) Poorly screened stock, abrasive material and filler such as glass and sand;

(4) Abnormally high shower pressure and needle type of showers over long periods of time;

(5) Improper crowning and sharp edges on rolls;

(6) Improperly aligned rolls and whipper assemblies;

(7) Guide mechanism not functioning properly;

(8) Cleaning methods which are harmful to fabric of the felts, such as strongly acid or alkaline solutions;

(9) Abrasion of the felt fibers due to the felts' becoming filled up or dirty.

Felts are worn out as a result of mechanical, bacterial, and chemical degradation. These often occur at the same time. Normal acidities used in paper making have no effect on wool, but alkalies are harmful. Above a pH of 9, wool loses its strength rapidly, especially in warmer climates, and therefore a strongly alkaline solution should be avoided. Bacterial effects are often aggravated by high operating temperatures.

Press Loading

The moisture content of a sheet leaving a press depends upon the pressure in the press nip. As it approachs a maximum, the moisture content of the sheet decreases almost linearly. The pressure in the nip, however, is a function of both the applied load and the width of the nip. The width of the nip is affected by the hardness of the rolls and their sizes. As two rolls are pressed together, the area of contact in the nip increases so that the rate of increase in pressure is not proportional to the applied load. Greater dryness may be achieved, however, by increasing press loading and by using harder rolls. Increasing the loading on the press will tend to cause crushing or blowing in the press and both heavier loading and harder rolls have a tendency to shorten felt life.

A roll is said to be crowned when it is larger in the middle then at the ends and gradually tapers from the middle to the ends according to a smooth curve. This crown is necessary to compensate for the deflection of the roll under the action of the following forces:

(1) Weight of the roll itself;

(2) Applied load;

(3) Pull of the tension of the felts;

(4) Vacuum of the inner suction box on the suction roll shell.

Any large press roll in a machine will sag somewhat because of its own weight and the pull of the felts. If they were ground perfectly straight and cylindrical, two press rolls would not touch except at the ends as a result of this sag. By means of proper crowning, a close approximation to uniform loading may be obtained across the width of the press. It is obvious that a press roll crowned for one pressure will not be properly crowned for another. Paper machine roll crown calculations are quite complex and technical [12,13].

Several so-called crownless press rolls have been developed which tend to minimize this difficulty. They are particularly applicable where a wide range of loadings is desired. Press loadings are adjusted to a value where good water removal is obtained with reasonable felt life. In many cases, some experimentation with press crowns and felt construction is necessary to achieve optimum results.

Press Moisture Profiles

It is important for subsequent pressing and drying operations that the uniformity of moisture coming out of a press be good from front to back of the machine. This can be checked by taking a series of moisture samples across the width of the machine at the press. On wide machines, the press profiles frequently have an M or W shape indicating a somewhat more complex problem. Not only the amount of crown but its distribution across the width of the machine is important. The shape of the profile can also be affected by the amount of press loading applied by the hydraulic or pneumatic cylinders. In some cases, it is helpful to measure the pressure profile by running a sandwich of carbon paper and white paper through the nip. The blackness of the impression gives an indication of the pressure at any point. Recently some other methods of measuring nip pressure have been developed which make use of NCR paper and embossed aluminum foil [14].

The amount of deflection of a roll varies directly with the pressure. Thus a roll can be correctly ground for only one pressure, and if a different pressure be applied in the roll, the crown will be incorrect. A given crown frequently is not suited to all operating conditions. The use of rubber covering increases the range of satisfactory operation of a roll with a given crown. Rubber increases the nip width, however, decreasing the pressure per square inch. This tends to increase felt life and correct for a faulty crown, but gives less dewatering action.

DRYER SECTION

As it passes from the press section, the sheet consists of about 32 to 35% dry fiber. From this point on, it is necessary to apply heat in order to reach the desired final state of dryness. The usual method of drying uses a series of cast-iron, steam-heated rolls, 48 to 60 inches in diameter. The sheet is passed over and under these until the desired dryness is reached, usually about 6% water content. The number of dryers is determined by the amount of water to be evaporated, the speed of the machine, and the weight of the sheet. The paper is held tightly against the drying cylinder by a cotton or woolen felt called a dryer felt which also helps in threading the paper through the dryer section.

Arrangement

Figure 12.35 shows a group of dryers divided into two sections. Each section has its own top and bottom dryer felt and felt dryers. The drives for these sections normally have provision for varying the speed slightly to allow for shrinkage as the paper dries. The felt serves the dual purpose of picking up moisture from the wet sheet as it is heated, and holding the sheet in contact with the dryers for good heat transfer. The top and bottom felts each have one or more "felt dryers" to help reduce the moisture content of the felt and improve its water-removing ability.

Another felt dryer, the Feeney, named after its originator, contacts the paper side of the felt at a point a few cylinders from the beginning of the section to dry the felt during its travel with the wet sheet.

At the beginning of the dryer section there is a small dryer roll called a "baby

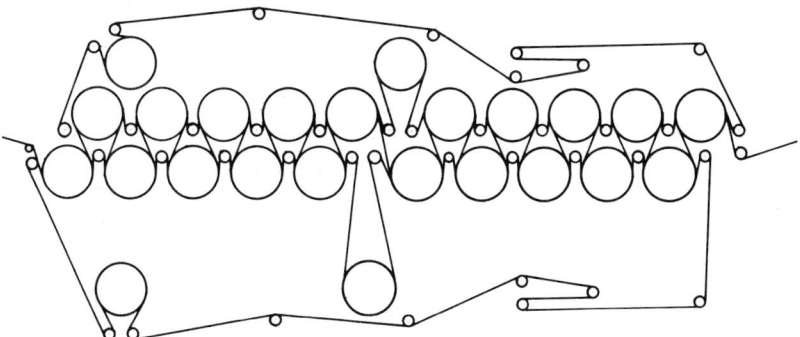

Fig. 12.35. Paper machine dryer section.

dryer" or receiving dryer, used as a lead-in from the press to the dryer section. A "spring roll" is located between the last dryer roll and the calender stack to take up any minor changes in tension and prevent breaking of the sheet. This small light-weight idler roll has its bearings mounted in springs so that it may be deflected some distance from its neutral position.

A rope carrier is arranged to thread a narrow tail of the sheet through the dryers when re-threading. This is a two- or three-rope device into which the operator drops a narrow "tail" at the beginning of the dryer section. The ropes grasp this tail and carry it through the press and dryers to the spring roll. After the tail is well started through the section, it is gradually widened out by moving the trim squirt on the Four-drinier wire.

On certain types of paper machines a "breaker stack" is located between dryer sections (Figure 12.36). This calender stack is actually a smoothing device to give the sheet the caliper and density desired by the consumer. The breaker stack is placed between the dryer sections at the point where the sheet is still damp enough to be pressed and compacted effectively.

Drying Cylinders

The standard paper dryer is a four- or five-foot diameter cast-iron shell or "can" machined to a smooth finish on the outer surface. It is also bored out at the inner surface to give a uniform wall thickness allowing for an even transfer of heat. This machining also serves to improve the important balance of the dryer.

The framework supporting the dryers is extremely heavy and rugged, for it must support not only the dryer journals themselves but all the piping and auxiliary equipment. The framing must also give accessibility to the dryer surface for repairs, for sheet handling, and for the unobstructed flow of air removing vapor from the felt and sheet.

Fig. 12.36. Paper machine "breaker stack." (*Courtesy Albemarle Paper Manufacturing Co. and Beloit Corp.*)

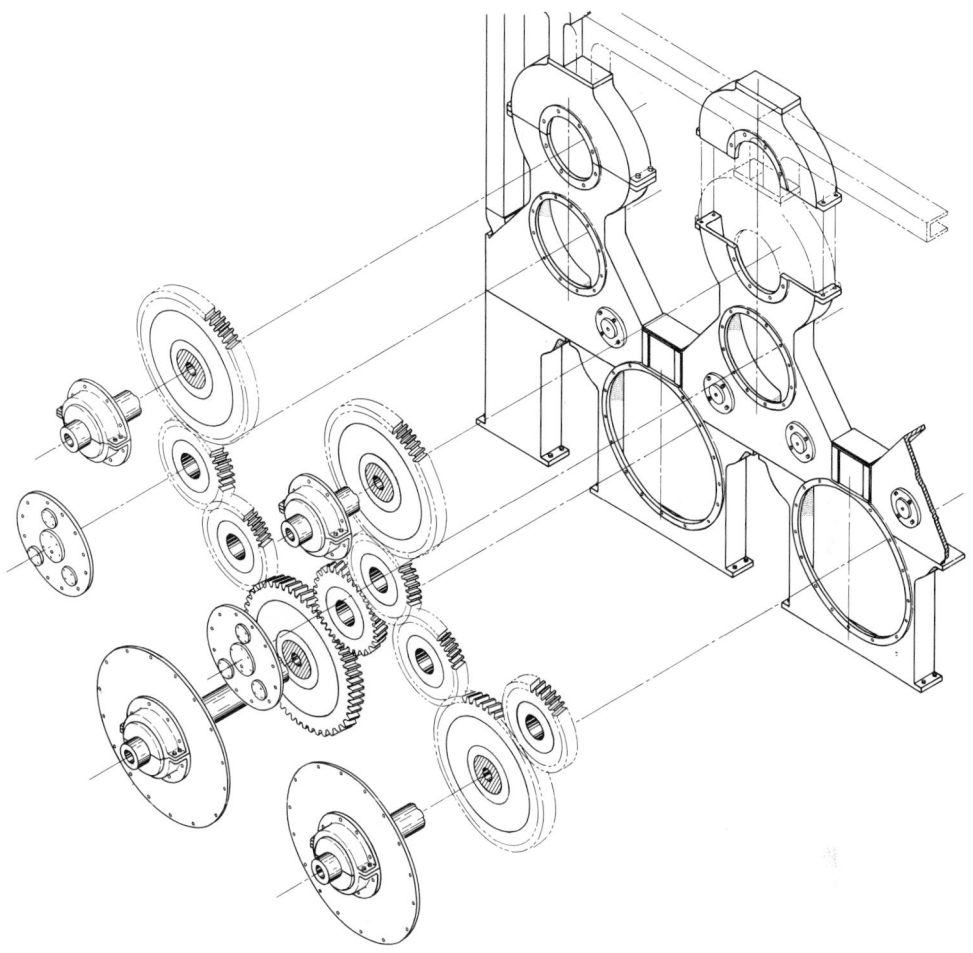

Fig. 12.37. Pinion gear drive. (*Courtesy Black Clawson Co.*)

Antifriction dryer bearings are used on all high-speed paper machines to minimize starting loads. The bearings are provided with a constant supply of clean lubricant. Continuous lubrication dissipates the heat given off by the dryer and carries away moisture which has been separated from the oil at the main filtration tank.

There are several methods of driving the dryer section. The oldest is an open gear train meshed together so that each dryer in the section is running at the same surface speed. Other dryer-section drives operate with chains and pinions, worm gears, or multiple gears between dryers. Modern high-speed machines use enclosed drive gears which provide more or less unobstructed access to the back side of the dryer section. Figure 12.37 is a view of a pinion gear drive.

Steam to heat the dryers is introduced through the hollow back journal, and the exhaust steam and condensate are removed through this same journal. Transfer of steam and condensate is accomplished by a device called a "steam fit" or "steam joint" (see Figure 12.38). The steam fit allows for the passage of steam into the dryer and the evacuation of condensate from the interior of the dryer. Today the spring-loaded carbon ring type has become universal in most steam joints. All steam joints

Fig. 12.38. Dryer steam joint. (*Courtesy Beloit Corp.*)

must be carefully aligned, since any undue strains will cause the carbon rings to wear and permit leakage. Removal of condensate from the dryer is extremely important, as it will form an insulating layer on the inside surface if its thickness is allowed to build up.

The wall of cast iron conducts heat 85 times as well as the same wall of water and 2,000 times as readily as a wall of air. Therefore, air and water must be effectively removed from the dryers for good heat transfer. Water also increases the power required to drive the dryers. This power increases until the water goes around with the dryer—a condition known as "rimming."

There must be a difference in pressure between the steam inside the dryer and the condensate line of about 2 psi to force the water up through the syphon pipe which, in its simplest form, is a small pipe bent down from the center line to a point just clearing the bottom of the dryer. Steam

condensate systems of this kind are based on a "blow through" principle to evacuate the condensate and noncondensable gases and create good steam circulation for uniform dryer temperature.

The revolving type of syphon consists of one or more curved syphon pipes secured to a fitting bolted to the dryer head. This syphon acts on the same principle as the stationary type, but revolves with the dryer and is frequently equipped with a small scoop to remove water from the inner surface of the dryer. It utilizes gravity, but is also affected by the centrifugal force acting on the rotating part. Almost all high-speed machines use revolving syphons.

Doctor blades are usually provided on dryers to keep them from becoming coated with fuzz, coating, and other materials which would reduce heat transfer. Such doctors are usually arranged so that the fuzz that accumulates on them can be removed without falling into the sheet. Every effort should be made to keep dryers clean and to prevent lint, scale, and fuzz from coming in contact with the sheet. For certain applications, an oscillating motion may be imparted to the doctor to increase its efficiency. This is accomplished by a motor or hydraulic oscillating device.

Dryer Felts

Dryer felts are used for the manufacture of most grades of paper. They serve to increase the contact pressure of the web of paper with the dryer face and, hence, the drying rate. The dryer felt absorbs a certain amount of water vapor and must also allow steam to pass through it to be carried away by the ventilating system. Cotton felts with single duplex or triplex weave are commonly employed. So-called asbestos felt, containing about 60% cotton and 40% asbestos, is used for certain grades of paper. The use of wool and synthetics in dryer felts is somewhat limited by their high initial cost. They have several advantages, however, since wool dryer felts give better finish, better drying efficiency and tend to hug the dryer more tightly in the areas where the sheet is the wettest.

Dryer felts are among the most difficult of paper machine accessories to manipulate. They are made of very hard and firm material and do not stretch like woolen felts except by wetting and drying.

Dryer felts should be provided with an automatic tightener roll. They are subject to a variety of conditions because of the heat of the dryers, the moisture of the paper, the speed of the machine, and such accidents as paper wrapping around a dryer. Consequently, the felt take-up must be sensitive and respond to all variations. Carrying rolls not in proper alignment with the dryer felt will cause it to travel from one side of the machine to the other, and in many cases to wrinkle. Dryer felts should be provided with automatic guides, similar to wire guides, which will respond readily to the slightest variation in location.

There are several methods of joining the ends of these felts when putting them on the machine. The clipper seam has become fairly universal because it is more rapid than sewing to form a lap or joint in the felt.

Air Hoods and Air Systems

The use of air in paper making is common to all mills. In a sense, it is the largest single constituent used in paper production. It accomplishes many important purposes in passing through the mill. For example, air is used to eliminate condensation and deterioration of building and equipment, to provide comfortable working conditions, and finally to pick up moisture liberated in the drying process before it is exhausted.

Air systems are arranged for the following purposes. In many cases, the same air can be re-used to accomplish several of these in succession.

(1) Heat and ventilate the room for the comfort and health of workers.

(2) Assist the machine dryers to evaporate water from the sheet.

(3) Remove, economically, the resulting vapor from the dryer section.

(4) Prolong the life of the dryer felts and prevent deterioration.

(5) Assist in maintaining uniformity of moisture content of the dried sheet.

(6) Perform other smaller, but equally important, duties such as cooling calender rolls and electric drives, and handling trim and dust from the machine.

In addition, much useful heat is recovered from the air as it leaves the mill.

The main purpose of a hood over a paper machine is to catch and confine the vapors from the machine before they have a chance to disperse in the room. In so doing, hoods often increase the production, improve the quality of the final paper, and make possible considerable savings in thermal energy. Care has to be taken in the design of a hood to see that the vapors are collected properly. The confinement of the vapors reduces to a minimum the deterioration of mill construction and equipment. In gen-

Fig. 12.39. Dryer section hood. (*Courtesy Wausau Paper Mills Co. and Beloit Corp.*)

Fig. 12.40. Enclosed dryer section hood. (*Courtesy International Paper Co. and Beloit Corp.*)

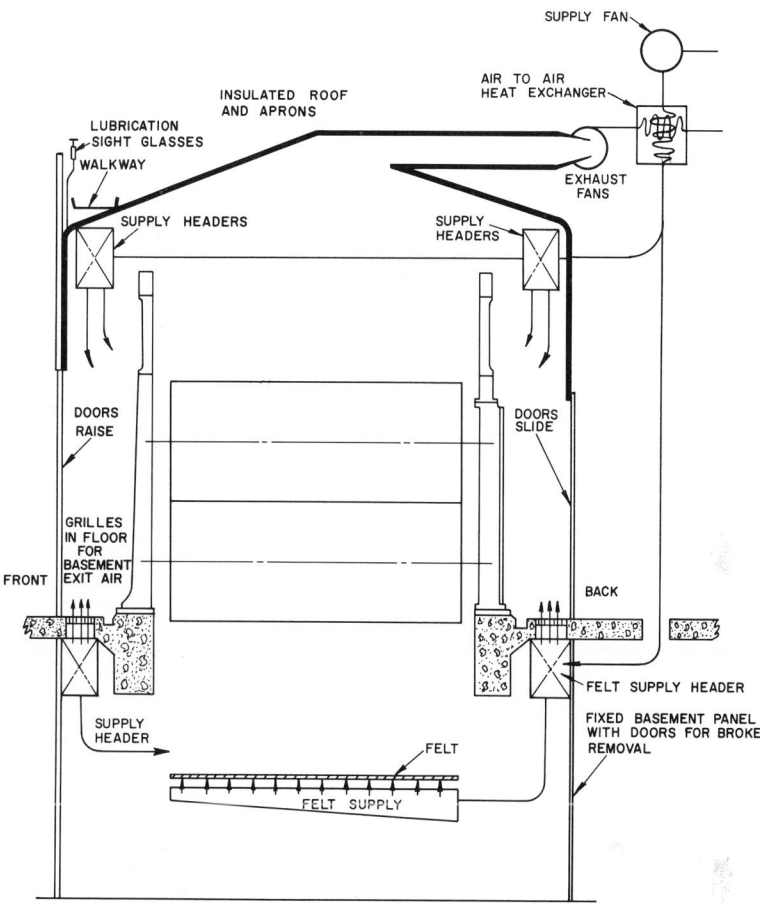

Fig. 12.41. Enclosed paper machine hood. (*Courtesy Beloit Corp.*)

eral, hoods can be described as open (see Figure 12.39) or totally enclosed (see Figure 12.40). There are also special designs of hoods for Yankee machines which do not fall within the generally accepted ideas of either of these types.

Open hoods are usually arranged with fairly wide overhangs on both the front and back side and are equipped with deep curtains to ensure catching the vapor (Figure 12.39). In general, these hoods are built up of asbestos board or aluminum panels on a steel structure supported, in most cases, from the machine frame. The top slopes up on both sides to a peaked ridge. Exhaust take-off ducts, located along the machine, extend horizontally to the rear under the crane, or may be extended vertically through the roof with slip joints to allow passage of the crane.

The closed hood (see Figure 12.40) has aluminum-insulated top panels with two sections of panels for each side. The top side sections are stationary on both the front and back of the machine. The lower front sections can be lifted vertically to provide a clear working space in front in case of a paper break. The lower back is made with sliding panels for occasional access. The basement area around the bottom felt must be completely closed to prevent chimney action which would cause excessive leakage of vapor to the machine room (see Figure 12.41). Considerable economy can be realized by the use of enclosed hoods, since lower volumes of air are required and increased efficiency and production are obtained. The amount of air necessary with an enclosed hood is approximately 50% of that for an open hood.

All the outside make-up air required for a closed hood can be applied to improve conditions in the operating areas such as the dry end, wet end, and center aisle. After the air has picked up heat in these areas it can go to the machine or to the roof. This means that the pick-up points for the felt system and roof systems should be at the hottest point.

Roof air is hot air blown out against the roof of the building to prevent condensation, dripping, and deterioration of the roof structure.

The felt air system applies heated air uniformly along the length of the dryer section in the basement under the machine. This heated air, passing upward on both sides of the dryer nest, picks up the water vapor coming out of the pocket between the dryers and felts, and carries it to the top exhaust ducts or exhaust hood. The heated air could be distributed along the floor under the bottom of the felts and satisfy the requirements, but it is usually blown directly against the felts where it will improve the rate and uniformity of drying and increase the life of the felts.

Vapor Removal System

On board machines without dryer felts it is possible to use nozzle pipes extending across the full width of the machine located in the pockets formed by the board and the dryers. A vapor absorption system will normally increase production by about 15 to 20% and help to improve the uniformity of drying across the web.

Various methods are in use to improve vapor removal from the pockets in dryers both with and without felts and to increase evaporation from the felt itself. Small nozzles with high-pressure, high-velocity air discharge from a point just outside the paper web are frequently used to force the vapor out of the pockets. This is the Grewin system, named after the Swedish inventor (see Figure 12.42). The pressure is about 1 psi and the velocities are about 20,000 fpm depending upon the size of the nozzle, diameter of the dryer, and the face width of the dryer. At the wet end where the sheet is weak and the draws are loose, the velocities must be reduced. Several systems have been proposed for blowing out hot air or pulling in air through the felt-turning rolls located between the dryers. It is important that the felt have some porosity for this application. Good results have been reported on installations of this type particularly where the dryer section is heavily loaded and the felt drying is limited.

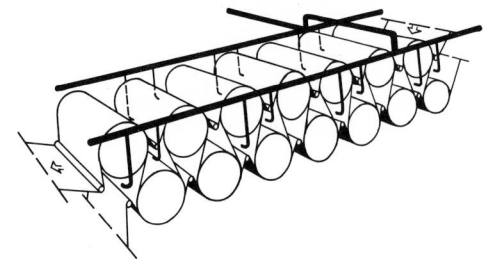

Fig. 12.42. Grewin system. (*Courtesy Beloit Corp.*)

Figure 12.43 shows a typical steam-condensate system based on the blow-through principle to evacuate condensate and noncondensable gases from the drying cylinders. In the arrangements shown, there are two stages of heating; however, three or more may be arranged as desired. Steam at the maximum desired pressure is fed to the dry end group of dryers. The condensate, gases, and blow-through steam are piped to a separator which takes out the water and permits the steam and gases to pass to the wet end group of dryers at a lower pressure. This lower pressure is maintained by a differential controller which admits some make-up steam from the dry end steam header, as shown, or from the main steam lines. The blow-through steam from the wet end dryers, as well as any flash steam, is condensed in the condensate tank and the gases are removed by a vacuum pump.

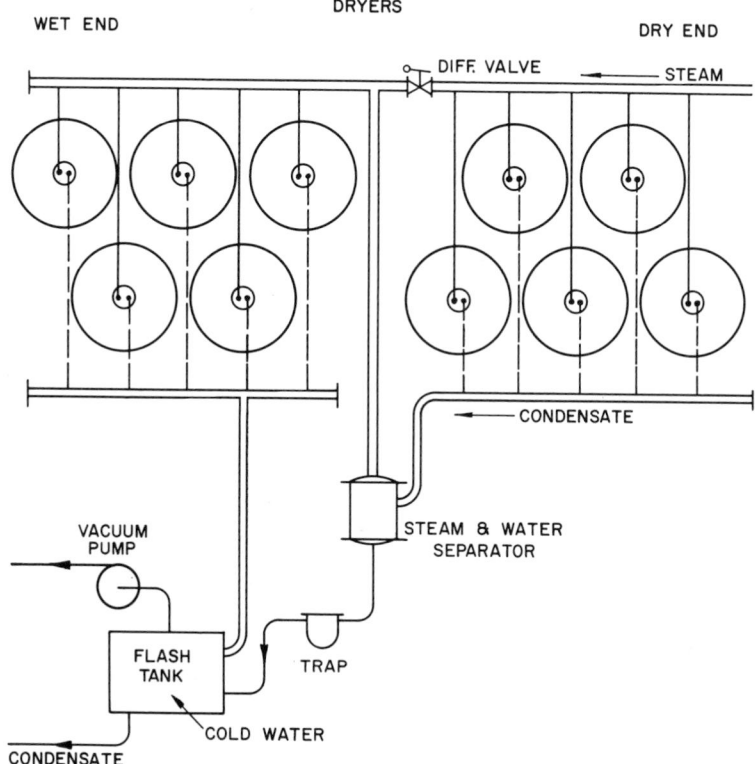

Fig. 12.43. Steam condensate system.

High Velocity Air Hoods

Air "hoods" or nozzle sections are being used over standard steam dryers to improve the rate or uniformity of drying.[15] Several designs are offered, but they are all based on using relatively large amounts of air impinging at high velocity (10,000 to 15,000 fpm) and at a high temperature (300 to 600°F).

One common feature of all these various hoods is the presence of air outlets (holes or nozzles) spaced from $\frac{1}{2}$ to 2 inches from the dryer surface. In some cases, they are arranged to vary the rate of drying across the width of the machine. Because of the close spacing to the dryer surface, these hoods are arranged so that they can be lifted away from the dryer to permit threading or cleaning. The effect of the high-velocity air is to improve heat transfer, in some cases, and to greatly expedite the removal of moisture. For a standard steam dryer,

the drying rate is increased from approximately 1 to 3 pounds to about 6 to 15 pounds per square foot per hour. The effectiveness of the high-velocity hood is dependent upon its location in the dryer section and the type of sheet being made.

One of the most promising uses of this equipment is for profile moisture control where the air hood can be used to compensate for variations in moisture content across the width of the sheet at the dry end. For these applications, the air hood is divided into a number of sections across the machine and the velocity of each is remote-controlled, as desired, to level the moisture profile.

YANKEE GLAZING AND CREPING DRYERS

The essential difference between a Yankee machine and a Fourdrinier machine is the method used in drying and finishing or surfacing the sheet of paper. The Yankee machine has one large-diameter dryer, sometimes as much as 16 feet in diameter, while ordinary machine dryers range from 4 to 6 feet in diameter. The Yankee dryer has a highly polished surface against which the wet sheet is pressed by one or more pressure rolls. The heat transfer is greatly improved and evaporations of 10 to 20 pounds per hour per square foot are common instead of the 1 to 3 pounds for the standard dryer arrangement.

Most Yankee dryers are not equipped with felts but make use of a high-velocity air hood which scrubs the vapor from the surface of the drying sheet as it makes its way to the surface. The paper may be creped off the surface of the dryer with a doctor blade in which case it has a bulky "pleated" finish used for tissue and towels. Paper creped off when the sheet is practically dry has a softer, lighter feel than that removed at higher moisture contents. Towels are usually made with a "wet" crepe requiring that the paper be further dried after removal from the Yankee dryer.

If the paper is taken off the dryer "flat" or without creping, the side of the paper next to the dryer will be machine-glazed or have an "MG" finish.

The speed and production of a Yankee machine is limited largely by the capacity of the big paper dryer. To allow increased production, conventional paper machine dryers are frequently added before the Yankee dryer. By means of these "predryers," the web of paper can be heated and brought to a reduced moisture content still sufficient to permit good adhesion on the surface of the Yankee. Dryers used after the Yankee result in a lower finish on the paper, but the production capacity of the machine is increased. Many modern Yankee machines produce tissue papers and creped wadding at speeds over 3,000 fpm. It is essential that the surface of the dryer be kept absolutely clean. In many cases, the dryer is supplied with some sort of polishing or cleaning apparatus to continuously buff or polish the surface.

Hoods

The hoods for Yankee dryers are usually of the high-velocity air-impingement type so arranged as to maximize the drying rate. Good removal of evaporated moisture will cool the surface of the sheet and improve the heat transfer through the Yankee shell. An effective hood for rapid vapor removal is essential to the high drying rates common to Yankee dryers.

Steam and condensate systems for Yankee dryers must be unusually efficient because of the rapid rate of heat transfer and heavy drying loads. Blow-through systems are used almost exclusively with a multiplicity of nozzles to handle the large volumes of condensate produced. It is important that the interior surfaces of the Yankee dryer be swept as free of condensate as possible.

Construction

The design and construction of Yankee dryers is quite specialized. To withstand pressure roll loadings of 250 to 400 pounds per inch of width and support itself rigidly, the dryer shell is two to three inches thick. Nearly all Yankee shells are made of high-quality cast iron having a tensile strength of about 60,000 psi. The dryer itself consists of several parts—the shell, two heads, and a strong center shaft which provides journals for rotation, supports the endwise thrust on the heads, and provides a conduit for steam and condensate handling.

In the United States dryers are limited in diameter to 12 feet for most locations because of transportation difficulties. A 12-foot diameter Yankee dryer will weigh approximately 53 tons.

SPECIAL DRYING EQUIPMENT

Minton Vacuum Dryers

At reduced pressure, water boils at temperatures below 212°F. By sealing up the

Fig. 12.44. Minton dryer. (*Courtesy Rice Barton Corp.*)

dryer section in a chamber and applying a vacuum, several advantages are obtained. For instance, at the usual vacuum of 28 inches of mercury, water boils at 100°F. For a given steam pressure and temperature within the dryers, a much greater temperature difference exists across the sheet and dryer; hence greater heat transfer is obtained, reducing the number of dryers required. Removal of vapor from the pockets within the dryer cylinders is also taken care of by the vacuum system, which evacuates and condenses the water vapor given off from the sheet.

The Minton dryer is a patented design used for some special applications. The dryer section, including rolls and felts, is enclosed in an airtight cast-iron chamber (Figure 12.44). At one end of this chamber an ingenious seal or trap allows the wet paper to pass through but does not admit any air. There is a similar contrivance at the other end of the chamber which allows the dry paper to emerge without breaking the vacuum pump. A powerful vacuum pump

and an efficient condenser maintain the vacuum in this chamber at about 28 inches of mercury. Doors and glass windows are provided at frequent intervals so that the passage of paper can be observed from the outside. The drying conditions can be immediately and accurately governed by the operator and are entirely independent of the weather. The first cost of such installations is obviously high.

Straight-through or Conveyor Dryers

Grades which are too stiff or brittle to pass around dryer rolls are frequently dried in straight-through or conveyor dryers, or tunnels. These have particular application to building board and pulp mats. This sheet is supported by wire mesh, mechanical conveyors or a system of air jets so that it passes directly through the drying region. Heat is applied and vapor removed by the impinging hot air. In order to conserve space, such dryers are sometimes built in several layers, the sheet passing through one bank and then dropping down to the next one traveling in the opposite direction. Such a drying method is not particularly adaptable to sheets which must be held flat to prevent cockling during the drying operation.

Infrared Drying

As the paper web becomes dryer and the water content approaches zero, the conductivity of the sheet decreases noticeably. To overcome this difficulty with conventional dryers, infrared radiation is finding some application. Heat radiators consist of gas burners, electrical sources and radiating surfaces heated by circulating liquids. Such dryers tend to be more expensive than conventional means of drying paper; however, they have been found to be suitable and economical for several applications.

Sweating Dryers

Sweating dryers are not dryers in the truest sense, although they are frequently found in the dryer section. A roll filled with cold or cool water will become covered with condensation or "sweat" in the humid atmosphere of a dryer section. This device is frequently used to re-introduce some moisture into the sheet to obtain the desired final moisture content.

HEAT RECOVERY EQUIPMENT

A large portion of the heat supplied in paper mills for comfort heating and the drying of paper is exhausted from the machine room with the moist air. The reclamation of heat in the vapor removed from the machines represents an important saving in thermal energy. It is particularly true of mills in the northern climates, where the use of vapor economizers is almost standard practice. The economizer acts like a large heat-transfer unit where incoming outside air is heated by the moist exhaust air. A cross-flow type of unit, consisting of a series of corrugated metal plates, is usually employed. The passage for the exhaust vapor is vertical and straight, and the passage for

the make-up air passes on the opposite side of the corrugated plates.

Water can also be sprayed before, over, or after the economizer to increase the heat recovery and provide warm water which can be used in heating the white water system. Approximately 10 to 15% of the thermal energy in the air can be recovered by an economizer for heating outdoor make-up air. The total heat recovery can be increased to approximately 30% for combined air and water heating.

CALENDERS

Paper made in the most simple way does not have a very smooth surface. It was found by the ancient Arabs, however, that "stone glazing"—a procedure which involved placing the sheet of paper on a square block of wood, after which it was rubbed with a piece of flint or glass—produced a surface of astonishingly high smoothness and gloss. This finishing process was so satisfactory that even today it is being used in special cases, the stone of course being moved mechanically over the sheet.

Calendering, in essence, is the application of pressure and some degree of friction, resulting in a smoother surface and compaction of the sheet. The usual calender "stack" consists of two or more horizontal rolls held in place by a rugged framework. Calender rolls are usually made of chilled cast iron of extremely fine grain and the arrangement is dependent upon the specific requirements. The sheet is often guided by angular steel fingers, called "ductors," into each roll nip. Emerging from the first nip, the sheet is guided back into the second nip and proceeds from nip to nip, coming out at the nip between the bottom roll and the roll above it on the reel side of the calender.

The bottom calender roll is usually the only driven roll in the stack, the others being driven by friction from this roll. The bottom roll is the largest in the stack and is sometimes called the "king roll." The top roll is frequently referred to as the "queen roll."

Most modern calenders are equipped to hold exacting nip pressures by hydraulic or pneumatic methods. A load is applied to the journals of the top roll and separate lifting arrangements may be fitted to the individual rolls in the stack.

The normal machine calender is placed after the dryer section and before the reel. It helps to control the bulk and density of the sheet before reeling and aids greatly in winding up uniform reels. A machine stack is also used immediately before a machine coater or size press to compact the sheet and control sheet porosity and smoothness.

Because of the heavy loads carried by the bottom roll in a calender stack it is crowned to compensate for deflection under load. In some cases, all rolls in the stack are crowned; in others the upper rolls are ground in cylindrical form and the bottom roll is crowned. Figure 12.45 is a picture of a typical machine calender stack. Calender rolls are heated by the sheet emerging from the dryer section and also by the friction of forces exerted at the paper nips. It has been found that adjustments in crowns and calender roll contours can be made by local cooling. This is usually done by a series of air pipes fitted with adjustable valves which can be used to cool the calender roll selectively. This may be looked on as a special trimming or crown adjustment on the operating calender stack.

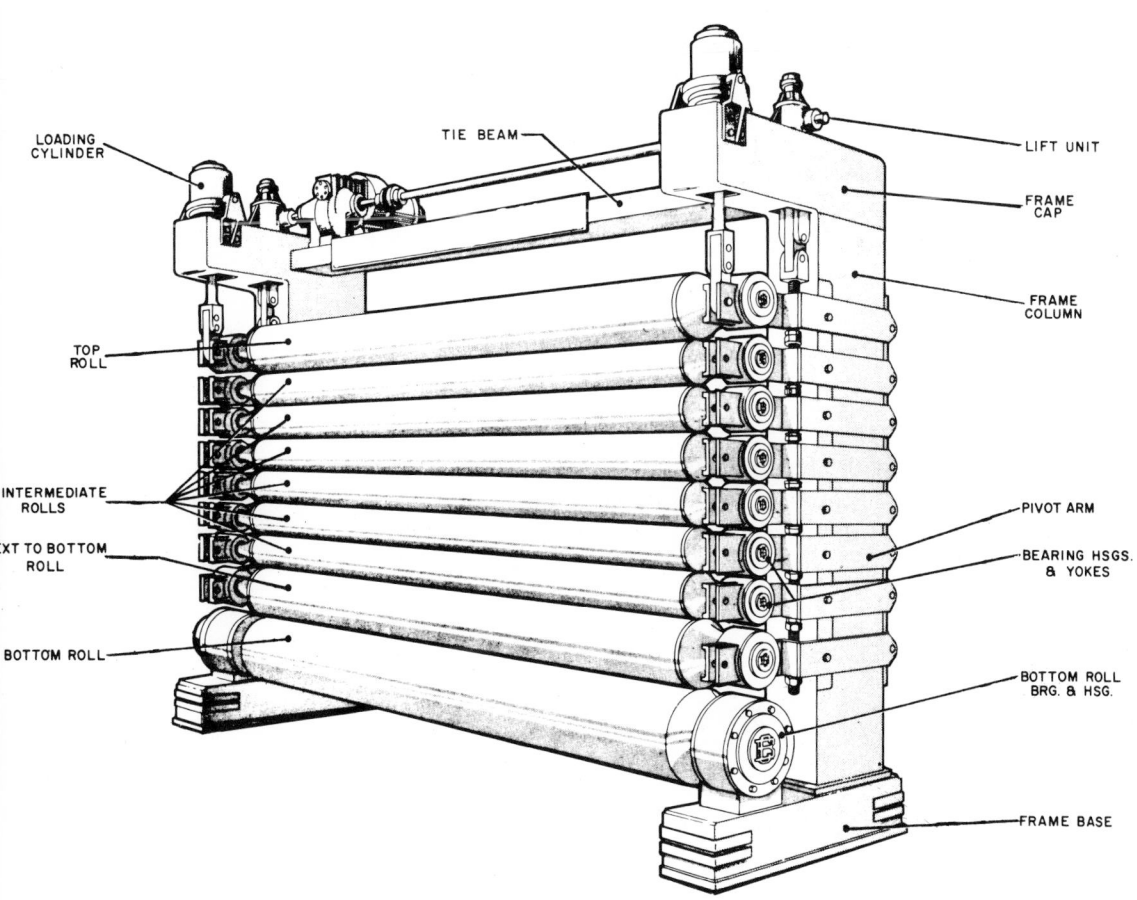

Fig. 12.45. Machine calender stack. (*Courtesy Black-Clawson Co.*)

REELS

Paper making is a continuous process from the headbox to the calender. After the sheet leaves the calender it must be put in a form that can be easily transported and handled. The first step in this process is to wind it on a reel.

The older types of machine reels consisted of a revolving core or drum driven by a friction clutch or slipping belt. For the purpose of classification this can be called a center wind reel. Two or more winder drums are necessary for continuous winding and the sheet transfer is not automatic.

As machine speeds have increased, it has become necessary to have a reel which will handle the sheet faster and more efficiently. This has led to the development of the surface-drive reel, in which the roll being wound is driven by the surface of the reel drum. The core or center shaft of the roll of paper being wound must be moved continuously away from the drum surface as the reel builds up. This can be done in several ways. Older reels used a primary and secondary arm arrangement, as shown in Figure 12.46. Many recent reels have a horizontal track device which supports the center shaft of the roll and load is maintained by means of pneumatic or hydraulic cylinders (Figure 12.47). Most modern reels are variations of the drum type with auxiliary roll handling equipment to do an efficient job of transferring the winding to a new core as each roll is finished.

Machine Winder

Rolls from the paper machine reel with breaks which must be spliced or which must be slit and trimmed to size are rewound on the machine winder. This involves unwinding and rewinding on a special type of winder or reel.

The full reel of paper is taken from the machine reel by a crane or a hoist and placed on the reel spool supports of the unwinding stand. The sheet is then threaded into the winder. As the roll on the winder grows larger, the roll on the unwinding stand diminishes in size. A brake assembly mounted on the unwind stand is used to control tension. Accurate tension control keeps the rolls hard and uniform.

Winders operate at two or three times the speed of the paper machine. Thus it is possible for a winder always to be well ahead of the sheet coming from the reel. In some mills the winder is the completion of the paper-making process and the slit rolls are taken directly to the shipping area where they are wrapped and shipped to the customer. Each winder is designed for the specific type and width of sheet it will be handling in the mill. Most modern machine winders are capable of speeds over 6,000 fpm and are able to produce a roll upwards of 40 to 60 inches in diameter. Special cutters trim and slit the sheet while being rewound. Shear type slitters are widely used. The sheet passes from the unwinding stand into the tension or lead-in roll arrangement through the slitters to the winder drums as

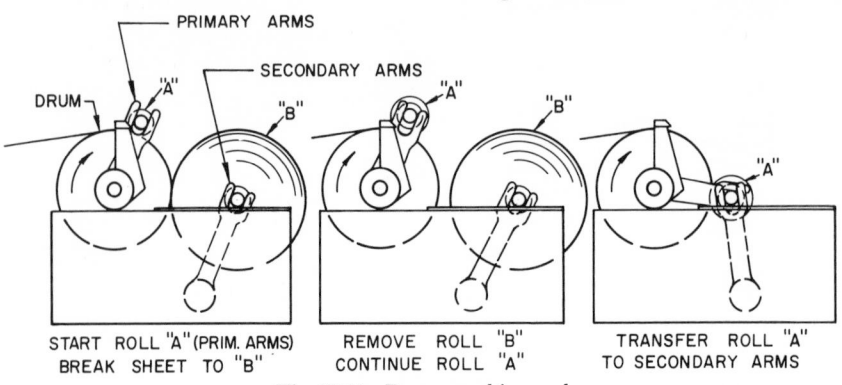

START ROLL "A" (PRIM. ARMS)   REMOVE ROLL "B"   TRANSFER ROLL "A"
BREAK SHEET TO "B"   CONTINUE ROLL "A"   TO SECONDARY ARMS

Fig. 12.46. Paper machine reel.

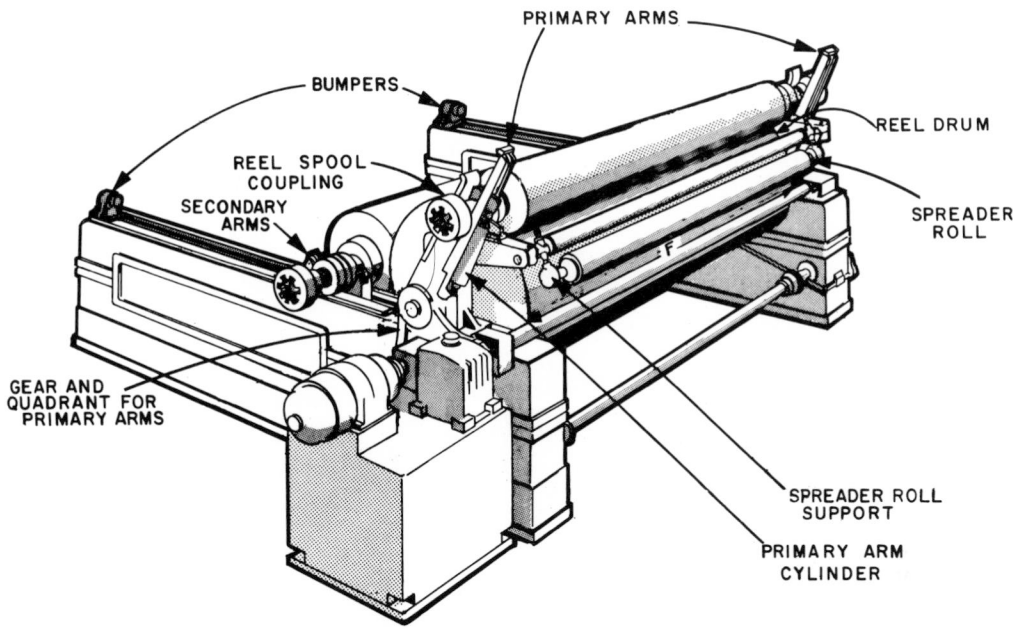

Fig. 12.47. Paper machine reel with pneumatic cylinder. (*Courtesy Black-Clawson Co.*)

shown in Figure 12.48. The winder drums are wormed and fluted to keep the sheet well spread out during the winding operation. The sheet is wound around the paper or metal core on the winder shaft. As the

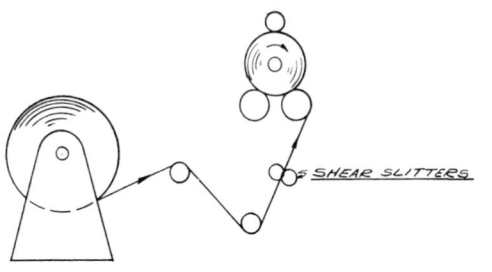

Fig. 12.48. Slitter rewinder. (*Courtesy Consolidated Papers, Inc. and Beloit Corp.*)

sheet is built up on the core, a constant tension or pressure is maintained by the rider roll. On high-speed machines this roll and the two bottom or bed rolls are driven rolls (see Figure 12.49).

The pressure or score type of slitter is also frequently used on winders. The slitter knives slit the sheet as it passes over a hard metal roll. The pressure of the knives against the roll is maintained by springs or air pressures (see Figure 12.50). Slitters are also used on the rider roll and in this case the sheet is slit as it is being built up on the winder shaft.

COATERS

Size Press

A size press is used to apply coatings to one or both sides of the paper web. The sizing is an aqueous solution applied to improve appearance, to prevent undue penetration of printing ink, and to produce a firm hard surface for easy writing. Surface sizing seals the pores of the sheet and improves its pick strength. It is frequently used as a prime coat in double-coated offset grades.

Surface sizing is accomplished by passing the web of paper between a pair of press rolls. If the rolls are placed vertically over each other it is known as a vertical size press; if they are horizontally placed it is called a horizontal size press (see Figure

Fig. 12.49. Rewinder. (*Courtesy Consolidated Papers, Inc. and Beloit Corp.*)

Fig. 12.50. Slitter arrangement. (*Courtesy Wausau Paper Mills Co. and Beloit Corp.*)

Fig. 12.51. Horizontal size press. (*Courtesy Patton Engineering Co.*)

12.51). The sizing material is applied to the surface of the rolls either by a dip roll or a spray pipe so that the ingoing nip is flooded with a sizing material.

One of the rolls in a size press is usually covered with a relatively high Durometer hardness rubber. The loading ranges from 100 to 250 pounds per linear inch.

There are many types of sizing agents, the most common being modified starch. Other materials are frequently blended with the starch solution for specific purposes. The average moisture content of the more common grades of paper is in the range of 8 to 12% when the sheet enters the size press. The amount of moisture picked up by the sheet as it emerges from the size press depends upon its degree of internal sizing, but it may vary from 5 to 10%. The total moisture in the sheet as it enters the after size dryer is in the range of 15 to 25%. The size press is usually located near the calender end of the dryer section and is followed by a series of dryers to complete the drying of the sheet.

The most usual type of on-the-machine coater is the roll coater. Several different configurations are used. In general, the coating color is spread from a pond carried between two roll nips and is transferred and split by means of several roll transfers until it is printed or rolled onto the surface of

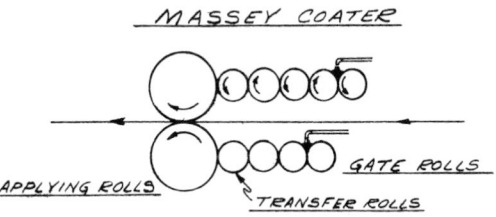

Fig. 12.52. Arrangement of rolls for machine coating.

the sheet by an applying roll. The Massey coater (Figure 12.52) represents a commonly used type of roll coater. In the arrangement shown, coating is applied to both sides of the sheet simultaneously. In some other variations, a shorter roll train is used and the coating is applied to only one side of the sheet at the time. The gate rolls and transfer rolls are usually run at a lower speed than the applying rolls, and some axial motion is frequently incorporated into the transfer rolls.

Blade Coaters

It has been found in some cases that improved smoothness can be obtained when applying a coating by means of a flexible

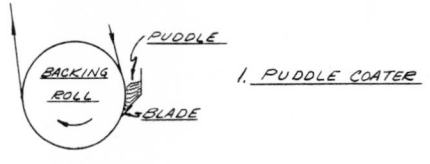

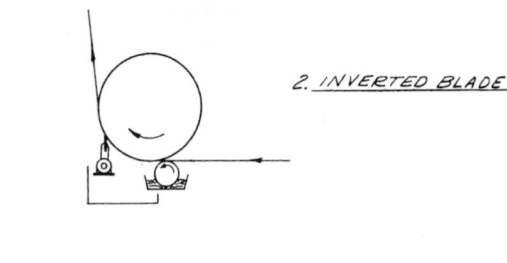

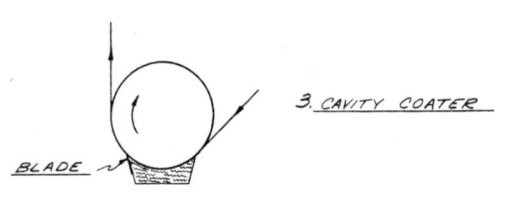

Fig. 12.53. Blade coaters.

trailing blade. The principle is very much like that involved in buttering toast. A smooth uniform surface is left after the thin blade trowels on a controlled amount of coating. The excess coating is removed by the blade. Although the principle of blade coating is similar in all cases, three main types of configuration are used. These are shown in Figure 12.53. In the puddle type of coater an excess of coating is applied during the time that the sheet passes down through the puddle. Excess coating is wiped away by the flexible blade. In the inverted blade

coater, an excess of coating is applied by the dip roll, which is then scraped off or metered and smoothed by the inverted blade. The third type of blade coater makes use of an enclosed cavity or chamber which is filled with coating under pressure. Coating is applied to the sheet as it enters this chamber through a narrow gap at the entering side. Again the excess is removed by the flexible blade at the outgoing side of the pressure chamber. The sheet must be dried after the application of coating. With the exception of vacuum dryers, most methods for drying paper have been applied to coating.

PAPER MACHINE DRIVES

Because stock is put on the wire at a uniform rate for a given machine speed, it is important that the speed of the machine be held constant in order to obtain proper sheet formation and constant weight on the wire.

The machine drives should also hold constant draws between sections, and transfer of the sheet should be accomplished without breaking the sheet or reducing its strength. The drives should have enough draw range so that different settings can be used for different weights of paper, and there should be enough flexibility in each section so that the drives do not have to be changed as the rolls are changed for grinding or recovering. When one is standing at the winder and looking toward the headbox, the drive on the right hand side indicates a right-hand machine; if the drive is on the left hand side, it is a left-hand machine.

There are two principal types of drives on the paper machine: line shaft and electrical. In its most common form, the line shaft drive has a single prime mover. A long shaft running the length of the machine is connected to enclosed right angle gear units on the operating floor and in shafts at each drive point on the machine by a system of belts and cone pulleys. This is a relatively old type of drive and is being largely replaced by electrical drives. The development of new "plastic" driving belts which permit much higher driving speeds and higher loads with good reliability has resulted in the rebuilding of many old drives and the installation of line shaft-belt drives on many new machines.

Variable pitch diameter V-belt sheaves are also used in a series of drives which are similar to the line shaft-cone pulley arrangement. Such an arrangement is relatively compact and efficient.

The differential mechanical drive is a line shaft drive in which a series of gear units located at the drive position of the machine are connected by a single line shaft driven by a prime mover. By means of differential gearing, speeds of individual sections can be regulated relative to the line shaft speed. In effect, the differential drive is a mechanical variable-speed drive making use of gears rather than cone pulleys for speed variation. Although installation costs for differential drives are quite high, they have a reputation for reliable performance, easy trouble shooting, and freedom from breakdowns.

Electrical sectional drives provide a separate drive motor at each drive position of the machine with no mechanical connections between sections. The draw or speed control at each section is maintained by a reference signal produced by a small generator on each motor. The speed voltage obtained from each section is compared to a speed reference voltage obtained from an electronically controlled supply. The output of a comparison circuit is used to feed a high-power amplifying section which makes the required adjustments in speed. Common accuracy among modern electrical drives is approximately .05%. It is important that electrical drives be made as insensitive as possible to sudden frequency and voltage disturbances.

Several electric drives have been built which are based on the use of a series of synchronous motors and a variable frequency supply of AC power. Individual draw between sections is obtained by a mechanical differential drive. This type of system is a combination of electrical and mechanical systems described above. Hydraulic drives are also used on some specialized paper machines.

Lubricating System

Lubrication plays an important part in pulp and paper mills. The progress made in the development of higher-speed machinery and equipment in order to increase production and lower the cost of operation has emphasized the necessity of correct lubrication. The wet end of a modern paper machine is provided with antifriction sealed bearings equipped with pressure grease fittings. With the exception of the table roll bearings which are of the ball-bearing type, the wet end rolls are carried on double roller bearings.

Lubrication systems for antifriction bearings on the dry end of modern paper machines are quite similar in over-all design. A typical mill lubrication system consists essentially of an oil storage tank from which the oil is pumped under pressure to both sides of the dryer section through headers, from which it is fed through regulating valves or metering devices to the individual bearings. The oil flows through the bearings and drains from the bottom or side of the bearing housing into a return oil header from which it returns to the storage tank. Here it is settled and filtered or centrifuged before recirculation.

The economics of increasing machine capacity have dictated greater machine speeds. These have been made possible by the use of higher steam temperatures. Also, new machines are much wider than old ones. These two factors have resulted in increased bearing temperatures and high bearing loads and have necessitated a change in the type of lubricant for use in this service in order to provide satisfactory bearing protection. The circulating oil used to lubricate the bearings in high temperature dryers is subjected to severe oxidation conditions. Present-day oils are compounded to improve stability and to keep oxidation at a minimum to ensure maximum oil service life. Factors which promote oxidation are high oil temperatures, use of copper parts in the circulating system, and finely divided iron in the oil in the presence of water. The two metals are oxidation catalysts which are considerably more active in the presence of water. Well designed oil lubricating systems have a properly designed settling compartment and means for temperature control. In many instances the lubricating system is also the cooling system for the machine bearings.

MACHINE START UP AND SHUTDOWN

Start Up Sequence

The sequence or order of starting up a paper machine after a shutdown depends to a large extent upon the particular machine and various mill procedures. Paper machines are commonly shut down on a regular schedule for routine maintenance and repairs. Some machines are run on a continuous basis with shutdowns as required for felt changes, wire changes, and other maintenance work. Other mills are run on a six-day basis with a Sunday shutdown. Here the problems of start-up are somewhat complicated if all the machines are started at the same time.

At the time the machine is shut down, it is thoroughly washed and all operating parts are inspected, particularly the felts and wires. Unless a machine is thoroughly cleaned, old stock and pulp remaining in the system and drying on various parts of the machine, will be very difficult to remove and will give rise to serious problems when the machine is restarted. Similarly there is economy in doing as much of the maintenance and repair work as possible during the scheduled shutdown. Unscheduled shutdowns are always costly from a production and manpower standpoint.

Assuming the machine has been properly cleaned and maintained during the shutdown period, the start-up usually involves the following steps.

(1) The dryer section is turned over slowly and steam is admitted to the cylinders gradually to bring them up to operating temperature.

(2) The machine chest is brought up to the operating level and the white water system and headbox are filled with water up to the point where it begins running out on the wire.

(3) The Fourdrinier wire, flatboxes, table rolls, and other wet end parts are thoroughly washed down; the showers are turned on. The wire is started with great care to see that it is tracking properly and that the wire tension is set at the proper level.

(4) The felts are wetted out and the tension properly adjusted after the vacuum pumps are started. The felt cleaners are also put into operation.

(5) With the dryer section and Fourdrinier turning over, the machine is brought up to operating speed and various vacuum and shower pumps started. The felt tension should be rechecked.

(6) With the machine operating at full speed and the headbox filled, heavy stock is admitted to the white water system bringing the headbox consistency up close to its operating level. At this point a sheet begins to form on the wire which is run into the couch pit until a satisfactory weight is obtained.

(7) The sheet is next threaded or tailed through the machine, widened out to full width, and started on the reel.

(8) The dryer steam pressures are adjusted to obtain proper dryness at the reel, basis weight is brought into control, and the machine Jordan is adjusted if necessary.

(9) Various auxiliary operations such as coating or impregnating are put into action once a satisfactory sheet has been achieved.

In general, the start up of a paper machine involves a sequence of operations and many checks over a period of several hours.

Stable operation is not achieved in many cases for a period of six hours.

Automatic Equipment for Start Up

Because of the complexity of start up and the expense of time lost if any delays occur, automatic equipment has been developed to control the machine during the start-up procedure with a minimum of delay. One particular installation has been described in the literature.[16]

Shut Down Practice

Shut-down procedures are quite similar to start up, but in reverse order. Heavy stock is removed from the white water system, and the sheet is allowed to "run out" on the Fourdrinier as the weight decreases rapidly. As the weight goes down, the sheet is either broken at the couch or the pick-up roll is lifted and the knock-off showers are started to drop the sheet into the couch pit. Steam is turned off in the dryer section and the machine is allowed to run while the dryers cool, the felts dry, the felt tensions are eased off, and the wet end of the machine is thoroughly washed. When the dryers have cooled sufficiently and the wet end is clean, the machine may be stopped and the felts further backed off. Some large Yankee dryers are kept running at low speed with some heat in them to minimize their tendency to go out of round when standing idle. At the time of a shutdown all available parts of the machine are cleaned and inspected, and needed maintenance work is ordered. Efficient operation requires that good use be made of available opportunities to inspect, clean, and service the equipment.

MACHINE EFFICIENCY AND MACHINE BREAKS

A large, complex piece of continuous-process equipment such as a paper machine usually becomes the "pace-setter" for the entire production operation. Any lost production time or interference with normal production due to web breaks, unscheduled repairs, off quality product, etc., results in a direct reduction of marketable product. The costly overhead expenses and operating expenses of the equipment go on in spite of these interruptions and may even be increased by them. Consequently, one of the most important factors in reducing production costs is to maintain high over-all machine efficiency. Every effort is made to make the paper machine and its auxiliaries as efficient as possible and operating methods should be such as to maximize productivity by any economical means.

Wet end breaks on a paper machine are usually defined as those occurring on the wet end through the press section. The causes are of two general types: (a) weight non-uniformities due to the malfunction of the stock system, white water system, or headbox and Fourdrinier table; and (b) web breaks due to excessive tension in the wet web which is usually caused by improper draws or speed relationship between sections or the sticking of the wet web to the Fourdrinier wire, or various roll surfaces.

Dry end breaks are also caused by improper draws giving rise to high or low tensions in the sheet and weak spots in the drying web. Weaknesses in the web can be caused by weight discontinuities, holes, or such things as water condensing in the hood and dripping back onto the sheet. Dry end breaks are particularly time consuming because of the necessity for cleaning scraps of paper out of the dryer rolls.

Additional equipment in the paper machine such as calender stack, coaters and size presses will inevitably reduce machine efficiency. Lost time on any one of the machine elements effectively prevents the other elements from producing during this period. It has been found uneconomical to include any low efficiency operation or "bottleneck" in a paper machine production line which could perhaps be performed more efficiently off the machine. As a result, some modern book paper machines are being built with off-machine coating equipment so that the coater efficiency does not directly affect the paper machine efficiency. Another way of looking at efficiency is to assign an efficiency to each portion of the machine or operation. The over-all efficiency is a product of the individual efficiencies, so that one low factor will strongly affect the result.

Acknowledgment: The author would like to acknowledge generous help provided by various equipment manufacturers and paper companies. He is particularly indebted to Mr. T. M. Jones, of the Beloit Corporation, Mr. W. H. Kennedy, of the Black-Clawson Company, and Mr. W. E. Bright of the Rice-Barton Corporation.

REFERENCES

1. McLenaghen, J. N., Clark-Pounder, I., and Salomon, S., "Pressurized Screening of Groundwood Pulp with the Bird Centriscreen," *Pulp Paper Mag. Can.,* **60**, No. 8, T236 (August, 1959).
2. McCulloch, C. D., "Cleaning Groundwood with Vorjets at Port Alfred," *Pulp Paper Mag. Can.,* **60**, No. 1, T21 (January, 1959).
3. Lee, C. F., (to Kimberly-Clark Corporation) U.S. Patent 2,865,260 (Dec. 23, 1958).
4. Ostertag, H. M., and Boylan, F. O. (to Scott Paper Company) U.S. Patent 2,418,600 (April 8, 1947).
5. Gerhauser, J. P., "Corrosion of Fourdrinier Wires," *Tappi,* **43**, No. 4, 207A (April, 1960).
6. Friese, J., "The Improvement of Paper Machine Wire Life," *Pulp Paper Mag. Can.,* **61**, No. 10, T467 (October, 1960).
7. Broadway, J. D., Friese, J., and Husband, R. M., "Some Studies of the Abrasion and Corrosion of Fourdrinier Wires," *Pulp Paper Mag. Can.,* **60**, No. 8, T231 (August, 1959).
8. Burkhard, G., and Wrist, P. E., "Investigation of High Speed Paper Machine Drainage Phenomena," *Pulp Paper Mag. Can.,* **57**, No. 4, 267 (March, 1956).
9. Taylor, G. I., "Drainage at a Table Roll and a Foil," *Pulp Paper Mag. Can.,* **59**, No. C, 172, (Convention Issue, 1958).
10. Locke, I. I., "Recent Suction Press Nip Theories Are in Opposition," *Paper Trade J.,* **146**, No. 12, 403 (March 19, 1962).
11. Wahlstrom, B., "A Long Term Study of Water Removal and Moisture Distributions on a Newsprint Machine Press Section—Part I," *Pulp Paper Mag. Can.,* **61**, No. 8, T379 (August, 1960).
 Ibid., "Part II," **61**, No. 9, T379 (September, 1960).
12. Gardner, D. M., "Paper Machine Roll Calculations," *Pulp Paper Mag. Can.,* **60**, No. 6, T187 (June, 1959).
13. Gardner, D. M., "Deflection Equation for Non-uniform Loadings," *Pulp Paper Mag. Can.,* **61**, No. 7, T356 (July, 1960).
14. Institute of Paper Chemistry, "Evaluation of NCR Paper as a Means for Measuring Pressure," *Research Bulletin,* **25**, No. 4, 222 (June, 1959).
15. Larsson, T., "Comparing High Velocity Dryers —Aspects of Theory and Design," *Paper Trade J.,* **146**, No. 38, 36 (Sept. 17, 1962).
16. Garret, G., Eastwood, M., and Gade, M. F., "Instrumentation for the Automatic Start-up of the Wet End of a Paper Machine," *Tappi,* **40**, No. 6, 403 (June, 1957).

SUGGESTED READING

Casey, J. P., "Pulp and Paper," New York, Interscience Publishers, Inc., 1960.

Mosher, R. H., "The Technology of Coated and Processed Papers," New York, Chemical Publishing Co., Inc., 1952.

Organization for European Economic Cooperation, "The Pulp and Paper Industry in the U.S.A.," Paris, Organization for European Economic Cooperation, Chateau de la Muette, 1951.

Stephenson, J. N., "Pulp and Paper Manufacture," New York, McGraw-Hill Book Co., Inc., 1950.

CHAPTER 13

Finishing and Converting

ROBERT C. STURKEN

Frank W. Egan & Company

When a roll of paper has been slit and wound on the mill rewinder, it is seldom in condition for use by the consumer, whether he is a printer, a packager, or a householder. The paper must first be passed through a series of finishing and, in most cases, converting operations.

As used in the paper industry, the word "finishing" refers to those operations performed in the paper mill finishing room in order to make the paper ready for shipment. The principal operations involved in finishing are supercalendering to improve the surface finish, secondary slitting and rewinding to produce rolls of a size desired by the customer, and cutting of the paper into sheets (sheeting) if the end product must be in sheet rather than roll form.

The term "converting" as used in the paper industry refers to the modification of the raw paper as delivered from the mill rewinder into an improved grade of paper with special properties, or its fabrication into a finished article. Thus, it might be said that there are two distinct types of converting. The first will be referred to as wet converting wherein the paper is handled in roll form and is modified and improved by such operations as coating, impregnating, laminating, and variations and combinations of these processes. The second will be called dry converting, wherein a finished product is made from the paper, such as a bag, box, or a household-size roll.

There are a great number of converting operations, and to describe them all fully would be beyond the scope of this book. In this chapter the principal converting operations in use for the more important types of paper products will be discussed.

General History, Background and Trends

The development of the finishing room has paralleled the tremendous growth during the past one hundred years in the volume of production and in the variety of paper products produced. In earlier periods paper was used almost entirely for printing and writing, and was manufactured in sheet form. The roll of paper from the paper machine reel on the early Fourdrinier machines was cut into sheets with a hand cutter and stacked by hand. The better grades were frequently sized by dipping the sheets in a tub of water solution of animal glue or gelatine and were then hung in a room or loft to be air-dried.

The rotary sheeter was subsequently developed during the late nineteenth century to permit operation at considerably higher speeds than had been possible with the hand operation. Supercalendering was introduced with the advent of coated papers to give a much needed improvement in surface finish for printing. The slitter-rewinder came into use about the same time, partly as a result of the development of roll-fed rotary printing presses, and also as a result of the de-

407

velopment of lower priced papers made from wood pulp instead of rags, which permitted the use of paper as a packaging material. These two developments—roll-fed presses and paper packaging—produced the demand for paper in roll rather than sheet form for the first time.

The first application of a conversion-processed paper, in addition to the tub sizing mentioned above, was probably the application of a pigmented coating during the early nineteenth century. These coatings were applied by hand application with brushes, followed by manual air-drying.

The expansion of converting processes and operations is closely related to the great increase in the production and consumption of paper products. The great multiplication of uses for paper has in most cases involved the development of new converting processes and equipment to make these products. Raw paper from the machine has limited usefulness, but after processing or conversion, it finds practical use in the many thousands of paper products being made today.

In the past the conversion of paper was commonly carried out in separate plants, to which the raw paper was shipped by the paper mills. For economic and commercial reasons, however, the trend during the past fifteen years has been toward the increasing conversion of products at the paper mill itself. Converting departments have been established at many mills, particularly for the heavier tonnage products, while the smaller volume specialties are still produced in separate converting plants.

There is also a trend toward carrying out, on the paper machine, operations that were formerly considered a part of converting. The most important of these are sizing and pigment coating. Here again, for economic reasons, it has been found that substantial savings in manufacturing costs can be achieved by performing these operations on the paper machine, as long as they do not interfere with its productive capacity. Other than sizing, pigment coating and some crep-

ing, however, converting operations are traditionally carried out on a completely separate basis.

Typical Finishing and Converting Sequences

Before describing the principal finishing and converting operations, the basic procedures used for the more important grades of paper products will be reviewed. It is important to emphasize that the number and complexity of converting operations tend to increase the cost of the finished product.

Newsprint, the cheapest and largest tonnage grade other than paperboard, is simply slit and rewound into rolls of the size required for newspaper presses. It is then ready for shipment directly to the printing plant.

Machine-coated book papers are almost invariably supercalendered and then slit and then rewound. In some cases they are sheeted. The better grades of printing papers receive a pigment coating in a separate operation off the paper machine and are either sheeted or slit and rewound. Supercalendering is always used.

Writing grades are commonly sheeted and the highest qualities are often given a separate tub-sizing treatment.

Packaging and wrapping papers are subjected to a wide variety of converting processes to improve their usefulness. These processes include the application of various protective and waterproof coatings, lamination to increase strength and to combine qualities, and pigment coatings to improve exterior printability. These packaging papers are then further processed into paper bags or cartons, liquid containers, and overwrap materials, in each case on special machines designed for these purposes. They are frequently decorated or printed in line with the container-making machine.

Another major class of paper products, the sanitary papers, are processed through a highly mechanized and specialized converting procedure, and because of their low cost this must be done with minimum handling. Toilet tissue and towels are rewound on continuous automatic machines from mill-size parent rolls. Paper napkins and facial tissues are similarly handled on specially designed automatic equipment which operates continuously from mill rolls and delivers a finished packaged product ready for shipment.

Building and structural papers are frequently impregnated for water-proofing and laminated to build thickness, strength and rigidity.

In addition to these principal grades there is, of course, a great variety of miscellaneous paper products which are passed through converting operations, including such items as carbon paper, photographic paper, wallpaper and others, which will be mentioned under the descriptions of the appropriate converting operations involved.

THE FINISHING ROOM

As stated previously, the paper mill finishing room includes those operations necessary to transform the mill roll into a form suitable for the next user, whether this user be the mill's own converting department, an independent converter, a printer, a package manufacturer, etc.

The mill finishing operations include slitting and rewinding of the web in most types of product. On the paper machine rewinder, the roll is slit into jumbo rolls which are large in diameter and usually one-third or one-quarter of the paper machine trim width. With the exception of newsprint and other large tonnage printing papers, these rolls must then be reduced further in size, both in width and diameter, to accommodate conventional printing and converting machines.

Sheeting from mill rolls is carried out in the finishing room for those grades of paper which are desired in sheet form. This includes principally the book grades, which will subsequently be printed in sheet-fed printing presses, and writing grades used in sheet form.

Inspection of the paper is an integral part of the finishing room operations. Inspection is carried out to some degree on the slitter-rewinder or on the sheeter, and higher-quality grades of sheeted paper are subject to further individual inspections and counting. Material handling and storage are major auxiliary functions of the finishing department.

One operation, which is basically a web converting operation, is nevertheless traditionally a part of the mill finishing room function, namely, supercalendering. It falls within the finishing room principally because so many grades of paper are supercalendered that this is logically carried out on mill-size rolls before the final finishing.

Supercalenders

Most grades of paper receive some calendering in the paper machine itself. The machine calender consists of a series of metal rolls and serves the purpose of smoothing the surface and compacting the web of paper (see Chapter 12).

On the other hand, the supercalender is used to impart a high degree of gloss and surface smoothness to paper. This process is carried out on practically all pigment-coated papers, both on-machine and off-machine coated, as well as on many uncoated grades. It should be noted, however, that supercalendering has the disadvantage of reducing brightness and opacity.

The supercalender accomplishes this smoothing action by passing the paper between a series of metal and resilient fiber rolls. A typical supercalender as shown in Figure 13.1 consists of a vertical stack of rolls through which the paper is threaded, with pressure applied to load the roll nips. The rolls are supported on a heavy frame. The top and bottom rolls, which support and apply the load, are of metal construction and are larger than the others in diameter. The remaining rolls are of alternating metal and fiber construction.

The metal rolls are manufactured of "chilled" iron which gives a hard, strong, dimensionally stable roll. These rolls are made of high-grade white cast iron, poured into a water-cooled steel mold. The sudden chilling produced by this method of casting gives the outer portion of the roll a very hard but somewhat brittle surface. The depth of "chill" can be controlled from about $\frac{1}{4}$ to 1 inch. The balance of the roll, which cools more slowly, consists of a softer

Fig. 13.1. Supercalender. (*Courtesy Appleton Machine Co.*)

but tougher cast iron which gives the roll body the necessary strength and toughness.

The fiber rolls, or so-called "filled" rolls, are fabricated on a steel base using specially prepared papers or fabrics as a filler. The material is cut into circular sheets with a central hole and these are stacked on a steel mandrel. They are then compressed by high pressure, hydraulically applied, and the steel heads of the roll are fastened in place. The surface of the roll is then finished by turning with a diamond tool followed by

sanding and polishing. These rolls can be made in all degrees of hardness, depending upon the type of filler paper or cloth used, to suit various supercalendering requirements.

The supercalender produces its polishing action as a result of this combination of chilled iron and resilient fiber filled rolls. Since the latter have a relatively low modulus of elasticity, they deform at the point of contact with the chilled iron rolls. This produces a nip of finite width rather than a nip of essentially line contact obtained with two metal rolls.

The higher elasticity of the fiber rolls then causes a relative motion or frictional action between the two rolls comprising the nip. It is generally believed that it is this frictional action that results in the high smoothing and polishing action produced on the surface of the paper by the supercalendering process.

On modern supercalenders the rolls are mounted in sealed antifriction bearings which are continuously lubricated. The older type double-column frame for supporting the rolls has been replaced in all new installations by an open or one-side frame construction with the bearings retained on slides or pivots. This permits rapid change of a roll with minimum shutdown time whenever regrinding or other correction is necessary.

The bottom calender roll is usually driven by means of a variable speed DC drive. Normal operating speeds range from about 600 fpm up to 2,000 fpm, depending upon product.

The number of rolls in a stack may vary from three to fifteen for single side finishing, again depending upon the amount of smoothing and finishing desired. It is also possible to finish both sides of the sheet by reversing the direction in the middle of the stack. This is done by placing two fiber filled rolls together. The reversing point can be varied upward or downward from the center depending upon the amount of finish desired on each side of the sheet. Double finishing stacks will have an even number of rolls, up to as many as sixteen.

Pressure is applied to the stack by loading of the top roll, which then transmits this force through all the intermediate rolls to the bottom. Mechanical application of pressure by levers or screw jacks was common in the past, but is giving way largely to the use of hydraulic pressure application on new machines. The use of hydraulic pressure has the advantages of being readily controllable and reproducible.

Supercalenders are also equipped with so-called fly rolls or blow rolls, which are idler rolls located at intermediate points along both sides of the stack. This permits threading the paper around these rolls before entering the next nip to equalize tensions and relax the sheet before further work is done upon it. This helps to prevent wrinkles and to give more uniform results.

Supercalenders are available in widths exceeding 200 inches. The common maximum pressures which can be applied are about 2,000 pounds per linear inch of face width.

The complete installation will include, in addition to the drive, an unroll and winder of the types described later in this chapter.

Some of the intermediate chilled iron rolls are frequently bored and equipped with rotary joints for heating by means of steam, since heat will soften the paper and accelerate the polishing action.

The moisture content of the paper is an important factor in obtaining the proper results in supercalendering since the amount of moisture directly affects the plasticity of the web. If the moisture content is too low, the web is not sufficiently plastic to obtain the necessary gloss and smoothness. If the moisture content is too high, it results in blackening of the paper surface.

The general practice is to dry the paper on the paper machine to a moisture content equal to or slightly below that desired for calendering. The amount of moisture then can be adjusted by the use of steam showers located on both sides of the web entering the calender. On certain products where even higher moisture contents are desired than can be obtained with steam showers, water boxes on the faces of the calender rolls or separate water applicator rolls can be used.

Slitting and Rewinding

On many grades of paper it is necessary that the rolls be slit and rewound again in the finishing room, after having once been slit and rewound on the mill rewinder at the dry end of the paper machine. This is true where the diameter or width of the rolls desired by the end user is too small for convenient operation on the large heavy equipment used in mill rewinding. On better grades of paper secondary rewinding is necessary for inspection of the paper, for removal of defects, proper splicing of breaks, etc.

The typical finishing room rewinder, although basically similar in design, is smaller and more precise than the machine room rewinder. It will generally accept jumbo mill rolls of about one-third or one-quarter of the paper machine trim.

A typical finishing room slitter rewinder is shown in Figure 13.2. It consists first of the backstand or unwind to hold the parent mill roll. In the most modern designs these are arranged for pneumatic chucking of the mill rolls without the use of shafts, as this results in a considerable labor saving. The supporting bearings can be located on a pair of pivoted arms which permits lifting the roll from the floor; this again gives appreciable saving in material handling cost.

Braking must be applied to the unwinding roll to control the tension of the web between the backstand and the winder, and also to prevent the roll from coasting when the rewinder is stopped. The mechanical friction brakes used in the past are largely being replaced by automatically controlled brakes to give constant tension. This automatic control is usually actuated through a dancer roll, which in turn controls the brake pneumatically, hydraulically, or electrically. Water cooling of the brakes is required on the larger, higher-speed machines to dissipate the energy absorbed.

Some provision must be made for side shifting of the parent roll so that it will line up with the slitters on the rewinder. Sometimes the rolls become dished or telescoped in handling after they leave the mill rewinder. The simplest method of accomplish-

Fig. 13.2. Slitter-rewinder. (*Courtesy Cameron Machine Co.*)

ing this is to put a hand-operated side-shifting device on the backstand which the operator can control according to the width of the trim which he observes at each side of the web. On the more sophisticated and higher-speed machines, however, this guiding is done automatically, with a hydraulic or electric shifter to move the roll, and either a pneumatic or photoelectric sensing device to control the position of the web.

The rewinding is generally carried out on a surface-driven winder of the two-drum type. Before reaching the winding station the web passes over idler rolls and through the slitting station.

The two principal types of slitters in use are the shear cut and the score cut. The shear cut slitters consist of a pair of driven overlapping sharpened blades which can best be likened to a pair of scissors in continuous rotating form. In the score cut slitting method a single rotating blade is held by pressure against a hardened steel backing roll. The blade is also hardened and ground to a slight radius rather than a true sharp point. The shear cut method is the more versatile and can handle a wider range of weights of paper and board. It does, however, require more care in setting and maintaining the knives. The score cut method gives a good slitting action on light to medium weights of paper with a good separation of the rolls. On heavier weights, however, this type of action causes flattening of the edges and lint-formation, which may be a serious objection for some uses.

In order to prevent interleaving of the paper, the slitters are located as close as possible to the two winding drums. In addition, it is frequently advisable to install a bowed spreader bar or spreader roll after the slitters and before the first winding drum to cause the webs to separate.

It is generally necessary to take a slight trim from the web at the finishing room slitter rewinder. This results from the fact that the roll width desired by the customer may not be an even multiple of the mill roll width, and also because of the fact that the web cannot be guided perfectly into the rewinder and a slight allowance must be made for side shifting.

The paper is commonly wound on paperboard cores which are precut to width and are lined up with the slitters. These cores will vary in diameter from 3- to 5-inch I.D. (internal diameter) for various grades of paper, and from 6- to 12-inch I.D. for paperboard. The winding core is supported on a shaft which in turn is held by sliding bearing housings on the machine frames. The core is held down against the winding drums by means of an ironing roll or riding roll.

Pressure can be applied to the riding roll by either weights or pneumatic cylinders. It is common practice to reduce this pressure as the roll of paper builds up in diameter, since the weight of the roll itself gradually increases the pressure against the winding drums. The tightness or hardness of the roll is controlled to a considerable degree by the total pressure or weight between the roll of paper and the bottom drums, and for this reason it is necessary to compensate for the increasing weight with increasing diameter. Both winding drums are driven, and on the larger and wider machines the riding roll or ironing roll is also driven. A differential speed is commonly provided between the drums in order to tighten the paper and, thereby, to wind a very tight roll, which is required so that it can be shipped without telescoping or flattening. This differential speed can either be a built-in fixed differential resulting from a difference in diameter of the drums, or can be provided by a mechanical speed variation between the drums. On the larger machines, separate motors may be used for both drums and also for the riding roll. This type of multiple motor drive permits good control of winding tension throughout the cycle and also helps to compensate for the increased weight by reducing the draw on the second drum.

Accessories commonly provided on the newer and larger machines include a roll ejector and roll lowering table for automatic handling of the finished product. Variable-speed direct current drives are the most popular for rewinding machines. These provide smooth acceleration to maximum speed and deceleration at the end of a roll.

The prevention of interleaving is an important problem on slitter rewinders. This is accomplished by proper design and location of the slitters and proper tension control of the incoming web. On many machines the winding drums are grooved with a variety of patterns to promote spreading of the rolls.

Variations in caliper of the paper are another common cause of problems at the slitter-rewinder. After the paper is slit, a thick section will tend to wind a larger diameter roll than a thin section, with the result that the rolls will try to turn at different speeds and will be wound respectively hard and soft. There is no good solution to this problem other than the correction of the caliper at the paper machine.

For certain specialty grades of paper a center-driven or a combination type winder may be used rather than a surface-driven winder. This choice is frequently made for tissue and other light weight sheets where an extremely tight wind is not desired.

Because of the strong tendency to interleave with center winding, the general practice is to use two winding shafts, alternating the slit webs between these two shafts. The cores are permitted to slip on the shafts using a differential friction device to compensate for variations in web caliper and roll diameter. With some units the winding rolls also rest against a surface-driven drum to give a combination surface-center winding effect.

For slitting certain very light webs, razor blades are sometimes substituted for shear-cut or score-cut slitters. These require frequent replacement, however, and are used only where the rotary types of slitters cannot be used because of difficulties with tearing, etc.

One of the important functions to be performed by the operator at the slitter rewinder on many grades of paper is that of inspection. He must watch visually for holes or tears in the paper, for dirt or other imperfections, for skips in coating, etc. When any such defect is observed the machine is quickly stopped and the defective portion cut out. The ends are then glued together with gummed tape on the rewound roll. The splice must be carefully made so that the paper can subsequently pass through printing or converting operations without tearing or wrinkling. Normally it is required that splices be marked in the rewound roll.

After the rolls have been removed from the slitter rewinder they must be given final preparation for shipment. Wooden plugs are commonly inserted into both ends of the paperboard core to prevent its collapsing from the combined effect of the high winding tension and jarring during subsequent shipment. The roll is then wrapped, the amount of wrapping being dependent upon the quality and cost of the product. A simple steel strapping may be used for the cheap grades, while on better grades the heads are covered with several layers of paper and the outer cylindrical surface wrapped similarly. Waterproof paper may be used if outdoor exposure is to be expected.

Hand wrapping is employed on the smaller rolls where a wide variety of sizes are encountered. In high production mills where a large number of rolls in the same general size range are shipped, heading and wrapping is carried out on automatic machines designed specifically for that purpose.

Sheet Cutting and Finishing

The bulk of high-quality printing is still carried out on sheet-fed, flat-bed printing presses, the use of rotary presses being limited to newspapers, magazines, packaging products, and other long-run items. The high-quality coated and book papers must, therefore, be delivered to the printer in sheet form and the same is true of writing and ledger papers.

It might be mentioned in passing that many of the medium-to-heavier grades of paperboard used in folding box manufacture, which are made at relatively low speed on the Fourdrinier or cylinder machine, are cut into sheets directly in line with the paper-making machine and are never wound.

In the typical finishing operation, however, mill rolls from the rewinder are fed through a high-speed rotary sheet cutter.

The mill rolls are unwound prior to sheeting on a multiple reel stand or backstand.

For reasons of production efficiency, a number of webs are usually fed to the sheeter at one time. From 5 to 8 backstands are generally provided. In some cases these are double backstands to permit loading new rolls while the finished rolls are expiring.

Because the sheeter operates at considerably lower speed than the slitter rewinder, the backstands are of simpler design with a simple shaft support for the roll and a mechanical friction brake. Manually operated side shifting is desirable to permit lining up the rolls.

The paper passes from the backstands over idler rolls and spreader rolls to remove wrinkles. It then passes through the nip of a pair of driven pull rolls which control the speed of the paper. On most sheeters, shear-cut slitters are provided for cutting the web into narrower widths in the longitudinal direction. The multiple webs of paper then pass to the sheet cutter itself. This consists of a rotating or fly knife and a stationary or bed knife. These knives are made of heavy tool steel with carefully ground sharp edges. The rotating knife is counterweighted for balancing. The clearance for proper cutting is obtained by adjusting the position of the bed knife. The sheet length is determined by the rotational speed of the fly knife in relation to the speed of the paper. This speed ratio is commonly adjustable by means of gears or any of a number of standard mechanical variable-speed devices.

As the sheets are delivered from the cutter they must be conveyed away from the knives and stacked. This is accomplished by means of a conveyor consisting of a series of parallel tapes. On high-speed units it is advisable to use the so-called overlapping delivery system where a first set of tapes operates at a speed slightly faster than the cutter and a second set operates at reduced speed to slow down the sheets prior to stopping, and this results in an overlap of sheets.

The sheets are received in a stacking device known as a layboy, so-called because this operation was formerly performed manually by boys. This device consists of a table with adjustable side guides which jog the sheets of paper into place. The table is automatically lowered as the pile of paper increases in height. When the full depth is reached, a set of fingers is inserted to hold the upper portion of the pile while the bottom is removed without stopping the machine.

Since sheeted paper is commonly sold by the ream rather than by the pound, it is necessary that paper sheets be counted. Although this used to be done by hand there are now a number of reliable automatic ream counters and marking machines available.

The higher-quality grades of book, writing, and ledger papers are inspected by hand. The inspector manually turns over each sheet of paper in the pile to look for any unacceptable defects such as holes, dirt, specks, etc.

For products which must be delivered in sheet sizes smaller than are conveniently cut on rotary sheeters, the paper is then transferred in piles to guillotine-type cutters. This type of cutter is also used where accurate trimming is required to a precise sheet size since the precision of the rotary cutter still is not sufficiently accurate.

Following inspection and cutting or trimming, the sheeted paper is then ready for wrapping and packaging for shipment. It is commonly wrapped first in paper and then in cartons to protect it during shipment.

PIGMENT COATING

One of the most important converting operations carried out on paper is the application of a mineral or pigment coating to its surface to improve its printability. These coatings improve the surface gloss and finish and in turn enhance the ink receptivity and the speed at which the paper can be printed in modern printing equipment with the latest types of fast-drying inks. These coatings also are very important for the printed reproduction of photographs both in black and in color. A good quality coated paper greatly improves the sharpness and fidelity of the reproduction of half-tone engravings.

Coated papers are equally important for use in the three basic methods of printing, namely letterpress, rotogravure, and offset lithography. The coatings are applied not only to publication papers for books and magazines but also for packaging papers where the external design is of importance in selling the product.

The basic mineral pigment coating used consists of a water suspension of a white pigment, usually clay, with a soluble binder. The binder used for many decades was casein. However, it was found that other binders would produce coatings of superior properties, not only in speed and ease of application, but in printing qualities of the finished product. Starch derived from corn began to replace casein, and more recently vegetable proteins and synthetic resins have become an important binder for paper coatings.

The basic pigment still remains clay. There are a wide number of varieties of clay from which to choose, both domestic and imported. The clay producers have refined their manufacturing processes to give good color control and good coating viscosity characteristics. Most coatings also contain titanium dioxide for whiteness and opacity as well as small amounts of other mineral pigments. Other pigments used in addition to, or instead of, clay include calcium carbonate, calcium aluminum silicate, satin white, and blanc fixe. For producing colored paper coatings, dyes are added.

The preparation of coating mixtures (traditionally called "coating colors") has become a highly refined art. The final mixture comprises dozens of ingredients including such materials as dispersing agents, preservatives, viscosity modifiers, antifoaming agents, leveling agents, softeners, and plasticizers.

The consumption of coated paper and

board has been increasing at a rate substantially above the general increase in the production of uncoated paper and board products. The approximate annual production of these materials in terms of tons of paper and board is shown in the following tabulation.[1]

	1940	1950	1960
Coated paper	300,000	1,000,000	2,000,000
Coated paperboard	30,000	1,000,000	4,000,000
Total	330,000	2,000,000	6,000,000

For comparison, total production of paper and paperboard is given in Chapter 1. This increase is due to a number of factors. The readers of books and magazines prefer a coated surface which reproduces both type and illustrations more effectively. Advertisers in magazines wish to have their illustrations clearly reproduced.

The development of the self-service market for food and other products has placed far greater emphasis on the external appearance of packages in addition to the more widespread use of packages themselves. To obtain a pleasing and effectively printed outer surface on packages which are largely made from cheap grades of board, the outer surface must be clay-coated prior to printing. Because clay is substantially lower in cost per pound than paper and since it enhances the properties of the paper substantially, it appears logical that the use of this type of coating would continue to expand. The only offsetting disadvantage is the cost of application.

The effects of a conventional domestic clay coating on the brightness and opacity of two different paper grades (A and B) are shown in the following tabulation.[2]

Coating Weight (lb/ream, 25 x 38—500)	Brightness (%) A	B	Opacity (%) A	B
0 (raw stock)	45.4	75.0	58.0	85.0
5	60.8	78.5	69.0	88.0
10	67.2	79.8	78.0	90.5
15	71.9	80.3	84.0	92.5

Thus it can be seen that a pigment coating produces a very significant improvement in the properties of raw papers (A) having poor brightness or opacity. The relative improvement is less in better quality papers (B) but is nevertheless still commercially important.

Coated papers were produced more than 100 years ago by hand operation. Coating was applied to sheets of paper spread out on tables by means of brushes. These sheets were then hung in lofts to be dried.

The first continuous coating machine was built in the late 19th century and was of the brush coater type. The coating was first applied to the web of paper by means of a roll revolving in a pan. The paper then passed through a series of brushes which smoothed and distributed the coating. After this it was hung in festoons in large rooms to dry. Brush coating was the principal process used for applying mineral coatings to paper until the early 1930's when the air knife coater was developed. During the intervening years improvements were made in the brush coater and particularly in the method of drying the paper. At first heat was added to the drying room. Later this was replaced by hot circulating air and the festooning operation was completely mechanized.

Also, during the 1930's the first successful applications of coatings on the paper machine were carried out by several paper companies. This had the advantage of reduced labor cost and reduced equipment cost. In order to coat effectively on the paper machine, it was necessary to develop high solids content coatings which would dry rapidly without offsetting onto the paper machine dryers. The application was carried out principally on the equivalent of a letterpress printing machine which in effect gave an over-all printing of the coating onto the surface of the paper. Other types of machine coaters were subsequently developed, as described in the preceding chapter. Today all the large tonnage grades of medium quality coated paper are coated on the paper machine.

Where heavy coating weights are desired or where special formulations or other conditions exist which do not permit application on the paper machine without slowing down or encountering drying difficulties, etc. papers are coated off the machine. There are several important off-machine processes for applying clay coatings in use today.

Air Knife Coater

This equipment was the first significant departure from the traditional brush coater. A typical air knife coating machine is shown in Figures 13.3 and 13.4. The coating is again applied to the paper by means of a roll revolving in a pan of coating. In many cases a second roll is used to meter the amount used; this reduces the excess, which is then carried over to the air knife doctoring station. The paper then passes around a breast roll or head roll where the air doctoring action is applied.

The air knife itself consists of a tube with a slotted orifice discharge. It is made of noncorrodible metals, such as bronze and stainless steel, to resist the minor corrosive action of the water and dissolved ingredients in the coating. Adjustments are pro-

vided across the full width for giving an accurate control of the slot opening. Air is delivered to the knife by means of a rotary turbine type blower at pressures varying from 0.5 up to 5.0 psi, depending upon the coating viscosity, desired thickness, and operating speed. The air doctor removes the excess coating and smoothes out the coating remaining on the sheet. The excess is blown off into a catch pan which must also have an exhaust system and spray collector. Operating speeds vary from about 500 to 1500 fpm. The coating solids content is usually in the range of 35 to 45% and the dry weight applied from 10 to 30 pounds per ream (25 x 38-500). The coating is then dried in an air-drying tunnel and wound on a continuous winder. These types of equipment will be discussed separately at the end of the chapter.

The air knife coater is widely used for applying the heavier weights of clay coatings to paper and board, above those which can be conveniently applied on the paper machine. It is by nature a one side coating machine but both sides can be readily

Fig. 13 3. Air knife coater. (*Courtesy Waldron-Hartig Div. Midland-Ross Corp.*)

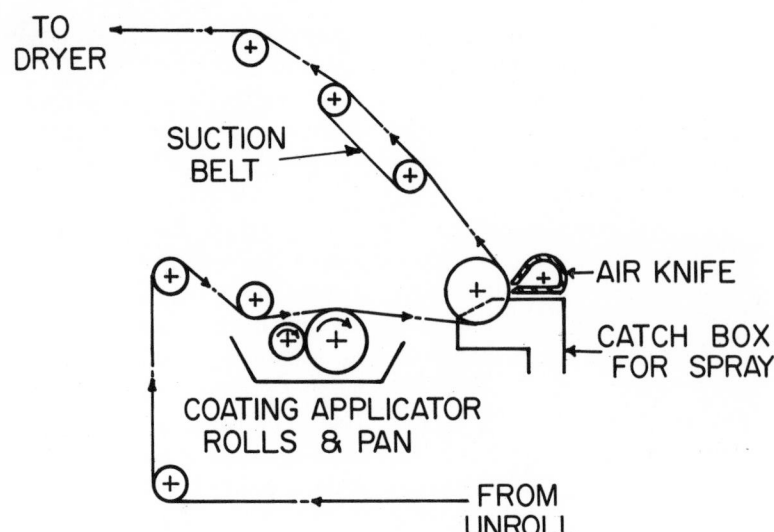

TO DRYER

SUCTION BELT

AIR KNIFE

CATCH BOX FOR SPRAY

COATING APPLICATOR ROLLS & PAN

FROM UNROLL

Fig. 13.4. Air knife coater.

coated, either by placing two air knife coaters and dryers in tandem, or by passing the web twice through a single coater.

Trailing Blade Coater

The trailing blade coater is a relatively new development having reached importance during the past ten years. A typical trailing blade coater is illustrated in Figures 13.5 and 13.6. During the coating process the web is supported by means of a rubber backing roll of relatively large diameter. The coating can be applied to the web from a fountain consisting of the blade support on one side and the paper supported by the backing roll on the other side. In other designs the coating is applied by means of an applicator roll or directly from a pan with the blade on the ascending side of the roll.

The coating is metered and smoothed onto the paper surface by means of a flexible trailing blade held in pressure contact with the paper. The blade is usually of spring steel construction and is supported in a rigid blade holder which is adjustable with regard to both pressure and angle.

The coater may seem at first to be simple, but actually a considerable amount of development went into the design of the machine as well as into the formulation of the coating materials. Originally this type of equipment was limited to very high solids content coatings and to very thin applications. Subsequent improvements, particularly in coating formulations and in drying techniques, have permitted the application of somewhat heavier coatings.

Because of the fact that it will handle high solids coatings of paste-like viscosity, the trailing blade has the advantage of greatly reduced drying requirements for water removal, which give substantial savings in both initial equipment and operating costs. It can also operate at very high speeds of over 2000 fpm. The high speed and low drying cost makes it advantageous to use this for off-machine coating of many grades at costs which can be competitive with on-machine coating.

As in the case of the air knife coater, the trailing blade is essentially a one-side coater. Two-side coatings can be obtained by tandem operation or by double passes through the machine. Because of the lower drying requirements with high solids coatings these materials can frequently be dried by passing over a steam-heated drying cyl-

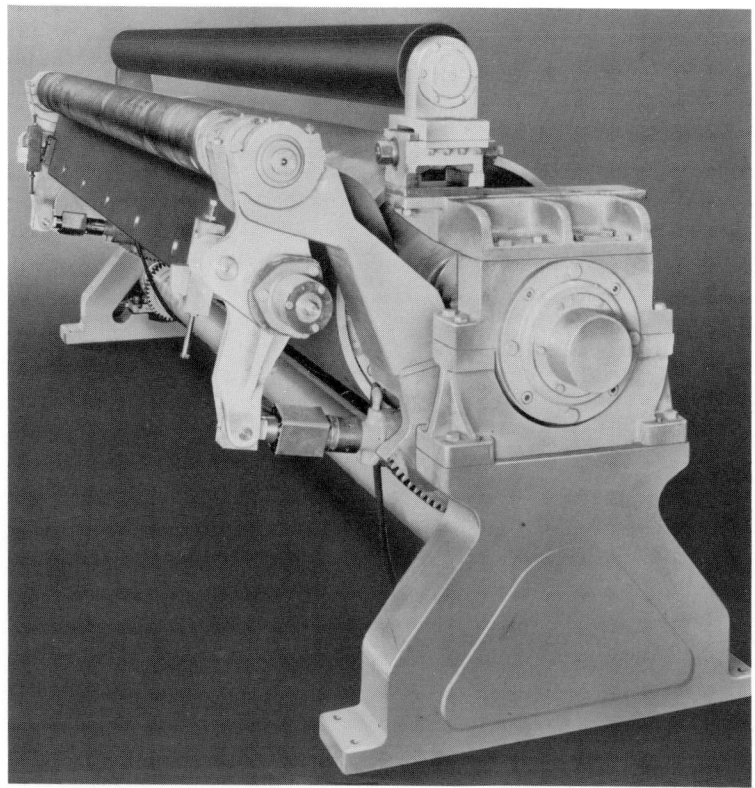

Fig. 13.5. Trailing blade coater. (*Courtesy Rice Barton Corp.*)

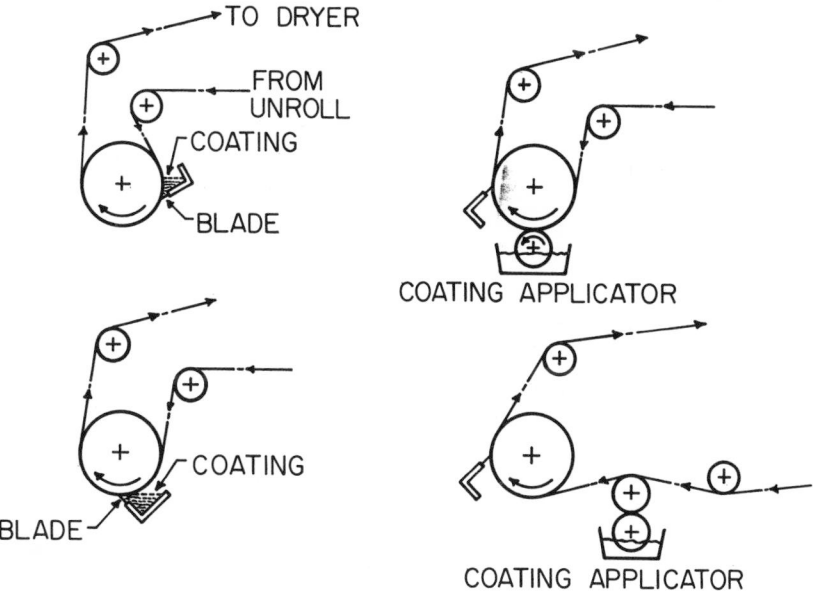

Fig. 13.6. Trailing blade coater.

inder with a high-velocity hot-air drying hood located over the cylinder. This arrangement is simpler than the long hot air tunnel required with low solids coatings.

Other Pigment Coating Processes

Several other coating processes and equipment are now in use for off-machine coatings which, although used in substantially lower volume than the air knife and trailing blade, are nevertheless commercially important.

One of these is the cast coating process and its modifications. In this process the clay coating is applied to the paper (which usually has a machine precoat) by means of a simple roll coater. The coated face of the paper is then pressed against a highly polished chromium-plated, steam-heated drying cylinder of large diameter. The paper is dried by diffusion of the water through the sheet and this must necessarily be a slow process.

The result, however, is that the finished surface of the paper is a true reproduction of the surface of the drying cylinder. This gives a coated finish of the highest gloss obtainable, far superior to that produced by other coating methods and supercalendering. Because of the complex equipment and low speed, however, it is quite costly.

Other modifications of the cast coating process recently introduced include application of the coating itself to the drying cylinder, followed by partial drying, with subsequent lamination of the paper onto the coating on the drying drum. A second process involves finishing of a paper which has previously been coated by partially moistening a coating and applying it under pressure to a polished drying cylinder, which again gives the desired high gloss finish to the end product. These two newer methods have the advantages of higher operating speeds because of improved drying conditions. In one sense the latter method is very similar to the Yankee dryer process for machine-glazed paper.

A variety of roll coaters and modified print roll coaters have been used for off-machine clay coating, but none of these is of great importance. These types are, of course, important for on-machine coatings where thin weights must be applied at very high speeds. One type of coater which is still in use, however, is the two roll double coater which will apply a clay coating simultaneously to both sides of the sheet. This is a simple two-roll stack, the bottom roll revolving in a pan and the coating being pumped up to a fountain formed by the upper roll and the web. A series of small driven smoothing rolls or bars follows the coater to level out the ribbed pattern produced on this type of coater. It is then dried in either a tower or floater type dryer, to be described later, since the paper cannot be contacted on either side until most of the moisture has been removed from the coated faces.

FUNCTIONAL COATINGS

The second major field of coating involves the application of a wide variety of functional coatings to paper, to improve its properties and its range of uses. Of primary importance are coatings that act as barriers to the passage of water, water vapor, and gases. These properties are of value in packaging food products as well as all other types of products which must be protected from the atmosphere.

The oldest types of coatings for these purposes were paraffin wax and bituminous asphalt. Subsequently, various lacquers and varnishes of both natural and synthetic types were developed for application to paper, not only to serve as barriers but also to give gloss and improved appearance.

Paper is also useful as a base for gummed tapes and adhesive tapes used for packaging and a variety of other purposes. Animal glues and rubber-base pressure-sensitive adhesives are applied to paper for producing these tapes. Greaseproof lacquer coatings and a wide variety of solutions and dispersions of the modern synthetic resins are available for use as paper coatings to suit almost any desired protective purpose. While paper itself is a poor barrier and has poor water resistance, a thin film of any of a number of coating materials greatly enhances its protective properties and expands its usefulness.

For applying these functional coatings to paper there are several principal types of processes and equipment in common use.

Roll Coaters

The basic roll coater is one of the oldest types of coaters, the coating applicator roll itself having been used in the early brush coaters and in most subsequent types. The single-roll coater is now seldom used alone because of its relative lack of control of the amount of coating being applied. There are literally dozens of different types of mul-

tiple-roll coaters with a wide variety of roll arrangements; among these there are three of primary importance, namely, the two roll coater, the reverse roll coater, and the gravure print roll coater.

A typical two roll coater is shown in Figure 13.7. It consists of two rolls arranged vertically in a stack with provisions for adjusting both the pressure and the clearance between the rolls. For most operations the paper is threaded between the rolls, although in certain cases it may pass over the top roll. In this latter case it serves as a so-called kiss coater, the coating being metered between the nip of the rolls. This type of coater finds its principal usage in the waxing of paper and in the application of glue and other gums for adhesive papers, such as gummed tapes and label papers. The coating is held in a pan below the bottom roll, which is frequently heated to maintain the temperature of the wax or gum. The rolls may consist of two steel or chilled iron rolls,

Fig. 13.7. Two-roll coater. (*Courtesy Dilts Div., Black-Clawson Co.*)

the latter being recommended for accuracy, or it may have one rubber-covered roll and one metal roll.

Waxed paper is produced in large quantities for bread wrapping and other food packaging, and for household use. For packaging it is printed with the desired pattern prior to waxing. The wax coating operation is carried out at high speeds employing molten paraffin wax, a petroleum by-product, as the coating material. The weight to be applied is controlled by the gap between the rolls. Speeds of the order of 2000 fpm are obtainable on modern high-speed waxing machines. The wax must be chilled quickly in order to give a glossy surface and to minimize penetration of the wax into the sheet. This chilling can be accomplished by dipping the wax into a bath of refrigerated water which gives the desired effect, followed by removal of the water with air blasts or scraper bars or both. The same rapid chilling with a different effect can be achieved by passing the paper over one or more specially designed cooling rolls which contain refrigerated water and have polished surfaces. The waxed paper is then ready to be wound.

Gummed paper is traditionally made on a similar two-roll coater, the paper passing over the top rolls in a kiss coating operation. Gumming speeds are limited by drying, since the gum must generally be applied as a relatively dilute solution. Speeds as high as 800 fpm are obtained with long arched hot-air dryers.

The reverse roll coater is shown in Figure 13.8 and two typical roll arrangements in Figure 13.9. This type of coater is the most accurate and versatile of the roll coaters for applying medium-weight coatings. The coating is applied by means of a casting roll which travels in a direction opposite to that of the paper, the paper being supported on a rubber roll to give uniform contact pressure. The thickness of coating on the casting roll is controlled by a separate metering roll whose surface is also driven in a reverse direction. Both of these rolls are made of chilled cast iron and are

Fig. 13.8. Reverse roll coater. (*Courtesy Waldron-Hartig Div., Midland Ross Corp.*)

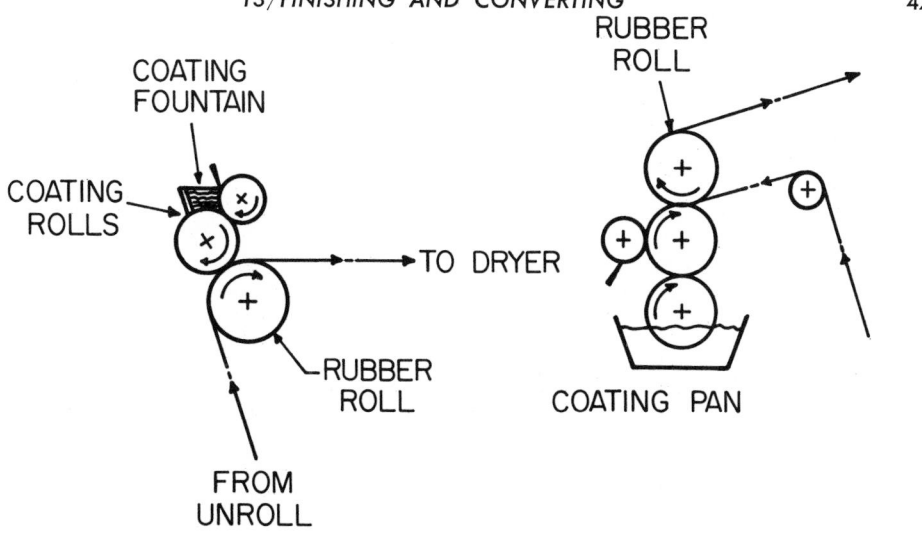

Fig. 13.9. Reverse roll coater arrangements.

ground to a precision of .0001 inch or better. Thus with this type of coater the thickness of coating to be applied depends only on the precision of the rolls and is not affected by the viscosity or film splitting characteristics of the coating or by the thickness or surface of the paper. This coater is widely used for applying a great variety of lacquers, varnishes, emulsions and suspensions as well as hot melts. It can apply materials with viscosities varying from slightly more than that of water up to several hundred thousand centipoises. The useful thickness range is about .001 inch minimum of .020 inch maximum wet thickness. Speeds in the range of 500 to 800 fpm can be obtained on reverse roll coaters without encountering hydraulic difficulties.

The print roll coater is a specialized type of coater of high precision for applying very light weight coatings. It consists essentially of a rotogravure or intaglio printing unit wherein the print roll is engraved with an over-all fine screen pattern. The print roll revolves in a pan of coating and the excess is removed by means of an oscillating doctor blade. The coating is then transferred to the paper with a rubber pressure roll nip. The resulting coating is actually a series of small dots which may not be suitable for some purposes. Some attempts have been made to smooth out this coating with a smoothing bar following application but these have not been altogether successful. It is also possible to use an offset gravure principle wherein the coating is transferred to a rubber roll and then to the paper. This operation has the tendency to spread the coating and blend the dots together into a continuous film. This is, of course, limited to coatings containing solvents which do not attack natural or synthetic rubber rolls. The gravure coater has the highest precision of any known type of coater but is limited to light weight coatings by the nature of the engraving process and is further limited by the dotted pattern effect. It is, however. used for application of coloring lacquers, prime and release coats for pressure-sensitive papers, and for applying adhesive to paper prior to lamination.

Extrusion Coating Machines

The extrusion coating process is a relatively new development in the application of functional coatings which has experienced a widespread expansion during the past ten years.

This process has enjoyed its widest use in the application of polyethylene plastic coatings to all grades of paper and paperboard. Polyethylene was found to have ideal

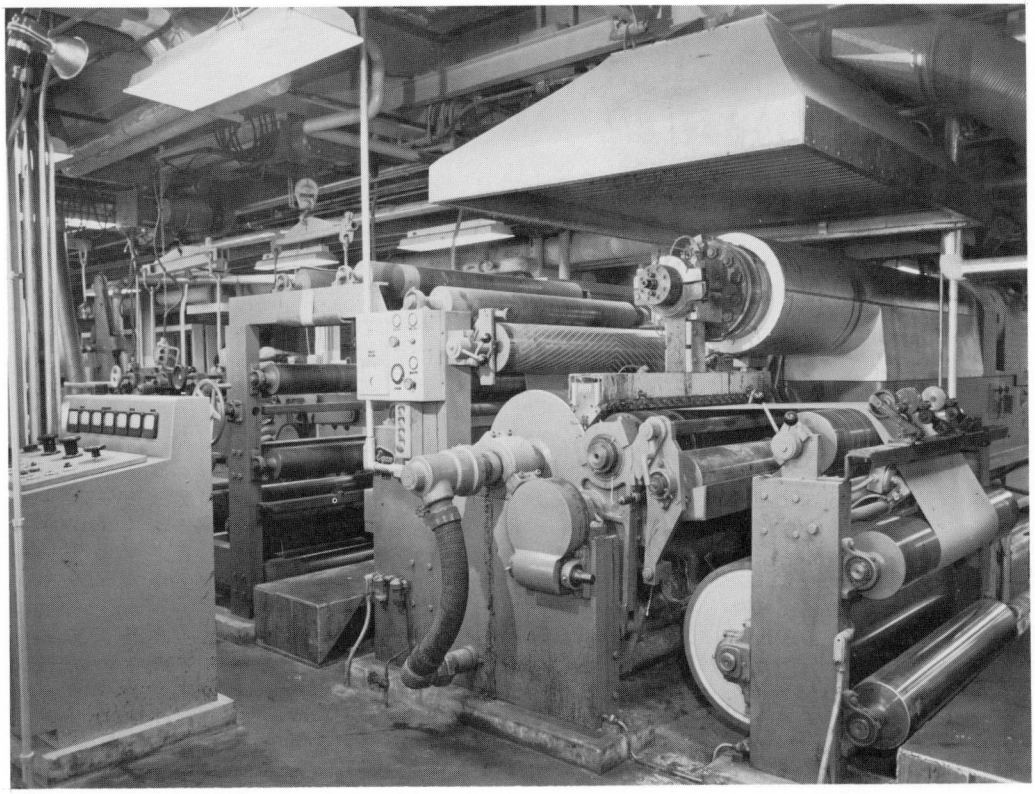

Fig. 13.10. Extrusion coating machine. (*Courtesy Frank W. Egan & Co.*)

properties for use in combination with paper as a packaging material. These properties include waterproofness and some degree of grease proofness, plus excellent barrier properties against transmission of water vapor and gases, good heat sealability and low-temperature flexibility, and freedom from odor and toxicity.

The following data [3] give an example of the effect of plastic coatings on paper properties for packaging.

	Moisture Vapor Tranmission Rate (gm/100 sq in.-day) (ASTM)	
Coating Weight (lb/ream, 24 x 36—500)	*Low Density Polyethylene*	*High Density Polyethylene*
7	3.2	1.6
10	2.2	0.9
15	1.6	0.6
20	0.8	0.5

Similar barrier properties are obtainable for gas transmission and grease resistance.

The marked increase in production of extrusion coated paper and board is evidenced by the following statistics.

	1956	1961
Tons of polyethylene applied to paper	6,000	14,000
Tons of polyethylene applied to board	200	12,500
Tons of paper and board coated with polyethylene	20,000	400,000

The extrusion coating process has been found useful for a number of other extrudable film-forming thermoplastics which have sufficient heat stability to pass through the equipment. These include the other polyolefins, polyamides, and styrene polymers and copolymers. Thus far, however, none of these have been produced in any significant commercial quantities as paper coatings. The vinyl chloride and vinylidene chloride

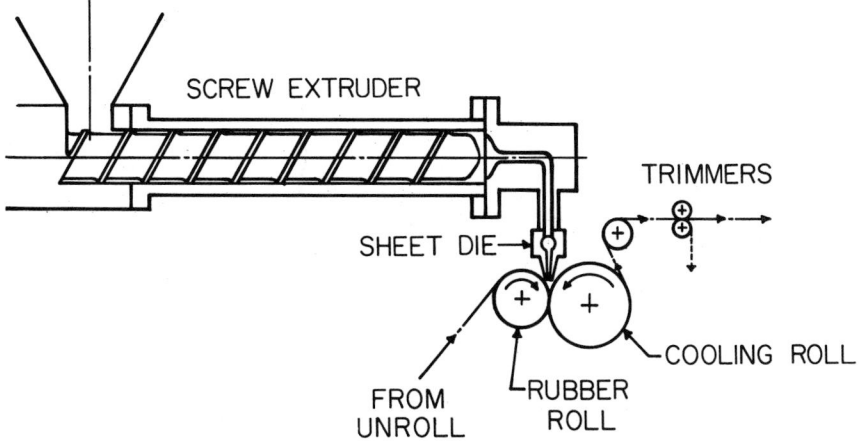

Fig. 13.11. Extrusion coating machine.

polymers have not been suitable because of poor heat stability for extrusion through the wide sheet dies used. A typical extrusion coating machine is shown in Figures 13.10 and 13.11.

The polyethylene resin is melted in a conventional thermoplastic extruder. This consists of a driven screw within an electrically heated cylinder which melts and compacts the resin granules and extrudes them in a continuous flow at high pressure. The resin is then discharged through a film-forming slot die consisting of a manifold with an adjustable outlet. The die is equipped with electric heaters with a number of precision temperature controls to give uniform temperature and viscosity of the plastic melt. The slot opening is also equipped with a number of adjustments across the width for maintaining uniformity.

The hot extruded film is then stretched and combined with the paper between a pair of rolls, one of which is a rubber-covered pressure roll and the other a water-cooled chromium-plated steel roll. The combination takes place so rapidly that a permanent bond is created between the plastic film and the paper due to the adhesiveness of the film before it has time to be cooled by the steel roll. This roll must be kept cold, as otherwise the plastic would adhere to the metal and could not be stripped off.

The combined web passes around the cooling roll and after cooling is ready to be wound in the usual manner.

In a manner similar to the cast coating process the surface of the film produces an exact reproduction of the surface of the cooling roll since it is soft when it first contacts this roll. For a high-gloss coating which is desired for many purposes, the cooling roll is given a mirror finish chrome-plated surface. Because polyethylene tends to be somewhat tacky when it is glossy, for certain types of products and packaging machines a high slip coating is desired. This is produced by giving the cooling roll a dull or matte chrome-plated finish which is transferred similarly to the coating. The coating produced by this method has high slip properties and is similar in appearance and feeling to a dull waxed paper.

The extrusion coating process has one inherent disadvantage in that the plastic film tends to thicken at the edges as it is stretched between the die and the chilled roll. This stretching is necessary since it has not been found practical to set the die opening at the very low final thicknesses desired. Commonly the die opening is set at .020 inch with the final coating thickness on the order of .001 inch or less.

Operating speeds on the order of 500 to 1500 fpm are commonly encountered, the upper limit being imposed either by lack of hot stretchability of the resin, or lack of adhesion to the paper which results either from excessive cooling or insufficient oxidation of the surface necessary to produce adherence to some webs.

The polyethylene extrusion-coating process initially found wide usage for kraft paper for multiwall bags, where it gave an excellent water and vapor barrier. Its use subsequently expanded to include a wide range of food packaging papers, and in addition, bags for hygroscopic chemicals and fertilizers. An important recent development is the adoption of extruded polyethylene coatings for milk containers made from bleached kraft paperboard. Because of the superior properties of this coating, it is replacing the wax coating now in use in these containers.

Other Functional Coating Processes

There exists a wide variety of other types of coaters used for applying functional coatings. One such coater is the air knife coater described previously for application of mineral coatings. Various plastic resin coatings can conveniently be applied to paper in the form of a water-base latex or emulsion. These are available in relatively high solids content (of the order of 50%) and, when dried, form a good protective plastic film. The air knife coater has been found very useful for applying these emulsions and latices.

Following the application, the coatings are dried as usual in a hot-air drying tunnel, and frequently they must be fused by application of increased temperature, often by radiant heat, to actually flash-melt the plastic particles deposited from the latex and cause them to fuse together to a film. With some products it is necessary to apply at least two coats to obtain satisfactory results. This process is particularly useful for vinyl and polyvinylidene chloride materials which cannot be conveniently extruded in the form of wide flat films for coating.

One of the oldest types of coaters which is still in use to a limited degree is the knife coater. In this type, the paper is drawn under a knife and is supported by a roll or a blanket or by its own tension. The coating material is poured onto the upper surface of the paper to form a bank in front of the knife and the thickness is metered by the web tension or pressure between the paper and the bottom of the knife. This is a very simple machine but has serious disadvantages with regard to uniformity of coating thickness, formation of streaks, etc. It is still in use, however, for the application of rubber-base, pressure-sensitive adhesives to paper and for applying vinyl plastisols to paper for the manufacture of artificial leather. For both classes of products, however, it is gradually being replaced by the reverse roll coater.

Other coaters, such as dip type and spray type, have been used to a limited degree for special grades of paper but are not of importance in the manufacture of any of the familiar large volume functional paper products.

OTHER WET CONVERTING PROCESSES

In addition to the coating operations already described, a number of other converting processes are carried out on paper in continuous web form, from roll to roll.

Paper and board may be impregnated or saturated with various types of resin or latex materials to make them suitable for packaging or structural purposes. Two or more webs of paper may be laminated together, either to give a sheet with properties derived from the combined materials or to give greater thickness and strength.

The surface of the paper may be embossed to improve its appearance for decorative purposes. Although most creping of paper is now carried out on the paper machine, the production of high-stretch crepe is carried out as a separate converting operation. An important specialized process involving a combination of converting operations is the manufacture of corrugated paperboard for box and carton manufacture.

Impregnating Equipment

There are various products which involve the impregnation of paper or board. One of the most important uses of impregnated paper is in the manufacture of high-pressure plastic laminates. These materials are widely used for electrical insulation and for various industrial and structural purposes and for decorative purposes, such as table and counter tops, furniture, etc.

Although some of the industrial laminates use cloth as a base, paper is the most important fiber base in this industry. These laminates consist of a number of sheets of paper which have been impregnated with phenolic resins and dried, and are then pressed together in high-pressure curing presses in thicknesses from $\frac{1}{16}$ up to 1 inch or more.

The familiar decorative laminates consist of a number of sheets of phenolic-impregnated kraft paper as a core, the outer sheets being made of alpha-cellulose paper impregnated with melamine resins. These are similarly pressed and cured into sheets having thicknesses in the range of $\frac{1}{16}$ to $\frac{3}{32}$ inch. The patterns used for decorative purposes are printed on a heavy alpha sheet prior to saturating, and a thin melamine-impregnated alpha sheet, called the overlay, is then placed over these printed sheets, which becomes transparent upon pressing.

A typical resin impregnating machine (referred to as a "treater" in the saturating industry) is shown in Figure 13.12. The paper is unwound and dipped into a pan of resin solution, either phenolic or melamine, with the solvent consisting of a mixture of ethyl alcohol and water. It then passes between a pair of large diameter precisely ground chilled-iron press rolls. These not only force the resin through the body of the paper but also meter the final quantity of resin retained in the paper.

The sheet then passes into a hot-air drying tunnel where the solvent is evaporated and where the resin is partially cured, with

Fig. 13.12. Resin impregnating machine. (*Courtesy Frank W. Egan & Co.*)

release of water vapor. In the case of phenolic-impregnated kraft it is then wound into rolls for subsequent sheeting on conventional sheeters. The melamine-impregnated alpha paper is quite brittle and is difficult to wind and is therefore sheeted as it emerges from the dryer.

A second important use for impregnated paper is the addition of various rubber-like latices to long-fiber papers which then serve as a strong base for structural purposes. These latices may be of either natural or synthetic rubber or can be emulsions of a variety of synthetic resin materials. Their purpose is to greatly increase the internal bond strength and tear strength of the paper. The equipment used for this purpose is somewhat similar to the impregnator used for treating of laminating papers. The sheet is, however, given a longer dwell time in the pan to increase the degree of saturation and penetration, since these papers are often quite thick. Longer drying time is also required to remove the water from the sheet; hence festooning dryers are still in use on heavier products of this type. Lighter-weight impregnated paper, however, can be dried in horizontal drying tunnels.

Papers which have been latex-impregnated in this manner are used as gasket papers, as a base for artificial leather, in the manufacture of shoe soles and inner linings, in producing various leather substitutes for manufacture of luggage, etc., and as a base for pressure-sensitive paper tapes such as masking tape.

Oiled papers are made on similar saturating equipment wherein the paper is dipped into a bath of molten paraffinic oil. It is then passed through squeeze rolls and cooled and wound up, no drying being required. These papers are used for meat wrapping and can also be used for wrapping machine parts.

Another important saturating operation is the manufacture of felt-like grades of paperboard for use as building papers. These materials, commonly referred to as roofing felts, consist of strong, long-fiber paperboard saturated with molten asphalt. Because the penetration is rather slow, the typical roofing felt saturating machine consists of a large tank with a series of dip rolls. The sheet is passed into and out of the tank a number of times over this series of rolls, during which operation it picks up a heavy content of asphalt. The sheet is then air-cooled to chill the surface to reduce its tackiness, and is then finally cooled on water cooled rolls prior to winding up. This type of paper is very widely used in the building industry both for roofing and as a barrier sheet in the siding of houses.

Still another saturating operation is the tub sizing of high grade bond and ledger papers. Although most sizing is carried out on the paper machine, the use of a separate continuous tub-sizing process is still required for the highest qualities of writing papers. This type of saturation is carried out on equipment similar to that used for latex saturation. The paper is first passed through a rather long tub of sizing solution to give the desired dwell time and then passes between a pair of squeeze rolls to remove the excess and to meter the amount absorbed. These papers are then dried in continuous air dryers either of the floating or running festoon type. It is found desirable to use this type of drying with relaxed tension of the sheet to give the desired "cockle" finish on many of these grades of paper.

Laminating Processes

There are several reasons for laminating together two or more sheets of paper or board. One is to produce a sheet with combined properties, as for example the lamination of a sheet of liner paper to a cheap grade of paperboard for making folding boxes; here the cheap board filler provides rigidity in strength while the liner gives the desired exterior surface.

Another reason for lamination is to build up the thickness and strength for structural purposes. Heavier grades of boxboard, for example, can best be made by laminating several finished sheets together with an adhesive rather than attempting to produce a thick sheet directly on the board machine. Heavy boards up to ½ inch thick are made by lamination for such uses as fiber drum heads, automotive interior panels, etc.

Still another use of lamination is the production of barrier papers both for packaging and for structural uses. In these products the laminant is asphalt, which serves as a barrier material as well as an adhesive. A widely used product is the so-called 30-30-30 asphalt-laminated kraft consisting of two 30-pound kraft sheets with a 30-pound layer of asphalt between them. This is then used in the manufacture of multiwall bags for fertilizer and other similar materials.

For special-purpose bags and for construction uses, two sheets of kraft paper are laminated with heavier coatings of asphalt. To give strength, fibers are often introduced between the two asphalt-coated sheets immediately prior to lamination to give reinforcement. Jute fibers were widely used for this purpose in the past but they are being largely replaced by fiber-glass roving, which is both thinner and stronger.

Still another widely used lamination is the combination of aluminum foil and paperboard. The aluminum foil provides an ideal barrier for packaging and also gives a bright glossy surface for exterior printing. A typical foil-to-paper laminating machine is shown in Figure 13.13. The adhesive is applied to the web by means of a conventional roll coater described previously. The excess adhesive is usually removed by means of a doctor blade or doctor rod. Although in the past, the metering of the amount of adhesive has not been carried out with any degree of accuracy, the trend now is to give far greater emphasis to the control of the adhesive application. This is necessary from the point of view both of maintaining product quality and of economizing in the cost of the adhesive consumed.

With a two-web lamination the adhesive is commonly applied to only one web, usually the less absorbent of the two. For laminations of more than two webs, the adhesive is applied to all but a single web to give the necessary number of adherent surfaces. Accurate control of the tension in each of the webs entering the laminator is

Fig. 13.13. Foil laminator. (*Courtesy Dilts Div., Black-Clawson Co.*)

of the utmost importance in every laminating operation. Since the sheets are permanently bonded together, any imbalance in residual tension will cause the final product to curl. This is corrected by applying accurate independent tension controls to each of the incoming webs.

Following adhesive application, the webs are combined in a press. For the thinner laminations this press consists of a pair of nip rolls, pneumatically loaded, with one steel and one rubber roll. High pressures are not required since the adhesives commonly used will develop the bond with minimum contact pressure. Sodium silicate solutions were once widely used as a laminating adhesive for paper and board, but these have largely been replaced by water solutions of starch, vegetable protein and synthetic resins. Where barrier properties are desired, paraffin wax and asphalt are applied in the molten condition as a laminating adhesive.

For sheets which are thin enough to be flexible after laminating, the next step is to pass them over a series of heated drying cylinders. This removes the moisture from the adhesive through the sheet and also helps to set the adhesive. Following this, these materials can be wound or sheeted.

The thicker laminated products cannot be conveniently passed around drying cylinders. For these a converted starch of higher solids content is used which will dry by absorption into the sheet and will set without further external drying. These types of products are generally laminated through two sets of press rolls which are both made of steel or chilled iron. Additional pressure is required to assure a good permanent bond with thick rigid products, since they are handled only in flat form after having been laminated. These products are always cut into sheets immediately after the laminating section.

In the case of wax and asphalt lamination, the sheet is passed around a series of cooling rolls instead of dryers prior to winding in order to set the adhesive. In the manufacture of reinforced asphalt-laminated papers, the reinforcing material is drawn into the nip of the press rolls. With this type of product both sheets are coated to assure continuity of the adhesive around the reinforcing material.

Laminations are commonly carried out in a width range from 40 to 120 inches. Operating speeds for adhesive, wax and asphalt laminations with flexible webs run from 1,000 to 1,500 fpm, but in the case of thick rigid laminated boards the speed is limited to about 400 fpm by the heavy rotary sheet-cutting equipment.

Embossing and Creping Processes

These two processes, although otherwise unrelated, are both used to deform the sheet of paper so that it is no longer flat.

Embossing is generally carried out for decorative purposes to give the paper a raised design on its surface. This is used extensively in making paper napkins which will be described later, in certain grades of writing paper and papeteries, and for fancy wrapping papers and exterior box liner papers.

Embossing is a simple process carried out by passing the paper between a pair of nip rolls. The upper roll is a heavy forged steel roll which has been mechanically engraved with the desired pattern. This roll is usually steam-heated to help soften the paper. The bottom roll is fiber-filled, similar in construction to a supercalender roll. The pattern is usually impressed into this roll by running the two rolls together for a time before commencing the embossing operation.

Creping is a wet-deforming process used to increase the stretchability of paper. Although low-stretch papers are creped in line with the paper machine, it is necessary that crepe with a high percentage of stretch be made as a separate converting operation.

To produce this type of paper, the flat sheet is first fed into a tub of water containing a small amount of size, to wet the paper thoroughly. It then passes through a press to remove the excess water and around a steam-heated drying roll which serves as the creping roll. During drying, the size causes the paper to adhere slightly to the creping roll. The paper is then removed from the roll by a doctor blade, called the creping knife. The angle and contour of the blade and the speed and sizing conditions control the percentage of stretch and the coarseness of the crepe obtained. In order to avoid removing the crepe the paper must then be dried in a completely relaxed condition. This can be done by either carrying it on felts over a series of drying cylinders similar to a paper machine dryer, or by carrying it through an air dryer on a slat conveyor which avoids the application of any tension to the sheet.

These high-stretch creped papers can be used for decorative purposes in which case a coloring dye is frequently added to the creping bath. They are also used as kraft paper liners for barrels and bags where the high stretch characteristics give them excellent resistance to tearing and bursting.

The Corrugating Process

The manufacture of corrugated paperboard has developed during the past fifty years to the point where it is now one of the major tonnage items of the paper industry. Its development has been made possible by the availability of high-strength, low-cost, unbleached kraft paperboard.

Because of its low cost and high strength characteristics corrugated paperboard has become an ideal material for manufacturing shipping cartons. Available in a variety of weights, it has gradually replaced wooden boxes and solid fiber boxes and barrels for shipping a tremendous variety of commodities. The corrugated paper carton has become one of our most familiar articles of commerce.

The sheet of corrugated paperboard consists of three webs of kraft paperboard. The center web is corrugated or fluted and is adhered to the two outer webs by means of adhesive. This gives a continuous thick sheet of truss-like structure which is resistant to bending and crushing.

A double-deck corrugating head, on which the fluted paper is formed and glued, is shown in Figure 13.14.

The webs of kraft paperboard are unrolled on standard unwinding devices. For the larger higher production machines, these unwinds provide for shaftless chucking and floor pick-up of the rolls.

The first operation involves the formation of the so-called single-faced corrugated sheet. The central or corrugating layer is first softened by exposure to live steam and passing around a heated roll. In the single-facing machine it is then passed between the nip of a pair of fluted corrugating rolls to produce the desired corrugated contour. This web must obviously be drawn in at a higher speed than the other webs since its length is considerably shortened by this process.

As the web emerges from this nip it follows the upper fluted roll to the glue applying position. A double roll coater is used to apply the glue to the top edges only of the fluted board, while it is still in contact with the corrugated sheet, with a rubber nip roll which presses it against the fluted roll. The resulting product is the single-faced corrugated sheet. The liner has been pre-heated by passing over a steam-heated roll to help set and commence the drying of the adhesive.

The single-faced sheet is then led to a storage conveyor consisting of tapes operating at reduced speeds. The material is overlapped in small festoons and permitted to stand on this conveyor so that the adhesive can set and dry. This intermediate storage also makes possible a separate operation of the double-facing step from the single facer to permit splicing new rolls, making changes at the dry end, etc.

The single-faced sheet is then passed through a glue machine or glue applicator unit. It must be carried under light tension through this operation to avoid crushing the fluted paper. The glue applicator consists of a conventional double-roll coater. The single-faced sheet is passed in light

Fig. 13.14. Corrugating machine. (*Courtesy Samuel M. Langston Co.*)

kiss contact over the applicator roll with the fluted side down so that adhesive is applied only to the upper edges of the corrugated web.

The bottom liner sheet is also passed over a pre-heating roll and is then brought into contact with the upper web to which the glue has been applied. This contact must be very light to avoid crushing.

The combining is carried out on a heated table between a pair of driven canvas belts, this unit being referred to as the double facer. The table consists of a series of steam-heated flat cast-iron chests which have been smoothly machined on their upper surfaces. The corrugated web is drawn over this table by means of a driven canvas belt. During this operation the final adhesive bond is created and the moisture in the adhesive is diffused through the board into the belt and evaporated during the return pass of the belts.

The board is then cooled by passing through a second section which is similar in construction to the first section. In this case, however, belts are provided both on the upper and lower sides of the web to draw it without friction. The cooling is largely accomplished by heat transfer from the board to the belts which are supported on idler rolls on both sides. The spacing between these idlers is accurately controlled to give positive draw without excessive pressure. Heat is then dissipated from the belts into the air of the room.

At the end of the cooling section the finished corrugated board must be cut to size. The sheet is first passed through a scoring and slitting unit, using shear cut slitters which cut the full width web into the desired finished width. It is also indented by means of scoring rings to facilitate folding into boxes at the desired locations.

Following this the sheets are cut to length in heavy-duty rotary sheet cutters similar to those used for cutting paper, except that they are considerably heavier in construction. The sheet length is varied as usual by adjusting the speed of the cutting knife in relation to the speed of the sheet. As with other types of converting lines, the complete corrugating line is generally driven by a direct-current variable-speed multiple motor drive.

Because corrugating plants must deliver boxes to order in a wide variety of sizes and on short delivery time, the machines frequently are equipped with duplex stations to permit rapid change of product specification. There are two principal sizes of corrugation used and many machines have corrugating rolls of both designs available. By duplicating the corrugating, gluing and cut-off units, rapid changes can be made in the product being manufactured.

The finished corrugated sheets from the corrugating line are then delivered to a machine known as a printer-slotter for conversion into a box blank. These machines include a sheet feeder followed by from one to four printing stations of the flexographic type. The blanks are then slotted at each end to provide for the top and bottom flaps and are scored again at right angles to the original scoring to permit folding.

The result is a finished printed carton blank ready for use.

DRY PAPER CONVERTING

In contrast to the wet converting processes described previously, there is a second complete field of paper converting called dry converting. This does not involve any modification of the paper web itself, but rather leads to the production of a finished article of paper from the web which may or may not have been subjected to previous converting operations. These finished articles consist of paper bags, boxes, and cartons, small rolls for household consumption, etc.

Bag-making Equipment

The manufacture of paper bags is a large consumer of paper. The two principal classes of bags are the familiar kraft paper grocery bag and the multiwall shipping sack. Various other fancy grades of single-wall bags are also made.

The basic operations performed in the manufacture of single and multiwall bags are the same, with the exception of the number of plies. A typical multiwall bag machine is shown in Figure 13.15. The rolls of paper are unwound at high speed on conventional unwinding equipment. Side guiding adjustment is required to assure accurate alignment of the webs. Bags must frequently be printed with identification or brand markings and these markings must almost always be in register with the bag length. This is accomplished by the installation of single or multicolor flexographic printers.

The webs of paper are formed into tubes on a unit known as a tuber. This consists of forming shoes over which the paper is drawn, which gradually will transform it from a flat sheet into a cylindrical tube. The glue is applied to the edge of each ply

Fig. 13.15. Multiwall bag machine. (*Courtesy H. G. Weber Co., Inc.*)

and the sheets are then flattened and passed through press rolls which seal the seams.

The finished bag is then manufactured on a bottoming machine. This is a complex automatic unit which cuts the tubes to length and folds, glues and seals the bottom of the bag. Many bags are gusseted to provide a convenient shape for handling and filling. This is done by the installation of additional guide plates on the tuber which tuck in the sides prior to flattening.

The finished bags are delivered at high speed from the bottomer and are ready for packaging and shipping.

Box and Carton Making

There are a great variety of designs and types of paperboard boxes and cartons in use, besides the corrugated type previously described. In general, paperboard cartons are produced by the converter and shipped to the user in the form of flat blanks. The production of these blanks is generally considered to be a paper converting opera-

tion, whereas the actual forming, filling and sealing of boxes is considered to be packaging.

A typical carton printing and blanking machine is shown in Figure 13.16. The roll of paperboard is unwound and fed to a single or multicolor printer. Because of its simplicity and ease of changing plates, the flexographic printer is the type most widely used. For higher quality products, however, rotogravure printing is used.

The printed board is then fed, still in register, to a scoring and die-cutting unit. The web may be slit to produce narrower widths at this point. The cutting and scoring units can be either of the rotary or flat type. The flat type involves less expense for dies and easier change-over, but it naturally results in a "start-stop" feeding of the board which requires lower speeds and web storage provisions.

On both these types of units, however, the carton blanks are die-cut from the web and are simultaneously scored to permit

Fig. 13.16. Carton blanking machine. (*Courtesy Champlain Co., Inc.*)

subsequent folding into carton shapes. This basic process is used for making practically all types of folding boxes as well as for liquid containers such as paper milk bottles.

Automatic Roll Winding

A large volume of paper products is ultimately used in the form of small rolls. Because of the large tonnage and the necessity of producing these products at low cost, complex automatic roll winding machinery has been developed.

Toilet tissue is probably the largest volume product produced in the form of small rolls. Other similar products include paper towels, counter rolls of wrapping paper, household rolls of waxed paper, adding machine paper rolls, etc.

A typical automatic roll-winding machine for toilet tissue is shown in Figure 13.17. The full mill-size rolls of tissue are unwound at the machine speed of about 1500 fpm. The web passes through slitters which cut the sheet to the desired finished roll width. The finished small rolls are wound on a center shaft winder, principally for

ease of automatic transfer. Long cores are fed automatically into the machine and are cut to length on the winding mandrel.

The winding mandrel then advances to the starting position. Glue is applied to assist in the transfer to the core. Before reaching the winding station the webs of material, such as toilet tissue and paper towels, are passed over a specially designed roll which perforates them to permit severance of the sheets when used. When a finished measured length has been wound, the unit automatically cuts the web and transfers it to the new winding core. The finished rolls are then automatically ejected from the machine.

In a modification of this process the tissue is wound full width rather than in slit widths. The finished roll, referred to as a log, is then cut to the desired width with an automatic log saw. This operation eliminates the necessity of matching the slit cores to the slit web on the machine.

These rolls are then delivered to automatic wrapping and boxing machines for direct shipment. Mechanical handling is used throughout for efficient operation.

Fig. 13.17. Toilet roll winder. (*Courtesy Paper Converting Machine Co.*)

Automatic Cutting and Folding

The second large group of sanitary paper products is used in the form of folded sheets. These include facial tissues and paper napkins, and also such products as industrial paper wipers.

There are two different processes for making these types of products. In the first, individual or two-ply webs are individually cut with rotating knives and then folded. In the second process, a large number of webs, as many as 100 or 200, the number to be contained in the finished package, are folded longitudinally in a continuous process and the resulting log is saw-cut to package length. Typical machines for these types are shown in Figures 13.18 and 13.19.

With a single web operation, as used for paper napkins, the web is unwound and is usually first embossed to give the desired pattern in a conventional paper embosser. This type of embosser is frequently equipped with two matched metal rolls, rather than one engraved roll with fiber backing roll, to give clear-cut two-sided embossing at high speed. The web then passes through a pair of cutting knives to give the desired sheet length and thence to an automatic folder to produce the finished size article.

In the multiple-web process a large battery of backstands must be provided, one unwinding position for each web, corresponding to the number of sheets in the finished package. The webs are passed through continuous folders which consist of a series of guides to fold the sheets to the desired shape. They are then pressed flat with nip rolls to make the fold permanent.

Two principal types of folds are used, namely, the "C" type fold and the overlapped fold for continuous withdrawal of the tissue from the carton. The product delivered from the folder is a continuous stack of folded sheets. This is then cut to length by means of high-speed saws and the in-

Fig. 13.18. Paper napkin machine. (*Courtesy Hudson-Sharp Div., FMC Corp.*)

Fig. 13.19. Facial tissue machine. (*Courtesy Paper Converting Machine Co.*)

dividual bundles are ready for boxing in automatic cartoning machines.

Other Dry Converting Processes

There are a considerable number of other paper converting processes for producing finished articles of lesser production volume than the items previously described. Paper cups are coming into increasing use as a sanitary means for serving hot drinks and soft drinks as well as water. These are produced from continuous webs of paper on special high-speed machinery. Paper plates for food consumption are produced by die-cutting and hot-pressing paper from a continuous web which has been moistened and heated to soften it. Envelopes are produced on automatic high-speed machinery which die-cuts the envelope from a continuous web, applies glue at the seams, and folds and glues the flaps.

AUXILIARY CONVERTING EQUIPMENT

There are certain components of converting equipment which are common to most of the processes described herein. Thus in every case, a roll of paper must be unwound before it can be fed to a converting machine.

Except for the cases where the end product is cut into sheets, the converted web must be re-wound into rolls for subsequent handling. For all types of coated and impregnated papers and for many laminated sheets where solvents or water are used, the web must be passed through a dryer to remove this solvent or water before the sheet is ready for winding and subsequent processing.

In addition, various web control techniques must be employed to ensure proper handling of the paper. These include side guiding of the web entering the machine, application of tension control not only to the entering web but at various stages through the process, proper choice of drives to give the desired speed and tension characteristics, etc.

These various web processing auxiliaries will be discussed in the following sections.

Unrolls

A number of designs of unrolls are available to serve the wide variety of converting needs. The simplest type is, of course, merely a single through-shaft with tapered cones to engage the paper core and with the shaft mounted in bearings on stands. A hand brake is mounted on the shaft to provide tension. This design is suitable for low speed unwinding with noncritical requirements for production, web tension, and side guiding. Frequently a double stand is provided so that a second roll can be made ready for splicing when the first one expires.

Because of the increasing demands for high-speed continuous operation of converting machines, however, the flying splice type of unwind is coming into far greater usage. There are two basic types of flying splice unroll, namely, the sliding type and the revolving or turret type. These are shown in Figures 13.20 and 13.21. In each case the new roll of paper is driven up to full web speed either by belts or contact rolls.

The roll is moved into splicing position as the previous roll expires and the leading edge is then fastened by glue. In most cases the tail of the expired roll is cut off automatically since it is seldom possible to time the splice exactly to the end of the previous roll.

It is always necessary to apply braking to the unwinding roll so that the web will be delivered under a positive tension to the converting machine. This is necessary to ensure accurate alignment of the web and to avoid wrinkling. The unwinding shafts are always equipped with brakes of the manual, pneumatic, or hydraulic type. On the more advanced machines these brakes are controlled automatically by a dancer roll to give constant tension. In many cases the web will pass over a pair of driven tensioning or hold-back rolls to provide greater tension than can be conveniently obtained by a brake on the shaft passing through the core.

The newest turret type unrolls are also equipped for floor pick-up of the mill roll of paper and for automatic chucking of the roll without the use of shafts. These features greatly reduce the amount of labor required on high-speed machines.

Side guiding is also often an integral part of the unroll. On all types of converting

Fig. 13.20. Sliding unroll. (*Courtesy Frank W. Egan & Co.*)

processes, it is necessary that the web be accurately aligned with the machine and not be permitted to weave from side to side. Frequently the mill rolls have telescoped slightly due to rough handling, and this misalignment must be corrected.

Fig. 13.21. Turret unroll. (*Courtesy Dilts Div., Black-Clawson Co.*)

The simplest arrangement is, of course, a manual side adjustment of the unwinding roll which the operator performs while watching the web. On most newer high-speed machines, however, it has been found desirable to carry out this side guiding automatically. The edge of the web can be determined either with a pneumatic sensing device or an electric eye and this in turn actuates a hydraulic or electric power unit which will shift either the individual roll of unwinding paper or the entire unwind unit.

Winders

As in the case of unrolls, there is also a wide variety of winder designs available for winding paper at the end of converting operation. There are two basic types, namely, the center-driven and surface-driven types, and either of these can be arranged either for manual roll changing or for continuous operation with flying roll starting.

The center-driven winder is the most versatile in that it will wind almost any type of web without damage and without winding it too tightly. It is also less affected by non-uniform thickness in the paper or coating. Center winding does have the disadvantages, however, of not being able to yield a very tight roll and of being limited by drive and tension considerations to a diameter build-up ratio of 6/1. In other words it is not desirable to wind a finished diameter larger than six times the outside diameter of the core, as otherwise the roll may become loose or may telescope.

The simplest type of center winder is, of course, a single shaft mounted in bearings with a drive and with cones to engage the paper. This can be expanded to comprise a two-shaft center winder with one shaft above the other, so that the web can be transferred manually from the finished roll to the new core at low speed without stopping.

A more advanced type is the turret type center winder where the two winding positions are mounted on arms on a revolving turret. This is very similar to the turret type unwind except that each winding position is equipped with a drive rather than a brake. To provide for continuous operation, the drive is arranged to bring the empty core up to full web speed. A pair of wrapping rolls is provided which wraps the web around the new core and an automatic cut-off knife then severs the web and tucks it into the nip formed by the core and one of the wrap rolls.

In order to control the speed and tension on center-driven winders, many special drives are available. The simplest and oldest types are mechanical drives using either a slip belt or a slip clutch. These must be manually adjusted by the operator to give the desired tension and winding characteristics. Better results are obtained, however, by using electrical or hydraulic drives, which give automatic control of speed and tension. For constant tension winding, it is necessary that the driving torque gradually be increased as the roll diameter builds up and the rotational speed decreases. In most cases a tapered tension rather than a true constant tension is desirable to avoid excessive tightening and telescoping of the inner layers. The latest type of electrical and hydraulic drives permits obtaining any degree of taper of the tension between the

Fig. 13.22. Continuous double drum winder. (*Courtesy Frank W. Egan & Co.*)

limits of constant tension and constant torque (maximum taper).

Surface winding is widely used on converting machines where large, tight rolls are desired and where the product is not particularly sensitive. There are two basic kinds of surface winders, namely, the single drum and the double drum types.

The single drum winder is similar to the surface-winding reel used on paper-making machines. The single winding drum is driven at line speed with provision for controlling the draw for winding tension control. The new winding core is started on top of the drum and the paper is cut and

wrapped around it by the use of a cord or by compressed air. Cutting can also be done automatically by a knife in combination with the use of an adhesive surface on the core. The roll is held against the drum on horizontal slides during the winding operation with controlled pressure applied hydraulically or pneumatically to control the tightness of the wind.

The double drum winder is basically the same design machine as is used for slitting and rewinding. Generally slitting is not attempted at the end of converting machines because this is basically a "start-stop" operation requiring careful alignment of cores and would tend to interfere with the smooth operation of the converting process.

Surface winders have the advantage over the center winders of being able to wind much larger rolls on small cores, and also to wind tighter rolls for shipment. In many cases the product wound on the double-drum winder can be shipped directly without further slitting and rewinding, whereas the center wound product must almost always be rewound on a double-drum winder before shipment.

A flying roll changer for double-drum winders has recently been developed which makes an ideal application for converting machines since it permits a continuous operation from roll to roll without stopping, and yet gives all of the desirable qualities in the finished roll which can be obtained by double-drum winding. A unit of this type is shown in Figure 13.22.

Surface-driven winders require no special drives since the winding drums operate at the same speed as the converting machine itself.

Dryers

Dryers are an essential part of many paper converting operations. In the application of pigmented coatings, these coatings are always dispersed in water and the water must be evaporated. Many functional coatings are dissolved in organic solvents which must be dried. In the impregnation of paper with resin or latex materials, the diluent must again be removed by drying.

Since most coating and saturating operations produce a wet surface which cannot be touched without damaging the product, the air dryer is the most widely used type of dryer. Heated drying cylinders such as are used on the paper machine can seldom be used for converted products because the sheet will adhere or the coating may offset on the dryer.

In the early history of paper coating and saturating, the drying was done merely by hanging the paper in lofts or in festooning chambers. The high inventory, lack of control, and high handling costs of these methods have gradually made it necessary to develop dryers which remove the water or solvent more rapidly.

This led to the development of the hot-air drying tunnel. In its most familiar form this consists of an insulated horizontal housing with a means for conveying the web through the housing, such as rolls or a slat conveyor. Air which has been heated by means of steam coils or gas burners is directed by rotary fans through a plenum system and discharge headers on to the upper surface of the paper. This produces rapid drying and efficient operation. The air is recirculated through the heaters with sufficient exhaust being maintained to remove the water vapor, and in the case of solvents to remain below the lower explosive limit.

For drying impregnated papers or double-coated papers it is necessary to handle a sheet which is wet on both sides. One method of doing this is to pass the sheet through a vertical drying tower, with hot air introduced to both sides of the web. This is limited in capacity by the height to which the paper can be carried without breaking or excessive fluttering.

Another method of handling impregnated and double-coated sheets is the horizontal floater dryer. With this arrangement, the bottom conveyor and rolls are eliminated and the air is discharged through slots below the web at a sufficient pressure to float the paper through the dryer. Here again there is a maximum length over which the paper can successfully be floated.

During the past five or ten years there has been a marked increase in the use of high-velocity air in drying tunnels for converted papers. It has been found that a substantial increase in velocity will give significant improvements in drying capacity. This makes it possible to use much shorter drying tunnels to achieve the same drying rate and, thereby, to increase production and to reduce the required floor space. A variety of nozzle configurations are available which permit directing the high velocity air effectively onto the sheet while still providing space for exhausting and recirculating the air.

Infrared drying has been used to a limited degree in the drying of coated and saturated papers. The infrared heat can be provided either from direct gas burners with ceramic tiles or from various types of electrical elements. These have the advantage of high energy input per unit area. More widespread use of this type of dryer has been restricted, however, by its high operating cost and difficulties of control, particularly with changes in web speed and during stoppages.

Since drying always involves the removal of vapors in addition to the application of heat, the most successful infrared dryers have involved a combination of direct application of radiant heat plus recirculation of heated air.

Drives

As in the case of the paper-making machine, the drive is an important part of every paper converting machine. Paper converting processes may operate at speeds varying from less than 100 to more than 2000 fpm.

Although the trend is toward more continuous operation in all converting processes these drives must all, nevertheless, be able to accelerate from zero speed up to the operating speed, and to change from one level of operating speed to another with smooth acceleration and deceleration, and to decelerate smoothly to a stop. Quick stops are also required if emergencies develop.

The early converting machines were equipped with line shaft drives for coupling the various components together. Cone pulleys or other mechanical speed changers were included to synchronize the various sections and to control the web tension between sections.

The prime mover for the lineshaft drive was generally an AC motor either of the wound-rotor variable-speed type or a constant-speed induction motor with a mechanical speed changer for controlling line speed.

Lineshaft drives are still in use today and are being provided on many new high-speed machines. They have the advantage of positive control and interlocking of the various sections of the machine. The modern lineshaft drives include accurate speed adjusting units for each section, such as PIV units in combination with differential gears, and the prime mover can be a variable speed DC motor.

The most widely used type of drive on modern converting machines is, however, the multiple motor DC drive of the Ward-Leonard system. With this type of drive, a motor generator set is provided to produce variable voltage direct current with an AC power input. The output voltage of the DC generator is varied by the operator to control the overall speed of the machine. This voltage is then fed to each of the motors driving the various sections of the converting line. A variety of means can be provided for controlling the tension and relative speed of the various motors. The simplest method is to furnish a field rheostat for each motor which the operator adjusts by hand. More elaborate drives use dancer rolls to control the individual motors or current regulators which automatically set the motor to hold a certain tension or load.

Various other electrical drives are available including variable speed AC motors, eddy-current clutches, etc.

Hydraulic drives are also in use to a limited extent where oil under pressure is provided by a master hydraulic pump. This then drives individual oil motors on each component of the line. The same control functions are available in this type of drive as are available in the DC electric drive.

REFERENCES

1. Castagne, M. R., *Pulp & Paper,* **35**, 39 (July 10, 1961).
2. TAPPI Monograph Series, No. 20, "Paper Coating Pigments."
3. Unpublished data, E. I. du Pont de Nemours & Co.; Union Carbide Plastics Co.

BIBLIOGRAPHY

Casey, J. P., "Pulp and Paper—Chemistry and Chemical Technology," Volume 3, New York, Interscience Publishers, 1960.

Mosher, R. H., "Specialty Papers," Brooklyn, New York, Remsen Press, 1950.

Mosher, R. H., "Technology of Coated and Processed Papers," New York, Chemical Publishing Co., Inc., 1952.

Stephenson, J. N., "Pulp and Paper Manufacture," Vol. 3, New York, McGraw-Hill Book Co., 1953.

Technical Association of the Pulp & Paper Industry, New York, TAPPI Monograph Series,

No. 5 "Resins for the Paper Converter";

No. 8 "Machinery for Paper Coating";

No. 11 "Preparation of Paper Coating Colors";

No. 17 "Starch and Starch Products in Paper Coating";

No. 20 "Paper Coating Pigments";

No. 22 "Synthetic and Protein Adhesives for Paper Coating";

No. 23 "Permeability of Plastic Films and Coated Papers to Gases and Vapors."

CHAPTER 14

Properties and Testing of Paper

KENNETH W. BRITT

Scott Paper Company

INTRODUCTION

It has been repeatedly emphasized in this Handbook that paper and paperboard are used in a great variety of forms, distinguished by a wide range of properties. There are literally thousands of paper grades and paper products differing from each other either very slightly or by gross and obvious differences. The identification and expression of these differences depend upon the application of standard test methods. Some of these tests are directed toward the performance of a paper item for a specific use; other tests are of a more basic nature and evaluate properties of general interest. It is the purpose of this chapter to relate testing procedures to the most significant properties of paper.

The testing of paper and the definition of its properties are noteworthy for several characteristic and peculiar features. First, most of the important properties are not physical absolutes, but depend on the testing instruments and on details of method. For example, such a simple property as tensile strength depends on both the rate of load application and the dimensions of the specimen, e.g. the longer the span under stress the greater the likelihood of finding a weak spot. So it is with many other properties such as brightness, gloss, tearing strength, folding endurance, stiffness, and permeability. The property is defined in terms of instrument and method. Hence, the terms "correct" and "incorrect" have reference to precise repetition of method and faithful maintenance of instruments rather than to some absolute value which should be the same regardless of method.

In spite of much striving for uniformity, paper is heterogeneous in structure and properties to a greater or lesser degree. It follows that precision in testing is dependent upon statistical considerations. A considerable body of paper industry literature will be found reporting the standard deviations and probable error in various paper tests [17]. Thus, the number of specimens used and number of tests performed has a significant bearing on the reliability of paper testing.

Finally, the enormous diversity in paper uses and the widespread nature of the paper industry have led to an almost unlimited proliferation of test methods. Practically all paper manufacturers, as well as converters and large buyers of paper, have invented test methods to evaluate desirable qualities. Some of these have remained intramural, others have spread to various segments of the industry, and a few have been refined, adopted widely, and universally recognized. It is with these latter, and only a few of them, that this chapter can concern itself. In the United States, the Technical Association of the Pulp and Paper Industry has adopted standard test methods for paper. Most of these correspond to similar methods adopted by the American Society for Testing Materials and by the Institute of Paper Chemistry. Progress is being made toward uniformity in test methods on the international level.

CLASSIFICATION OF PAPER BY TYPE

In the classification of paper, there is some overlapping of function and some items could be placed in more than one category.

Despite the great variety in the use of paper, it is possible to classify papers in general categories determined by the primary use or purpose. The terms used are those common in the trade and defined in standard texts.[3,4]

(1) Papers primarily for carrying of printing, illustrations, writing and drawing, including such items as cover stock, envelopes and labels. This function was the original purpose of paper, and was the impetus behind its invention and the stimulus of its widespread use. Some of the more important grades are listed below.

Album	Ledger
Announcements	Magazine
Blanks	Maps
Bond	Mat board
Book	Mimeograph
Boxed	Mounting board
Bristol	Music
Card	Newsprint
Cloth-lined	Offset
Cover	Safety
Document	Tag
Drawing	Text
Duplication	Tracing
Envelopes	Writing
Labels and seals	

(2) Papers primarily for wrapping, enclosing, protecting, sealing and carrying other materials. This function is a modern development in the use of paper and has come about from the great abundance of paper in recent decades and the ability to impart to paper good barrier and durability properties. This area has been one of the fastest growing in the paper industry.

Some of the more important examples of this category follow.

Bags and sacks	Gummed tape
Boxes and cartons	Kraft wrapping
Car liners	Milk containers
Containers (Food)	Multiwall sacks
Creped wadding	Plates
Cups	Shipping boxes
Fiber cans, tubes, cones	Spoons and forks
Fiber drums	Tea bag paper
Foil laminates	Waterproof paper
Glassine and greaseproof	Waxed papers

(3) Papers primarily for absorbing, wiping, cleansing and filtering purposes. Cellulosic fibers are naturally absorbent toward water, and this property combined with the porous nature of paper, provides an excellent absorbing medium. During the early days of paper making, the relative scarcity of paper prevented the widespread use of new paper for this purpose. With the present abundance of paper, this area is a large scale and rapidly growing category of paper use. A list of representative products follows.

Blotting	Industrial wipers
Filter	Napkins
Crepe wadding	Place mats
Diaper liners	Sanitary napkins
Dental bibs	Toilet tissue
Drop cloths	Towels
Dusting papers	Windshield wipers
Facial tissue	

(4) Paper and paperboard used as materials of construction as part of a structure having a permanent location.

Building paper
Building board

(5) Papers used primarily as a carrying medium for other functional material.

Carbon paper
Decalcomania paper
Photosensitive paper
Saturating paper
Soap-impregnated paper

(6) Paper used for a decorative function.

Creped streamer paper
Hanging (wall paper)

(7) There remain a number of miscellaneous items used for special purposes; representative of this class are:

> Condenser paper
> Electrical insulation paper
> Glass fiber paper
> Matrix paper
> Tyman paper
> Twisting paper.

RELATIVE HUMIDITY IN RELATION TO PAPER PROPERTIES

It is appropriate to introduce a discussion of paper testing with a section devoted to the effect of moisture content upon the properties of paper. Cellulosic fibers are hygroscopic, that is, they are capable of absorbing water from the surrounding atmosphere. The amount of absorbed water depends on the relative humidity and the temperature of the air in contact with the paper. Further, under the same humidity and temperature conditions, a sample of paper may have different moisture contents, depending upon whether the sample approached these conditions from a more dry state or from a more moist state (hysteresis). Finally, most physical properties of paper undergo change as a result of variation in moisture content.

Water has the effect of plasticizing the cellulose fiber and of relaxing and weakening the interfiber bonding. Hence, the moisture content of paper has a very marked effect upon such properties as folding endurance, tearing strength and stretch. These tests increase (improve) at relatively high humidities (80 to 90% R.H.) and decrease at low humidities (30 to 40% R. H.) when the fibers become more stiff and brittle. The tensile strength decreases moderately with higher humidities, presumably because of the weakening effect of water upon the interfiber bonding. Naturally, the purely structural properties such as porosity and formation are essentially unaffected by humidity, as well as such chemical properties as alpha-cellulose content, copper number, and acidity. Most physical properties of

paper rise or fall with changes in relative humidity—in other words, the changes are reversible. There are some properties, however, in which the change produced by high humidity is irreversible. Gloss is an example of this: some papers undergo a permanent loss in gloss when exposed to relative humidities of 85% [1].

It should be kept in mind that this discussion is limited to the moisture range in paper from the completely dry state to that prevailing under relative humidity conditions up to about 95% and at room temperatures. Any additional wetting leads to the presence of free water in the sheet resulting in more profound and more permanent effects.

Hysteresis

Figure 14.1 shows moisture sorption isotherms for a typical paper formed from rel-

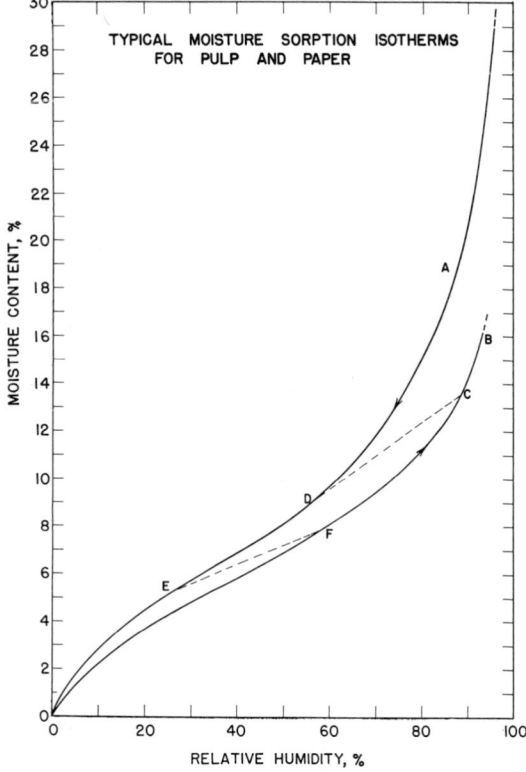

Fig. 14.1. Relation of moisture content of paper to relative humidity. (*Courtesy Institute of Paper Chemistry*)

atively pure cellulosic fibers [2]. The desorption of cellulosic material that has never been dried is shown in curve A, which together with adsorption curve B, define the outer boundaries of the equilibrium area. Upon subsequent cycling in relative humidity, the moisture contents of the sample fall within this area. Partial adsorption to a relative humidity corresponding to point C, for example, followed by desorption, results approximately in the course of the dotted line CD and, similarly, partial desorption to the point E, followed by adsorption, results approximately in the course shown by the dotted line EF. All cellulosic materials so far as is known exhibit hysteresis and similar sigmoid shape isotherms.

Table 14.1 shows moisture content values for several types of paper at various relative humidity values [2]. These figures indicate the well recognized fact that purer and more crystalline forms of cellulose hold less water under given atmospheric conditions than do the forms containing more amorphous and encrusting materials.

TABLE 14.1.

Temperature 73°F	100% Rag Paper	Bleached Sulfite	Ground-wood
	Moisture Content (%)		
52.4% RH desorption		8.37	
52.6% RH desorption	5.86		
52.4% RH adsorption		7.88	
48.0% RH desorption		7.89	
48.0% RH adsorption		7.62	
50.0% RH adsorption			9.70

Effect of Temperature [2]

The effect of temperature upon the properties of paper has received less attention than the more obvious effects produced by changes in humidity. This is evidently due to the relatively slight changes in moisture content due to variations in temperature normally encountered in testing rooms. Wink [4] has reported the effect upon several physical properties of paper over the temperature range from 63 to 120°F under conditions in which the moisture content of the paper was held constant at a level corre-

sponding to standard conditions of 50% R.H. and 73°F. The results showed a marked increase in stretch (7.30%) and a marked decrease in tensile strengh (7.20%) in going from the lower to the higher temperature. This would seem to indicate that the plasticizing effect upon fibers and upon fiber to fiber bonds of a given quality of water increases considerably at higher temperatures.

Standard Conditions

As a result of a survey conducted by TAPPI in 1940, the standard conditions for testing of paper in the United States have been etablished as 50% ± 2% R.H. and 23 ± 2° C approached from below 25% R.H. (Standard Method T402)*. Previously the most common testing condition in the U.S. had been 65% R.H. and this level of humidity for paper testing is still prevalent in European countries.

DIMENSIONAL STABILITY OF PAPER

An important consequence of the sorption and desorption of water by paper is the change in dimension that usually accompanies changes in moisture content. Such changes in dimension may seriously affect register in printing processes and interfere with the use of such items as tabulating cards. Uneven dimensional changes cause undesirable cockling and curling. For these reasons, much study and effort have been devoted to elucidating the causes for shrinking and expansion of papers and to devising means for increasing dimensional stability.

Dimensional changes in paper originate in the swelling and contraction of the individual fibers. It has been observed that cellulosic fibers swell in diameter from 15 to 20% in passing from the dry condition to the fiber saturation point. It is impossible to be precise about the degree of this swelling because paper-making fibers differ con-

* Designations of this type refer to methods adopted by the Technical Association of the Pulp and Paper Industry (TAPPI), New York.

siderably in this property, and because the irregular cross-section of fibers creates difficulty in defining diameter. Moreover, the definition of fiber saturation point is not exact. However, in contrast to the considerable expansion in fiber diameter or in lateral dimension, the longitudinal expansion is practically negligible, being estimated at no more than 5% of the lateral swelling.

Even though the swelling of fiber is the cause of expansion and contraction of paper, there is no direct relationship between the two phenomena. Paper samples made from the same fiber and presumably having the same fiber swelling characteristics may exhibit either negligible or maximum dimensional changes, depending upon conditions of stock preparation and conditions of sheet forming and drying. The following factors are considered to be most important in dimensional stability of paper.

(I) Shrinkage During Drying. It is well recognized that a freshly formed wet sheet of paper, allowed to shrink freely during drying, undergoes a considerable degree of contraction and also shows a high degree of hygroexpansivity upon rewetting. Likewise, when such a sheet is constrained from shrinking during drying, the hygroexpansivity is reduced. In fact, there is a fairly direct relationship between shrinkage during drying and the hygroexpansivity for paper made from the same stock and under otherwise similar conditions.

In machine-made paper it is obvious that the tension acting to pull the sheet through the machine tends to constrain shrinkage, whereas in the cross direction there is no corresponding force. As a result, machine-made papers shrink more in cross direction and show from two to three times greater hygroexpansivity in the cross direction than in the machine direction. In addition to the effect of greater shrinkage in the cross direction, the tendency of fibers to be preferentially oriented in the machine direction also contributes to greater cross direction hygroexpansivity because of greater lateral swelling of the individual fibers.

It is impossible to give exact figures for the amount of expansion and contraction undergone by paper because of the many factors which contribute to this property. However, it is common for papers to show dimensional changes from somewhat less than 0.5% to about 1% in the cross direction in passing from a very dry atmosphere to a very moist atmosphere. Corresponding changes in the machine direction could range from negligible to about 0.5%.

(2) Degree of Interfiber Bonding. It is well recognized that paper made from highly beaten, slow stock shows a high degree of shrinkage during drying and a high degree of hygroexpansivity. Paper made from free stock shows less shrinkage during drying and greater dimensional stability. It has been shown [31] that the equilibrium moisture content of highly beaten fiber is only very slightly greater than that of unbeaten fiber and, hence, cannot afford an explanation for greater hygroexpansivity. The greater inter-fiber bonded area of sheets made from highly beaten stocks or from pulps high in hemicellulose results in a condition where changes in dimensions of fibers are communicated directly to the rigid structure of the sheet. In contrast, fibers in a lightly bonded sheet are more free to move and, hence, their dimensional changes have less effect on the structure as a whole.

(3) Cross Linkage of Cellulose. Since the origin of dimensional instability of paper lies in the swelling characteristics of fiber, a reduction in that swelling should be beneficial. The swelling of cellulosic fibers when exposed to moisture may be reduced by chemical means, such as cross linking of the cellulose structure by formaldehyde or by resins. Moderate improvement in dimensional stability may be achieved by such treatment (similar to the development of wet strength in paper), but elimination of swelling in cellulose fiber by chemical means is accompanied by drastic changes in fiber properties which would be detrimental to tear strength and folding endurance. The subject of reduction of swelling by chemical means is reported in a recent article by Stamm [32].

(4) Non-Swelling Fiber. Again, since fiber swelling is the origin of dimensional changes, the use of a non-swelling fiber such as nylon, polyethylene or glass suggests itself. Papers made of such fibers do show dimensional stability, and if the higher cost is permissible, they represent a solution to the problem. Considerable benefit has also been reported from incorporating small amounts of non-swelling synthetic fiber in wood pulp furnishes. In this connection, a note of caution should be sounded. Since non-swelling fibers are also nonbonding, it may be that improvement in dimensional stability is due to reduced interfiber bonding (see above) and be accompanied by considerable loss in strength.

The interested reader will find further information on dimensional stability in recent review articles by Brecht [33], Rance [34] and Nordmann [35].

SUBSTANCE AND QUANTITY MEASUREMENT OF PAPER

Basis Weight

The weight or substance per unit area is obviously fundamental in all paper products. From the earliest use of paper in the printing trade, paper has been measured in *reams*, originally comprising 480 sheets (20 quires) but now also used to signify 500 sheets (long ream). Hence, *ream weight* is a common term to signify the substance of a lot of paper. It happens that the printing trades use a great variety of sheet sizes and hence there are a multitude of ream weights. Paper having the same weight per unit area (basis weight) can have numerous ream weights, depending upon sheet size and whether the ream count is 480 or 500. The most common "standard" reams are:

$$24 \times 36 \times 480 = 414{,}720 \text{ square inches}$$
$$24 \times 36 \times 500 = 432{,}000 \text{ `` ``}$$
$$25 \times 38 \times 500 = 500{,}000 \text{ `` ``}$$

Data using any of these reams may be encountered in publications and the reader must be alert in comparing other tests to make sure that the basis weight figures are comparable. In the paperboard industry the most common method of expressing substance is in *pounds per 1000 square feet*. In most European countries and in many laboratories in North America, the basis weight of paper is reported as *grams per square meter*. Table 14.2 gives comparative basis weight ranges of typical papers.

TABLE 14.2.

Paper Grade	Basis Weight (lb)
	24 x 36 x 500
Carbonizing tissue	5¾-25
Facial tissue	9-10
Manifold tissue	10-20
Tea bag tissue	8-12
Blotting paper	114-266
Bond	25-60
Book, uncoated	27-91
Book, coated 2 sides	45-109
Bristol, postcard	135
Envelopes	16-40
Grease proof	20-50
Newsprint	30-35
Multiwall bag stock	40-70
Kraft wrapping,	18-250
most common	25-80
Cover stock	66-216

The determination of basis weight is described in TAPPI Method T410m45. The sample to be tested is brought to equilibrium in the standard conditioning atmosphere. The specimens of paper to be weighed shall consist, whenever possible, of ten sheets, each of at least 100 square inches in area. The weighing of the specimens shall be carried out on a balance permitting an accuracy of one part in 400 of the total weight of the sample. Figure 14.2 shows a balance designed particularly for the determination of the basis weight of paper.

The paper weight shall be expressed in at least two of the following ways: (1) the equivalent basis weight in pounds for a ream consisting of 500 sheets, 25 x 40 inches

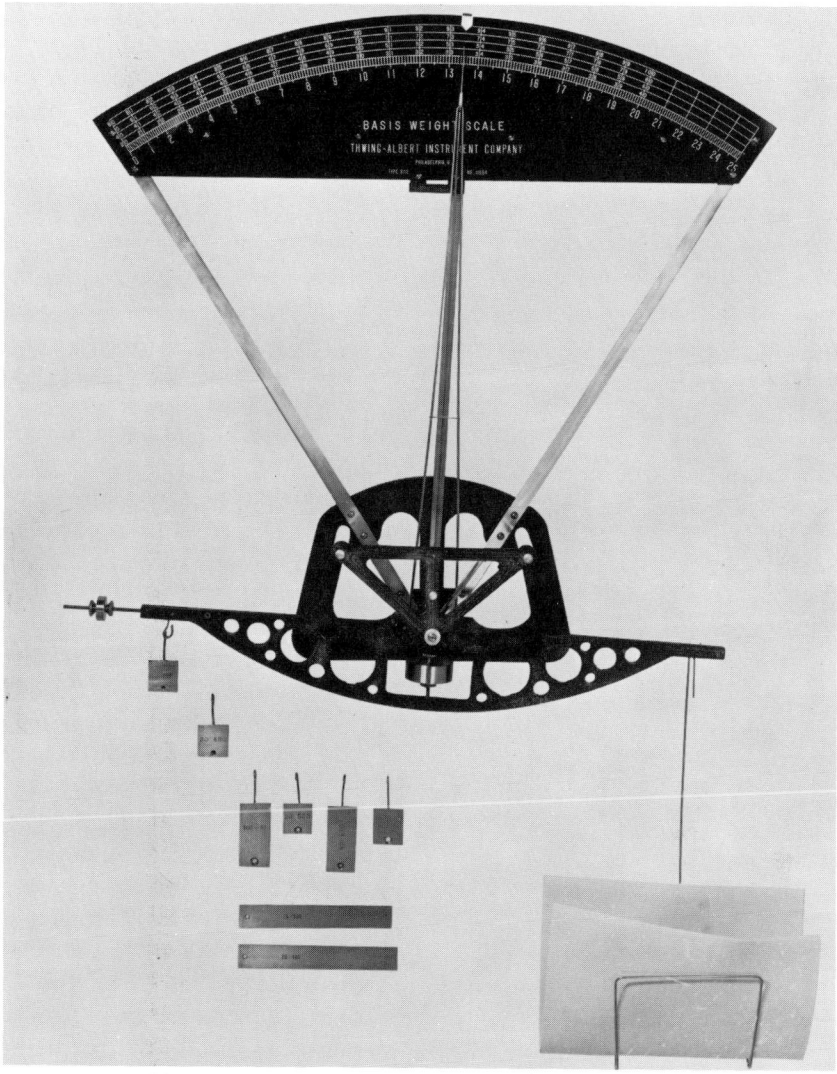

Fig. 14.2. Basic weight scale. (*Courtesy Thwing-Albert Instrument Co.*)

in size, (2) the weight in grams per square meter, (3) the equivalent weight for the ream size commonly used by the paper industry for the particular grade of paper. The weight of paperboard is reported in pounds per 1000 square feet.

Thickness and Density of Paper

The thickness of paper or paperboard is the caliper of a single sheet when placed under a steady pressure within the range of 7 to 9 psi between two circular and parallel plane surfaces. Details of the appara-

tus and method for this test will be found in TAPPI Method T411m44 (Figure 14.3).

The *density* of paper, or paperboard, is the weight per unit volume or the apparent specific gravity. Density is calculated from basis weight and thickness in accordance with the following formula:

$$D = \frac{W_1}{T_1 \times 18.08} = \frac{W_2}{T_2}$$

$W_1 =$ basis weight in pounds (25×40—500)
$W_2 =$ basis weight in grams per square meter
$T_1 =$ thickness in mils (0.001 inch)
$T_2 =$ thickness in microns (0.001 mm).

The thickness of paper at constant basic weight, hence the density, may range over relatively wide limits. For example, the density of glassine may be as high as 1.4 as one extreme, while that of creped wadding may be as low as 0.1. The density of paper is increased by the use of pulp that is characterized by fine, easily hydrated fiber and by extensive beating. Fibers which tend to

thickness. The search for greater uniformity in weight distribution both across the width of the paper machine and in the length-wise direction of the sheet has led to the use of scanning devices using beta rays and dielectric properties of paper for continuous determination of weight of the traveling sheet on the paper machine. See Chapter 15.

STRENGTH AND DURABILITY PROPERTIES OF PAPER

The resistance of a paper to rupture when subjected to various stresses is an important property in practically all grades of paper. Most papers require a certain minimum strength to withstand the treatment received by the product in use, but even where the use requirement for strength is not severe, the paper must also be strong enough to permit efficient handling in the various paper-making, converting, or printing operations involved in its manufacture.

Tensile Strength

The resistance of paper to rupture when subjected to tensile stress is measured in accordance with TAPPI Methods T404m50 for dry paper and by T456m49 for paper in the wet condition. A number of suitable testing machines for subjecting the paper specimen to measured tensile stress are available. Some of these machines are equipped to measure the total stretch undergone by the specimen at the breaking point and to draw a stress-strain curve from which the elastic modulus can be calculated (see Figure 14.4).

The following precautions are important in the tensile test.

(1) Sampling. There is some non-uniformity in the best of papers and hence samples must be sufficient in number and adequately distributed to give an accurate test.

(2) Conditioning. Tensile strength of paper is sensitive to moisture content and hence due regard must be given to proper conditioning of the sample.

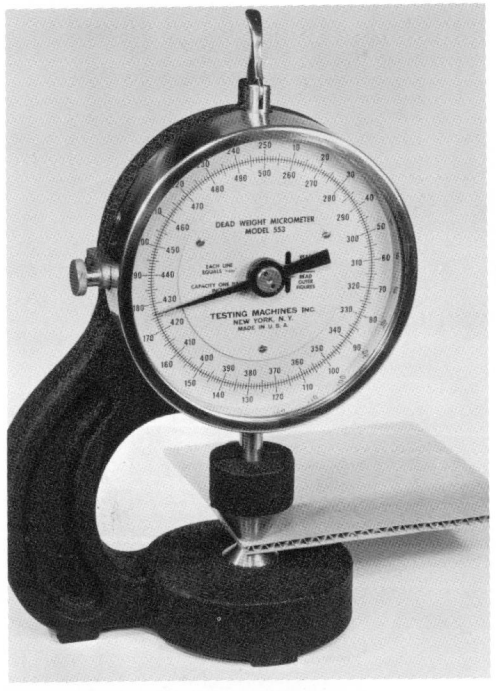

Fig. 14.3. Thickness gauge for paper. (*Courtesy Testing Machines, Inc.*)

remain stiff in the wet state, such as groundwood and some high yield pulps, produce papers that are bulky and less dense. Subjecting the sheets to wet pressing or calendering obviously increases the density. Physical treatments such as creping and some types of embossing reduce the apparent density of paper.

The nature of the paper-making process is such that perfect distribution of fiber and of other constituents of the sheet is difficult to attain. Hence, the *uniformity* of basis weight and of thickness is often of as much practical value as the *average* weight or

(3) Cutting of Specimens. The normal width of strip for tensile testing is one inch. Attention must be given to accurate cutting; an error that is barely noticeable may be an appreciable fraction of an inch.

(4) Rate of Loading. Paper shows plastic properties when subjected to stress, and hence the ultimate strength is appreciably affected by rate of loading.

(5) Grain. Machine made paper has "grain"—that is, it shows different physical properties in the two directions. Hence, tensile testing must be performed in both the machine direction and the cross machine direction of the paper. The ratio between these two values of strength is an important property of paper.

The results obtained from the typical tensile test are in terms of pounds per inch width or kilograms per 15 millimeters. For manufacturing control purposes and for judging the use performance of a paper product, such data are usually adequate. However, when one wishes to compare various pulps or various treatments and methods for efficiency in producing tensile strength, it is necessary to combine the observed tensile results with the basis weight to obtain a factor. A common expression for this result is the "breaking length," expressed in meters, which is the calculated length of material that would be self-supporting. This value takes into account the basis weight of the material and is theoretically independent of the specimen width.

Factors Affecting Tensile Strength. The tensile strength of paper is determined by the combined effect of the following factors: (1) the strength of the individual fibers of the stock furnish, (2) the average length of the fibers, (3) the inherent bonding ability of the fiber surface both in terms of bonded area and of strength per unit of bonded area, (4) a factor determined by the formation or fiber orientation within the sheet.

The great importance of the interfiber bonding in paper has led to the belief that this is the predominant factor in tensile strength, fiber strength playing a secondary role. A study by J. A. Van den Akker,[5] in which the percentage of ruptured fibers in a paper break is determined, showed that fiber strength is a substantial component of fiber strength. Also, it is well recognized that fiber may be chemically degraded and weakened in the pulping and bleaching processes. Such fiber produces weak paper,

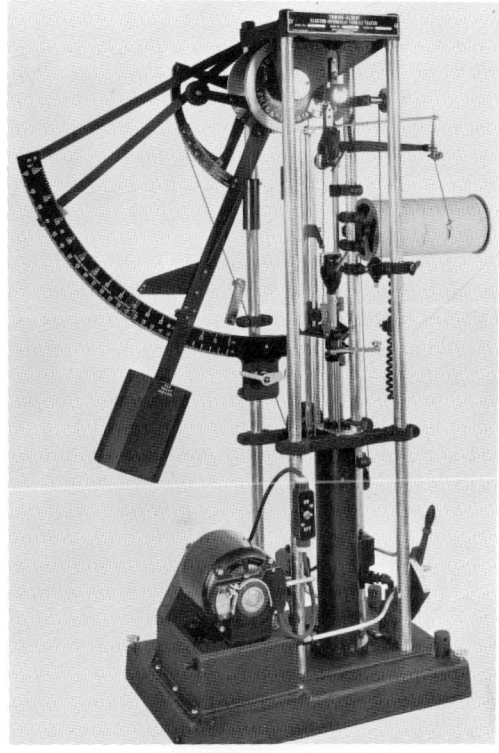

Fig. 14.4. Tensile strength and stretch measuring instrument for paper. (*Courtesy Thwing-Albert Instrument Co.*)

not only because the fiber is easily ruptured in the testing of the paper but also because the fiber cannot withstand the beating and refining action that is an essential preliminary to paper manufacture.

A long fiber is essential for making strong paper, and no papers of high strength are made from short-fibered furnishes. However, there is a limit to which longer fibers will contribute to paper strength because they result in sheets with "wild" and uneven formation. A poorly formed sheet with thick and thin areas will have poor strength. The limit of fiber length for most paper making is in the order of $\frac{1}{8}$ to $\frac{1}{4}$ inch. This value varies considerably due to such factors as ratio of fiber length to diameter, head box consistency, and presence of colloidal (surface-active) agents.

The inherent bonding ability of the fibers of a paper stock is of outstanding importance in paper strength. It is well recognized that some pulps have a strong tendency to form interfiber bonds while others have only a slight tendency to do so. The beating and refining action has the effect of swelling the fiber by increasing the imbibition of water, of rupturing and fibrillating the fiber surface, and of rendering the fiber more flexible and better able to mat and contact neighboring fibers. All these effects enhance the interfiber bonding ability of the stock. Pressure exerted upon the wet sheet is also an important factor in promoting bonding. The bonding ability of a paper stock is increased by the addition of adhesive agents which can be adsorbed by the fiber surface and act as a cementing agent between fibers (see Chapter 11).

Stretch of Paper

It is common in performing the tensile test to determine the elongation of the test specimen while it is undergoing the test. This elongation is usually expressed as per cent stretch to rupture. The tensile machine may also be equipped to draw the load-elongation curve (see Figure 14.4). The importance of the stress-strain curve is becoming increasingly recognized in predicting the durability performance of many paper products. The area under the curve resulting from plotting stress versus elongation is a measure of the work done or the energy absorbed in breaking the paper. For many uses, the energy absorption is more important to durability than is the tensile strength. There are numerous paper-making factors that influence the stretch of paper, such as fiber elasticity and strength, the density of the paper, formation and the con-

ditions of drying, particularly whether the sheet is allowed to shrink during drying or is held taut. For papers in which a high degree of stretch is sought, it is necessary to perform a physical disruption of the sheet subsequent to its formation, usually a type of creping by blade, roll or belt or by special types of embossing. It is also possible to obtain high values of stretch in paper by using elastomeric bonding agents (rubber) as the principal cementing agents between fibers.

The stretch of normal flat paper does not usually exceed 5%. Special multiwall bag stock is being made with stretch over 10%, and creped papers can be made with over 100% stretch in the machine direction.

Wet Tensile Strength

Because some paper products are subjected to wetting by water in their normal use, wet tensile strength testing has become of importance and is described in TAPPI Method T456m49. This test is essentially the same as the dry tensile test except that the test specimen is wetted to complete saturation over a prescribed distance between the jaws of the tensile tester. This test is primarily for absorbent papers, such as paper towels, sanitary tissues, filter paper and the like, which readily become wet and whose strength when wet is of importance. It is important to distinguish between the strength of paper in the wet state and the retention of strength by a paper because it resists wetting. Practically any paper will become wetted eventually if soaking is sufficiently prolonged. Paper that has not been especially treated for wet strength shows a value in this property of from 4 to 8% of its dry strength. By treatment of the paper by small quantities (1 to 5%) of thermosetting aminoplast resins, it is possible to increase the wet strength to about 40% of the dry strength.

Zero Span Tensile Strength

This method, described in TAPPI Methods T231sm-60 and T481sm-60, provides means for determining an index of the average ultimate strength of individual fibers either in a pulp test handsheet or in a commercial paper sample. Also, it may be used to indicate the degree of bonding between the fibers of a sheet, by the ratio between normal and the zero span breaking lengths of the test sheets with randomly oriented fibers.[6]

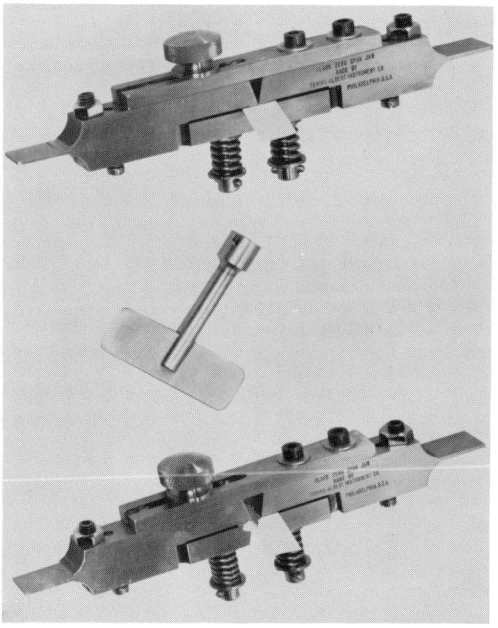

Fig. 14.5. Instrument for testing zero span strength of paper. (*Courtesy Thwing-Albert Instrument Co.*)

The means for accomplishing this test are a specially constructed pair of supplementary jaws which are inserted in the jaws of a conventional tensile testing machine. They are so designed that they clamp adjacent areas of the test strip with zero jaw separation at the start of the test (Figure 14.5).

When this test is properly conducted, the strength obtained will always exceed the normal tensile strength of a paper sample, usually by a substantial amount. It has been estimated that the zero span test is about $3/8$ of the ultimate fiber strength of the fibers composing the sheet.[5]

Transverse Tensile Test

Normally we consider a paper sheet to have two directions of strength, namely, the machine direction (x axis) and the across-machine direction (y axis). Another direction of strength exists at right angles to the plane of the sheet (z axis or transverse tensile strength). The importance of sheet strength or coherence in this direction has long been recognized in the printing industry where picking of fibers from the surface of the sheet is an undesirable paper quality.

The time-honored method of determining the resistance of paper to picking consists in depositing upon the surface of the paper a series of waxes having graded degrees of adhesive strength and determining which wax will just lift off fibers from the paper surface (TAPPI Method T459m45). This test is valuable as a practical use test, but the results are obviously only approximate and are of limited usefulness in determining the structure of paper.

It has long been recognized that a reliable method of determining transverse tensile or "bonding strength" of paper would be of great value, and several publications have appeared concerned with this subject.[7] The method consists essentially of a mounting jig in which a sample of paper is cemented to holding members that can be inserted into the tensile tester, which then pulls the paper apart at right angles to the plane of the sheet. Although the principle of the test is simple, difficulties have been encountered in finding a suitable adhesive. The requirements of such an adhesive are listed below:

(1) The adhesive must have a tensile strength substantially higher than that of the specimen being tested.

(2) Adhesive penetration into the specimen must be slight, but intimate contact must be made with the surface.

(3) If curing of the adhesive is necessary, it should not require elevated temperature and pressure.

(4) No solvent must be released after bonding is initiated.

Bursting Strength of Paper

One of the oldest and most widely used of the strength tests for paper and paperboard is the bursting test, usually called the Mullen test from one of the early instruments used for its determination. TAPPI Method T403m53 defines bursting strength as the hydrostatic pressure in pounds per square inch (psi) required to produce rupture of the material when the pressure is applied at a controlled increasing rate through a rubber diaphragm to a circular area, 1.20 inches in diameter, of the material under test, the test area being initially flat and held rigidity at the circumference but free to bulge under the increasing pressure of the test (Figure 14.6). The method is designed to measure the bursting strength of paper and paper products having a strength of 250 psi and in the form of flat sheets not over 0.025 inch thick.

The primary function of the bursting test is to indicate the resistance of a paper product to rupture in use. It is quick and easy to perform and one test is sufficient for both directions of machine-made paper, whereas average tensile strength requires testing in both principal directions of the paper. For these reasons, the burst test has found almost universal use throughout the paper industry even for the testing of laboratory hand sheets where the purpose of testing is to determine fundamental relationships rather than to predict in-use performance of the particular paper. The bursting test is the result of a combination of factors. Obviously the amount of interfiber bonding and individual fiber strength is of predominant importance in bursting strength, as it is in tensile. However, burst is also affected by the ratio of machine and cross direction strength and by the stretch of the paper, and probably by other properties. The tensile and burst curves in the beating cycle of pulp are roughly parallel, but they also show divergences that can be only approximately explained. A recent article reports

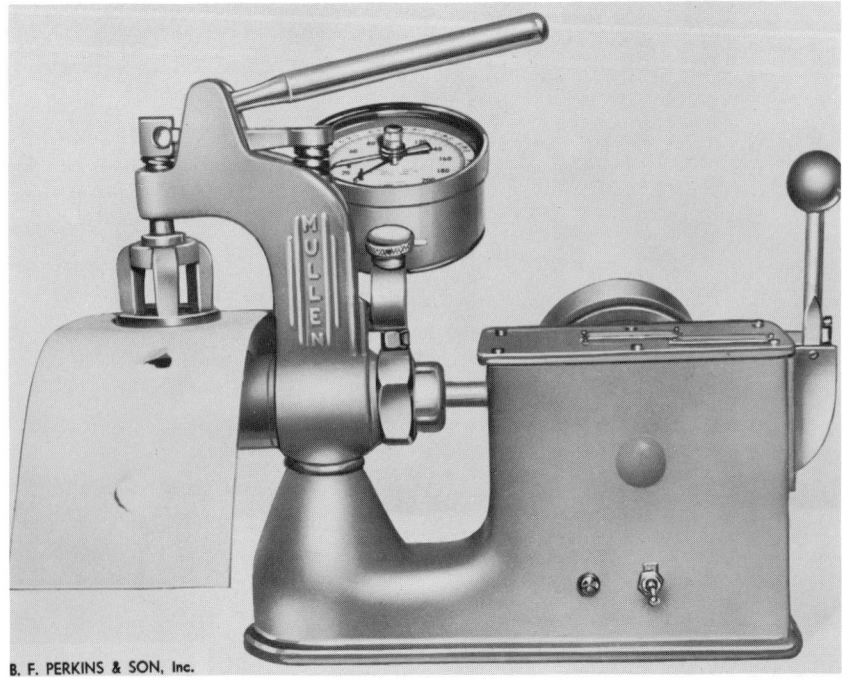

B. F. PERKINS & SON, Inc.

Fig. 14.6. Bursting strength tester for paper. (*Courtesy B. F. Perkins and Sons, Inc.*)

data for various strength factors of pulp, including burst and tensile, under various beating conditions.[8]

Experience has shown that it is difficult to obtain good correlation between different bursting test instruments, and this has led to considerable criticism of the test in the technical literature of the industry.[9, 10, 11, 12] Since the expansion of the rubber diaphragm of the instrument requires some force, the test is not suitable for very light, weak papers where the force to rupture the paper is of an order of magnitude similar to that of the diaphragm expansion.

Tearing Strength

Another test of significance in determining the resistance to rupture of paper is that for *tearing resistance*. TAPPI Method T414m49 is designed to determine the average force in grams required to tear a single sheet of paper after the tear has been started. The results obtained by this procedure are usually designated simply as "tearing resistance." More properly the results should be called "internal tearing resistance" as distinguished from "initial" or "edge" tearing resistance described in TAPPI Method T470m54.

The most common form of instrument for determining tearing resistance is the Standard Elmendorf tear tester (see Figure 14.7). This apparatus comprises a stationary clamp and, suitably aligned therewith, a second movable clamp carried on a pendulum, formed by a sector of a wheel or circle, free to swing on a substantially frictionless bearing. The pendulum carries a circumferential scale, graduated from 0 to 100 to read against a pointer which shows the retarding effect upon the swing of the pendulum of the tearing of the paper specimen.

It will be noted that the retarding of the pendulum swing is a measure of work done, that is, the product of the force and the distance through which it acts. However, the scale is so calibrated as to indicate the average force required to tear one sheet of paper when the tearing test takes place

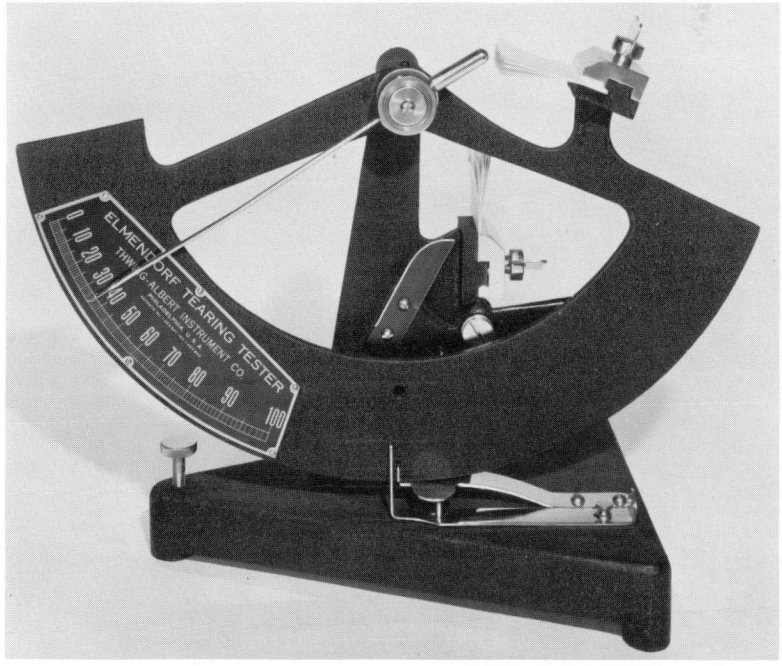

Fig. 14.7. Elmendorf paper tear tester. (*Courtesy Thwing Albert Instrument Co.*)

through a standard distance. The standard sample is specified as sixteen sheets of paper each to be torn through a distance of 4.3 cm. When a sheet of paper is torn a certain distance, one sector having held fast while the other sector moves, the force acts through a distance twice that of the tear. Hence, the total distance of the tear test is $16 \times 4.3 \times 2 = 137.6$ cm. Accordingly, if the reading on the scale after performing the test is 50, then the work done is $50 \times 137.6 = 8800$ gram-cm.

It is essential that each instrument be calibrated to make sure of the correct ratio between scale reading and work done. (For calibration directions see T414m49.) It is unnecessary to repeat the calibration of the instrument providing it is kept in adjustment and no parts become changed or worn. The tearing distance from the point of the initial slit and the edge of the sheet should be frequently checked. The instrument must be level.

The results are reported as grams force required to tear a single sheet. Since the scale readings are made $\frac{1}{16}$ the actual values; this is calculated by multiplying the average instrument reading by 16 and dividing by the number of sheets tested. The force required to tear a sheet of paper is an indication of its performance in use. Heavier papers will naturally have more tearing resistance than light papers. It is often important to determine the inherent tearing quality of fiber independent of the factor of sheet weight. In TAPPI Method T220m60, Physical Testing of Pulp Handsheets, a *tear factor* is determined from the equation:

$$\text{Tear factor} = 100 \, e/r$$

where e is the force in grams to tear a single sheet as described above and r is the basis weight in grams per square meter. This factor, which has been called the "tearing area" is equivalent to the number of square decimeters (100 sq dm = 1 sq meter) of paper, the weight of which, if applied to a single sheet, would cause a tear to progress. Thus it is analogous to the concept "breaking length" in tensile strength testing.

Factors Influencing Tearing Strength. As with many performance tests of paper, tearing strength is the result of a number of factors which are incompletely understood. The tearing test is very sensitive to the physical properties of the fiber. It is traditional in the industry that alkaline-cooked pulps have higher tear than corresponding acid-cooked pulps even when other durability tests are quite comparable. Any degradation of fiber in cooking or bleaching shows up dramatically in loss of tear. It is assumed that acid-cooked pulps suffer greater fiber degradation than do alkaline-cooked pulps. The tearing strength of finished paper is reduced by such influences as heat and acidity to a much greater degree than is tensile strength.

Fiber length and interfiber bonding are both important factors in tearing strength. That longer fibers improve tear strength is well recognized. The explanation is straightforward: longer fibers tend to distribute the stress over a greater area, over more fibers and more bonds, while short fibers allow the stress to be concentrated in a smaller area. The role of interfiber bonding is more complex. A low degree of interfiber bonding gives low tear because the fibers pull apart easily. As the interfiber bonding increases, the tear value rises to a maximum and then decreases. This phenomenon is often exhibited in beating cycle of a pulp (see Chapter 11). In the "beating curve" the increased interfiber bonding is accompanied by reduced fiber length, which adds to the reduction in tear value.

The tensile-tear relationship is an example of the situation often confronting papermakers in which two desirable characteristics are mutually contradictory and some degree of compromise is necessary. If a papermaker goes "all out" to get maximum tensile strength from a given stock, the resulting sheet will be low in tear. Conversely, a sheet formed at maximum tear value of the stock will be low in tensile.

One of the important consequences of this problem is the use of artificial bonding agents which permit the development of high levels of tensile strength with less beating and refining of the stock than otherwise would be needed. As a result, the fiber length of the furnish is preserved. Among the artificial bonding agents widely used at the present time are starches, proteins, natural gums, synthetic resins and latices (see Chapter 11).

Fig. 14.8. M.I.T. paper fold tester. (*Courtesy Testing Instruments, Inc.*)

Folding Endurance

Another important test relating to the durability of paper is *folding endurance* described in TAPPI Method T423m-50. This test is again a performance test based upon a particular instrument and indicative of a combination of physical properties of the sheet. It derives its importance and widespread use because of the frequency with which the ability to endure folding occurs in the use of paper products.

This method provides for use of two different forms of apparatus: the Schopper type for papers not more than 0.01 inch in thickness and the M.I.T. (Massachusetts Institute of Technology) type which can be adjusted for paper of any thickness. There is no constant relationship between the test values obtained by the two instruments. Figures 14.8 and 14.9 show the two types of folding endurance instruments.

Both instruments mechanically produce double folds at the same points in a strip of paper while subjecting the strip to tension after each fold. The result is expressed in the number of folds before rupture at the crease. The tension in the Schopper tester is 1 kg. The tension in the M.I.T. tester can be adjusted from 0 to 1.5 kg.

Abrasion Resistance

Another index of the durability of paper is the resistance to *abrasion*. For wrapping and packaging paper and paperboard this is usually referred to as scuff resistance. For writing and drawing papers the property of *erasibility* is of importance. Rubbing resistance is of importance in towelling and wiper paper, and, in this instance, wet rub is of special importance.

The abrasion resistance of paper is particularly difficult to reduce to standard testing conditions, and it is difficult to obtain meaningful quantitative results. No method has so far received official sanction.

PAPER PROPERTIES EXHIBITED PRIMARILY BY TOUCH

This section is concerned with several properties of paper that are generally evident by touch and can be evaluated by tests that do not destroy the paper. These properties are closely related to the texture.

Fig. 14.9. Schopper fold tester. (*Courtesy Testing Instruments, Inc.*)

Rigidity, Stiffness and Softness of Paper

The resistance of paper to a bending force is evident in all the various operations of its manufacture and in the manifold uses of paper. The range in this property extends from very soft, flexible tissues to rigid boards. It is obvious that thicker and heavier sheets tend to be stiff and rigid while soft, flexible papers are light and thin. However, even among papers of the same weight there can be considerable differences in flexibility due to the structure of the sheet.

The *rigidity* of a paper is its property of resisting an applied bending force and is proportional to EI where E is Young's modulus and I the moment of inertia.

The *rigidity factor* is proportional to the modulus of elasticity (E) or modulus of rigidity, which is a measure of the rigidity of the structure of the sheet, being a specific property of the material and the way it is put together inside the sheet.

The *stiffness* of paper is its ability to support its own weight, the inverse of flabbiness or limpness. It is proportional to EI/W, where W is the basis weight.

Softness is the subjective property of paper exhibited by the feeling of softness when a sheet is crumpled in the hand. This depends upon the ease of crumpling (flexibility), together with the absence of sharp edges in the crumpled sheet. It is inversely proportional to the rigidity modified by a function of the thickness of the sheet. With two sheets of the same stiffness, the thicker of the two feels softer.[13]

Methods of Measurement. Numerous methods have been proposed for the measurement of stiffness in paper. These generally fall into three categories: (1) the bending of a strip of paper under its own weight when suspended at one end as a cantilever, (2) the effect upon the period of a torsion pendulum of the torque-producing type in flexing a sample of paper, and (3) the deflection produced by an externally applied bending moment or, conversely, the bending moment required to produce a certain deflection. TAPPI Method T451m-60 utilizes (1) to determine "critical length" (L) which is the overhang of a test strip which will fall from one side to the other when the holding clamp is rotated through an angle of 90° (see Figure 14.10).

Fig. 14.10. Clark paper stiffness tester. (*Courtesy Thwing Albert Instrument Co.*)

The *flexual rigidity* of a strip of paper (or beam) is the bending moment required to produce unit curvature of bend. *Rigidity* as a property of paper is its ability to resist an applied force and is determined fundamentally by the flexural rigidity per unit width of sheet.[13]

The equation for deflection of a uniformly loaded cantilever is as follows:

$$y = L^4 w/8EI$$

y = deflection at end of a cantilever due to its own weight
w = weight per unit length of the cantilever
L = overhanging length
EI = flexural rigidity
E = Young's modulus
I = moment of inertia of section of strip.

The radius of curvature, r, is proportional to L and may be expressed $r = kL$. Likewise, the horizontal distance from the point of support to the center of gravity of the cantilever, a, is proportional to L and may be expressed as $a = k_2 L$.

The *bending moment* is expressed as

$$M = a L w$$

and also from basic theory of bending

$$M = EI/r$$

therefore

$$a L w = EI/r$$
$$EI \text{ (flexural rigidity)} = aLwr$$

then

$$EI = k_1 k_2 L^3 w$$

w is proportional to W (basis weight). *Clark Rigidity*, $L^3/W 1000$ (cf T-451m60) is therefore proportional to EI.

Flexural rigidity in dynes per square centimeter per centimeter of sheet width may also be derived from the torsion pendulum test.[13, 14] This device is a symmetrical mass suspended from a wire, its vibration is rotational about a vertical axis coincident with the torsion wire. The period, T, of such a pendulum is determined by the moment of inertia of the suspended mass, I_o, and the restoring torque per unit of angular displacement, r. If a paper strip is clamped to the suspended mass in such a fashion that the strip is bent when rotation occurs, the added restoring torque caused by the bending of the strip causes a reduction in the period of rotational vibration. The flexural rigidity of the strip may be computed from the periods T and T_o of the pendulum with and without the test strip.

$$EI = 4\pi^2 I_o \, [b^3/b(b+a)^2] \times \left[\frac{1}{T^2} - \frac{1}{T_o^2} \right]$$

Flexural rigidities determined by this method were found to be proportional to Clark rigidities.[13]

Ratliff [14] describes a modified torsion pendulum and uses the formula,

$$EI' = \frac{4\pi^2 I(b/3)}{T^2}$$

where EI' is the flexural rigidity in dynes per sq cm, I is the dynamic moment of inertia of the pendulum, b is the specimen length in cm and T is the period of oscillation in seconds. The flexural rigidity of typical papers is given as follows:

24#	Plasticized glassine	164
22#	Opaque glassine	214
25#	Tracing	379
30#	Glassine	626
40#	Glassine	1300
50#	Glassine	2850
	Sulfite bond	2610
40#	Wet strength sulfite	3820
	Glassine-foil laminate	115700

The purpose of this rather extended discussion is to point out that the term "flexural rigidity" refers to a physical property of paper that can be determined accurately by different methods. It is more than empirical "stiffness units" as determined by particular testing device.

Unfortunately, in the general area of stiffness of sheet materials, there are several subjective properties that are not susceptible to direct physical measurement. These properties include "softness," "handle," "texture," "drape," "surface feel." It is obvious that flexibility (flexural rigidity) is related to softness, but it is equally obvious that other factors play a part. If we have two sheet materials of the same flexibility but of different thicknesses, the thicker material will feel softer. It is likely that the factor of *compressibility* plays an important part. Thick materials of low density are likely to be easily compressible and to feel soft for that reason. In evaluating the property of softness subjectively, the surface feel of paper plays an important part. Surface feel is more closely related to smoothness, surface friction, and compressibility than to flexibility. The relationship between physical factors and softness has

been discussed for paper by Clark [15] and for textiles by Peirce.[16]

Factors Influencing the Stiffness of Paper. The bending of a sheet of paper may be compared to the bending of a beam. In the mathematical treatment of deformation, it is usual to treat the deformed body as being composed of homogeneous material. In contrast, paper is a structure composed of discreet elements (fibers) which may differ from each other in size, shape and elastic modulus. The structure exists only because it is welded together by bonds that have properties such as area, strength per unit area, and frequency.

When a beam is bent by an applied couple, the structure of the beam is compressed in the region nearest the inside of

Fig. 14.11. Bending of a beam.

the curve and extended in the region nearest the outside (see Figure 14.11). The filament which experiences no change in length when the curvature is applied is termed the *neutral filament* or *neutral axis* (A-A' in Figure 14.11). It is clear that stiffness in a sheet of paper is actually resistance to deformation both in elongation and compression. Further, to the extent that paper is anisotropic, the stiffness can be increased or decreased compared with an isotropic structure. For example, if paper is considered to have a laminar structure, the lamina near the surface are more significant than the lamina near the center in contributing to stiffness.

The stiffness of a beam of rectangular cross section varies as the third power of the thickness. This is approximately true of paper, although some deviation is to be expected because of the practical difficulty of keeping all other properties of paper constant while varying thickness. In any event, thickness has such a profound effect upon sheet stiffness that in making observation on other factors, thickness must be most carefully measured and taken into account. It may be assumed that the flexibility of individual fibers affects sheet flexibility and that fiber flexibility is the combined result of fiber geometry and their average elastic modulus. This relationship of fiber-sheet flexibility remains obscure for several reasons. No reliable method for determining a quantitative index of fiber flexibility is available. Further, fiber flexibility has a profound effect upon interfiber bonding and this change in bonding may have more effect upon sheet flexibility than does the change in fiber properties. In a qualitative sense, it is well recognized that strong, well-bonded sheets are less flexible than lightly bonded sheets. Because of the many other factors that also influence flexibility, there is no direct relationship between strength and sheet stiffness.

Finally, the relationship between sheet density and sheet stiffness is anomalous. It is common to associate density with stiffness; however, with paper, several contradictory factors come into play. Generally, paper of high density also has a high degree of interfiber bonding and this increases stiffness. However, at the same basis weight, a dense sheet has a lesser thickness and this tends to decrease stiffness. If the density of a sheet is increased by compression in the dry state (calendering), no appreciable increase in interfiber bonding occurs; the decrease in thickness markedly decreases stiffness and the denser sheet is also the more flexible.

The stiffness of paperboard has a considerably different meaning than does the stiffness of paper. The method commonly used for paperboard is described in TAPPI Method T489m60. The test measures the flexural rigidity or stiffness of paperboard by determining the bending moment in gram-centimeters necessary to deflect the free end of a vertically clamped specimen 1.5 inches wide a distance 15 degrees from the center line when the load is applied 5 cm from the clamp.

Significance of Paper Stiffness. Stiffness is a highly desirable characteristic of many paper products. The protective quality of many packaging papers and paperboard stocks is dependent upon stiffness or rigidity. In many instances the basis weight is determined by the stiffness required, and means to increase stiffness would permit lower basis weight and saving of material. Stiffness is an important characteristic of tabulating cards, index cards, mounting paper, paper cups and many other items. The stiffness or "rattle" of bond, ledger, writing and similar stocks is taken as a sign of quality or "character" of the paper. Conversely, sanitary papers, towels, napkins and similar papers require cloth-like properties and a maximum of flexibility. Glassine paper is frequently required to conform to the shape of other objects, and plasticizers are often used to increase its flexibility.

Surface Texture of Paper. In most of the uses of paper the character of the surface is of great importance. It is common to say that paper has a "smooth" or a "rough" texture. The terms "finish" and "pattern" are frequently used in describing the contour or appearance of paper surfaces. Formation and compressibility, although not strictly surface characteristics, have an important effect on the behavior of the paper surface in such processes as printing.

The surface requirements of printing papers are highly varied. In order that the type or other printing surface make complete contact with the paper, a certain minimum degree of smoothness is required. Halftone illustrations, which may have up to 300 lines per inch, require smoothness of a high order. The finest printing papers result from a compromise of various qualities in relation to printing conditions and use requirements. A printing paper of perfect smoothness, such as that of polished optical glass, would probably be disappointing because printing presses depend upon some roughness to carry paper through the presses and to aid in keeping the printing in register. Compressibility is a desirable feature in printing papers because it aids in obtaining intimate contact between the paper and the printing surface. However, highly compressible papers also tend to stretch easily, which is detrimental to good register. Although various physical tests, such as smoothness, are useful guides in the evaluation of printing paper, there are no tests or combinations of tests which can determine the "printability" of paper. For this reason, this property is usually determined by actually performing test printing.

In other paper products, the surface is important in permitting "slip" for trouble-free passage through sorting machines (example: tabulating cards). The easy travel of pen or pencil over the surface is significant in writing and envelope papers. With paper stock for shipping sacks, too much slip is undesirable since it permits slippage of bags piled together. For this reason bag stock is sometimes treated to increase surface friction.

In the area of sanitary and absorbent papers, the surface should be pleasing to the touch; it should not have an abrasive feeling, but should have a surface contour and texture similar to cloth and quite distinct from the smoothness of a film. It is obvious that surface contour can have many meanings. One surface may be rough, sharp, jagged and hard, while another may be rounded, undulating and soft. Even though the two surfaces may have the same depth of profile, the surface "feel" of the two would be quite different.

Methods of Measuring Surface Texture. Both direct and indirect methods may be used in measuring the surface texture of paper. Direct methods employ a tracing or profile of surface irregularities, whereas indirect methods make use of some over-all effect presumed to be related to surface smoothness, such as air flow, light reflection, friction, or electrical capacitance.

TAPPI Method 479sm-48, "Smoothness of Printing Paper" covers the determination of smoothness by three different instruments: Bekk, Gurley-Hill S-P-S, and Williams. The basic principle of all three instruments is the flow of air along the surface irregularities of the paper.

The Bekk smoothness tester consists of a mercury manometer connected by a three-way valve to a vacuum pump, a glass anvil, and the atmosphere. The anvil, where the sample of paper is mounted, is made of optically flat plate glass, in the center of which is a tapered hole, having a diameter of 11 mm at the top and 1 mm at the bottom. The manometer shows in millimeters of mercury the difference between the pressure in the chamber and the atmospheric pressure. Two chambers are provided to cover different ranges.

With the air chamber at reduced pressure, the valve is turned to the position connecting the anvil with the manometer and air chamber. Now a pressure differential exists between the opening at the center of the anvil and the outer edge, and air will flow between the surface and a sample of paper clamped thereto at a rate depending upon the roughness of the paper surface and the pressure difference. In operation an average pressure difference of 370 mm (0.5 atmosphere) is used. The pressure on the paper is 1 kg/sq cm and the air chamber is so designed that a flow of 10 cc of air into it will cause a drop in pressure of 20 mm. By definition, the smoothness is then taken as the time for 10 cc of air to pass between the 10 sq cm of polished glass and the paper surface under an initial pressure of 370 mm, the paper being subjected to a pressure of 1 kg/sq cm. The smaller of the two chambers is so designed that the flow of 1 cc of air will cause a pressure drop of 20 mm.

In the Gurley-Hill S-P-S rapid smoothness test, eight thicknesses of paper are perforated and held between the upper orifice plate and a solid lower plate which houses an annular ring stated to be optically flat. The test does not differentiate between felt and wire side smoothness but gives an average value for sixteen surfaces. By means of the lever arm, unweighted, a pressure of 3 psi is provided over the contact area of 1 square inch. The smoothness value is defined as the time in seconds for 50 cc of air to pass.

In the Williams instrument, although the air-flow principle is employed, the truly flat test surface is dispensed with, and the air is passed between two surfaces of the paper to be tested. Compressed air is applied to the center of a clamp holding a folded test specimen of the paper under standard pressure. The time in seconds required for the passage of 25 ml of air is determined.

Table 14.3 shows smoothness values for a series of typical printing papers. It will

TABLE 14.3. SMOOTHNESS OF VARIOUS PAPERS

Paper		Basis Weight (lb)	Caliper (0.001 inch)	Bekk Smoothness (sec)
Mimeo				
(17 x 22—500)	A	21	5.60	11.3
	B	21	4.58	18.1
	C	21	4.94	16.5
	D	21	4.63	16.3
	E	17.5	5.47	8.1
Newsprint				
(24 x 36—400)	A	32	5.56	4.8
	B	32	3.52	47.4
	C	32	3.87	27.6
	D	32	3.96	58.4
	E	32	3.61	56.3
Machine finish book				
(17 x 22—500)	A	50	3.33	182.4
	B	45	3.60	78.2
	C	43	2.85	290.5
	D	62	4.12	155.6
	E	40	2.87	146.2
Supercalendered book				
(25 x 38—500)	A	60	3.33	589.5
	B	40	2.48	538.9
	C	40	2.54	403.3
	D	50	3.00	448.5
	E	60	3.37	270.5
Coated book				
(25 x 38—500)	A	70	3.57	862.5
	B	70	3.39	1129.0
	C	70	3.43	1576.8
	D	70	3.34	640.7
	E	70	3.37	928.7

be noted that there is a general relationship between sheet density (thickness at a given basis weight) and smoothness. In the series, mimeo, machine-finished book, and supercalendered book, the progressive increase in calendering shows up in markedly increased smoothness. The prime purpose of the coating of paper is to improve finish beyond that possible by calendering. Note the marked increase in smoothness of coated book as compared with supercalendered book without any reduction in caliper.

PENETRATION OF PAPER BY FLUIDS

Because paper is composed of a randomly felted layer of fiber, it follows that the structure has a varying degree of *porosity*. Thus the ability of fluids, both liquid and gaseous, to penetrate the structure of paper becomes a property that is both highly significant to the use of paper and is also capable of being widely varied by the conditions of manufacture.

In the early history of paper making, when the product was used exclusively for writing and printing, the need to limit the spreading of ink resulted in "sizing" the paper with gelatinous vegetable materials which had the effect of sealing or filling the surface pores. Later, the term "sizing" was applied to the treatment of paper stock prior to the formation of the sheet with water-repellent materials such as rosin or wax (engine sizing, internal sizing). As the use of paper was extended to wrapping and packaging, additional requirements were encountered in protecting the contents of the package from the effects of fluid transfer through the paper wrapping. In some instances this has resulted in the demand for complete impermeability of the package to the transfer of any liquid or gas. In another direction, the use of paper as an absorbent medium for wiping up liquids, for filtering, and for saturating has created a demand for maximum wettability and permeability toward water and other liquids, as well as toward air and other gases. All this in turn has brought about the need for a variety of tests to indicate these properties.

By way of background, it is important to remember that cellulosic fibers are by nature hydrophilic, that is, they are readily wetted by water and they readily absorb and transmit both liquid water and water vapor. Thus, a sheet of paper formed from pure fiber and water, with little or no beating (waterleaf paper), is found to be highly absorbent toward water and other low-viscosity liquids.

Swanson[18] has reviewed the factors governing the penetration of liquids into porous structures such as paper and derives the equation

$$\triangle P = \frac{2\gamma/L \cos\theta}{r}$$

where $\triangle P$ is the pressure differential across the liquid interface and is the force causing the liquid to advance into the capillary, γ/L is the specific free surface energy of the liquid, θ is the *contact angle* between the solid and the liquid, and r is the radius of the capillary assuming a perfect cylinder.

The rate of penetration is given by the Washburn equation[19],

$$\frac{dl}{dt} = \frac{r\, o \cos\theta}{N\, 4\, l}$$

where

$\frac{dl}{dt}$ = rate of penetration of liquid

r = radius of capillaries or pores
o = surface tension of liquid
θ = angle of contact between liquid and solid
N = viscosity of liquid
l = depth of liquid penetration.

The contact angle, θ, between a solid and liquid is illustrated in Figure 14.12. If θ is zero, perfect wetting of the solid by the liquid occurs. When θ is finite, the attraction between the solid and the liquid is less than the attraction between the molecules of the liquid. At a value of θ of **90°**, the solid-liquid attraction is only one-half the cohesional attraction within the liquid itself. A 180° contact angle is obviously impossible. This would imply no attraction between the solid and liquid molecules. It has been established that all molecules and atoms attract others to an appreciable extent.

The actual measurement of contact angle is usually limited to those solids that have a smooth uniform interface with the liquid. Because of the relatively rough and heterogeneous nature of paper, it is more satisfactory to measure the rate of penetration directly. Even though the component factors of the above equation are seldom measured directly, it is important for the technologist studying the penetration of liquids into paper to differentiate among the effects due to these various factors.

Factors Influencing Water Resistance of Paper

A pure cellulosic surface is hydrophilic and easily wettable, that is, it forms a very low contact angle with water; hence, the natural condition of a paper composed of such fibers would be highly absorbent. Actually this condition seldom prevails, since much of paper and paperboard production is treated with sizing additives to increase the resistance to penetration of water (see Chapter 11). Also, paper-making pulps contain materials other than cellulose, some of which may be adsorbed upon the fiber surface. When so adsorbed, they create a hydrophobic condition, that is, a high contact angle between the surface and water.

The subject of paper sizing and numerous theories to account for observed phenomena have received much attention in the literature of the industry. For detailed review of this literature the reader is referred to the book by Casey[20]. The steps listed below describe essentially the process of paper sizing.

(1) Preparation of a size precipitate in a form dispersible in water and capable of exhibiting low surface energy. Partially saponified rosin acids (principally abietic acid) are commonly used for this purpose, as well as emulsified petroleum waxes.

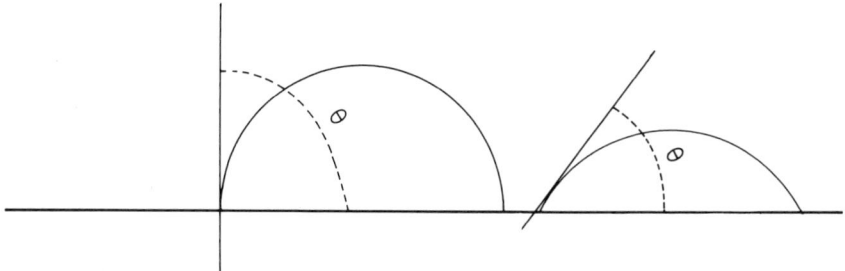

Fig. 14.12. Contact angle between liquid and solid.

(2) Retention of the size precipitate upon the fiber surface. This is accomplished by the addition of alum (aluminum sulfate) to the stock furnish in sufficient quantity to create a mildly acid condition in the stock.

(3) Orientation of the fatty acid molecules upon the fiber surface so that the hydrocarbon chain is presented outward and the molecules are anchored in that position with sufficient strength so that water does not cause a reversal, the polar carboxyl group extending outward. Aluminum hydroxide is considered to coordinate between the hydroxyl group of the cellulose and the rosin acid to produce a stable anchoring.

Change in water resistance of a paper with age is often encountered. It frequently happens that both sized and unsized papers increase in water resistance with age. Occasionally, sized papers lose water resistance with age (fugitive sizing). The "self-sizing" of absorbent papers is attributed to a redistribution of natural pitch or resin present in the sheet. Swanson and Cordingly [21] postulated that the migration of rosin, fatty acids, and certain low energy neutral materials present in the unsized paper becomes redistributed throughout the surfaces of the fibrous structure by a process involving evaporation and adsorption. The presence of multivalent ions, such as calcium, magnesium and aluminum, as well as the phenomena of oxidation and polymerization may also participate in the process. "Fugitive sizing" is attributed to a disruption in the orderly array of surface molecules due to insufficient anchoring.

Methods of Measurement of Water Resistance

Because of the extreme range in the rate of penetration of water into paper, extending from practically instantaneous absorption by certain absorbent papers to scarcely perceptible rate of some hard-sized papers, no single test is suitable for all conditions. Over the years a great number of test methods have been published. The interested reader is referred to the standard bibliography of the subject [22]. Only a few better known methods will be discussed here.

TAPPI Method 458m59 describes the measurement of surface wettability of paper by the angle of contact method [23]. A sample of paper to be tested is mounted in a horizontal position on a microscope slide. A drop of water of about 0.05 ml is placed on the paper and the image of the drop, magnified with a microscope 25 to 30 times, is projected upon a screen holding a sheet of transparent paper. A horizontal line is drawn on the paper coinciding with the image of the base of the drop. The two tangents at the points of contact between drop and base are drawn and the interior angles between tangents and base are measured (angle of contact). The method provides for determining rate of change of wettability with time. It is stated that at contact angles less than 90° the paper is likely to show feathering of an ink line, whereas at angles above 110°, skipping of an ink line is likely to occur.

TAPPI Method 433m44 describes the dry indicator method for determining the time required for water to penetrate a sample of paper. The indicator is prepared by mixing 1 part methyl violet dye with 45 parts sugar and 5 parts soluble starch; all ingredients are to be completely dry and finely powdered when mixed and are to be stored over calcium chloride pending use. The nearly colorless dry indicator becomes deep violet in contact with water. The test is performed by sealing the four edges of the test specimen with wax, sprinkling a thin, uniform layer of indicator upon the surface, and then floating the specimen, indicator side up, upon a vessel of water. The time interval from the instant of contact of the test specimen with water until the rate of change in the color of the indicator is at a maximum.

The Cobb test for papers of higher degree of water resistance is described in TAPPI Method T441m60. The weighed sample of paper is clamped upon a metal plate with a rubber mat between sample and plate by means of a metal ring 10-cm inside diameter and 2.5 cm high. Thus the sample forms the bottom of a cup the sides of which are formed by the ring. The test is started by pouring 0.5 to 1.0 cm of water into the ring and starting a stop watch. At the end of the test period, normally two minutes, the water is poured from the ring, the sample removed and weighed to an accuracy of 0.01 gram, after removal of surface water by mopping with a soft cloth. The absorptiveness of the paper is calculated as the average weight of water absorbed in grams per square meter for the test period. This test was designed for non-bibulous papers and paperboards; but satisfactory results have been obtained with up to about 20 sheets of highly absorbent papers stapled together and tested for 60 instead of 120 seconds. For very hard-sized or specially treated papers, the test may be extended to periods up to 18 hours to increase sensitivity.

In the *curl test* (TAPPI Method T466m52) a specimen of paper of standard dimensions is brought into contact with water on one side, whereupon the ends of the specimen curl upward to a maximum position, then reverse and move down again. The elapsed time from contact to maximum curl is a measure of water resistance.

Oil and Grease Resistance of Paper

In some instances the rate of penetration of liquids other than water is the property to be measured. The permeation of paper by oil-base printing ink is determined by TAPPI Method T462m43. The grease resistance of paper is determined by the rate of penetration of turpentine (TAPPI Method T454m60).

Whereas the resistance of paper to the penetration of water is greatly affected by surface treatment of the fibers by materials having low surface energy and with little or no effect upon porosity, the penetration of oily materials is little affected by such treatments. Oil and grease resistance is attained by reduction of porosity of paper. So-called "greaseproof" paper is made by beating an easily hydrated pulp to extremely low freeness, resulting in a closed sheet with a minimum of void space.

Absorbent Papers

Grades such as towelling, sanitary tissue, blotting and filter papers are commonly tested for absorbency according to TAPPI Method T432m45. A 0.1-ml drop of water is placed on the surface of the paper, which is supported in a manner so that the support does not touch the paper opposite the point of application of the drop. The time is measured from contact of the drop with the paper until the disappearance of the reflection from the drop surface indicates complete absorption. For light-weight tissues the size of drop is reduced to 0.01 ml.

It is customary to subject absorbent papers to "accelerated aging" tests in combination with the above absorbency test. This consists of exposing the sample to some elevated temperature, usually 110°C, in an oven or on a hot plate. The purpose is to simulate the well-known "self-sizing" effect (see above) that often occurs with absorbent papers. Although the correlation between the accelerated test and natural aging is not perfect, it still constitutes a useful guide in the manufacture of absorbent papers.

As pointed out previously, in the manufacture of absorbent paper it is important to keep the presence of resins, fatty acids and other hydrophobic materials in the pulp to a minimum. Maintaining a high degree of porosity in sheet and a textured surface are essential to high absorbency. Here again the paper maker is confronted with contradictory properties both of which are desirable. A high degree of absorbency in paper calls for low density and high porosity, which means a low degree of interfiber bonding and consequent low strength.

Since absorbent papers are expected to become wet in normal use, the strength property when wet is of prime importance. Methods have been discovered for modifying the interfiber bonding with thermosetting synthetic resins to increase wet strength with little effect upon the total bonded area or porosity of the paper (see Chapter 11). It is also likely that the wet strength resin has relatively little effect on absorbency. However, there is a marked tendency for wet strength resins to coprecipitate with natural hydrophobic fatty acids and thus to reduce absorbency.

It is also common to add "rewetting" agents to absorbent papers. Numerous such materials are offered to the paper industry. There are two ways in which a rewetting agent may act: (1) by dissolving in the advancing water film, thereby reducing its surface tension, (2) when bound to fiber surface, by increasing the free surface energy and thus reducing the contact angle.

PERMEABILITY OF PAPER TO GASES

Air permeability of paper and other sheet materials is the ability to allow the flow of air through the structure of the sheet under a pressure differential. It depends upon the number, size, shape and distribution of the pores or air passages within the sheet structure. "Porosity" is often used interchangeably with air permeability. This is not strictly true since, in a specific sense, the word porosity means the ratio of pore volume to total volume of the material. Likewise, "density," meaning weight per unit volume, although bearing some relationship to air permeability, is far from being equivalent. Density is affected by the specific gravity of the solid fraction as well as closed or nearly closed air cells or pockets that contribute little to permeability.

The usual method of test for air permeability is the measurement of the volume of air that flows in unit time through unit area under unit pressure difference. A method and apparatus for this measurement is described in TAPPI Standard Method T460m49. (ASTM Designation D-726.) The instrument consists of an outer cylinder which is partly filled with oil, and an inner cylinder sliding freely in the outer cylinder. Air pressure for the test is provided by the weight of the inner cylinder. The instrument is arranged to furnish air pressure to the paper specimen held between clamping plates having a circular orifice with an area of 1.00 square inch. The movable inner cylinder is graduated in units of 50 ml. It is 10 inches high with a total range of 350 ml. The average number of seconds required for the passage of 100 ml of air through 1 square inch of paper is reported as *air resistance*.

Because of the ease and rapidity of the test, air permeability is widely used as an approximate indication of the permeability of paper to other fluids such as oils and other organic liquids. It is also useful to indicate weight uniformity during manufacture and processing of paper.

It is used as an indirect means of estimating the filtering characteristics of industrial and analytical filter papers, of evaluating the impregnating qualities of saturating papers, and of indicating of ink penetration and spreading in printing papers.

Air permeability is of direct importance in bag papers for use on automatic filling machines where the displaced air must escape through the paper, and in building papers that must prevent air infiltration.

Moisture vapor permeability (MVP) is of great importance in many packaging papers and paperboards. With many commodities it is important that the packaging material prevent the entrance of moisture vapor from the atmosphere and preserve the contents of the package in a dry state. In other instances it is required that the packaging material prevent the loss of water from the contents by evaporation. Either way, a paper or paperboard packaging product may be required to present a barrier to the passage of moisture vapor.

Cellulose, even when formed into a film that is impervious to air (cellophane), is still not a barrier to the passage of moisture vapor. This results from the hygroscopic nature of cellulose, which causes it to adsorb atmospheric water vapor. The sorbed water migrates readily through the cellulose structure and will evaporate from the opposite surface of the film or sheet provided the atmosphere on that side is less humid than on the first side. Thus, cellulose in the form of fiber or film will act as a conductor of water vapor from a more humid to a less humid atmosphere. Even though a paper is made "closed" and dense with very little pore space, it still does not have barrier properties toward water vapor.

When paper is required to have moisture vapor barrier properties it is processed by one of the following methods:

(1) Impregnated with wax, normally paraffin;

(2) Coated with a solution, emulsion or hot melt of a hydrophobic solid material such as resin, latex, wax or asphalt;

(3) Laminated with a continuous film or foil that is impervious to moisture vapor and capable of strongly adhering to the paper surface (examples: polyethylene film, aluminum foil).

Water vapor permeability of paper is measured by sealing a specimen of the paper to be tested in the form of a cover to a dish containing a desiccant. The increase in weight of the desiccant represents the moisture transmitted by the paper sample. Successive weighings are made until a constant rate of gain is attained. The water vapor permeability is reported as grams per square meter per 24 hours with the test apparatus

Fig. 14.13. Vapometer cup for measurement of MVP of paper.

exposed to a relative humidity of 50% and a temperature of 73°F. Complete details of the test method will be found in TAPPI Method T448m49 (see Figure 14.13).

The influence of temperature and humidity on the water vapor transmission of most sheet materials is often nonlinear. Hence, results obtained at standard paper test conditions (50% R.H., 73°F) cannot be extrapolated to predict water vapor transmission under hot, damp conditions. TAPPI Method T464m45 gives the details of water vapor-permeability test at 100°F and 90% relative humidity.

It is normal for wrapping and packaging materials to undergo creasing during the packaging operation. Since creasing may have a disruptive effect upon the barrier film or layer, the moisture vapor permeability of the creased material is of more significance than the test of the flat sheet. TAPPI Method T465-5m52 provides a standard method of creasing of paper products prior to the permeability test.

Table 14.4 gives the MVP values for a few typical packaging materials. Recent years have seen a vigorous growth in packaging both in volume and in diversity. Keen competition for advantages in this field has brought about many advances in methods and materials for treatment of paper (see Chapter 13).

OPTICAL PROPERTIES

Brightness

The appearance of paper to the eye is determined by its behavior toward light, or, in other words, by its optical properties, the most important of which are brightness, color, opacity and gloss. Many methods and instruments have been developed for evaluating them. In this volume, description will be confined to the most widely recognized methods and to those physical principles of importance to these properties.

One of the classic scientific discoveries of all time was by Sir Isaac Newton more than two hundred and fifty years ago that sunlight could be separated into a "spectrum" of pure colors by passing the light through a glass prism. He also found that light of any of the colors, say green, could be passed through a second prism without being split into other colors. However, if the light *reflected* from an intensely green, opaque object is passed through a prism, all colors of the visible spectrum are represented to some degree. Whereas the color of a body or sheet may appear as pure as that of one of the spectral lines discovered by Newton, the body actually reflects all components of the visible spectrum to some degree. The color is due to reflecting some wave lengths to a greater degree than others.

The radiations of visible light are a small part of a large family of electromagnetic waves that travel through space at a common speed of 299,796 kilometers (186,000 miles) per second. The various members differ from each other only in wave length or frequency; visible light comprises the very small range of wave length from slightly less than 400 to slightly over 700 millimicrons (mμ).

TABLE 14.4.*

PAPER		ADDITIVE		
Type	Basis Weight (lb)	Type	Basis Weight (lb)	MVP gm/sq m/24 hr 100°F-90% R.H.
Glassine	27.1	Paraffin wax	7.2	1.1
Glassine	25.7	Paraffin wax	3.3	7.0
Freezer paper	35.8	Paraffin wax	11.5	10.0
Freezer paper	31.0	Paraffin wax	10.5	23.0
Kraft	50	Polyethylene film	16	18.7
Kraft	50	Polyethylene film	8	35.1
Kraft	50	Polyethylene film	5	70.2
Laminate kraft-asphalt-kraft	63.4	Asphalt-paper	30.2	39.0
Moisture-proof cellophane	31.2			18.7
Board		Acrylic-modified vinylidine chloride coating	7.5	0.95-14.1
White sulfite	24	Paraffin wax	5	6.0-12.5
		Polyethylene film	4.5-5.0	
Pouch paper	40	.0007-in. metal foil		0.8

* These tests were performed on the samples in the uncreased condition. After creasing, the samples treated only with paraffin wax would lose considerably in moisture resistance, whereas the samples with polyethylene film would remain practically unchanged. For methods of treating paper to improve MVP see Chapter 13.

The wave lengths of monochromatic light in millimicrons associated with the principal hues are: violet, from lower limit of visibility to 421; blue-violet, 439; blue, 473; blue-green, 498; green, 515; yellow-green, 568; yellow, 577; orange-yellow, 592; orange, 600; red-orange, 631; red, 644 to limit of visibility. These values are necessarily approximate, since the hues of the spectrum change continually and gradually with wave length.

The term "brightness" has come to mean the reflectance of white or near-white papers and paperboard to light of the blue end of the spectrum. The quantitative measurement of this reflectance depends upon an instrument of specified geometrical characteristics, using light of specified wave length and calibrated with a master instrument. Brightness measured in this way is usually found to correlate well with subjective estimates of the relative whiteness of paper.

The measurement of brightness of paper and paperboard is described in TAPPI Standard Method T452m-58. The essential features of the method are as follows: the specimen of paper is illuminated by light of wave length $457.0 \pm 0.5\,m\mu$ with a mean angle of incidence of rays upon the test specimen of $45 \pm 1°$. The specimen aperture is circular with a diameter of 0.480 inch. The exit aperture of the optical system which accepts reflected rays for measurement is concentric and coplanar with the sample aperture and somewhat less in diameter so that light reaching the photoelectric cell does not include that from the rim of the specimen. The angle of rays reflected from the specimen and accepted by the optical system of the photoelectric cell is between 0 and 1° with the normal to the plane of the sample aperture.

Because of variations inherent in any light source, as well as in the photocell, and the geometry of the system, continual calibration of a reflectance meter is essential. Method T452m-58 specifies that secondary standards provided by the Institute of Paper Chemistry having brightness values accurately established by the master brightness instrument be constantly available.

Factors Influencing the Brightness of Paper. Cellulose is colorless, which means that it does not absorb any of the wave lengths of white light preferentially. Furthermore, most papers are optically heterogeneous, that is, they have many reflecting surfaces. Paper appears white for the same reason that snow appears white as compared with the same thickness of ice. Sheets of highly purified cellulose fiber may exhibit brightness values over 90% as compared with the standard MgO block.

Paper pulp is seldom pure cellulose. The noncarbohydrate portion of wood contains material that shows both a higher absorption of light and hence lower reflectance and also a tendency to absorb the wave lengths in the blue region of the spectrum, giving a yellowish cast to pulps containing such materials. It should also be noted that the noncellulosic constituents of wood and of pulp are highly susceptible to the developments of dark-colored bodies by chemical action. Lignin in particular may undergo condensation reactions under both acid and alkaline conditions and may form addition compounds with chlorine, all of which result in darkening of color. Pulp fibers may also adsorb colored materials such as iron, copper, manganese as well as dissolved organic substances from the surrounding water. Pulp samples have been known to drop as much as 5 points in brightness upon dispersion in tap water containing considerable iron.

As previously pointed out, it is impractical to remove all noncellulosic materials from wood in the pulping operation. Therefore, all pulps requiring high brightness are given a separate bleaching operation (see Chapter 10). There are two distinct types of bleaching action that may occur with wood pulp. The first method depends upon removal of lignin and other colored or color-generating materials in the pulp. The brightness increases progressively with removal of noncellulosic material and reaches ultimate brightness as the pulp approaches pure cellulose. Chlorine, hypochlorite, chlorite and chlorate are chemicals of commercial importance in purification bleaching. Chlorine is usually supplemented by an alkali for solubilizing and removing reaction products.

It is also possible to decolorize the noncellulosic materials of pulp to a considerable degree without actually removing them. Oxygen in the form of peroxide, other percompounds, and ozone will do this. Strong reducing agents, such as hydrosulfite, exhibit a decolorizing action which may be used advantageously in sequence with oxidizing agents. The recent emphasis upon high-yield pulps has led to great interest in the decolorizing type of bleach, since the use of chlorine defeats the very purpose of high yield [24]. Although the decolorizing type of bleach has not been able to equal the purification type in brightness, it is apparently possible to approach 80 brightness in some high-yield pulps. One of the important factors in getting high brightness with decolorizing bleach on high-yield pulps is the prevention of conditions in pulping that lead to darkening of the noncellulosic materials. Once this darkening has taken place, the only recourse is the dissolving and removal of the colored material by chemical means.

The brightness of paper is materially affected by the incorporation of white pigments either as "fillers" in the paper stock (see Chapter 10) or as coatings (see Chapter 13). The effect of white fillers is by no means a substitute for bleaching, and their effect is more pronounced with respect to *opacity* than brightness.

In recent years fluorescent dyes have come into widespread use for the improvement of paper whiteness. These dyes have little or no color in the usual sense of the term, but do have the ability to absorb light of one wave length and to reflect the energy in a different wave length. Figure 14.14 shows spectral reflectivity curves for a group of papers, four of which contain fluorescent dyes and three of which do not. The curve for Sample D shows the effects of the "fluorescent whiteness" to a marked degree. The dye absorbs strongly in the violet and ultraviolet regions and the fluorescent radiation appears in the blue region.[24a]

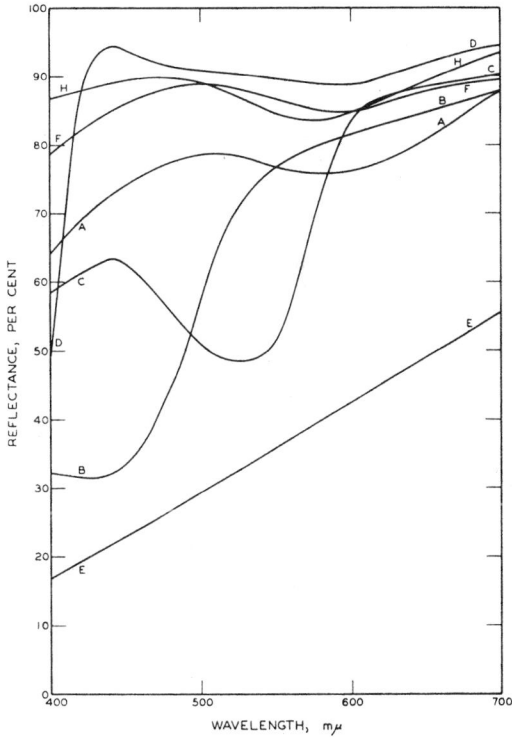

Fig. 14.14. Spectral reflectivity curves obtained with the GERS-R (Reversed System).

Identification of Paper Samples

Sample	Identification
A	White bond paper with a small amount of "fluorescent whitener" added
B	Fluorescent yellow bond paper
C	Fluorescent pink bond paper
D	White bond paper with a large amount of "fluorescent whitener" added
E	Unbleached kraft paper (no fluorescent dye)
F	White bond paper (no fluorescent dye)
H	Cost coated paper (no fluorescent dye)

Measurement of Color

The sensation of color depends upon the distribution of the energy of light entering the eye among the wave lengths making up the visible spectrum ("spectral reflectance"). The "spectral reflectance" of an object is characteristic of the object itself. It is quite independent of the illuminant and of personal variations among observers.

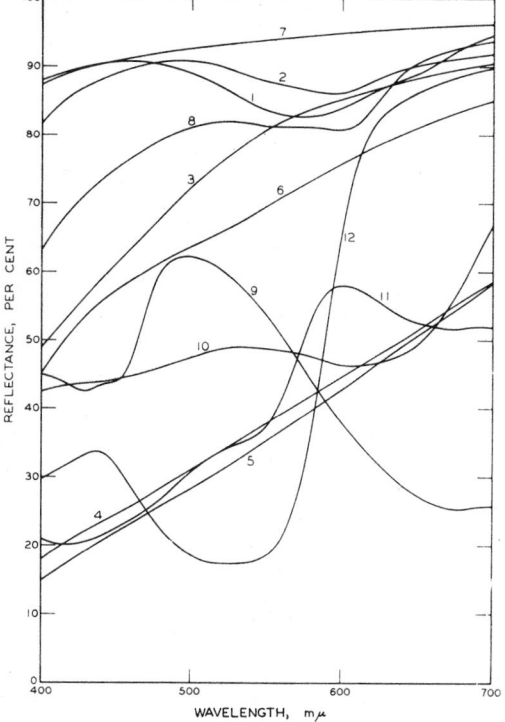

Fig. 14.15. Spectral reflectivity curves for a group of papers and handsheets. 1-Cast coated. 2-Bond. 3-Newsprint. 4-Unbleached kraft. 5-Unbleached kraft handsheet. 6-Sulfite handsheet. 7-Whatman filter paper. 8-Facial tissue. 9-Blue bond. 10-Gray bond. 11-Brown bond. 12-Red bond.

The "color" of objects varies with illumination and is a subjective attribute of observers.

Spectral reflectance is usually expressed in the form of a curve (spectrophotometric curve), the reflectance being given as a function of wave length over the range 400 to 700 mμ. Reflectance is the ratio of the amount of monochromatic light reflected by a body to the amount reflected by a standard surface of magnesium oxide under standard geometrical conditions of measurement (see TAPPI Method T442-m40). Figure 14.15 shows spectral reflectivity curves for handsheets from various pulps and for various colored papers.[24a] Note curves 4, 5, and 6 of papers made from unbleached pulp showing nearly straight line increase in reflectance from violet to red. Curves 1, 2, and 7 show a high and uniform reflectance due to being composed of pure cellulose and/or the presence of white pigment. Curves 9, 11, and 12 show the characteristic effect of the addition of dyes. Dyes color paper by reducing reflectivity in certain regions of the spectrum. For example, Curve 12 for red bond paper shows a deep dip in the blue and green wave lengths with reflectivity in the red being practically the same as for bright white papers. Curve 9 shows a deep dip in reflectivity in the red and yellow and a peak in the blue. This peak is much lower than the reflectance of bright white paper, which would indicate a dull hue.

Opacity

The quality of opacity is one of the most desired of all the properties of printing and writing papers. Satisfactory performance of a printing paper requires that there be little or no "show-through" of images from one side of the sheet to the other. The thickness or weight of sheet required to provide sufficient opacity is probably the principal determinant of ream weight in most printing paper. Thus, the weight of a book or magazine and the amount of postage required to carry them to the consumer is largely determined by the requirement for opacity in the paper.

In a physical sense, opacity is defined as a *contrast ratio*. Two contrast ratios are of importance to the paper industry: (1) TAPPI opacity, which is the reflectance of paper sample backed by a black body of substantially zero reflectance divided by the reflectance of the same sample backed by a white body of absolute reflectance of 0.89;

and (2) printing opacity, in which the white body is replaced by a pad of the paper of sufficient thickness to be completely opaque.

TAPPI Method T425m-60 describes in detail the procedure of determining the opacity of paper and of the calibration of the instrument (Bausch and Lomb Opacimeter). The results are expressed by the equation:

$$C_{0.89} = 100 \ (R_o/R_w)$$

where $C_{0.89}$ is the contrast ratio or TAPPI opacity, R_o is the reflectance of the specimen backed by totally absorbing black cavity, and R_W is the reflectance of the specimen backed by a white body of absolute reflectance of 0.89 as compared with magnesium oxide taken as reflectance of 0.98.

Light falling upon a sheet of paper may be reflected back, or it may be absorbed by the material, or it may be transmitted through the sheet. The following conventional symbols are used for expressing the optical relationships in paper:

R_o = reflectance of a sheet of paper when backed by a black body.

R_w = reflectance of a pad of paper of sufficient thickness to be opaque.

$R_{0.89}$ = reflectance of a sheet of paper backed by white body of 0.89 absolute reflectance.

S = scattering coefficient, the limiting value of light scattered backward from imaginary layer within the sheet as thickness becomes very small.

X = caliper.

SX = scattering power, sometimes SW replaces SX.[24b]

S' = specific scattering coefficient, $SX/$ basis weight.

K = absorption coefficient, the limiting value of light absorbed by imaginary layer within the sheet as the thickness of the layer becomes very small.

K' = specific absorption coefficient, $KX/$ basis weight.

The relationship among the various reflectances and scattering power has been derived from the original Kubelka-Munk formula [25] and has been put into chart form by the National Bureau of Standards.[26] Knowing R_o, $R_{0.89}$, caliper and basis weight, one can readily determine the scattering coefficients.

Other factors being the same, the opacity of a sheet of paper increases progressively (although not linearly) with increase in specific scattering coefficient. S' is a linear function of the specific surface area of the particles composing the sheet of paper that are not in optical contact. This is based on the fact that light is refracted or scattered only at interfaces between two materials of differing refractive index, for example, fiber and air. When the surfaces of two media of the same refractive index are brought into optical contact, light scattering at the interface does not occur. It is accepted that the surfaces of fiber within a sheet of paper exhibiting interfiber bonding are also in optical contact. It is well recognized that beating and wet pressing, which increase the fiber-to-fiber bonding, decrease the scattering coefficient and the opacity. The use of the scattering coefficient as a means for arriving at the total fiber-to-fiber bonded area in a sheet has been suggested.

This fact leads to one of the contradictions common in the art of paper making in which two properties, both desirable, are to some degree incompatible. Thus, optimum opacity would be accompanied by minimum interfiber bonding, or minimum strength. Obviously, a sheet of paper possessing practical use properties represents a compromise between opacity and strength.

The amount of light transmitted by any layer within the sheet is reduced in proportion to increase in the absorption coefficient, K. Thus, unbleached pulp is more opaque than bleached pulp. Also, since dyes perform their function of producing color by absorption of selected wave lengths of light, it follows that papers containing dyes are more opaque than the same papers would be without dye. This brings about another contradiction between opacity and brightness. With a *constant scattering coefficient,* a sheet of high brightness will be less opaque than one of lower brightness at the same basis weight. The function of dyes in increasing the opacity of paper is described in a recent publication.[27]

Gloss

The terms *gloss, glare, finish* and *smoothness* are used more or less interchangeably in describing the surface characteristics of paper. The broad term *finish* refers to the general surface characteristics of the sheet. *Smoothness* refers to the absence of surface irregularities under either visual or use conditions. *Gloss* refers to surface luster and connotes a generally pleasing effect. *Glare* is used for a more intense reflection and a more unpleasant effect.

Since all these terms are essentially subjective conceptions, they cannot be expressed in exact physical units. Referring to a surface as being glossy definitely conveys the idea of high reflectance. The continuity of the reflecting surface rather than its planeness is the more important characteristic in producing gloss. Calendering and coating are important paper-treating methods that affect gloss.

Light travels in straight lines which change direction only when reflected or refracted at a surface. Upon striking a surface, a certain portion of the light is reflected according to the well-known law that the angle of incidence is equal to the angle of reflectance. Another portion of the incident light enters the surface and is refracted in a direction depending upon the angle of incidence and the refractive index. As the angle of incidence (the angle between the approaching light beam and the surface) becomes less, the specular reflection becomes greater. The angle at which all the light is reflected is known as the "critical angle."

TAPPI method T480m51 describes the instrument and method for determination of papers of medium and high gloss. The angle of incident light is 15° (75° from a line perpendicular to the specimen) and the results are expressed in per cent reflectance by comparison with standards of known gloss furnished by the National Bureau of Standards.

The following table gives a comparison of gloss and brightness for several different cover-type papers.

Type of Paper	Color	Finish	Brightness	Gloss
Enamel cast coated	White	Very smooth	82.3	97
Uncoated opaque	White	Dull	85.5	9
Ripple finish	Black	Smooth	2.3	39
Ripple finish	Grey	Smooth	18.6	39.5

These data illustrate the well-known facts that black or dark-colored surfaces may have considerable gloss and that white and bright surfaces may be low in gloss.

CHEMICAL PROPERTIES OF PAPER

Aging Tests

Because of the use of paper for books, documents and records of all sorts, the *permanence* of paper with years and even centuries of aging is of great significance. That paper does deteriorate, at least in color, is evident to anyone who examines old books and papers. The exact extent of this deterioration and the causes for it are by no means clear. Cellulose itself, when protected from bacterial, fungus or chemical attack, appears to be quite resistant to deterioration with age. Linen cloth from the tombs of Egypt is found to be in good condition after thousands of years, and considerable quantities of such mummy cloth were actually used as paper-making rags.[1] In fact, the purity of the paper fiber in terms of cellulose has been considered the most important factor in aging. When wood pulp began to replace cotton and linen rags for paper making about a century ago, the tendency of paper to discolor with age was immediately noticeable. It is natural that this should lead to the conclusion that paper containing considerable quantities of non-cellulosic material ages poorly. This is certainly true so far as color or brightness is concerned, but whether it is likewise true for various durability properties is open to question.

For several obvious reasons there is very little exact information on the aging of paper over long periods of time. Many of the test methods for paper have been in existence for relatively few years. Hence, it is impossible to compare the present properties of old papers with the original values. Also, neither the original conditions of manufacture nor the conditions of storage are known exactly.

Because of the slow process of accumulating data on natural aging of paper, an accelerated aging test has been suggested in which a paper sample is heated in an oven at $100°C$ for periods up to 72 hours (Ref. T453m41). The National Bureau of Standards has published data on a number of paper samples in which the results of the accelerated test are compared with natural aging for periods up to 26 years.[28] These tests indicate a general qualitative relationship between the accelerated and natural aging. It is interesting to note that even the best papers in the Bureau of Standards study showed a considerable loss in folding endurance (embrittlement) over a period of 26 years, and for many of the papers the fold test dropped to a small fraction of its original value. Most of the paper samples showed no loss in tensile strength, and in those showing a loss, it was relatively slight. It would appear that the loss in fold was due to an attack upon, or some change occurring in, the fiber structure.

An interesting theory to account for deterioration of paper with age has been proposed by W. H. Langwell.[29] It is postulated that SO_2 in the atmosphere is catalytically oxidized to SO_3 through the agency of iron, copper, manganese or other metals present in the paper, and this brings about deterioration of fiber. Evidence is submitted to show accumulation of sulfate in the edges of book pages and in papers containing metals exposed to SO_2 fumes. The prevention of deterioration would be accomplished by any of the following: (1) making paper free of metal contamination, (2) incorporation of buffers to neutralize acid, (3) sealing of paper from contact with atmosphere, (4) incorporation of catalyst inhibitors, (5) air conditioning to remove SO_2.

Two recent publications [30] describe an extensive study of the durability of book paper and offer the following rules for judging of book paper intended to have a high degree of permanence.

(1) The paper must be free of groundwood and unbleached fibers.

(2) On the basis of a minimum of 15 test strips, from 15 different sheets selected at random from a ream, initial folding endurance of conditioned strips shall average not less than 300 folds in the weakest direction as measured on the M.I.T. test of $\frac{1}{2}$ kg tension.

(3) On the basis of a minimum of 12 test strips (selected as in 2) and tested by 5 tears through 4 strips, initial tear resistance of conditioned strips shall average not less than 60 grams in weakest direction as measured on the Elmendorf tester.

(4) After artificial aging at $100 \pm 2°C$, the average strips (selected and tested as in 2 and 3) shall not show less than the following fold and tear for the days of aging indicated:

Days	*Fold*	*Tear (gm)*
12	200	53
24	140	48
36	100	43

(5) The pH of the paper shall not be less than 6.5 at the time of manufacture, and after heat aging (as in 4) for three days shall show no sharp decline.

(6) Opacity of the paper shall not be less than 90.

(7) Procedures for testing shall follow TAPPI (standard methods) unless otherwise indicated.

Artificial aging data on a variety of papers sized under various conditions are presented in a recent article.[36] Papers of various pH values (acidity), sized both by conventional rosin and alum, and by "Aquapel" neutral sizing, were subjected to artificial aging at 105°C for periods up to 48 days. No definite correlation was found between the acidity of the paper and resistance to aging. The authors consider that acidity or alkalinity of paper is of secondary importance in aging, and conclude that structure of the sheet appears to be the determining factor.

The permanence of paper is obviously a property of considerable importance in many grades. It is equally obvious that there is no universal agreement as to the causes of deterioration of paper with age. Not the least of the obstacles to understanding the aging of paper is the necessity for depending upon accelerated tests to estimate the permanence of paper, together with the meager amount of test data from natural aging.

In the interest of adding to the knowledge of the permanency of paper, Table 14.5 gives test values for the paper upon which this book is printed, taken at the time of manufacture. At the end of the book are a few blank pages that may be used for testing in the future, after the lapse of considerable time, for comparison with the tests given below. This will also serve to compare artificial aging tests with natural aging. It would also be of interest to know as much as possible of the environmental conditions or geographical location under which aging has taken place.

Flammability

The *combustible nature* of paper is one of its most obvious characteristics. For most uses this is no disadvantage, and in the matter of disposing of waste paper, it is even an advantage. However, for various decorative uses and in certain environments, it is essential to reduce the *flammability* of paper. The flameproofing of paper is quite similar to that of cotton textiles. Two general classes of flameproofing agents are recognized: (1) water-soluble materials, not durable to weathering or laundering, (2) insoluble or permanent agents not removed by exposure to water. Since paper products requiring flameproofing are not normally exposed to weather or to laundering, the materials of class one are usually used for paper. It must be remembered that the term

TABLE 14.5. PHYSICAL PROPERTIES OF SILKOTE OFFSET 290M—60 LB STOCK ON WHICH THIS BOOK IS PRINTED

Paper Made	Nov. 25, 1963	Tested	Nov. 27, 1963	Conditions T402—50% RH 23°C
Test	TAPPI Method	Units	As Mfg'd	Artificially Aged 12 Days * at 100°C
Basis weight	T410m-45	pounds, 500 sheets 25 x 38 inches	60.9	
Tear	T414m-49 Elmendorf	grams force	55.2 m.d. † 57.2 c.d. ††	46.4 m.d. 45.6 c.d.
Fold	T423m-50 MIT-½ kg	number of folds	998 m.d. 784 c.d.	563 m.d. 608 c.d.
Burst	T403m-53	psi	40.4	33.7
Brightness	T452m-58	points MgO = 100	79.0	72.8
pH	T435m-52	pH units	6.9	7.2

* This is supposed to be equivalent to 100 years of natural aging.
† m.d. = machine direction of paper, or with grain.
†† c.d. = cross machine direction of paper, or against grain.

"flameproof paper" means that the paper will char when exposed to ignition temperature but will not burst into flame; such paper will not withstand or endure any higher temperature than ordinary paper.

The principal agents used for flameproofing paper are salts such as ammonium sulfate, ammonium sulfamate, and various ammonium and amino phosphoric acid compounds. The quantities required are of the order of 10 to 20% of the weight of the paper. It is generally considered that these compounds at high temperature catalytically decompose cellulose into carbon and water with marked reduction in volatile combustible gases normally characteristic of burning paper.

The standard test for flammability of paper and paperboard is described in TAPPI Standard T461m-45.

Anti-Tarnish Paper

Paper may come into contact with metal products as a wrapper, container or wiping towel. In some instances it is important that no tarnish, stain or corrosion be caused by the paper. Among the agents which might occur in paper and which would cause corrosion or tarnish of metal are sulfides and acids. TAPPI method T444m-41 describes a method to determine whether a sample of paper will tarnish silver. A moist sample of paper is placed between two sheets of brass plated with silver, and the assembly is placed in an oven until the paper is completely dried. The surface of the silver is examined for evidence of tarnish. Metals other than silver may be used and evidence of corrosion noted. TAPPI method T406m-60 describes the determination of sulfide sulfur in paper by evolution of hydrogen sulfide, absorption on lead acetate filter paper, and estimation of quantity colorimetrically.

Acidity of Paper

The presence of acid in paper, or to put it another way, paper possessing an acidic reaction, is a property of special importance. Not only may the presence of acid affect the aging properties of paper, but it also may act upon materials that come into contact with the paper. In addition, the sizing of paper, wet strength treatment, and dye and filler retention usually depend upon the addition of alum or other acidic materials to the beater furnish (see Chapter 11). Hence, many papers are acidic to various degrees at the time of manufacture. The author has also observed that paper formed under neutral but unbuffered conditions develops a slight acidic condition upon natural aging for a few months. The ability to measure acidity, or pH value, of paper and to control this property during manufacture is of considerable importance. Since the determination of pH of paper is an empirical test, it is necessary to relate use performance of various paper products to test records.

Measurement of pH of Paper

There are two types of pH measurement generally used with paper: (1) extraction of a certain quantity of paper with distilled water (hot or cold) and determination of the pH of the extract by a pH meter or other suitable means and (2) application of a pH color indicator solution to the paper and estimating pH colorimetrically by comparison with standards. These two methods are described in TAPPI Standard T435m-52 and Routine Control Method 274 respectively. The extraction method has the objection that the proportion of water to weight of paper is necessarily quite large and hence the usual lack of buffering in paper makes the test liable to error. The colorimetric method, since it depends upon an operator's judgment of color, is somewhat subjective and it is not suitable for colored papers.

It is also possible to determine the quantity of acid in paper, in contrast to the pH value, by titrating an extract of the paper with standard alkali solution. It will be recalled that pH is a measure of hydrogen ions present, which depends both upon the amount of acidic material and upon its degree of ionization. Hence, pH does not measure the amount of acid present. Since it is the "activity" or "intensity" of acid that is usually of most interest, the pH value is the more common test.

Fiber Analysis of Paper and Paperboard

It has always been of considerable importance to be able to determine from a sample of paper the fibers or pulps used in its manufacture. Some papers are bought with a specification of pulp furnish; with others, fiber analysis is of interest in interpreting physical tests.

Fiber identification is accomplished (1) by distinctive color reaction of various pulp fibers when exposed to certain dyes and to a variety of stains based upon iodine and (2) by morphological characteristics observed in a microscope. A systematic procedure for fiber identification is described in TAPPI Standard T401m-60. The distinctive color reactions of fibers when exposed to stain depends upon the chemical and physical experience undergone by the fiber during the pulping and bleaching processes. With the many innovations that have occurred in wood pulping in recent years, it is essential that fiber analysis be performed with constant reference to known samples of presently available pulps and by a microscopist of sound judgment and experience. This is also true in forming judgments of fiber morphology where identification depends upon familiarity with microscopic appearance of fine structural details (see Chapter 2).

The following tests are among the more common ones used to determine the composition of paper;

T418m-50—Organic Nitrogen in Paper. This indicates such components as glue, casein, urea-formaldehyde and melamine—formaldehyde resins.

T419m-60—Starch in Paper. Starch is frequently used for surface sizing and for internal bonding of paper.

T413m-58—Ash in Paper. An indication of amount of mineral filler present in paper.

REFERENCES

1. Institute of Paper Chemistry, "Instrumentation Studies XII, Effect of Relative Humidity upon Physical Properties," *Paper Trade J.,* 104, No. 15, TS209 (April 15, 1937).
2. Wink, W. A., *Tappi,* 44, No. 6, 171A (June, 1961).
3. "The Dictionary of Paper," American Paper and Pulp Association, 122 East 42nd Street, New York (1951).
4. "The Paper Yearbook," Eighteenth Edition, Duluth, Minnesota, The Davidson Publishing Co., 1960.
5. Van den Akker, J. A., Lathrop, A. L., Voelker, M. H., and Dearth, L. R., *Tappi,* 41, No. 8, 416 (August, 1958).
6. Clark, J. d'A., *Paper Trade J.,* 118, No. 1, 29 (January 6, 1944).
7. Institute of Paper Chemistry Report No. 31 to American Paper and Pulp Association, New York, Part I February 3, 1941; Part II January 27, 1942; Part III March 3, 1942; Part IV January 17, 1952; Part V February 13, 1956.
8. Wultoch, F., and Schmut, R., *Tappi,* 44, No. 1, 38 (January, 1961).
9. Carson, F. T., and Worthington, F. V., *J. Res. Nat. Bur. Std.,* 6, 339 (1931).
10. Carson, F. T., *Paper Trade J.,* 102, TS253 (1936).
11. Clark, J. d'A., *Tech. Assoc. Papers,* 4, 367 (1932).
12. Tuck, N. G. M., and Mason, S. G., *Pulp Paper Mag. Can.,* 50, No. 11, 132 (Convention Issue 1949).
13. Institute of Paper Chemistry, "Instrumentation Studies XXXV," *Paper Trade J.,* 110, No. 7, TS77 (February 15, 1940).
14. Ratliff, F. T., *Tappi,* 43, No. 10, 831 (October, 1960).
15. Clark, J. d'A., *Paper Trade J.,* 100, No. 13, 41 (March 28, 1935).
16. Peirce, F. T., *J. of Textile Inst.,* 21, T377 (1930).
17. Brandon, C. E., *Tappi,* 40, No. 3, 168A (March, 1957).
18. Swanson, J. W., *Tappi,* 44, No. 1, 142A (January, 1961).
19. Washburn, E. W., *Phys. Rev.,* 17, 273 (1921).
20. Casey, J. P., "Pulp and Paper Chemistry and Chemical Technology," Second Edition, Vol. 2, New York, Interscience Publishers, Inc., 1960.
21. Swanson, J. W., and Cordingly, S., *Tappi,* 42, No. 10, 812 (October, 1959).
22. Institute of Paper Chemistry Bibliographic Series No. 165, "Sizing of Paper," Appleton, Wisconsin.
23. Codwise, P. W., *Tech. Assoc. Papers,* 13, 200 (1930) and 22, 246 (1939).

24. Giertz, H. W., *Tappi*, **44**, No. 1, 1 (January, 1961).

24a. Institute of Paper Chemistry, Instrumentation Program Report 17, Part XIV to American Paper and Pulp Association (November 20, 1961).

24b. Van den Akker, *Tappi*, **32**, No. 11, 498-501 (November, 1949).

25. Kubelka, P., and Munk, F., *Z. tech. Physik.*, **12**, 593 (1931).

26. Judd, D. B., *Paper Trade J.*, **106**, No. 1, 39 TS5 (January 6, 1938).

27. Hayek, M., Deutsch, A. S., Neary, J. P., *Tappi*, **45**, No. 8, 149A (August, 1962).

28. Wilson, W. K., *et al.*, *Tappi*, **36**, No. 9, 543-8 (September, 1955).

29. Langwell, W. H., *Tappi*, **38**, No. 9, 190A (September, 1955).

30. Virginia State Library, Richmond, Virginia, "Deterioration of Book Stock: Causes and Remedies," 1959; "The Manufacture and Testing of Durable Book Papers," 1960.

31. Campbell, W. B., Pidgeon, L. M., *Pulp Paper Mag. Can.*, **29**, No. 6, 185 (February 6, 1930).

32. Stamm, A. J., *Tappi*, **42**, No. 1, 44 (January, 1959).

33. Brecht, W., "Fundamentals of Papermaking Fibres," *Brit. Paper Board Makers' Assoc., Proc. Tech Sect.*, 241 (1958).

34. Rance, H. F., *Tappi*, **37**, No. 12, 640 (December, 1954).

35. Nordmann, L. S., *Tappi*, **41**, No. 1, 23 (January, 1958).

36. Dixson, H. P. Jr., and Nelson, J. C., *Tappi*, **45**, No. 10, 753 (October, 1962).

GENERAL REFERENCE

American Society For Testing and Materials. Special Technical Publication No. 60-B Paper and Paperboard. 3rd Edition. Philadelphia, 1963.

CHAPTER 15

Process Instrumentation for the Pulp and Paper Industry

EARL W. PRINCE

Champion Papers, Inc.

The use of properly applied instrumentation is rapidly becoming a "must" in the paper-making industry. The batch system, made obsolete by higher machine speeds, is being replaced by continuous processes where variables must be controlled quickly and accurately. It is being proved every day that instrumentation is a vital factor in product uniformity and cost reduction. Modern paper mills are designed with instruments in mind. The use of centralized, enclosed control stations places the operator at a distinct advantage. The important variables can be easily noted, and with a graphic panel and miniature instruments, the complete process flow diagram can be displayed. This obviously gives a clear picture of the operation, and any upset can be speedily corrected. If the major variables were placed on automatic control, the process would indeed become continuous and free from the element of human error.

It is the purpose of this chapter to present typical methods of process instrument application. Instrument requirements vary from mill to mill due to type of product, speed of machines and variations in the type of equipment used. Therefore, each instrument application should be tailored to fit the process, for only in this manner can the full benefits be realized.

GENERAL CONSIDERATIONS

An attempt has been made in this chapter to show a cross section of the various types of instruments which are available from some of the manufacturers serving the paper industry.

The user has a wide selection from which to choose and his choice depends on many factors. Perhaps indicators are sufficient for a particular process; perhaps indicator-controllers will fill the need. Where past history of the variable is wanted, then recorders or recorder-controllers are necessary. In some cases a non-indicating controller will suffice.

Both regular size instruments and miniatures are available in most lines, as are the composite types and transmitter-receiver combinations. Also, the user has a choice in many cases between pneumatic and electronic systems. Space limitations permit only a discussion of the more important variations.

Regular Size vs. Miniature

Both regular and miniature sizes are available in the pneumatic variety for most applications. The electronic types are usually miniatures. However, there are exceptions and these will be discussed.

Regular size instruments have been in use

for years and still are popular. The large chart (usually circular) is easily read. The charts for the most part are of the 24-hour variety and the past record can easily be checked at a glance. The strip chart, which all miniatures employ, must be unwound or unfolded in order to back-check more than several hours. The 24-hour circular chart must be changed daily, whereas strip charts will run about a month, depending on their speed.

Although the regular size case requires considerable panel space, the depth is shallow, averaging about six inches. This facilitates mounting in some instances. Another advantage of this size is that several elements may be incorporated in the same case. It is common practice to use dual, triple or quadruple recorders, dual controllers or combinations.

The miniature instrument has the advantage of requiring very little frontal panel space. The depth requirement, however, is greater (16 to 18 inches) and additional space for maintenance must also be provided at the rear. Miniatures are especially advantageous when used in conjunction with a graphic panel on a complex process. Many brands of this type are plugged in from the front and some employ plug-in control elements which may be removed from the rear of the case. These features obviously facilitate maintenance and reduce down time.

Composite Types vs. Transmitter-Receivers

A prime example of the composite type is the widely used temperature indicator/recorder whose sensing element (bulb) is connected to the case element by means of capillary tubing. Another example is a pressure recorder whose pressure element is connected directly to the pipe line tap by means of piping or tubing. This type is used mainly where it is desirable to mount the instrument near the point of measurement.

The transmitter-receiver combination employs a sensing element and transmitter (mounted at, or close to, the point of measurement) which sends a signal to the remotely located receiver. In pneumatic systems, the receivers are all 3 to 15 psi pressure indicator/recorders (or controllers) using appropriate charts for the particular variable. The transmitters transmit a 3 to 27 psi signal proportional to the variable being measured.

Electronic systems operate similarly except that the signal is electrical in the low millivolt range. Needless to say, since all receivers are identical (in each category), the spares inventory is minimized. The main disadvantage is that both transmitter and receiver must be maintained and calibrated. There is no question that the transmitter-receiver combination lends itself well to centralized control station installations. This approach is the modern trend. Such control stations are usually in a separate room or far enough away from the process to provide clean, dry surroundings.

Pneumatic vs. Electronic

Many heated debates arise between the proponents of pneumatic and those of electronic instruments. Both types are capable of excellent performance.

The pneumatic type (controller or transmitter) has been in use for many years and is known for its simplicity of design, dependability and ease of maintenance. Pneumatically operated final control elements (valves, dampers, positioners, etc.) also have proved to be excellent performers. The use of pneumatic transmitters and receivers obviously requires pneumatic final control elements. The only requirement necessary for years of good performance is an ample supply of clean, dry air. One cannot expect an instrument to operate faultlessly when fed on a diet of water, oil and dirt.

The electronic type is gaining in popularity as a result of several factors. The improvement in component reliability, component miniaturization and the use of solid state devices is significant. The fact that the electrical output of electronic transmitters is compatible with modern data-logging apparatus (for computer use) gives added impetus to their popularity. Extremely fast response is yet another characteristic; however, many paper mill processes do not require this type of response. A disadvantage is that a transducer is necessary in order to utilize the reliable, easily obtained and proven pneumatic valves and operators. Electrically operated valves require a separate control amplifier for any mode other than on-off control.

MEASUREMENT METHODS

There are many instruments widely used in the paper industry that are electronic by nature. Among these are instruments for measuring temperature (thermocouple, radiation elements, thermistors, etc.), load (strain gauges), pH, ORP, conductivity, turbidity, flow (magnetic flow meter) and others.

In addition there are certain instruments that do not lend themselves readily to miniaturization. In this category are the multi-record units where the number of receiving elements and pens dictate the case size or where so many variables are recorded that a large chart is required for proper delineation.

Since a full discussion of all the measurement methods would constitute a book in itself, only a brief outline will be presented on those methods which are in widespread use in the paper industry.

Flow

The orifice plate is used for many paper mill applications, particularly for steam and water flow measurements. The mercury type instrument, which has been used for many years to measure the drop across the orifice, is giving way to the differential-pressure (D/P) transmitter. The force-balance principle is employed. The system is rugged and has fast response. The range is adjustable, thus making it highly versatile. The output (3 to 15 psi of air) is fed into a suitable receiver.

For corrosive liquids and slurries (stock, coatings, etc.) the magnetic flowmeter is now the acknowledged leader. The main advantages are: (1) no pipeline restrictions, (2) permits measurement of any fluid whose conductance is above a certain very low minimum, and (3) extreme accuracy throughout its range. The only requirement is that the meter body be kept full. The measurement principle is analogous to that of an alternator (a moving wire in a magnetic field). In this case, the fluid passing through the magnetic field produces a voltage which is proportional to the average velocity.

The area type flowmeter (rotameter) is also in wide use for measurement of gases and fluids at relatively low flows from hundredths of a gallon to several hundred gallons for a liquid, and tenths of a cfm (cubic foot per minute) to 400 cfm or higher for a gas. This is a simple device consisting of a calibrated tapered glass tube containing a float or rotor. The rotameter itself is an indicating device, but it can be supplied with a suitable float extension and recorder/controller. The float extension serves as an armature in an inductance bridge in electrical instruments, or as a magnet for magnetic coupling in pneumatic control actuation.

Level

The continuous air purge or bubble tube system is widely used on open tank level applications. This is a simple, inexpensive and foolproof method and is wholly satisfactory. The system consists of an open-ended pipe fastened inside a tank with the pipe end within several inches of the bottom. The pipe also can be mounted externally and tapped into the side of the tank, close to the bottom. A continuous flow of air is applied to the pipe through a combination flow indicator-restrictor. When the air bubbles from the open end, the pressure in the pipe will correspond to the pressure of the liquid head in the tank. A pressure recorder or controller (calibrated in inches or feet of level) is connected to the pipe after the flow restrictor. A combination of air and water may be used for purging where high consistency fluids are present.

The diaphragm type is also widely used and can be of the 1 to 1 ratio type (where the transmitted air pressure corresponds to the pressure of the liquid head) or the D/P cell type whose output is 3 to 15 psi air, proportional to level.

For closed tanks the differential pressure cell is used. The transmitter signal is 3 to 15 psi of air which is proportional to the level. Internal tank pressure is cancelled out. An example would be boiler drum level or digester level. Another type, used primarily for Weir or Parshall flume applications is mechanical in nature. A float operating in a stilling well is cable-connected to a pulley on the pen or pointer positioning shaft of the instrument.

Pressure

The typical pressure instrument consists merely of an expansible element mechanically linked to the pen or pointer. Depending on range and sensitivity desired, this element may be a semi-circular, hollow, spring-like tube (Bourdon tube), a bellows, a spiral or a helix. In most cases (whether composite or transmitter types), the element is piped directly to the point of measurement. For corrosive service, a diaphragm seal or isolator is required. A similar diaphragm seal is used for high consistency or viscous service.

Temperature

There are many methods of measuring temperature. The most widely used type is the filled system. In this category are the liquid-expansion (mercury, xylene), vapor-pressure (volatile liquids such as the ethers) and the gas-pressure classes. All operate on the same principle and all employ a bulb connected to the instrument element by means of a capillary. The element is a pressure-sensitive spiral or helix similar to that in a pressure instrument. An increase in temperature causes the pressure to increase within the system and so expands the ele-

ment. Again mechanical linkage is used to operate the pen or pointer.

The vapor-pressure class is most widely used because of its range (-300 to $+600°$F), fast response, sustaining accuracy and simplicity. No compensation is necessary if the measured temperature does not cross the ambient. The capillary may be 100 feet or more in length. A characteristic of this class is that the response is of the expanding scale type. Thus the chart is more open and easy to read in its upper portions.

The gas pressure class covers a usable range of from $-450°$F to $+1000°$F. The response is linear, thus affording an evenly scaled chart. The general construction is the same as for the vapor pressure type. Gas pressure systems are particularly useful in temperature transmitters because of the linear response (transmitter output is 3 to 15 psi air, proportional to temperature).

For high temperature applications such as lime kilns and sulfur burners, the radiation pyrometer is the popular choice. This device converts radiant energy into electrical energy. The sensing element is comprised of small thermocouples connected in series upon which the radiant energy is focused. The generated voltage is fed into a millivolt or potentiometer type instrument calibrated in terms of temperature.

pH

The measurement and control of pH in the paper industry is of prime importance in order to yield a more uniform product along with savings in raw materials. An example of this is controlling the amount of alum required for proper sizing of the sheet.

A pH measurement is electrical, and, to put it simply, a pair of specially designed electrodes is immersed in the solution being measured. A sample flow chamber is used for continuous measurement. One electrode produces a constant potential regardless of the solution (reference electrode). The other (glass electrode) produces a potential which varies in proportion to the hydrogen ion content of the solution (pH is the logarithm of the reciprocal of the hydrogen ion content in grams per liter). The output of the electrodes is fed into a suitable amplifier and recorder/controller. Automatic temperature compensation is accomplished by means of a resistance thermometer placed in the sample chamber along with the electrodes.

Oxidation Reduction Potential

The measurement of ORP is similar to that of pH. The main difference is that a platinum electrode instead of the glass is used in conjunction with the reference electrode. The instrument is calibrated in millivolts. This measurement is valuable in pulp bleaching since an excessive ORP of the bleach causes cellulose degradation.

Conductivity

The measurement of conductivity is a useful tool in several areas of the mill, for example, where the condensate from an indirect heated digester is re-used in the boiler plant. Any leakage of the acid cooking liquor in the heat exchanger into the condensate would be disastrous. A conductivity alarm would signal such a condition and automatically dump the condensate into a sewer.

The conductivity or resistance of the media is measured by a cell (using carbon or platinum elements) connected to an a.c. bridge. The change in voltage across the bridge due to an increase of conductance is detected and used for alarm or control purposes. Various types of cells are obtainable for insertion in the flow piping and for specific applications. Where media temperature variations are a factor, automatic temperature compensation is available. Recorders and indicators can be calibrated directly in micromhos.

Gas Analysis

A popular method of measuring oxygen and combustibles uses the thermal conductivity method. Two cells are used, the oxygen present in the gas sample is measured by one cell, and the other measures the combustibles present. The cells contain a platinum filament by which the gases are burned catalytically. The cell measuring the oxygen is purged with hydrogen. Both cells are legs of a.c. bridge circuits which are connected to an amplifier and suitable two-pen recorder which provides continuous and independent measurement of per cent oxygen and per cent combustibles. Where continuous measurement of only oxygen or excess air in a gaseous mixture is required, a single hydrogen purged cell is required.

For the measurement of the percentage of one gas present in another, the thermal conductivity type may be used. The gas sample is passed through a cell which contains a filament which senses the rate at which the gas conducts heat. This is compared to the conduction rate of a reference gas (gas to be analyzed). Both the sample filament and reference filament are part of the instrument input bridge circuit. As various gases differ in relative conductivity the instrument is adaptable to such gases as carbon dioxide, oxygen, etc.

THE SULFITE PROCESS *

Sulfur Dioxide Manufacture

Sulfur dioxide is used in the manufacture of sulfite digester liquor. This is obtained by burning sulfur either in a rotary or spray type burner.

One way of controlling the variables is shown in Figure 15.1. The temperature of the sulfur in the melter and in the storage tank is controlled (TRC-1 and TRC-2) as is the level of the sulfur in the burner (LRC-1). These are the important variables. The temperature of the gas leaving the combustion chamber is continuously recorded (TR). Control of secondary air is accomplished by an automatic gas analyzer.

Figure 15.2 shows a slightly different approach. TIC-1 and TIC-3 control the temperatures in the melter and storage tanks.

* See Chapter 6 for additional details of sulfite process.

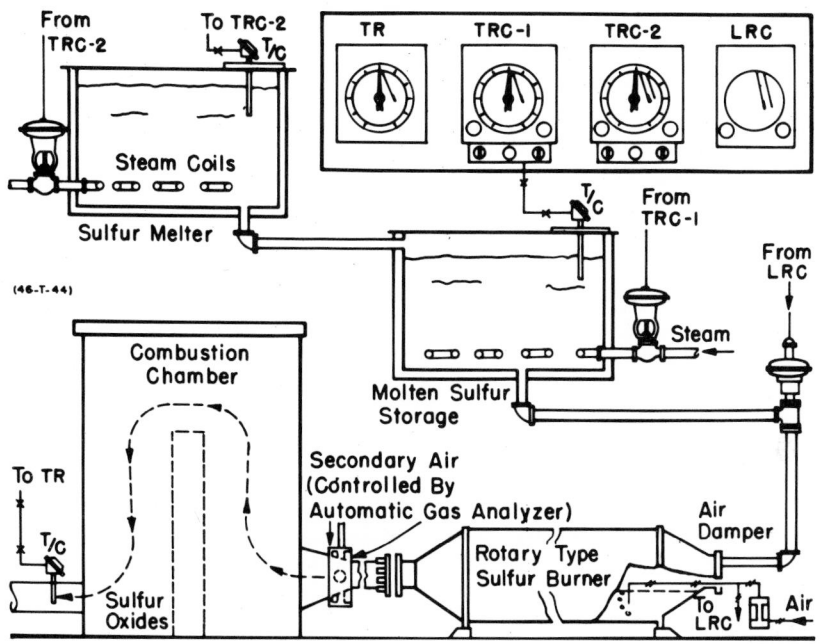

Fig. 15.1. Sulfur burner controls. (*Courtesy Minneapolis-Honeywell*)

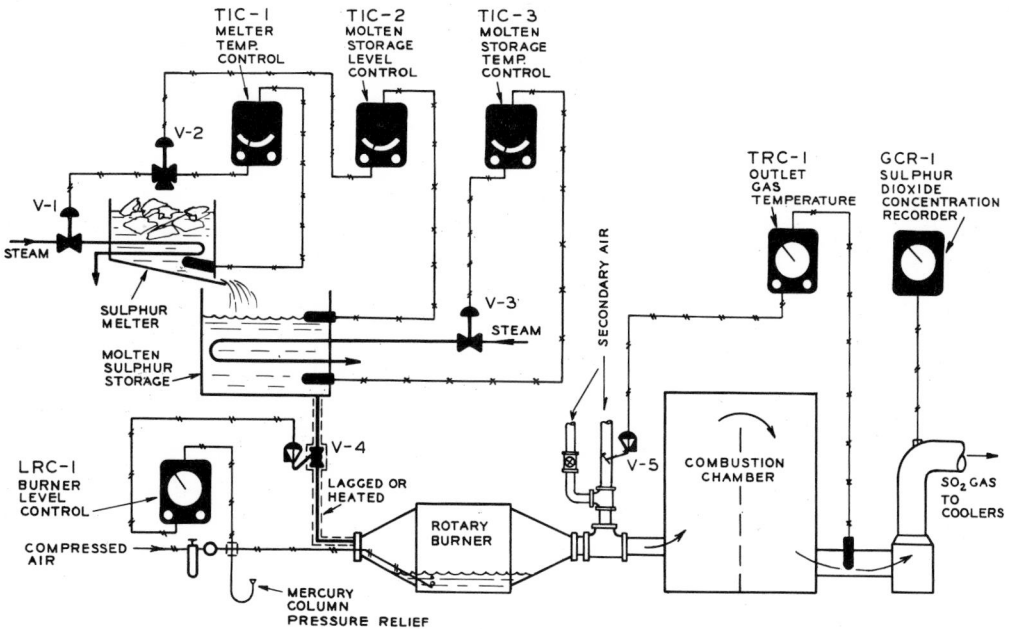

Figure 15.2. SO_2 system controls. (*Courtesy The Bristol Co.*)

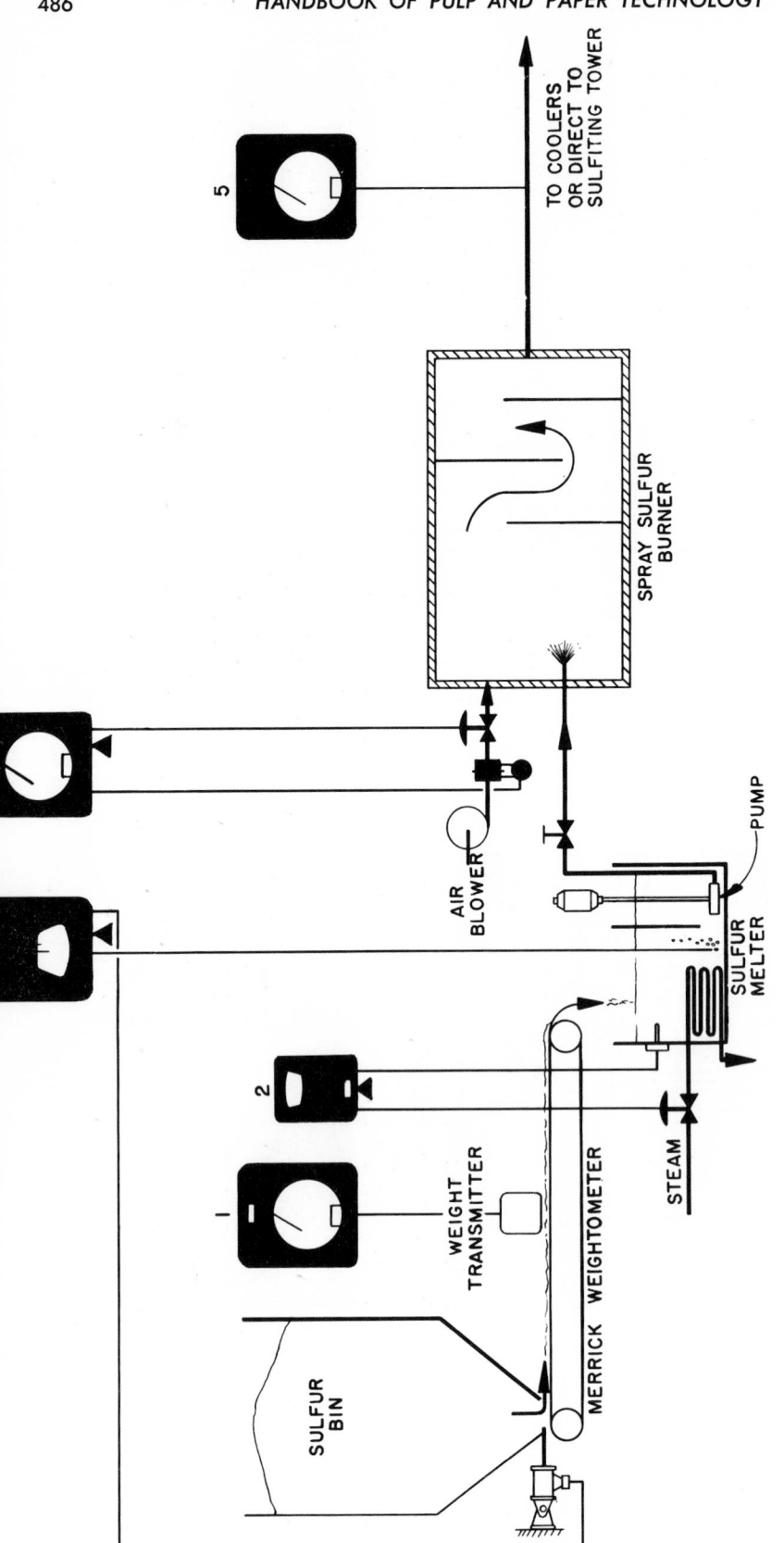

Fig. 15.3.   Spray sulfur burner instrumentation.   (*Courtesy The Foxboro Co.*)

1   DRY SULFUR WEIGHT RECEIVER RECORDER WITH INTEGRATOR.

2   SULFUR MELTER TEMPERATURE CONTROLLER.

3   SULFUR MELTER LEVEL CONTROLLER — VARIES· FEED OF DRY SULFUR.

4   AIR FLOW CONTROLLER

5   EXIT GAS TEMPERATURE RECORDER

▲ = 20 PSI AIR SUPPLY

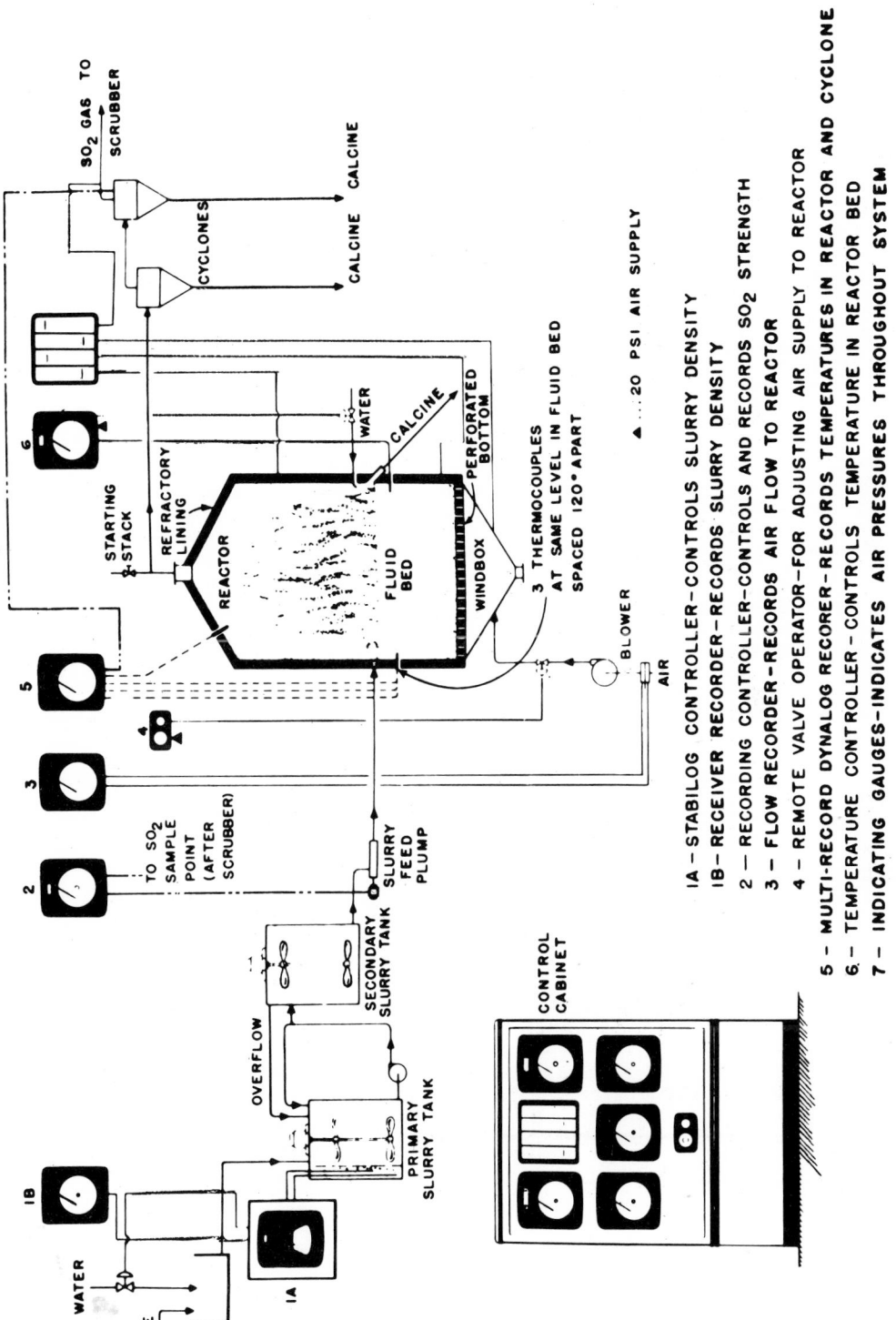

Fig. 15.4. Pyrites ore roasting instrumentation. (*Courtesy The Foxboro Co.*)

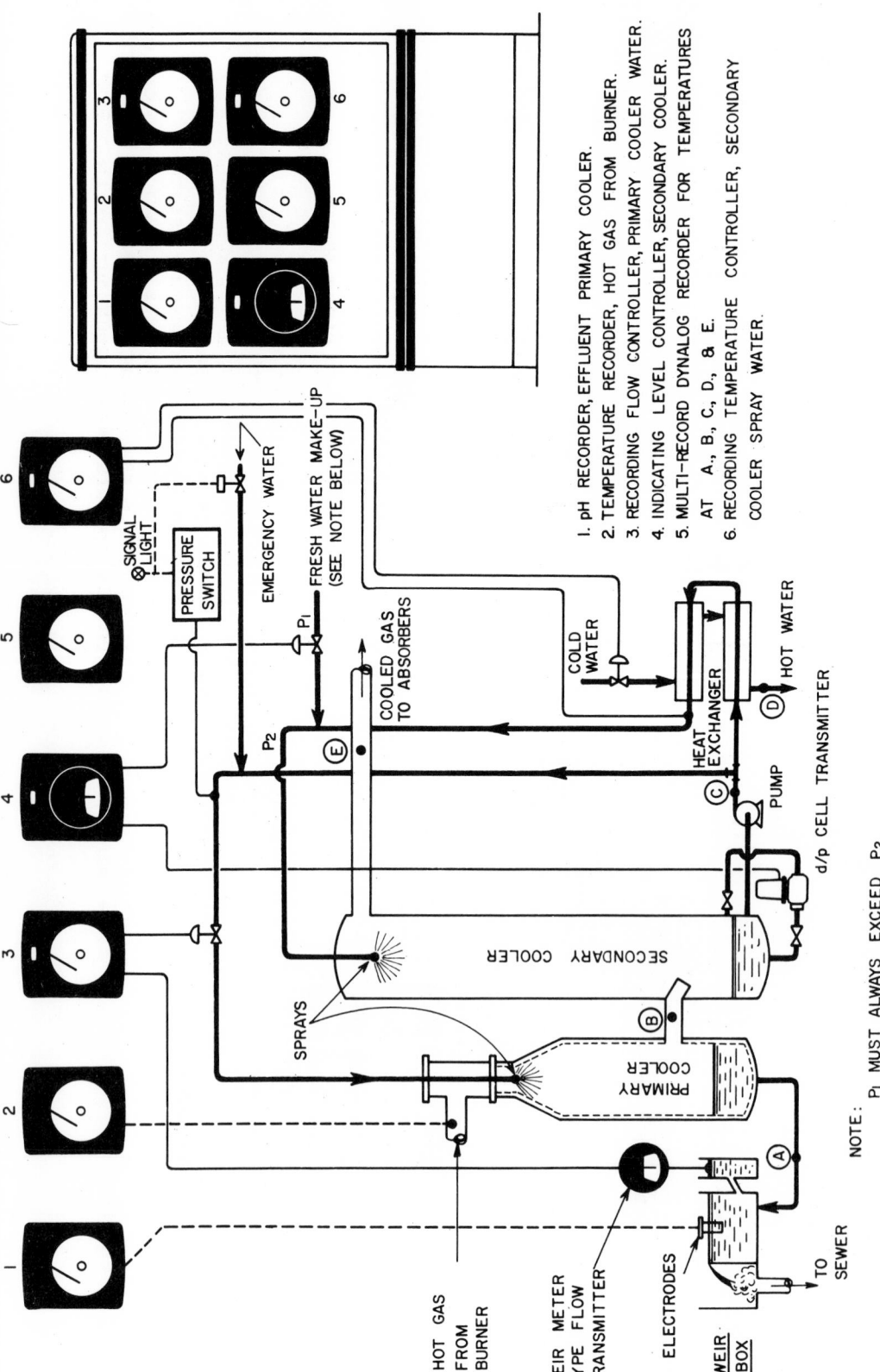

Fig. 15.5. Sulfur dioxide gas cooling system instrumentation. (*Courtesy The Foxboro Co.*)

By using a temperature bulb to sense the level of the storage tank, TIC-2 and V-2 control the amount of molten sulfur delivered. LRC-1 is the burner level control, while TRC-1 controls secondary air by sensing the combustion chamber discharge temperature. GCR-1 is a gas concentration recorder serving as a guide in setting TRC-1.

Figure 15.3 illustrates typical instrumentation for spray type burners. The method of dry sulfur feed is one of several. Combustion air is controlled, and the exit gas is recorded.

In those areas where sulfur bearing ores are readily available, SO_2 may be obtained economically by the Dorrco "Fluosolids" process of roasting the ore. As indicated in Figure 15.4, ore slurry density, slurry feed and bed temperature are controlled. Measurements important to proper operation include windbox air flow, system air pressures, reactor and cyclone temperatures.

Spray-type Gas Coolers

The hot gas leaving the burner is cooled quickly under controlled conditions in order to hold chemical losses to a minimum. The instrumentation is indicated in Figure 15.5. A pH recorder (1) gives a continuous record of the primary cooler effluents. This aids the operator in balancing flows and temperatures to prevent chemical losses which are indicated by an excess of sulfuric acid in the effluent. The temperature recorder (2) serves as a guide to the operation of the sulfur burner. Control of cooling water to the primary cooler is accomplished by flow recording controller (3). Enough water is needed to cool the gas but an excess will form waste acid which is lost in the effluent. A weir type flow transmitter with plastic coated float is used.

An indicating level receiver-controller regulates the amount of make up water to the secondary tower to counteract losses and maintain desired level. The multi-record temperature recorder (5) displays the temperatures at various critical points to enable the operator to maintain proper operating conditions. Temperature controller (6) regulates the heat exchanger cooling water. An emergency tower cooling water supply con-

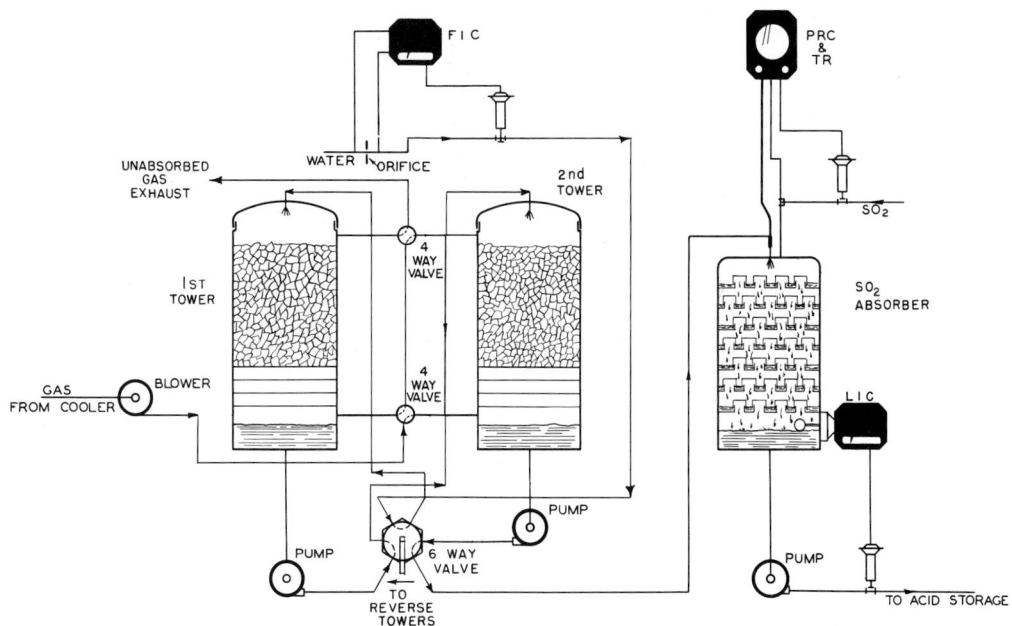

Fig. 15.6. Reversible absorption system for SO_2. (*Courtesy Taylor Instruments Co.*)

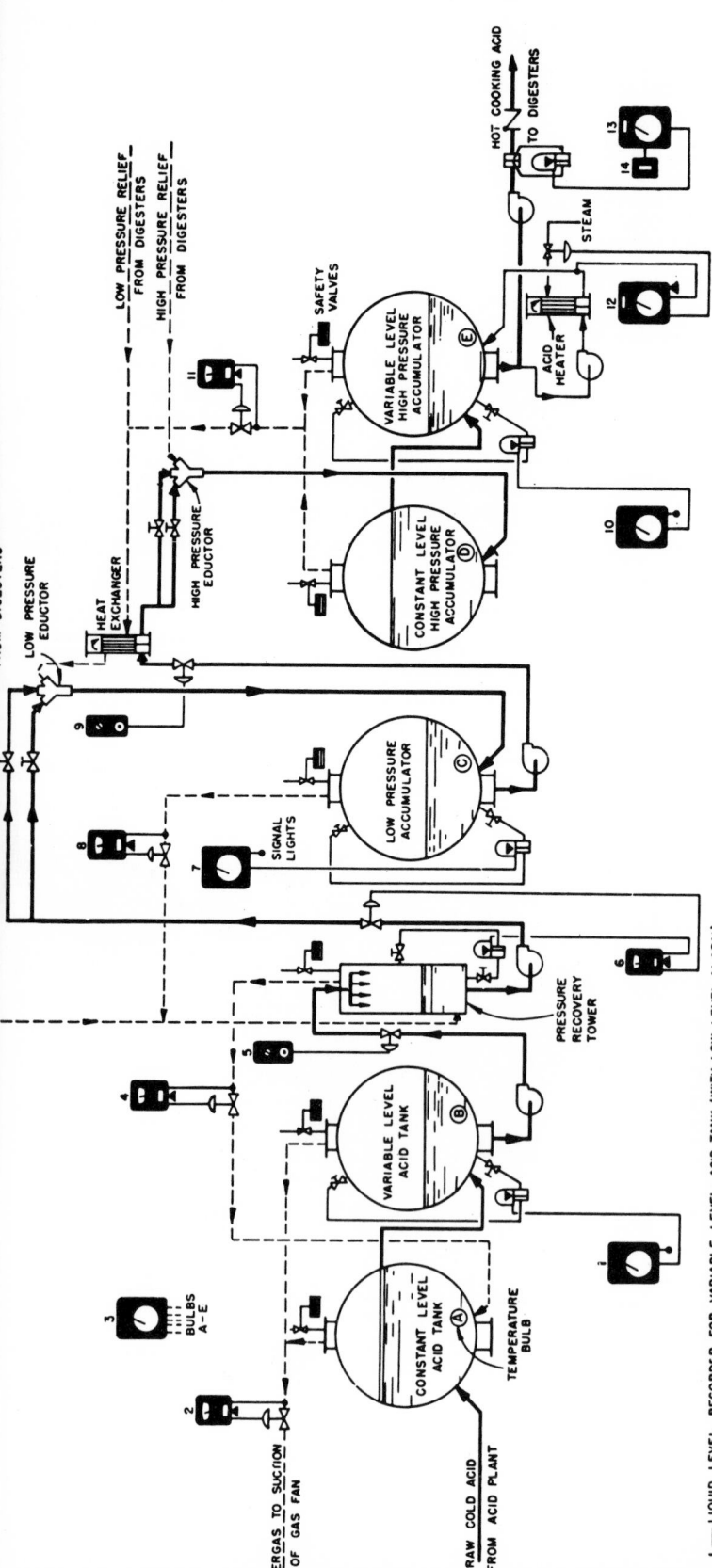

1 — LIQUID LEVEL RECORDER FOR VARIABLE LEVEL ACID TANK (WITH LOW LEVEL ALARM).
2 — INDICATING PRESSURE CONTROLLER-ACID TANKS.
3 — MULTI-RECORD ELECTRONIC TEMPERATURE RECORDER-ACID TANKS, LOW AND HIGH PRESSURE ACCUMULATORS
4 — INDICATING PRESSURE CONTROLLER-PRESSURE RECOVERY TOWER.
5 — REMOTE VALVE OPERATOR FOR ADJUSTING FLOW OF ACID TO PRESSURE RECOVERY TOWER.
6 — INDICATING LIQUID LEVEL CONTROLLER - PRESSURE TOWER.
7 — LIQUID LEVEL RECORDER, LOW PRESSURE ACCUMULATOR WITH LOW LEVEL ALARM.
8 — INDICATING PRESSURE CONTROLLER-LOW PRESSURE ACCUMULATOR.
9 — REMOTE VALVE OPERATOR FOR ADJUSTING FLOW OF ACID FROM LOW TO HIGH PRESSURE ACCUMULATORS.
10 — LIQUID LEVEL RECORDER VARIABLE LEVEL HIGH PRESSURE ACCUMULATOR WITH LOW LEVEL ALARM.
11 — INDICATING PRESSURE CONTROLLER-HIGH PRESSURE ACCUMULATORS.
12 — RECORDING TEMPERATURE CONTROLLER, HIGH PRESSURE ACCUMULATOR REGULATES STEAM TO ACID HEATER.
13 — FLOW RECORDER WITH AUTOMATIC TOTALIZING SHUT-OFF FOR ADDING CONTROLLED AMOUNT OF COOKING ACID TO DIGESTERS.
14 — ACID BATCH SETTING MECHANISM.
ALL ACCUMULATOR AND PRESSURE TOWER LIQUID LEVEL TRANSMITTERS WITH WATER FILLED EXTERNAL LEGS

- - - - GAS LINES
——— ACID LINES
▲ = 20 PSI AIR SUPPLY

Fig. 15.7. Chemipulp system for heat, liquor and SO_2 recovery. (*Courtesy The Foxboro Co.*)

trol is also shown as a safeguard if the normal supply should fail.

Absorption System

Figure 15.6 shows a reversible absorption system using two towers. Gas from the cooler enters the bottom of the towers and rises to the top through the limestone. Weak acid is sprayed in at the top of the first tower. In like manner, the gas, after passing through the first tower, enters the bottom of the second tower and fresh water is sprayed in at the top. The unabsorbed gases exhaust into the air from the second tower. Fresh water flow is controlled by FIC, and although not shown, the temperature should also be controlled. The amount of SO_2 absorbed depends on the pressure and temperature in the absorber. PRC-TR performs this function and can be a ratio pressure controller whose set point can be changed by variations in incoming liquor temperature. LIC is the absorber level control.

Accumulators

Recovery of heat, liquor and SO_2 from the digester relief gas is desirable for efficient operation. A system (chemipulp process) is shown in Figure 15.7. The variables are indicated, recorded or controlled as shown on the diagram.

Sulfite Digesters

Digesters may be classified as direct steaming (with natural or forced circulation) or indirect steaming.

Direct-steaming, natural circulation types tend to give nonuniform results due to steam channeling. Thus, the temperature bulb, which is located in the side of the digester, does not give the average temperature and defeats the purpose of the time schedule controller. Figure 15.8 shows a direct-steaming, forced circulation system. The temperature bulb is located in the re-

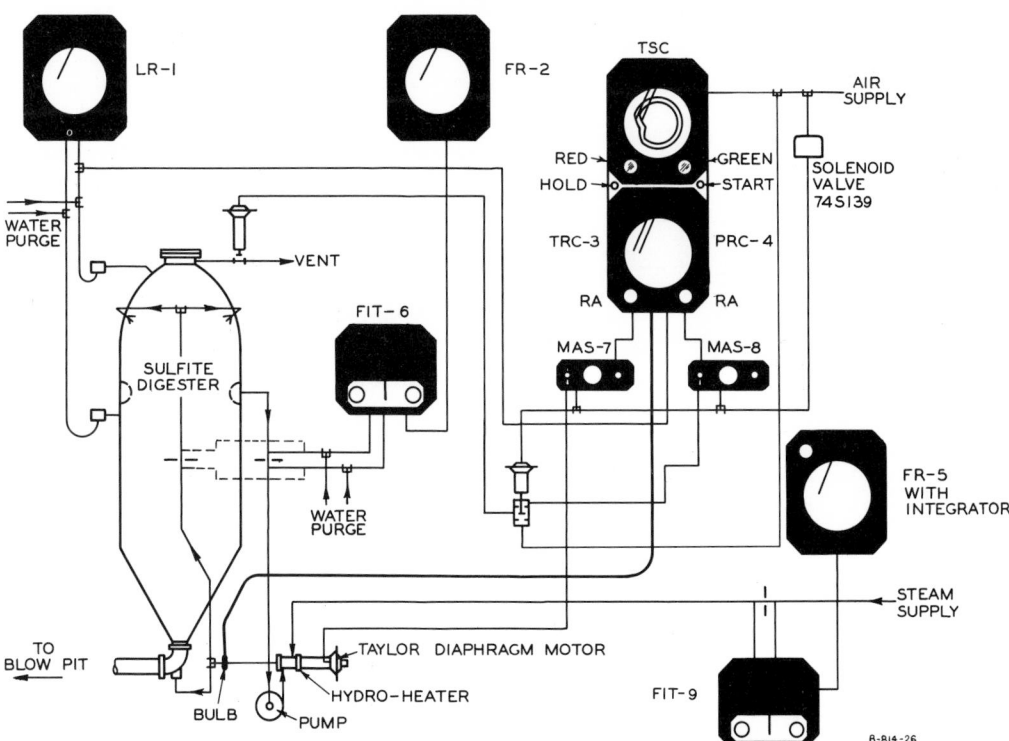

Fig. 15.8. Direct steaming forced-circulation system for sulfite. (*Courtesy Taylor Instrument Co.*)

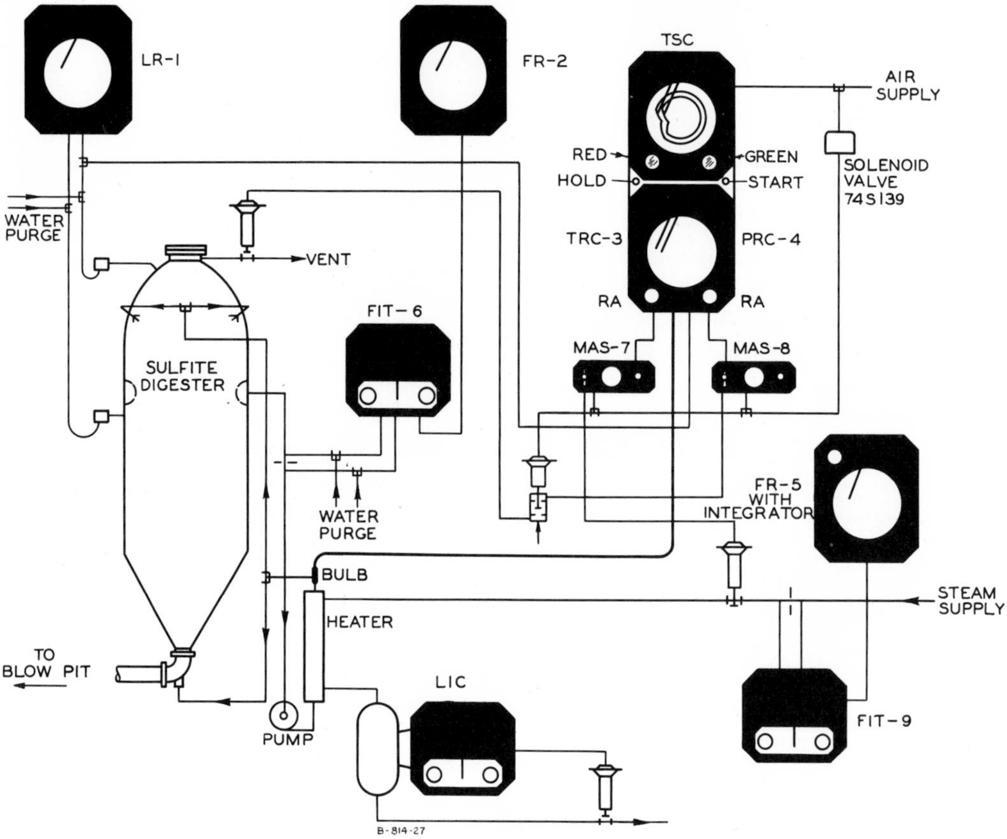

Fig. 15.9. Indirect-heating digester system for sulfite. (*Courtesy Taylor Instrument Co.*)

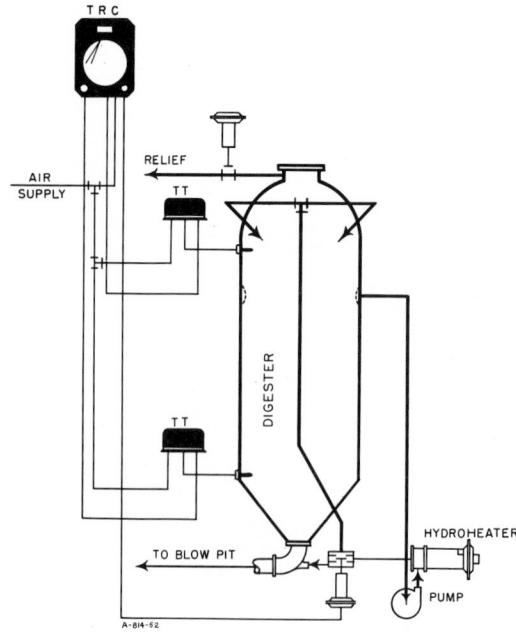

Fig. 15.10. Temperature equalization method for sulfite digesters. (*Courtesy Taylor Instrument Co.*)

circulating line, thus providing a more representative temperature of the cook. As indicated on the diagram, instrumentation includes digester level (LR-1) to indicate when the digester is full and for liquor draw-off purposes. Liquor circulation flow is recorded (FIT-6, FR-2) for a check on performance. Plugged strainers can be readily detected. Steam flow is recorded and integrated. The steaming controls are the time schedule type, and pressure is controlled by venting.

An indirect-heating digester system is shown in Figure 15.9. This system has the advantage of not diluting the cook. The controls are conventional. However, FIT-6 could well be of the Magnetic Flowmeter type, and a conductivity measurement of the heat exchanger condensate may be used to detect tube leakage and by means of a three-way valve automatically dump the condensate into a sewer. Even with forced

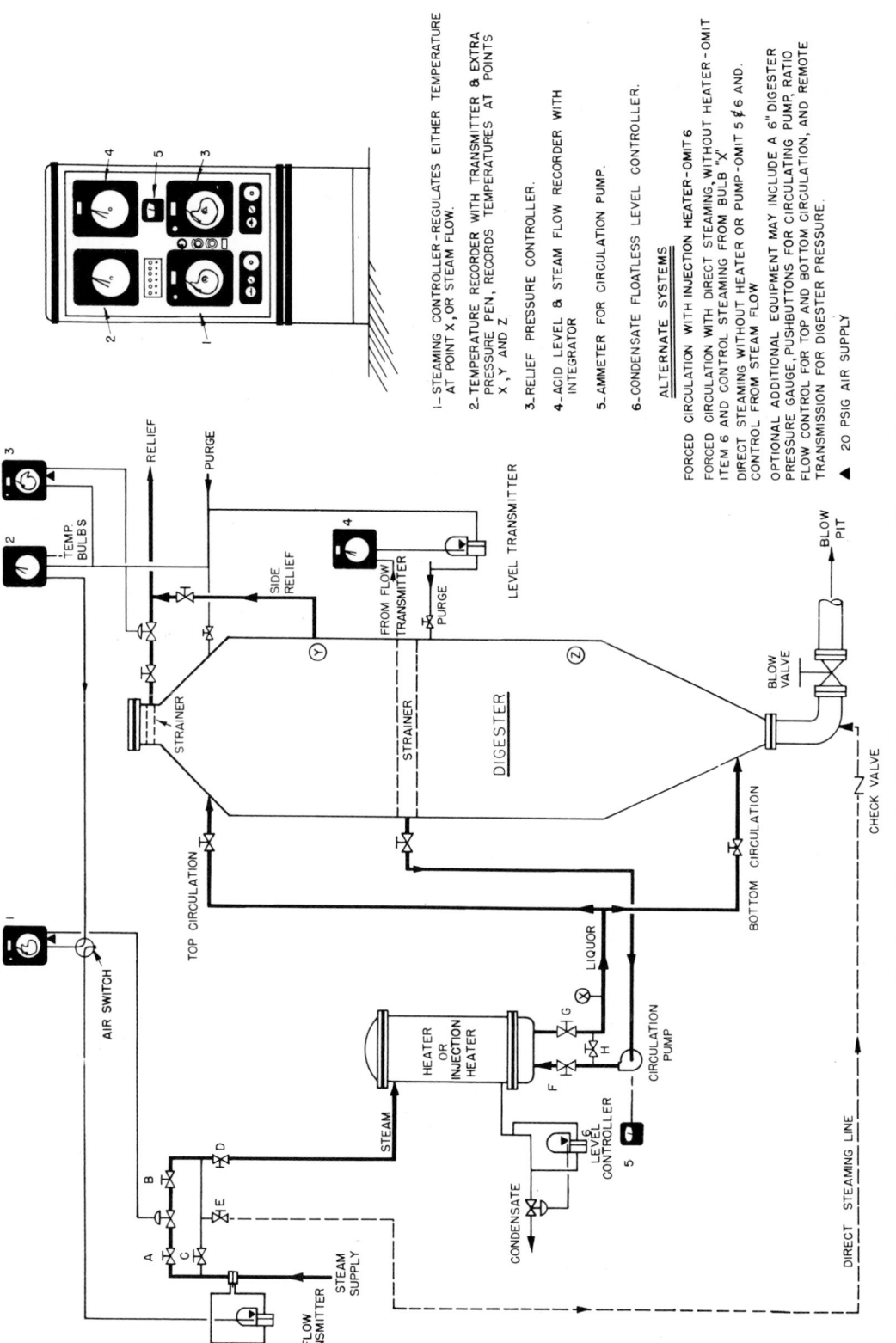

Fig. 15.11. Universal sulfite digester control systems. (*Courtesy The Foxboro Co.*)

circulation it has been found that the temperature distribution in the digester is not always uniform.

Figure 15.10 shows a method of equalization by use of top and bottom temperature transmitters. The output of each is connected to receiver bellows and one side of a differential bellows. The receiver records the top and bottom temperatures while the differential records the difference between top and bottom. The control mechanism is actuated by the differential temperatures and throttles the three-way valve.

Figure 15.11 is a universal sulfite digester control system which provides extreme flexibility. The digester may be operated as direct or indirect steaming. When operating on forced circulation, indirect heating, the steam flow is controlled by instrument No.

1. The temperature is measured at point "X" by instrument No. 2 which transmits the measurement signal to No. 1 through the air switch. Temperatures at points "Y" and "Z" are recorded on No. 2. Instrument No. 3 is a pressure controller and operates the relief valve. This allows more SO_2 recovery through controlled relief. Instrument No. 4 records liquor level as a guide to side relief and also records and totalizes steam flow. Instrument No. 5 indicates the recirculating pump load and No. 6 controls the heater condensate discharge.

On direct steaming, control is switched to "steam flow" by turning the air switch from "temperature" to "steam flow" and changing cans. Thus, Instrument No. 1 will control the steam flow on a predetermined schedule.

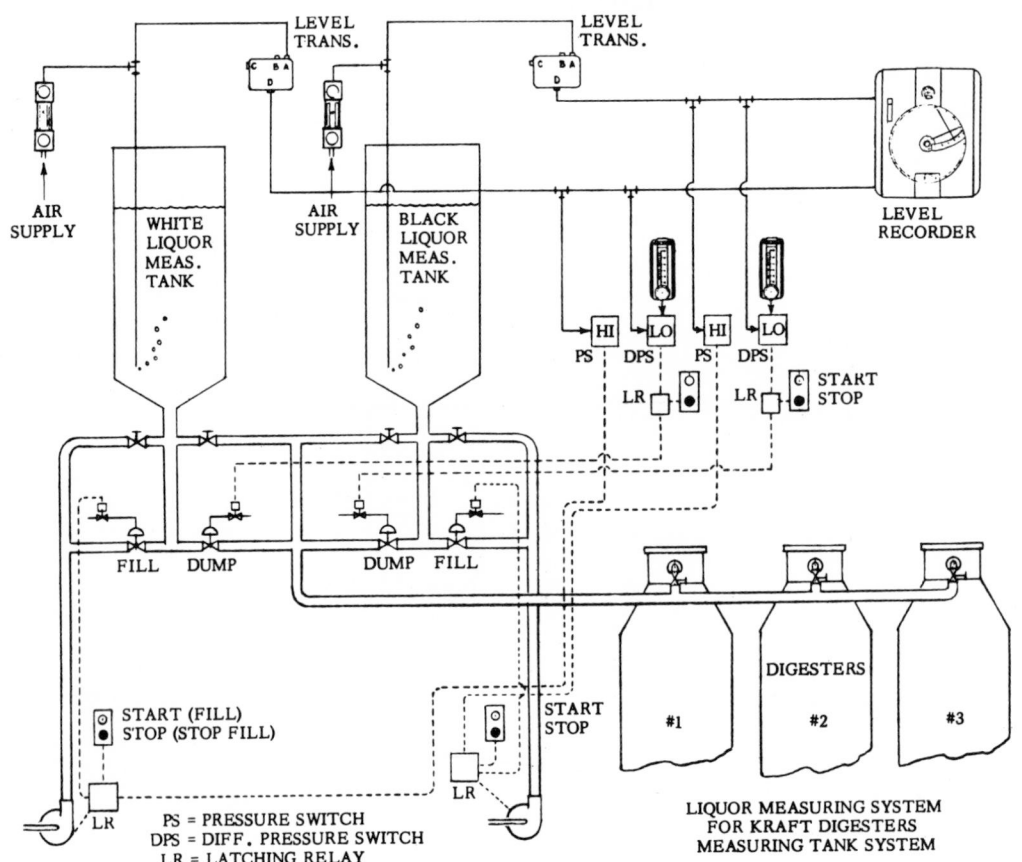

Fig. 15.12. Automatic batch system for kraft digesters. (*Courtesy Bailey Meter Co.*)

THE ALKALINE PROCESS *

It is customary to use white liquor from the recovery process and black liquor, in the proper ratio, to make up the cooking liquor charge to the digester. This can be done by several methods: automatic measuring tanks or flow ratio.

Figure 15.12 illustrates an automatically batched system. Each tank is identical in operation. The operator, starting with full tanks sets the desired quantity required on the manual loader and pushes the "start" button. The manual loader is connected to one side of a differential pressure switch and the liquid level signal from the level transmitter is connected to the other side. The "start" button opens the dump valve of the measuring tank and is held open by

* See Chapter **7** for additional details of the alkaline process.

the latching relay. When the tank level has reached the preset level, the signal from the level transmitter equals the manual loaded signal, and the differential pressure switch trips the latching relay, closing the dump valve. To refill the tank, the pump starter button is pushed, the fill valve opens, and the tank fills until the preset level pressure switch trips the latching relay, stopping the pump and closing the fill valve. Selection of the digester to be filled can be done remotely by using solenoid air valves to operate the pneumatic digester valves.

Figure 15.13 shows a flow ratio method of liquor charging. This system permits the operator to set the desired quantity of white liquor necessary for the cook and then to set the corresponding ratio of black liquor to make up the charge. The control system then admits the primary liquor until an integrated contact in the recorder sends

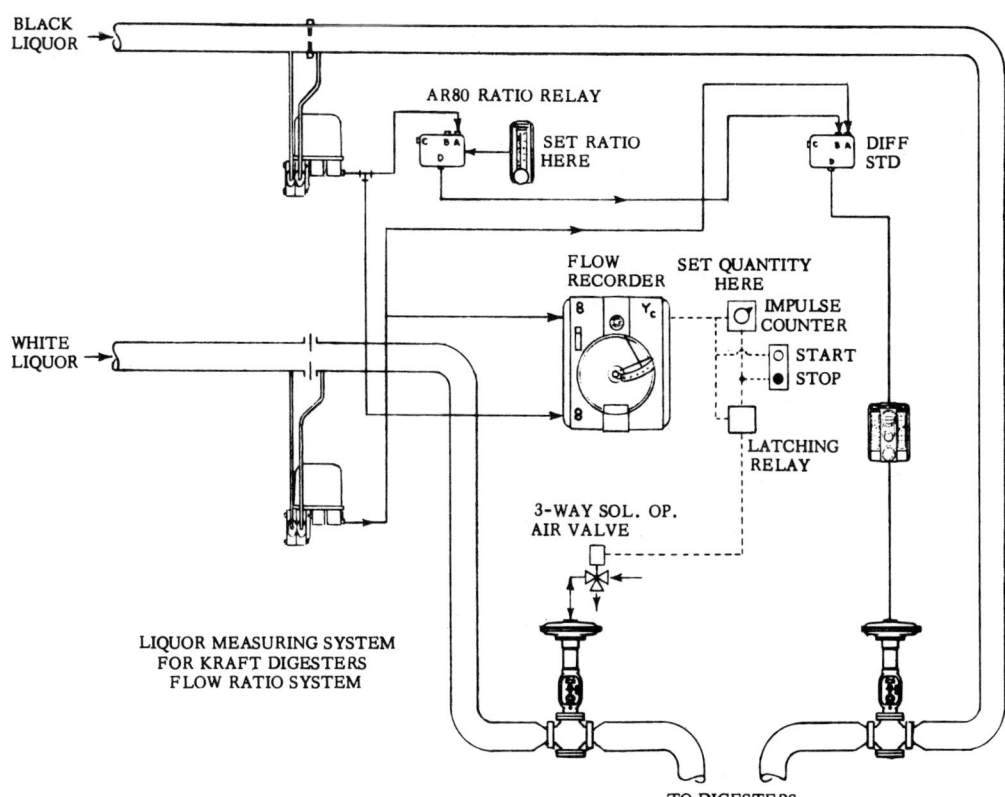

Fig. 15.13.   Flow ratio method of liquor charging. (*Courtesy Bailey Meter Co.*)

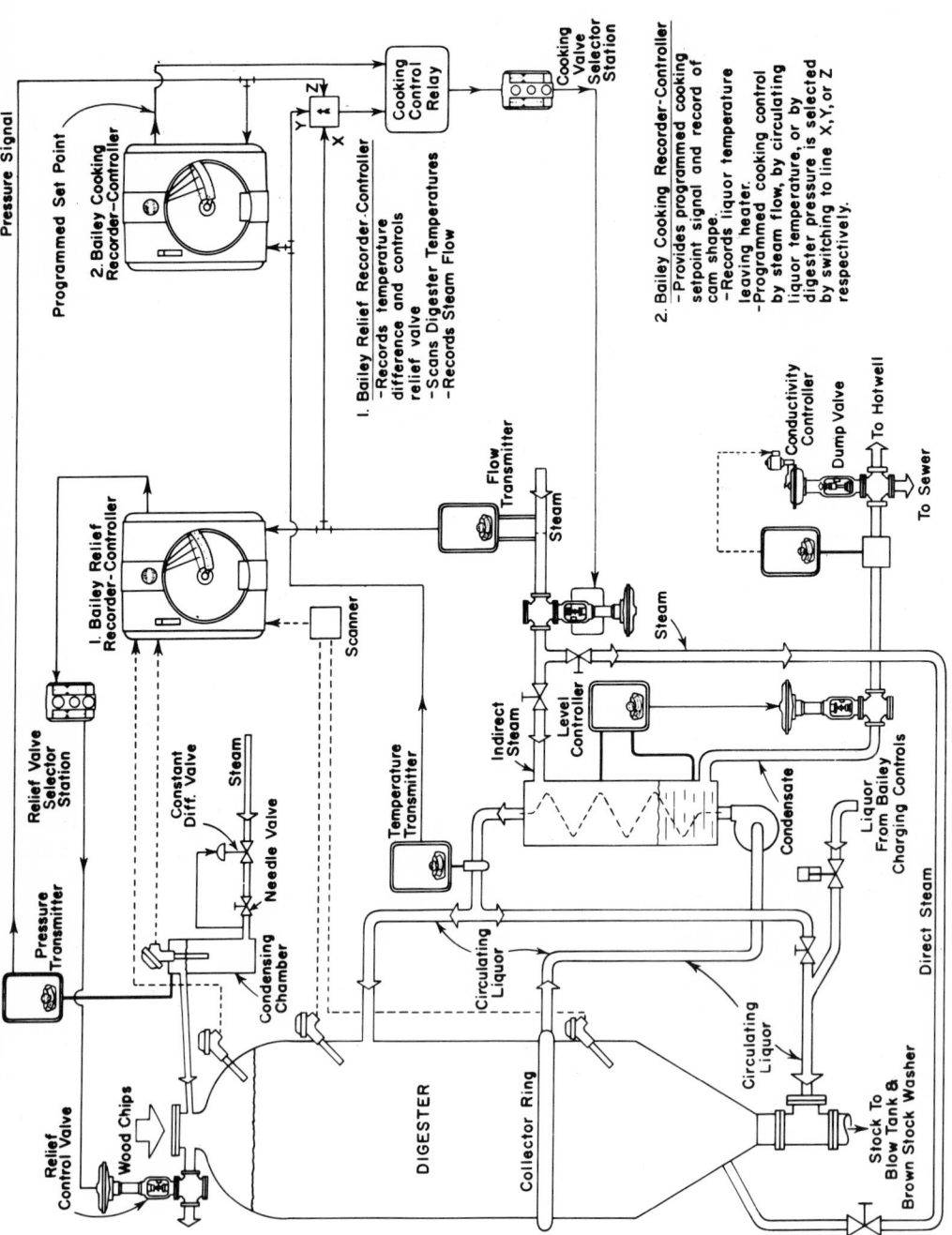

Fig. 15.14. Indirect-heated digester controls. (*Courtesy Bailey Meter Co.*)

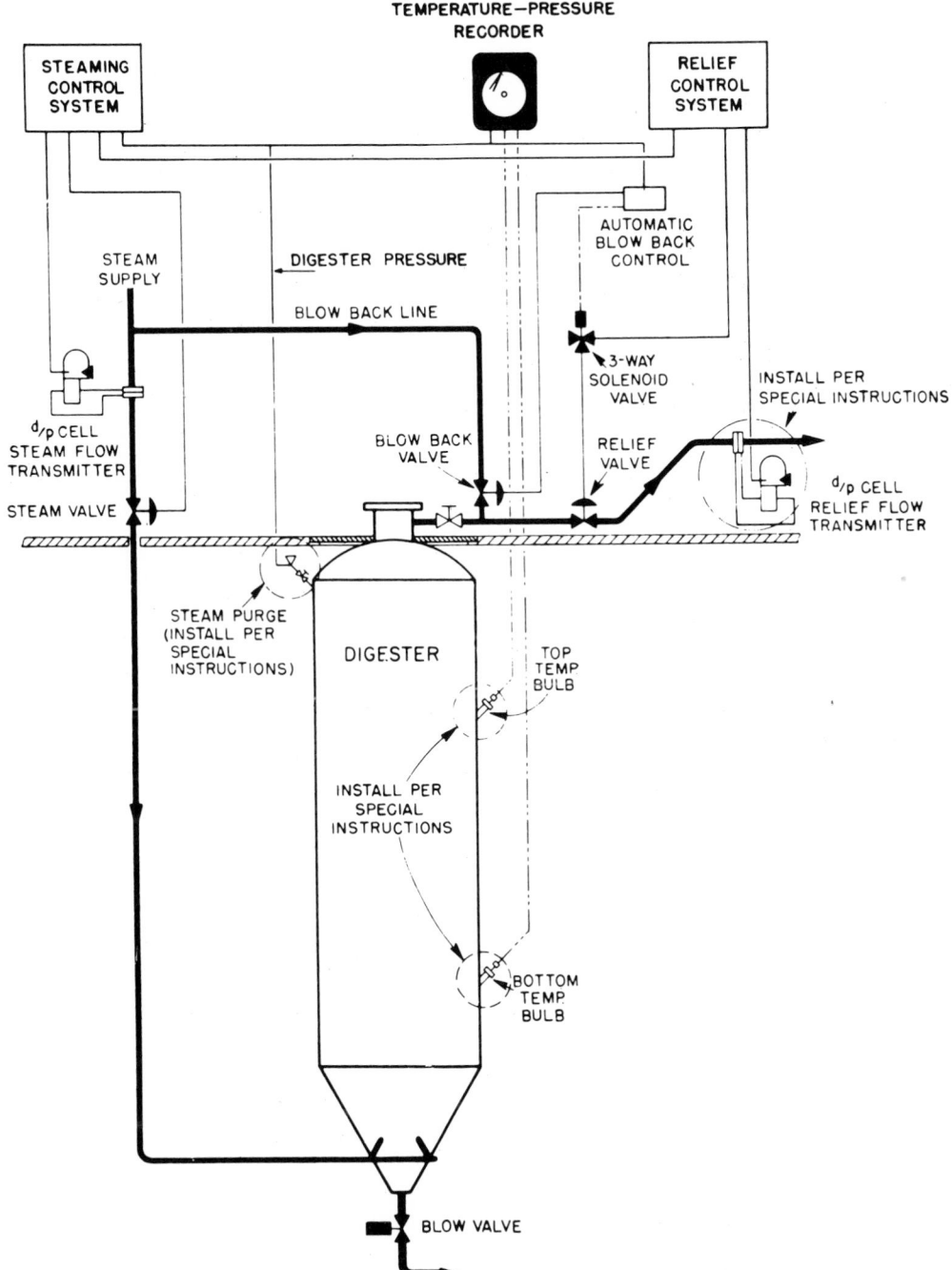

Fig. 15.15. Kraft digester relief control. (*Courtesy The Foxboro Co.*)

the required impulses to an impulse counter (each impulse represents a certain number of gallons) which causes the valve to close. If pumps are required, additional controls are necessary to start and stop the pumps.

An alternate system, using two sets of flow measuring equipment and associated components would permit simultaneous control of both liquors.

Alkaline Digesters

Digester control for alkaline pulping processes is similar to that used in sulfite pulping. Although direct steaming is in wide use, present day practice is toward the indirect method. This not only facilitates control, but eliminates dilution of the cook. Obviously more uniform cooking results, and there will be less load on the evaporator portion of the recovery system. Figure 15.14 illustrates an indirect heated digester which also can be operated as direct heating. The temperature of the liquor leaving the heater is used for control purposes. Temperature measurements at the digester side walls are used to indicate temperature distribution in the digester. The purpose of the various instruments is clearly noted on the diagram.

The relief system is of the differential temperature type. The digester total pressure is converted to equivalent steam temperature theoretically expected in the dome by placing a temperature element in a condensing chamber purged with steam. Since water is present in the condensing chamber, the chamber takes up the desired saturated temperature equivalent to the total of all partial pressures in the dome. Thus, if the actual dome temperature is noted to be below this figure, it is known that noncondensable gases are present. This system of relief offers simplicity in operation and maintenance.

Another method of relief control is shown in Figure 15.15. A flow controller regulates the flow of relief gases at a rate such that liquor pull-over is negligible. This is accomplished by the control mechanism which

changes the rate of flow of the relief gases inversely to the change in rate of steam flow to the digester. As the relief valve opening for any given rate of relief flow depends on (1) digester pressure, (2) the amount of screen plugging and (3) the back pressure in the relief header, this system automatically positions the relief valve correctly for any combination of these variables. Automatic blow back is also incorporated as a part of the control system.

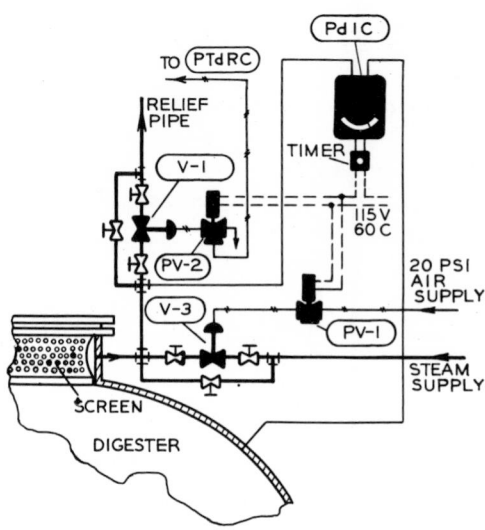

Fig. 15.16. Blow-back controls for pulp digester. (*Courtesy The Bristol Co.*)

Figure 15.16 shows a method of blow-back control that can be incorporated into any system not so equipped. A differential pressure controller measures the dome pressure and the relief line pressure. Thus, by measuring the pressure drop across the screen during relief, screen plugging is readily detected. When the pressure differential rises to a value found to indicate a plugged screen, a contact in the controller (PDIC) closes and operates solenoid valves PV-1 and PV-2. These valves control the air pressure to control valves V-1 and V-3, closing the relief valve V-1 and opening the blow back valve V-3. A timer holds this condition for a predetermined time until the screen is clean and the foam is settled. At the end of this time, normal operation is automatically resumed. The air line marked "To PT & RC" is the control line from the relief controller.

Continuous Digesters

In the past ten years much progress has been made in the continuous digestion of wood chips. Many mills have converted from the batch to the continuous method.

Figure 15.17 illustrates the instrumentation applied to one of several methods available (chemipulp). The chips are forced by screw feed into the preheating chamber where the cooking chemicals and steam are introduced. The compressed chips rapidly absorb the steam and chemicals. From this point the chips are conveyed through a series of reaction chambers by feed screws. Uniform cooking and mixing is thus obtained.

Steam pressure to the first reaction chamber is recorded and controlled and the temperature is recorded by the dual instrument PRC-TR. The pressure indicating controller PIC is a safety measure to prevent steam blowback past the preheated feed screw and into the chip bin by operating Solenoid Valve No. 8 which shuts off the steam supply.

Steam flow is measured and integrated by the combination of flow indicating transmitter FIT and recorder integrated FRI. Speeds of the feed screw and the reaction chamber screws are measured by tachrometer generators whose outputs are recorded on a dual pen speed recorder.

Figure 15.18 shows another approach to continuous digestion. It is completely automatic and employs the conveyor principle to carry the chips through the vessel. This provides sequential cooking combinations

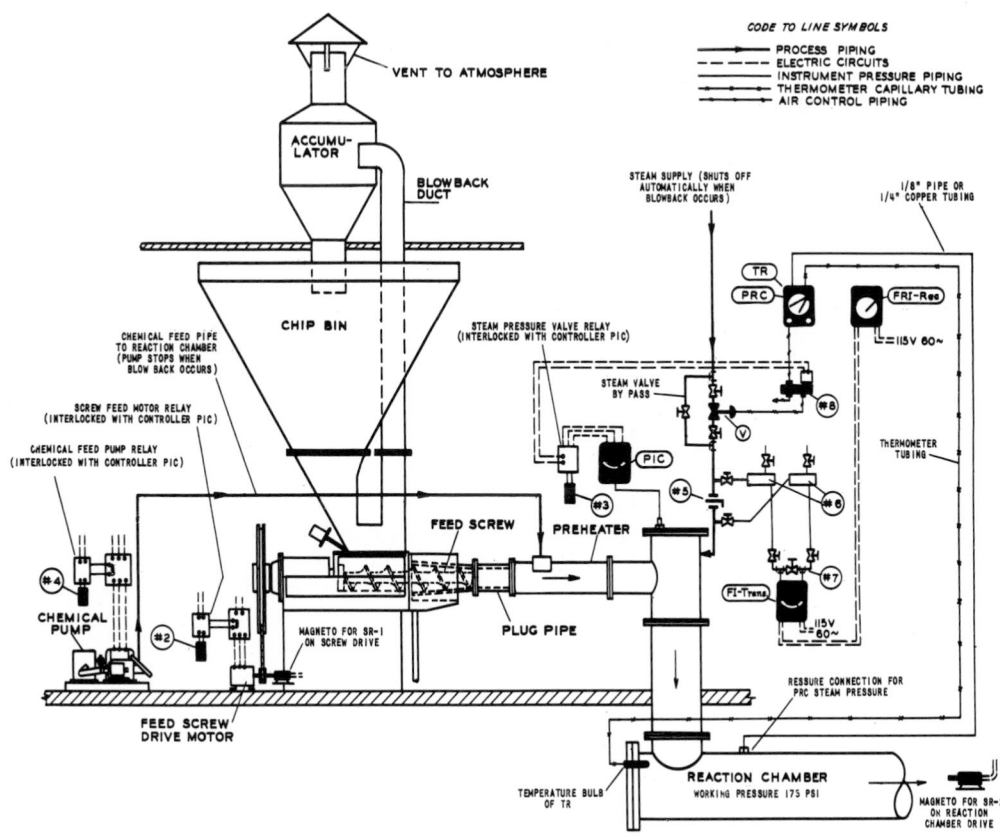

Fig. 15.17. Continuous digester controls. (*Courtesy The Bristol Co.*)

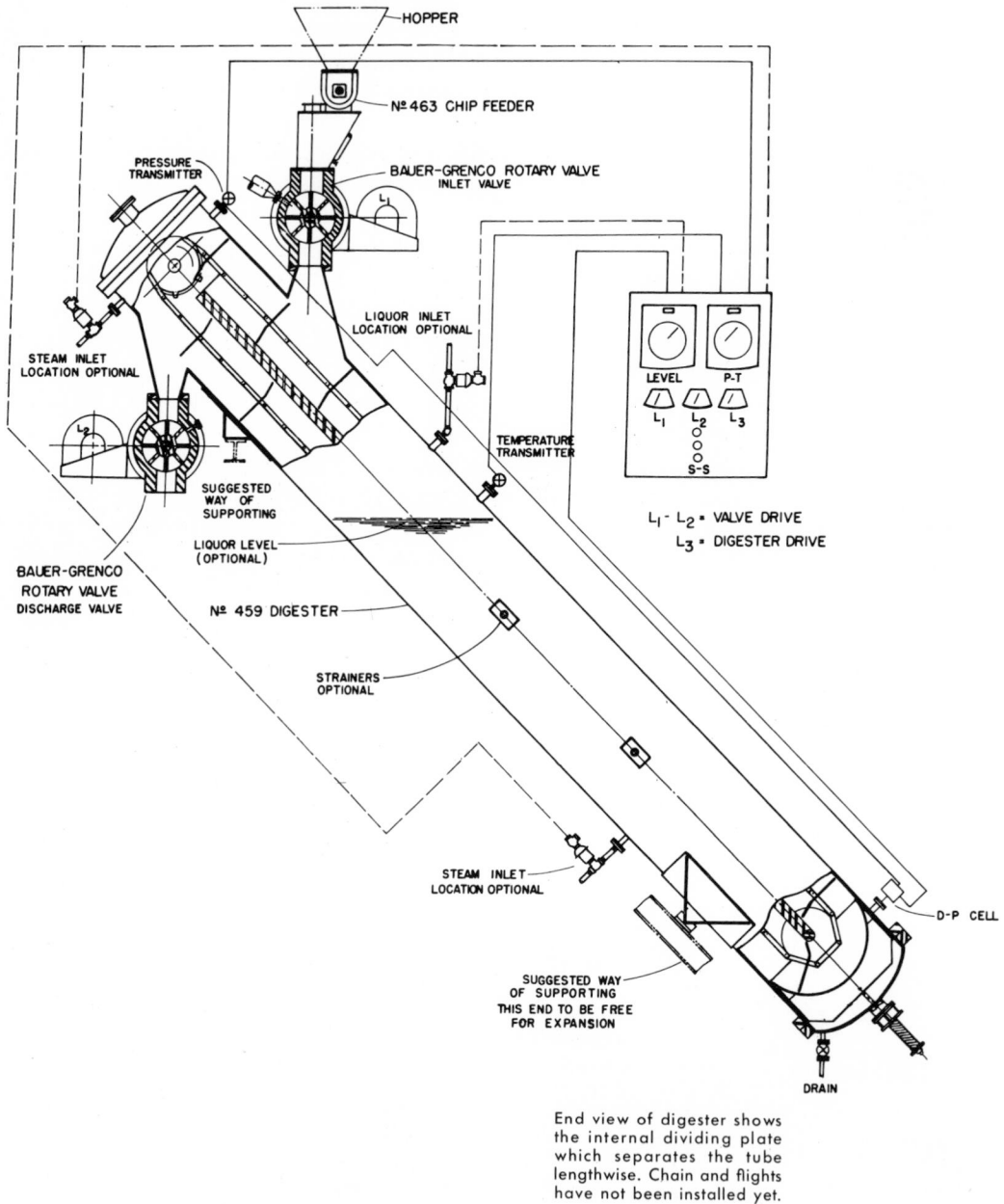

End view of digester shows
the internal dividing plate
which separates the tube
lengthwise. Chain and flights
have not been installed yet.

Fig. 15.18. Continuous digester controls. (*Courtesy The Bauer Bros. Co.*)

integrated into zones for steaming, impregnating, and vapor phase cooking in the same vessel. Single phase or wide range variation of the three cooking combinations is possible. Both temperature and pressure are recorded and controlled by the dual instrument (P-T). Vessel level is recorded and controlled by a separate instrument. Note the use of transmitters for temperature and pressure and the differential-pressure cell for level. Although not shown, the complete installation would also include make up liquor flow control which is tied into the chip feed rate. Thus, liquor flow would be automatically changed by a change in feed rate.

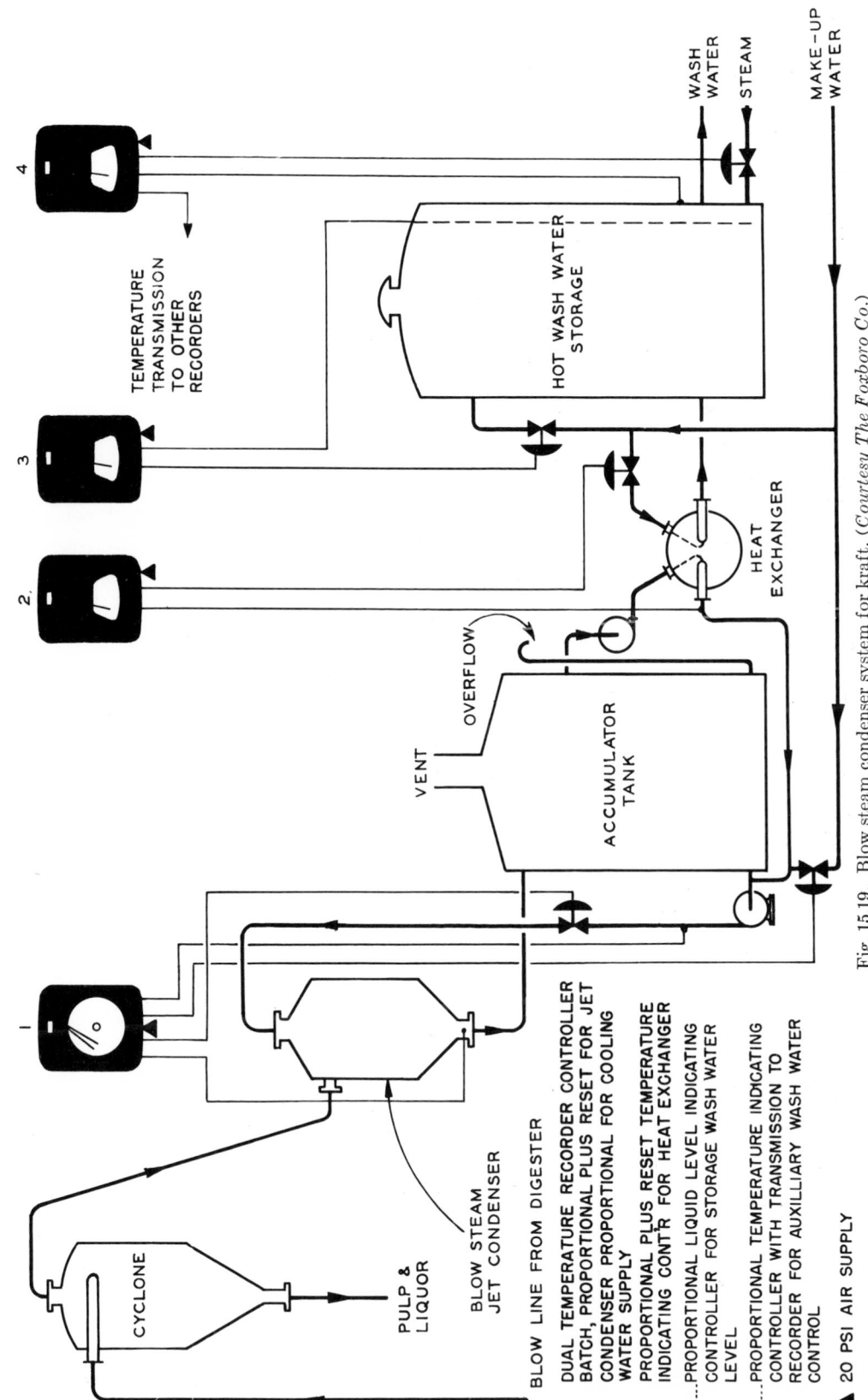

Fig. 15.19. Blow steam condenser system for kraft. (*Courtesy The Foxboro Co.*)

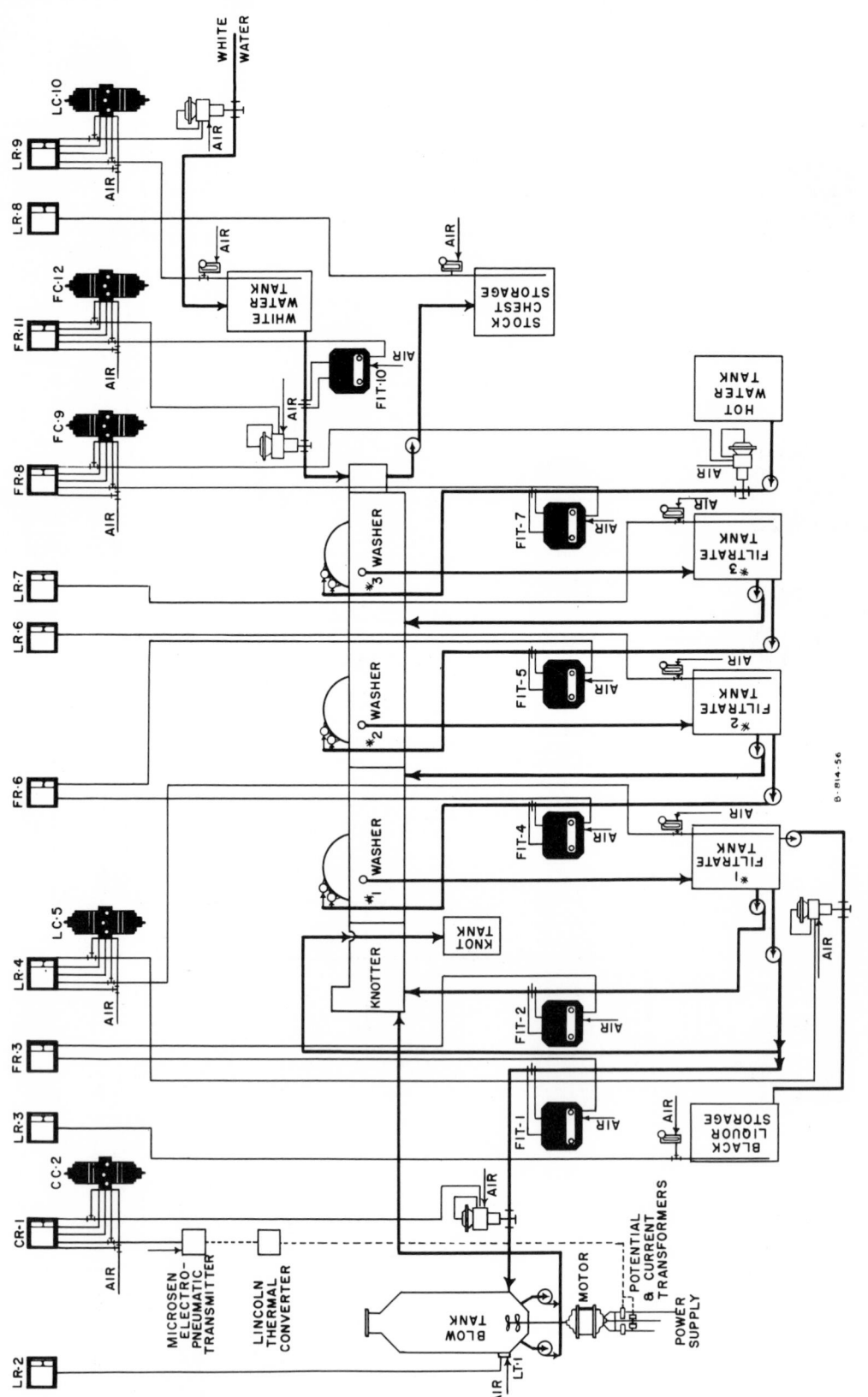

Fig. 15.20. Stock washing control system for kraft pulp. (*Courtesy Taylor Instrument Co.*)

Heat Recovery

In order to recover maximum heat from the digester blows, a system such as indicated in Figure 15.19 is employed. One bulb of the dual temperature instrument (No. 1) is located in the outlet of the jet condenser. When this bulb senses the blow heat steam, the condenser water valve is opened rapidly. The second bulb of this dual unit (No. 1) measures the water from the accumulator tank. If the water is too hot, a valve in the make up water line is opened. Temperature controlled No. 2 measures the accumulator outlet water temperature from the heat exchanger and regulates the flow of clean cold make up water to attain maximum heat recovery. Level controller No. 3 maintains the storage water level at a desired level regardless of the wash water demand. Temperature recorder No. 4 provides auxiliary heating if the demand exceeds the capacity of the blow steam system.

Brown Stock Washing

Efficient washing is necessary for removal of all traces of liquor and impurities from the pulp. If the pulp is to be bleached, thorough washing reduces the amount of bleaching agent required. When the liquor is to be recovered, removal of as much liquor as possible with a minimum of dilution is necessary in order to reduce the evaporator load.

As may be noted in Figure 15.20, the consistency of the stock from the blow tank is controlled by CR-1 and CC-2. Levels in the black liquor storage tank, the No. 1 filtrate tank, and the white water tank are controlled as shown. Level recorders are used on the remaining tanks and stock storage chest. Flows from the hot water tank and white water tank are controlled while the flows from the filtrate tank to the preceding stages are recorded. Miniature instruments (recorders) are shown here using the transmitter-receiver-controller combination.

Evaporators

Efficient multiple effect evaporator operation requires proper instrumentation. Due to variations in design and operating characteristics, each installation should be individually engineered to assure continuous and smooth operation.

Figure 15.21 illustrates a sextuple effect unit with suggested instrumentation. Effects 3 and 4 have been omitted for reasons of space limitation. Temperature recorder TR-1 is a multi-point strip chart recorder

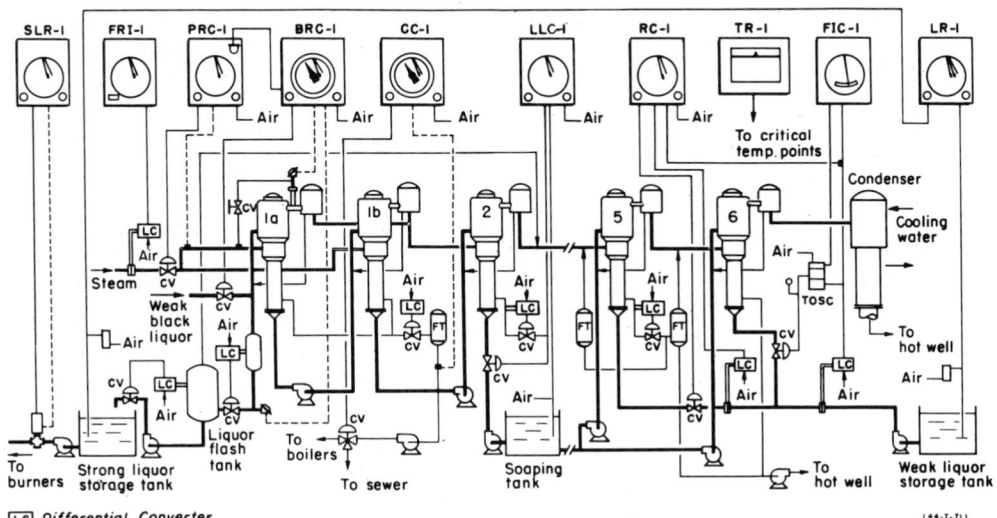

LC Differential Converter

Fig. 15.21. Multiple-effect evaporator. (*Courtesy Minneapolis-Honeywell*)

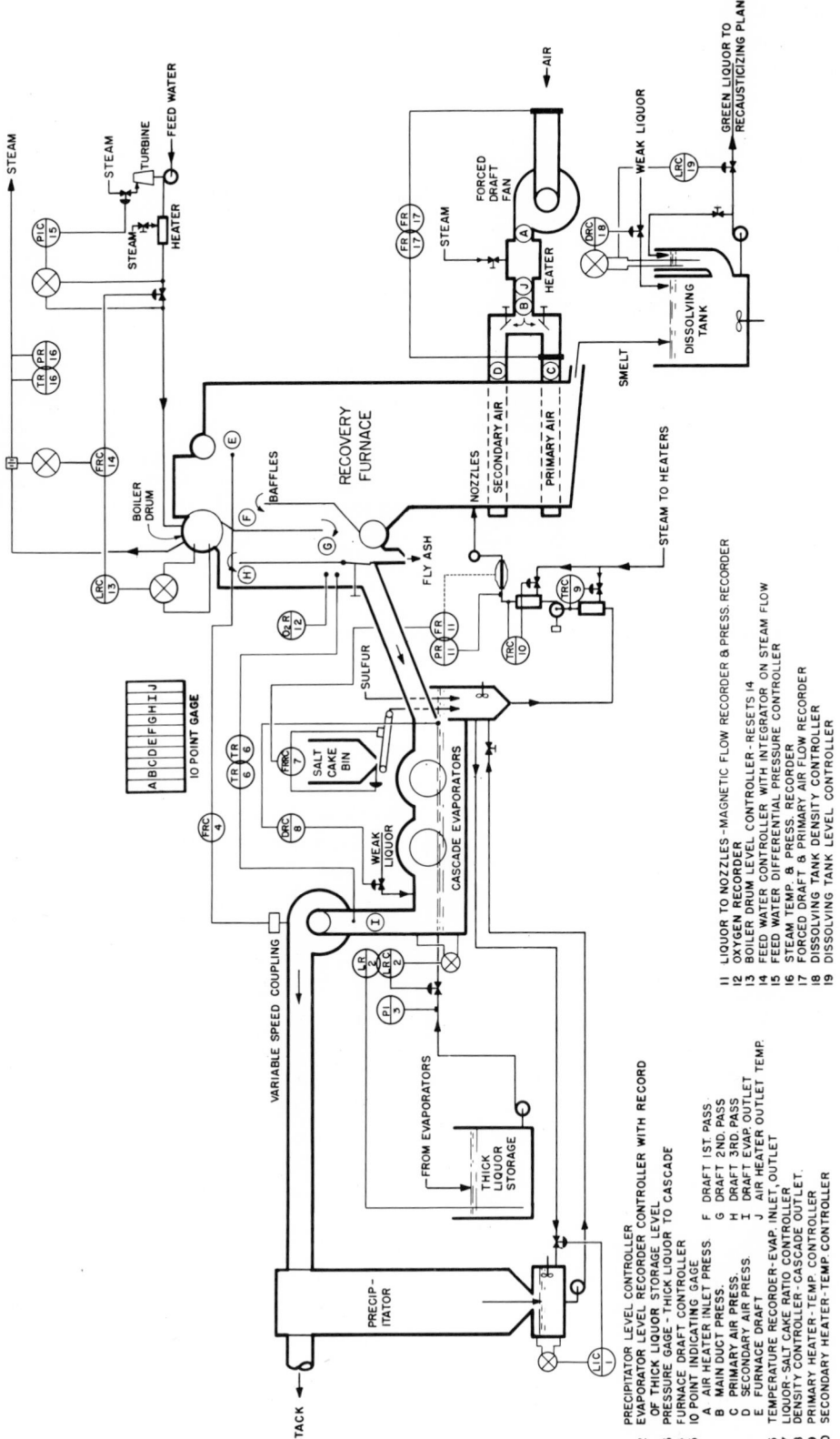

Fig. 15.22. Recovery furnace and cascade evaporation control system. (*Courtesy The Foxboro Co.*)

which measures the temperature at various points throughout the system. These include temperatures of the feed liquor, water to the condenser, water in the hot well, liquor and steam in each effect. The concentration recorder-controller BRC-1 measures the boiling point rise in the first effect and resets the steam pressure controller PRC-1 accordingly to keep the strong black liquor at the desired concentration; it also positions a control valve to admit weak black liquor should the concentration be too high. Flow controller, FRI-1, records and totals the steam flow to the evaporator. FIC-1 indicates, controls, and integrates the flow of weak black liquor to the evaporator. RC-1 is a ratio controller for black liquor flow which controls the ratio of liquor flowing through effects 4 and 5 and is reset by the main liquor flow controller (FIC-1). SLR-1 is the strong liquor flow recorder, recording the flow of strong liquor to the recovery furnaces. LR-1 is a two-pen level recorder showing levels in the strong and weak storage tanks. LLC-1 controls the level in the soap tank. CC-1 is a condensate conductivity controller which diverts the condensate to the sewer if contamination occurs. Differential converter transmitters (LC) are used as non-indicating controllers in the downleg condensate lines to insure liquid in the lines and prevent blowouts.

Recovery System

Figure 15.22 illustrates a typical recovery furnace and cascade evaporator control system. Black liquor from the evaporators is fed into the cascade evaporator where hot furnace gases are used to increase the Baumé of the liquor to the furnace nozzles. Precipitator tank level controller (1) admits the proper amount of liquor to dissolve the dust precipitated from the stack cases. A dual pen recorder-controller (2) maintains proper level in the cascade evaporator and records thick liquor storage level. A ratio recorder-controller (7) maintains the optimum ratio between liquor flow to the nozzles and salt cake addition. Proper Baumé of the liquor

leaving the evaporator is maintained by a density controller (8) which varies the addition of weak liquor. The dissolving tank density is controlled similarly. Liquor temperature to the nozzles is controlled and the rate of flow is manually adjusted by varying the liquor pump speed. Other instruments necessary for efficient boiler operation are noted on the diagram.

Recausticizing

Instrumentation plays an important part in the recovery of the process chemicals. A continuous recausticizing system for the kraft process is shown in Figure 15.23. The raw green liquor storage tank is level controlled by LR-1 as is the flow to the green liquor clarifier (FRC-1). TRC-1 controls the temperature of the green liquor to the slaker. Flow of white liquor to storage is recorded and integrated and storage tank levels are recorded (FR-2, LR-3). Wash water temperature and flows are controlled (TRC-2, FRC-3, FRC-4). The level of the lime mud filter is controlled by bleeding air into the suction of the vacuum pump.

Lime Recovery and Lime Kiln

Figure 15.24 illustrates a system for lime recovery. Temperature recorder controller TRC maintains optimum wash water temperature by controlling steam to a heat exchanger in the heating tank. The level in the lime mud washer is recorded by LR. Control of lime mud wetness (for proper kiln operation) is controlled by LRC. This instrument controls the level in the filter by varying the amount of vacuum to the filter. Speed is also recorded as an aid to adjusting the filter to the capacity of the kiln.

Basic instrumentation for the rotary lime kiln is shown in Figure 15.25. Kiln temperature is sensed by a radiation type detector and recorder by a high speed recorder (TR). This permits the operator to maintain optimum fuel flow at all times. A furnace pressure controller (PIC) indicates and controls the draft within the kiln through damper operator (M). A speed recorder (SR) pro-

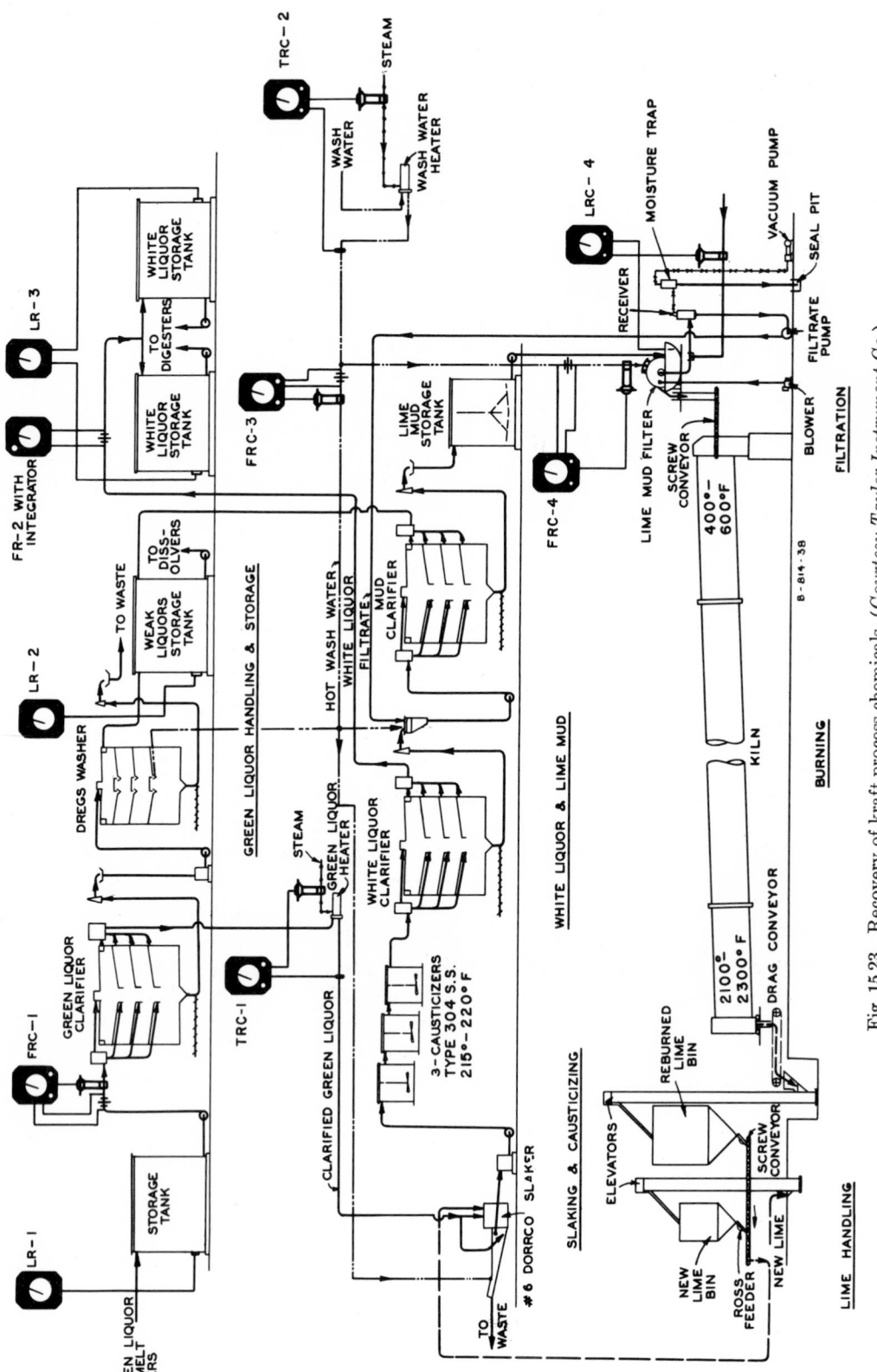

Fig. 15.23. Recovery of kraft process chemicals. (*Courtesy Taylor Instrument Co.*)

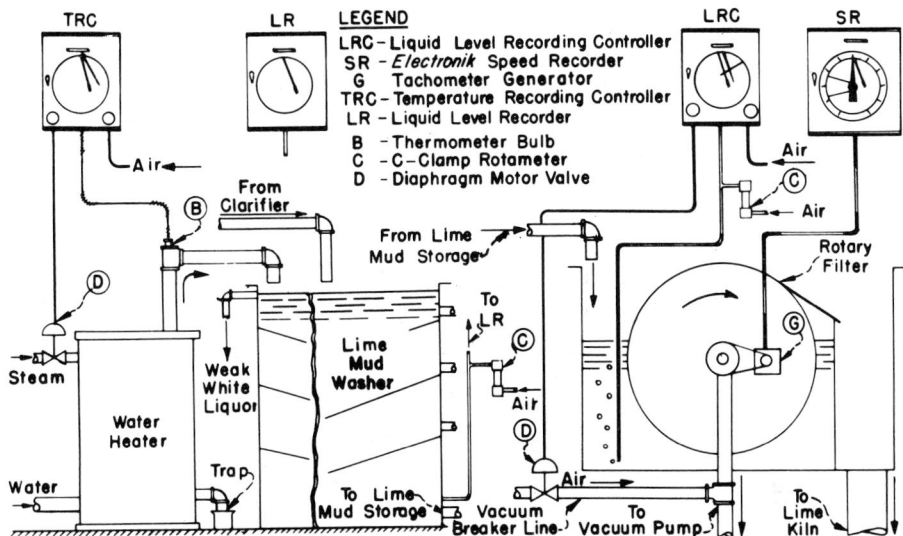

Fig. 15.24. Control system for lime recovery. (*Courtesy Minneapolis-Honeywell*)

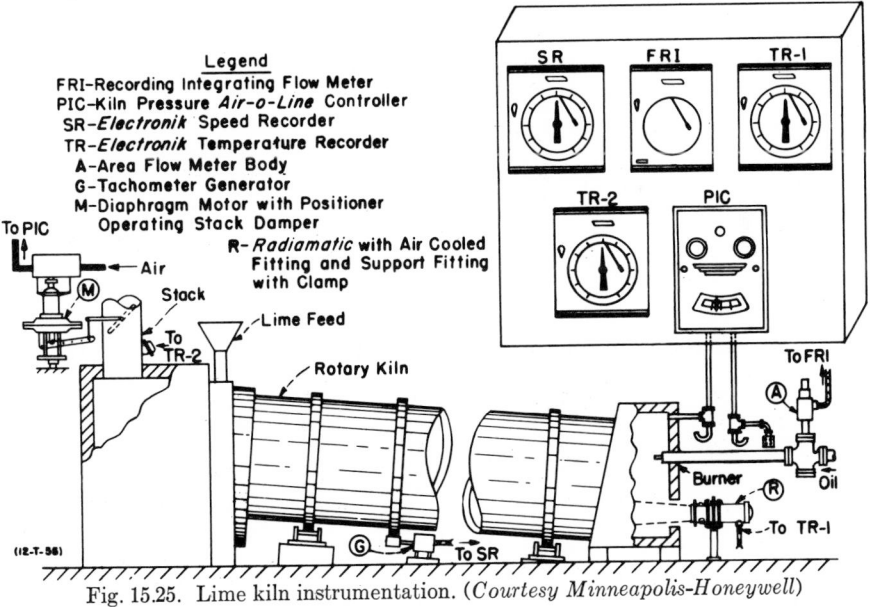

Fig. 15.25. Lime kiln instrumentation. (*Courtesy Minneapolis-Honeywell*)

vides the operator with adequate means of controlling the relationship between kiln temperature and the time the lime is subjected to temperature.

The Flow Meter (FRI) records and integrates the fuel to the burner. An area type meter may be used for oil and a differential type for gas. Figure 15.26 shows a similar system with the addition of an oxygen analyzer, primary air flow recorder and additional draft indication.

Bleaching

It is impossible to include in this chapter all of the bleaching processes in use today. The three stage system as shown in Figure 15.27 is perhaps most typical. The instrumentation is clearly noted on the diagram and includes those which are necessary for continuous bleaching operation. The use of a magnetic type flow meter in the stock line to the chlorination tower insures accurate

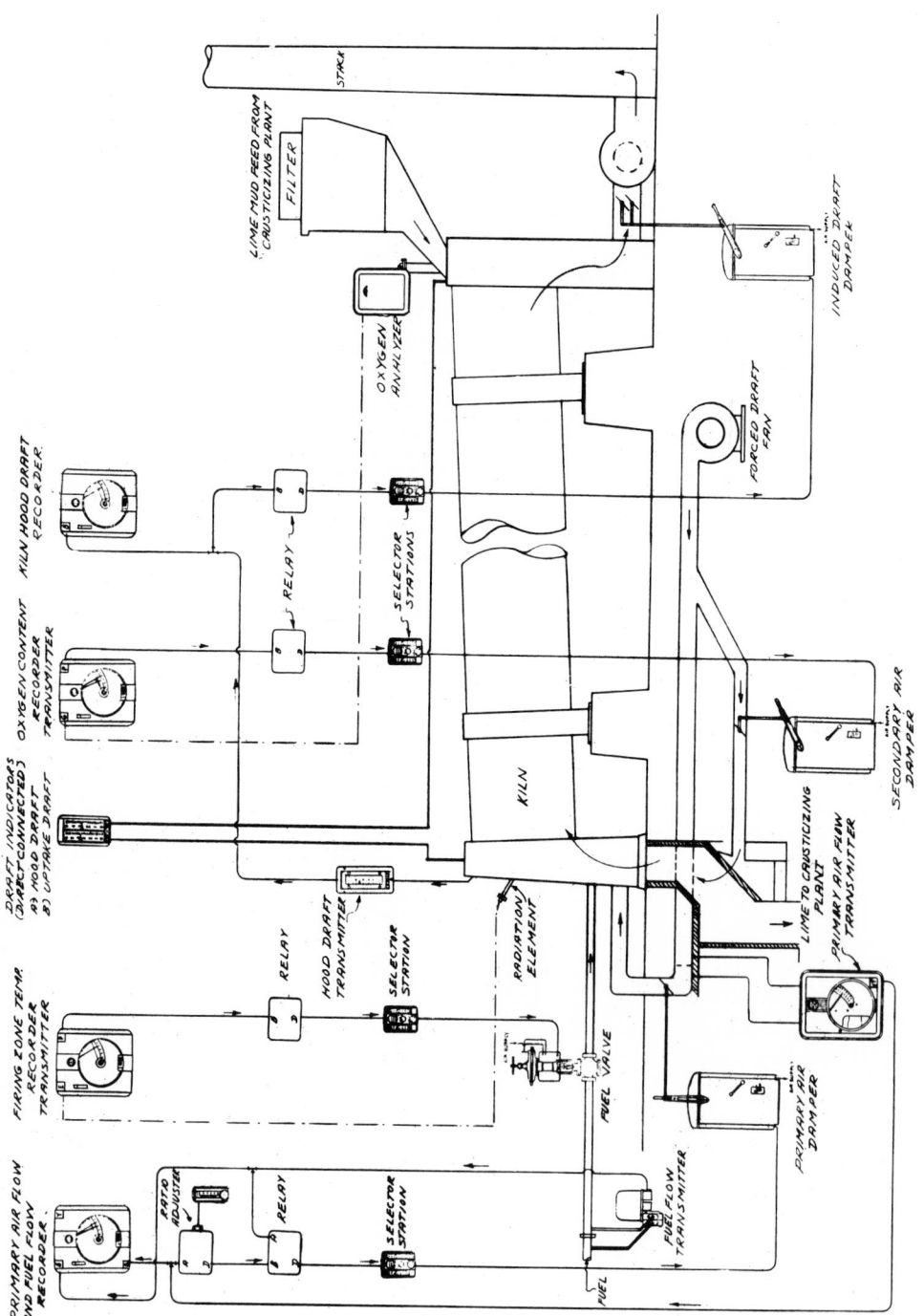

Fig. 15.26. Lime kiln control. (*Courtesy Bailey Meter Co.*)

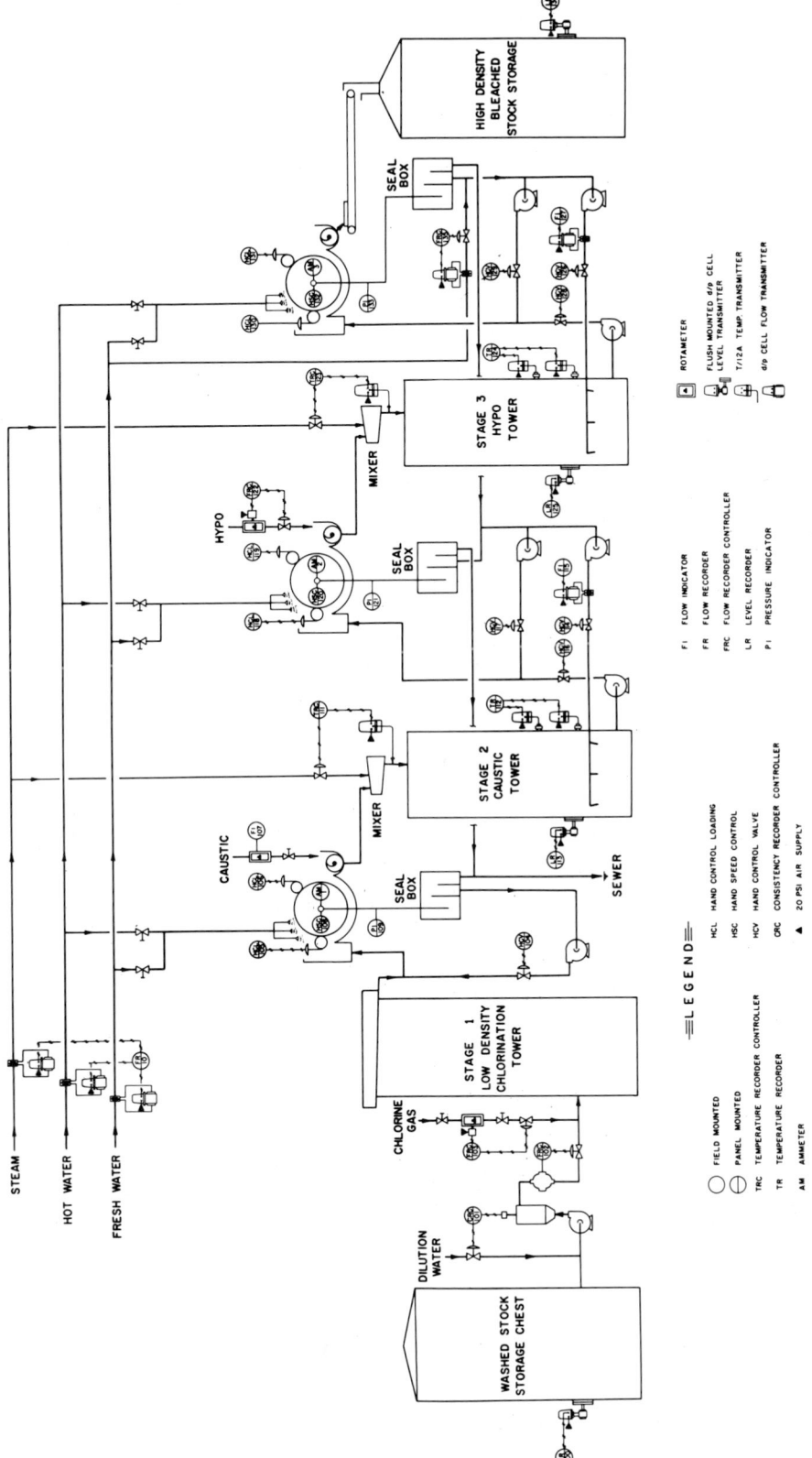

Fig. 15.27. Three-stage bleach system. (*Courtesy The Foxboro Co.*)

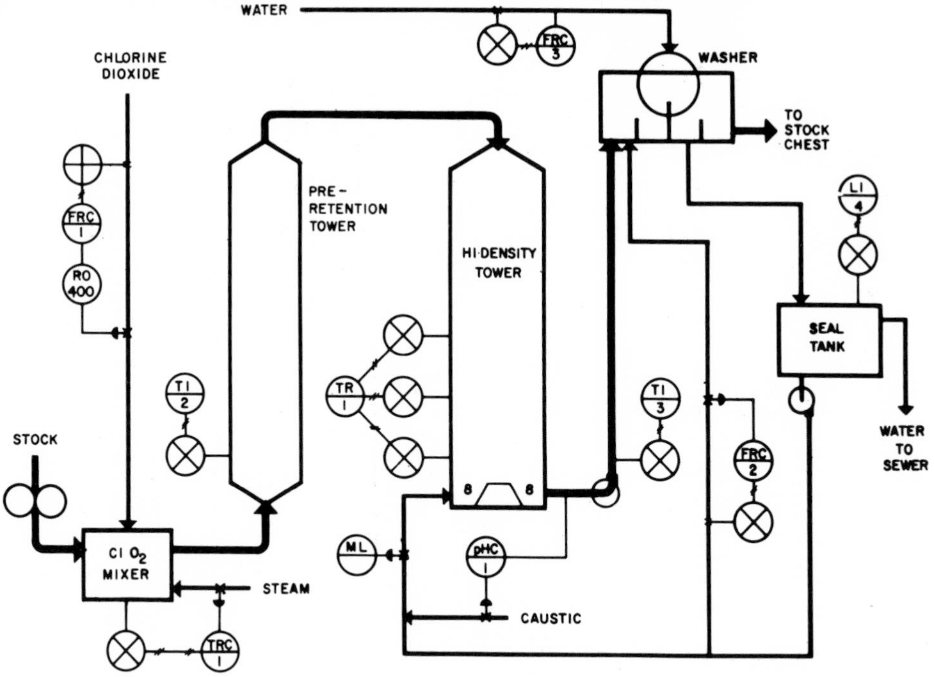

Fig. 15.28. Chlorine dioxide installation. (*Courtesy Minneapolis-Honeywell*)

measurement and control of the stock without purges or seals. For chlorine, caustic and hypo flow control, the rotameter type of flow meter is particularly adaptable.

The use of chlorine dioxide as a bleaching agent has become quite popular in the past few years due to its ability to produce high brightness with a minimum of cellulose degradation. The process is usually the last stage of the multistage bleach plant. Figure 15.28 shows such an installation. Stock from the previous stage flows through the ClO_2 mixer and into the pre-retention tower. ClO_2 flow is controlled (FRCI), as is the temperature of the mixer (TRCI). Interlocks are provided which permit ClO_2 and steam flow only when the mixer and high density stock pump are functioning. The temperature of the pre-retention tower is indicated while the temperature of the bleached stock is measured at three points to show the level to which dilution water rises. The stock must be neutralized before entering the washer; a pH controller is used for this purpose, and it controls the flow of caustic. Dilution water to the washer is controlled

by FRC2. The remaining instrumentation is clearly indicated.

Figure 15.29 is an excellent example of modern bleach plant instrumentation. Note the use of miniature instruments and transmitter-receiver combinations. This highly instrumented process utilizes practically every type of measurement possible. The legend explains clearly the functions of the various components.

STOCK PREPARATION

Pulpers

There are several types of pulpers available for slushing pulps and waste paper. Figure 15.30 shows a method of automatically measuring and handling of the water when a separate dilution water measuring tank is required.

Instrument No. 1 has adjustable high and low level contacts by means of which solenoid valves are operated to drain or fill the tank. In the type "A" system, operation of the "drain" button at the control station (2) will open the drain valve. When the

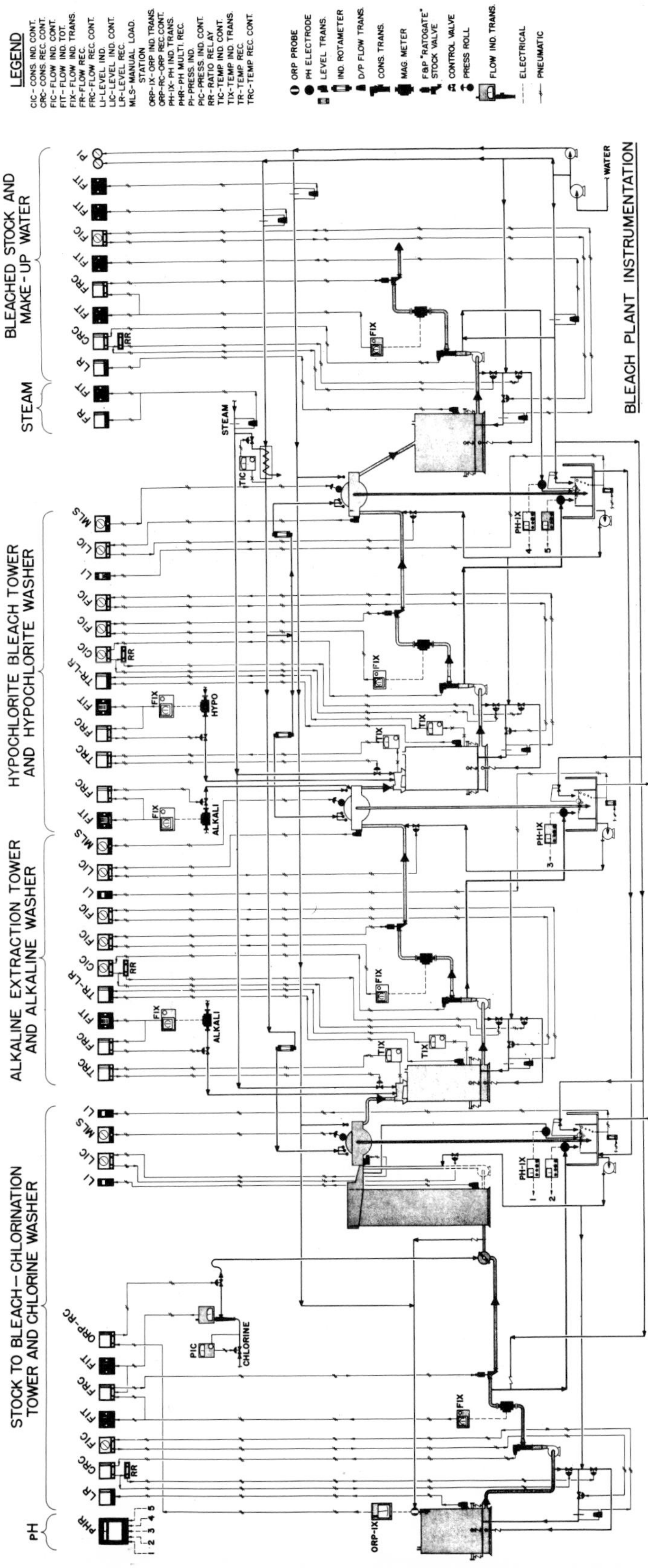

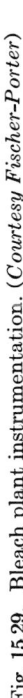

Fig. 15.29. Bleach plant instrumentation. (*Courtesy Fischer-Porter*)

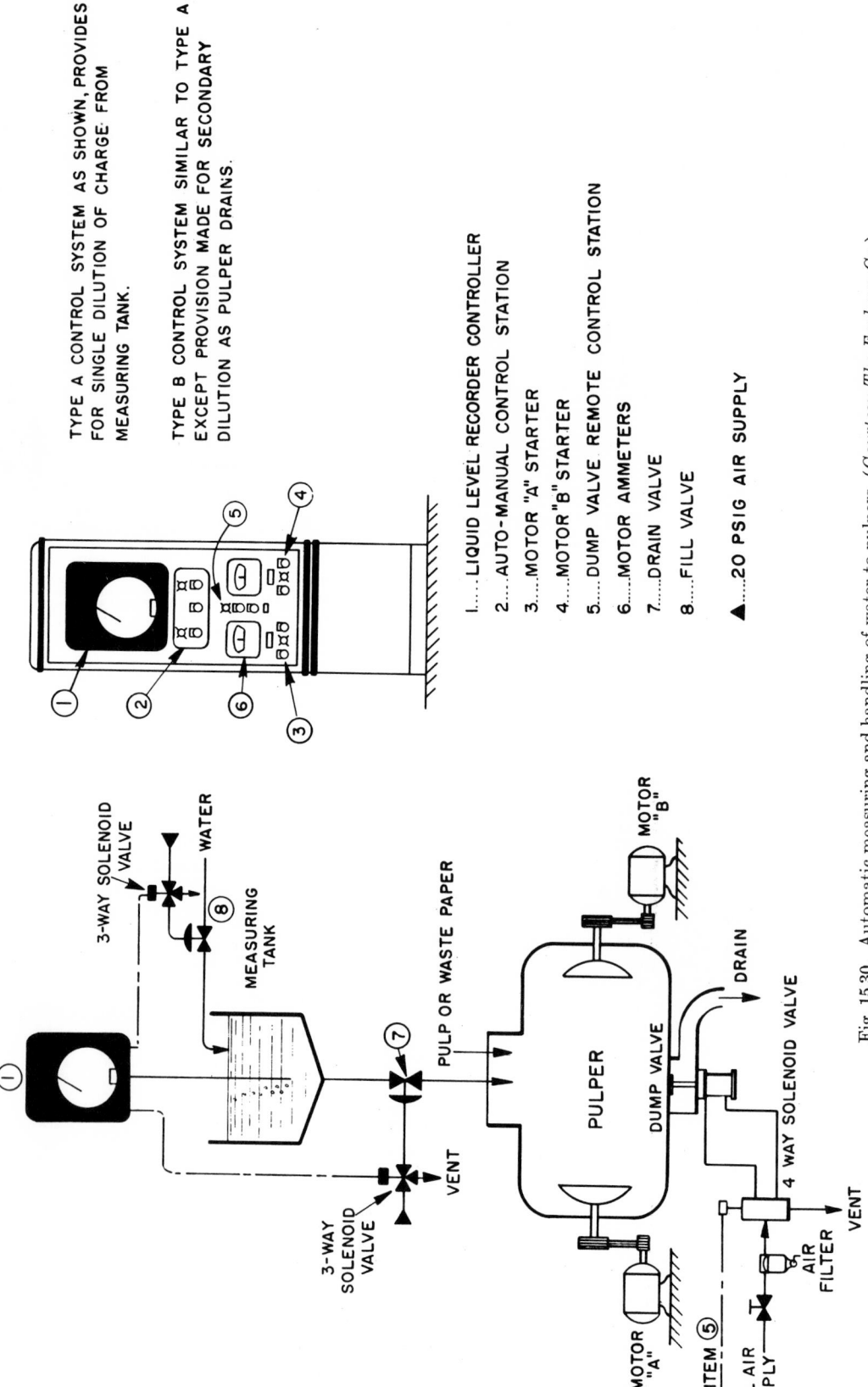

Fig. 15.30. Automatic measuring and handling of water to pulpers. (*Courtesy The Foxboro Co.*)

level has dropped to the point representing the desired dilution, the drain valve closes and the "fill" valve is automatically opened to restore the level. The control can be modified to give a secondary dilution cycle if desired (type "B").

Beaters

Automatic control of the beater may be attained by maintaining the same roll pressures for each batch. This may be done by positioning the roll by either pneumatic cylinders or a positioning motor operated by a pressure controller. The roll pressure is sensed by a load or force measuring element. Incorporation of a time schedule arrangement will maintain a predetermined schedule of pressure and time.

Jordans

As the clearance between the plug and shell is very small during normal operating conditions, every slight variation in stock consistency affects the processing pressure of the Jordan and, consequently, the stock treatment. Also, knife wear requires plug adjustment. By maintaining the processing pressure between the bars of the plug and the shell at the value best suited for each furnish, more uniform mechanical working of the fibers can be obtained. In most cases the force exerted by the loading screw on the end of the plug is a measure of pressure applied to the fibers. In this case a load or force element can be installed between the end of the loading screw and the thrust bearing on the plug shaft. A pneumatic cylinder or diaphragm motor is used to position the plug. In those instances where the plug tends to "pull in," due to Jordan pumping action and certain inlet and outlet pressure conditions, electric motor positioning is prescribed.

Another system uses electric motor plug positioning to keep the Jordan drive motor input power (or current) constant. Couch

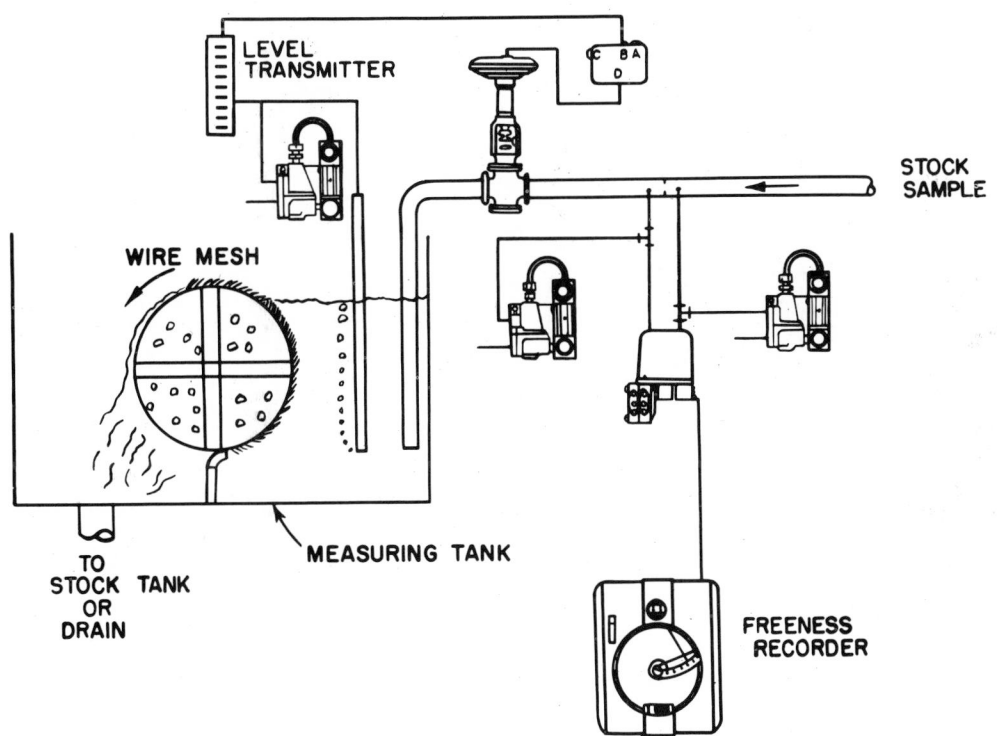

Fig. 15.31. Continuous freeness recorder. (*Courtesy Bailey Meter Co.*)

vacuum variations may also be used to alter the plug position.

Freeness

The continuous measurement and control of freeness is becoming more and more of a necessity due to modern refining methods, higher machine speeds and stock blending systems. Figure 15.31 is a basis diagram of a freeness recorder recently placed on the market.

A stock sample at a controlled consistency and temperature is pumped into a miniature rotary filter or decker. The rotating drum is sealed on the sides and bottom. Thus, the water drained from the stock must pass through the screen on the surface of the drum. A film of stock is formed on the surface simulating the conditions on a Fourdrinier wire. The level ahead of the drum is kept constant by the level controller. Thus,

the flow of stock in the sample line varies with the amount of water passed through the film of stock and screen. The measurement of this flow is used as the index of freeness.

Freeness control has been accomplished by using the flow recorder signal with auxiliary apparatus to position the Jordan plug.

Figure 15.32 shows a system which uses a different method of measuring the variations in drainage. A miniature "decker" again is used. The stock enters the headbox where it is diluted with water to a consistency of 1 to 2%. The diluted pulp flows to the cylinder vat in which a constant level is maintained by means of an overflow weir. A sheet is formed on the cylinder after which the sheet is couched off and returned to the stock system. The water drained through the cylinder is held at a constant

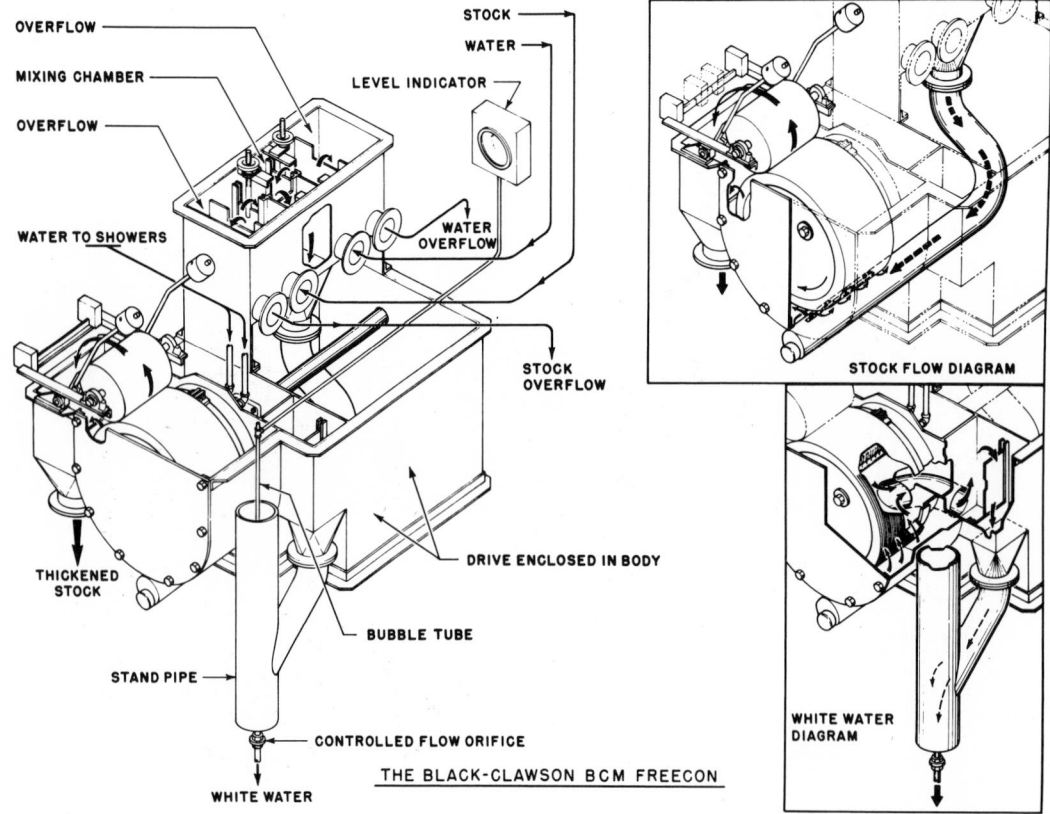

Fig. 15.32. Freeness control. (*Courtesy Black-Clawson Co.*)

level by an overflow weir; thus a constant head differential is maintained between pulp and filtrate across the face of the cylinder. The filtrate leaving the overflow is collected in a stand pipe which has a fixed orifice at the bottom. Thus, any change in the drainage rate (freeness) will change the level in the stand pipe. By using a level recorder controller and auxiliary apparatus, the Jordan plug can be altered to control freeness.

Stock Proportioning

The use of continuous proportioning for varieties of pulp and additives is increasing rapidly. Accurate control of the various percentages make for uniformity of product. In addition, saving in raw materials and reduction in operating costs have been reported by many mills.

Figure 15.33 illustrates a mechanical method of continuous proportioning which has been in use for many years. The system is comprised of as many individual positive displacement metering compartments as needed. The compartment rotors are driven by individual PIV's which in turn are connected to the variable speed shaft of the master PIV. Thus, the speed of each compartment can be easily adjusted to give the required proportions. This may be carried out at the unit or remotely at a centralized control panel. The master PIV is controlled by the machine chest level controller and speed recorders are used to record the proportions.

The flow metering method of continuous proportioning is shown in Figures 15.34 and 15.35. The use of the magnetic type flow meter provides high accuracy of measurement and requires no orifices or other restrictions in the pipe lines.

Figure 15.34 shows a system utilizing chest level as a common master signal to the various ratio flow controllers. Thus, each instrument automatically controls the rate of one flow at a preset ratio to the magnitude

Fig. 15.33.   Freeness control. (*Courtesy Trimbey Machines*)

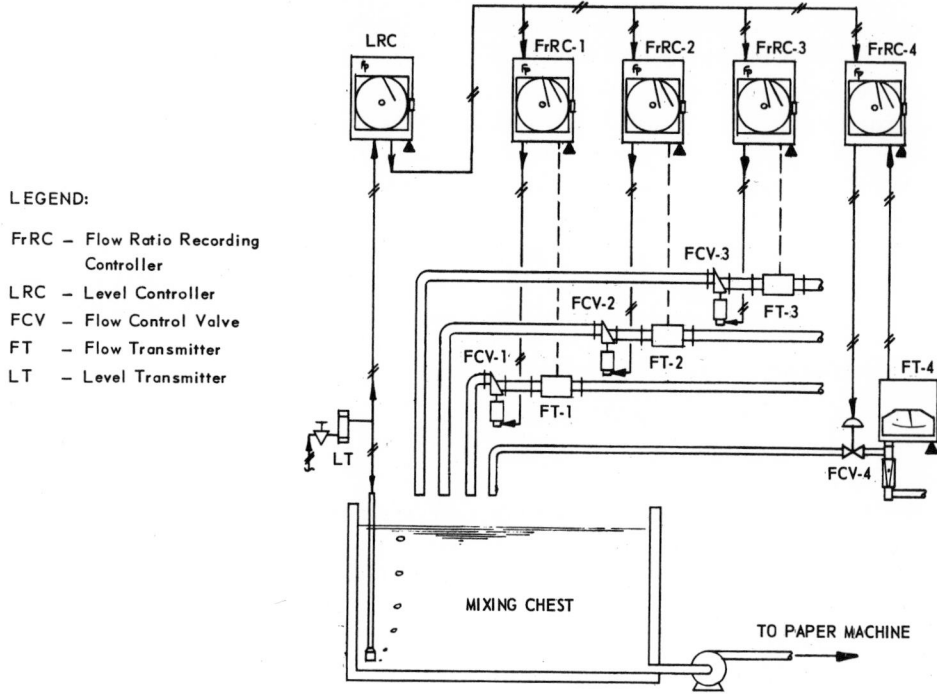

LEGEND:

FrRC — Flow Ratio Recording
          Controller
LRC — Level Controller
FCV — Flow Control Valve
FT — Flow Transmitter
LT — Level Transmitter

Fig. 15.34. Stock proportioning system. (*Courtesy Fischer-Porter*)

of the level signal. Direct reading ratio dials can therefore be used and each flow rate setting can be made directly in "per cent of total stock."

A similar system is shown in Figure 15.35. For operator convenience and extreme accuracy of setting the proportions, external indicating gauges and controls are used. The stock gauges are calibrated in "per cent of stock flow" and the additive gauges may be calibrated as shown. The total furnish flow recorder is optional.

With any system of proportioning, the consistencies of the various stocks must be controlled.

Consistency Regulators

Consistency control at several stages of the pulp and paper mill is essential in order to obtain a uniform product. Where automatic stock proportioning is used, such control is necessary for accurate measurement of the various stock percentages and total tonnage.

In the pulp mill, consistency is controlled in the blow tank by measuring the current demand of the agitator drive motor. A thermo-converter is used to supply a millivolt signal to an electronic recorder-controller which in turn operates a valve in the liquor dilution line.

This system also can be used in bleach towers and stock storage tanks where the agitator is covered at all times.

Another system for use on bleach towers and in the paper mill measures the torque effect on a constant speed agitator immersed in the stock. This system may be either the "in line" or "open" type. The latter may be level controlled or have constant head overflow. The movement of the torque arm actuates a pneumatic transmitter whose output is fed into a two pen recorder controller which operates the dilution valve. Both input and output signals are recorded; thus there is an indication of incoming and outgoing consistencies. Figure 15.36 illustrates this method.

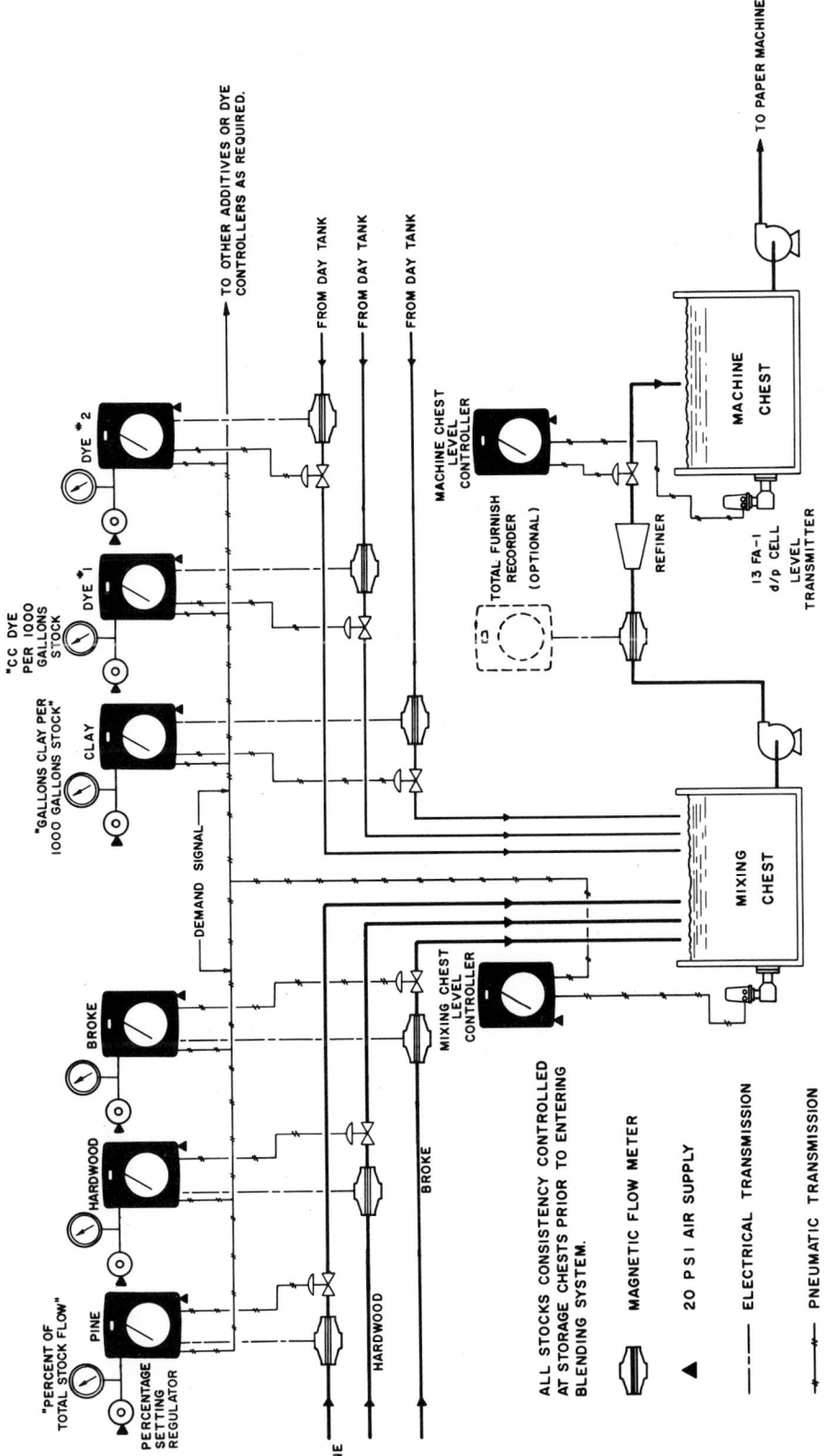

Fig. 15.35. Stock blending system. (*Courtesy The Foxboro Co.*)

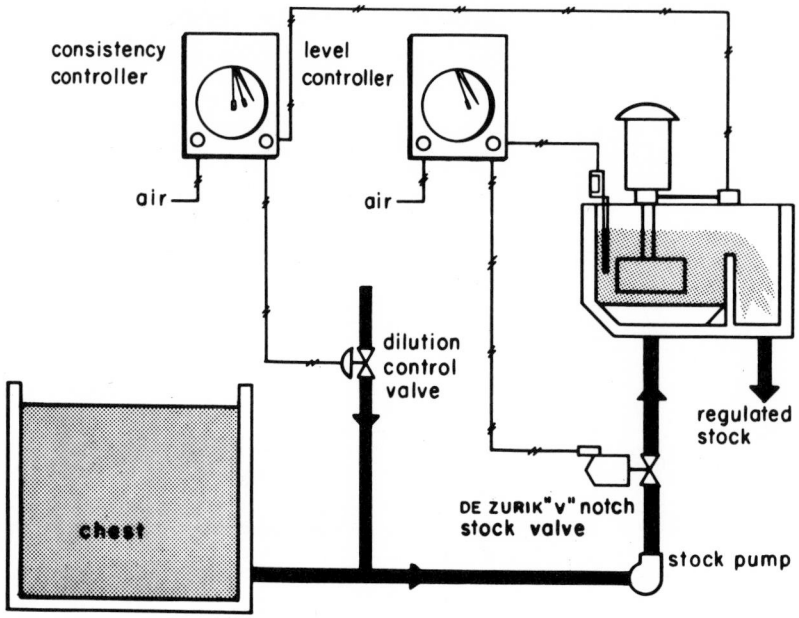

Fig. 15.36. Consistency regulator. (*Courtesy Minneapolis-Honeywell*)

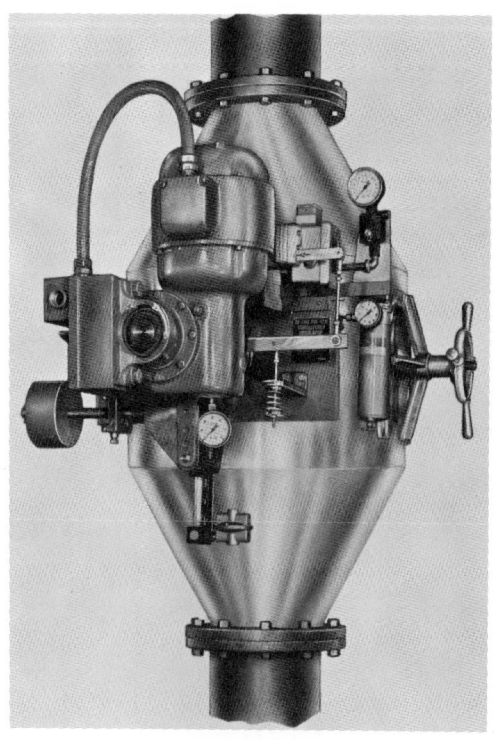

Fig. 15.37. Consistency regulator. (*Courtesy Trimbey Machines*)

A system utilizing a smooth disk whose plane is on the axis of stock flow is shown in Figure 15.37. This unit may be obtained for either "in line" or "open" operation. The disk is protected from direct stock impingement by a deflection baffle which eliminates the effect of stock velocity. By use of a specially designed motor gear reducer and torque arm, the torque created by the stock on the disk operates a pneumatic transmitter. The two pen recorder controller records the "incoming" and "outgoing" signals and operates the dilution valve. This unit is designed to operate in the 2 to 6% consistency range.

A recent development in pipe line consistency regulators uses a unique "shear float" design which permits wide variations in flow rate, temperature and freeness without significantly affecting the performance. The unit, Figure 15.38, is designed to operate in the 2 to 8% consistency range and regulate within 0.1% consistency. The shear float (resembling a turnstile) is contained within a "tee," on top of which is mounted the force transmitter. The movement of the float due to consistency changes, causes the force

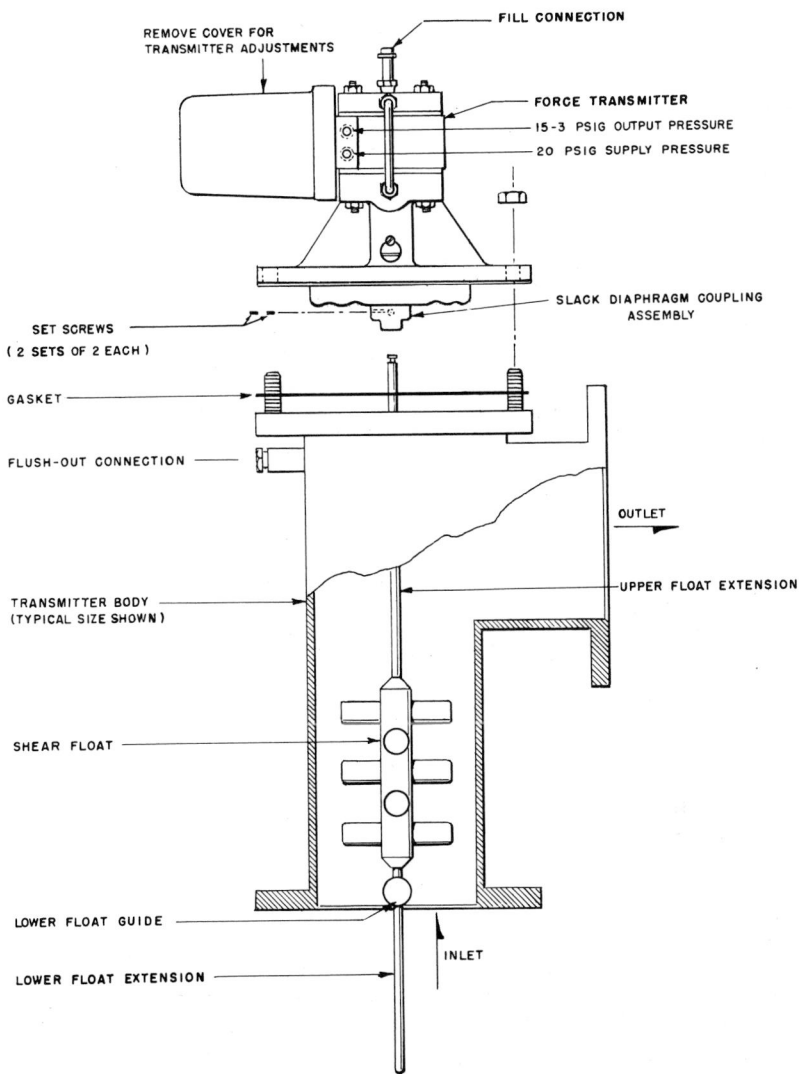

Fig. 15.38. Consistency regulator. (*Courtesy Fischer-Porter*)

transmitter to send a pneumatic signal to the recorder-controller which in turn operates the dilution valve.

Another method, Figure 15.39, used by many mills is the "pressure drop" method. The operating principle is that stock viscosity changes with consistency, and by measuring the variable pressure drop along a predetermined length of pipe caused by the deviations in viscosity, the corresponding consistency can be controlled. The installation is simple and compact since all components can be installed in a straight section of pipe. The flow of stock is maintained constant.

THE PAPER MACHINE

Wet End Controls

A highly instrumented wet end system is shown in Figure 15.40. The drawing is simplified to some extent by omitting the measuring elements for consistency, pH, and basis weight in addition to the control sys-

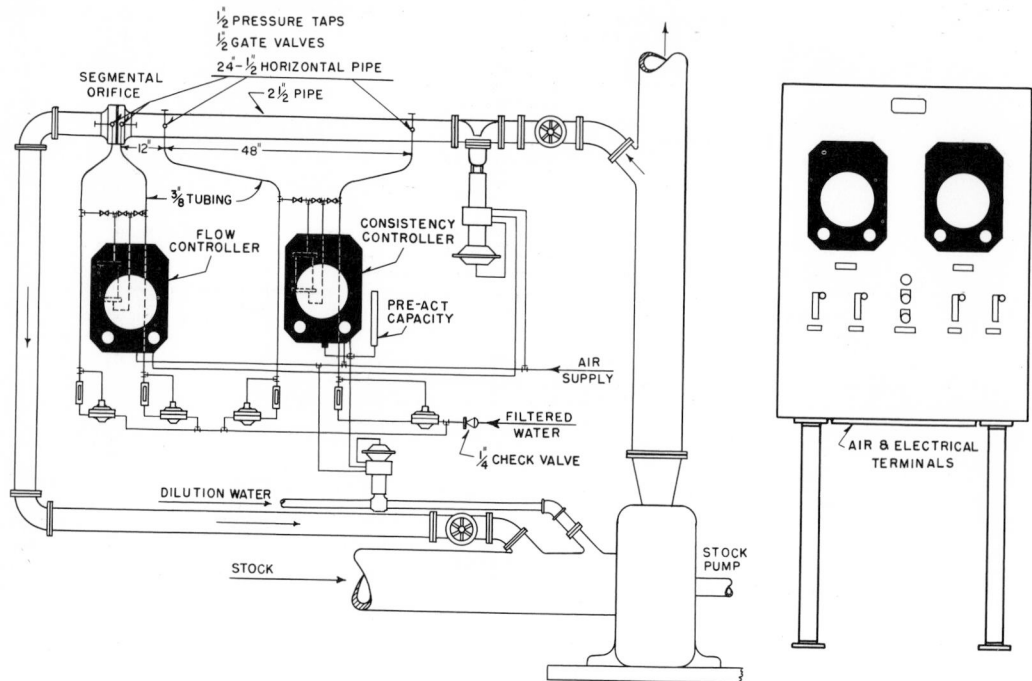

Fig. 15.39. Pressure drop method of consistency control. (*Courtesy The Taylor Instrument Co.*)

tems for save-all speed, Jordan plug positioning, etc. A magnetic flow meter (10) is used to advantage in controlling the stock flow to the fan pump and is reset by the Basis Weight Profiler. On machine breaks the couch pit level controller (18) senses the rise in couch pit level and pumps the stock back to the broke chest. Save-all level is controlled by varying the speed of the screen. If save-all filtrate is used for shower, instrument No. 2 automatically admits makeup water if the save-all is shut down. The notations on the diagram clearly indicate the various functions.

In those instances where pressure or vacuum head boxes are used, a simple pressure or vacuum controlled is used instead of the level controller shown.

Drying Controls

It is impossible to portray all the variations of *dryer controls* in this chapter. Instrumentation for single or multi-section machines can be fairly simple or complex, depending on whether maximum steam economy or operating flexibility is the governing factor. Steam to the dryers may be controlled by pressure or by temperature. Present-day trend is toward the differential pressure method although control by temperature is widely used.

Figure 15.41 shows the differential pressure instrumentation for a machine consisting of a main dryer group and two groups of flash dryers. This arrangement offers economy of steam usage but does not permit too low an operating pressure. Methods are available for uniting the flash groups, thereby permitting lower pressures in the main group.

A three section machine is shown in Figure 15.42. This permits flexibility at the sacrifice of some steam economy.

Felt dryers are not shown in either figure; however, such dryers are best operated separately with their own control and drainage system. In instances where the first few dryers must be operated at low temperatures to prevent picking, independent control and drainage systems are also required.

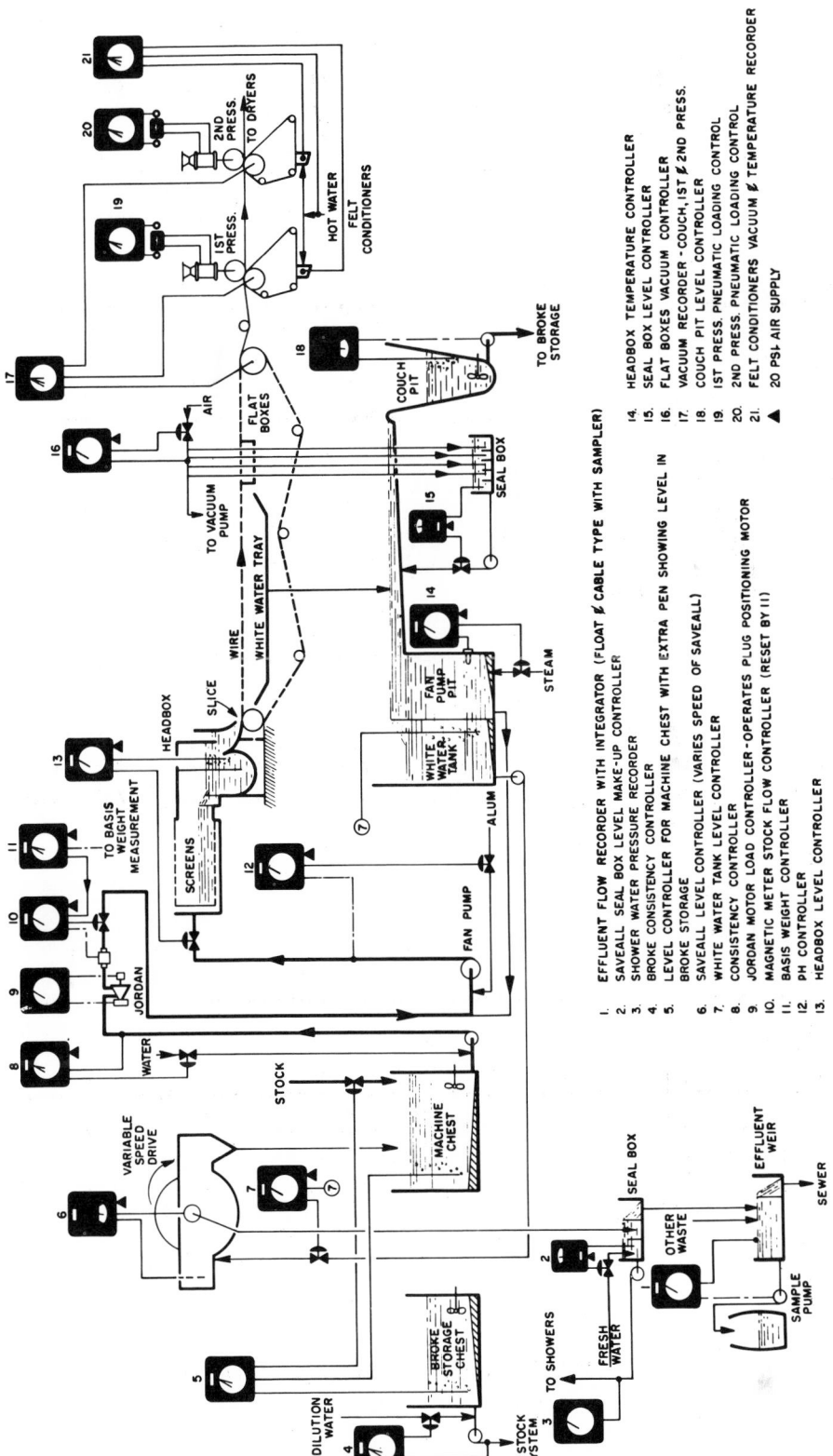

Fig. 15.40. Fourdrinier paper machine wet end controls. (*Courtesy The Foxboro Co.*)

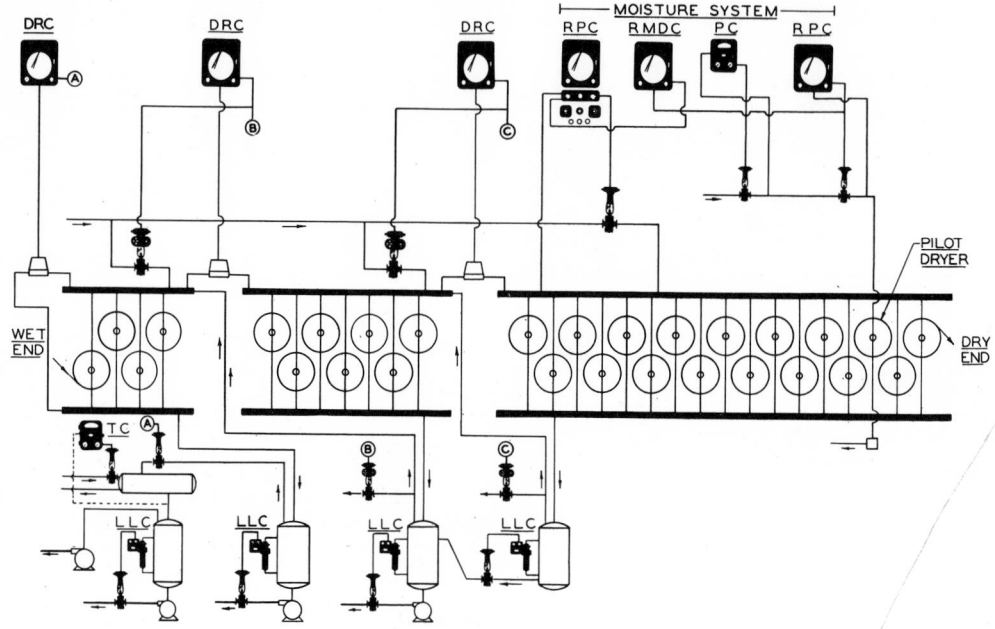

Fig. 15.41. Paper machine dryer controls. (*Courtesy Mason-Neilan*)

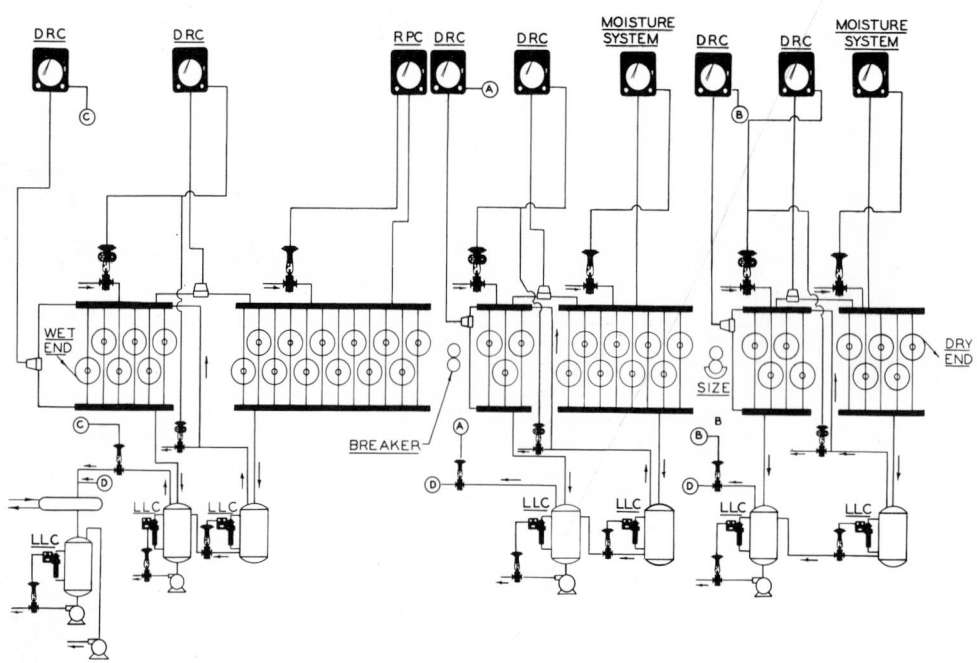

Fig. 15.42. Three-section dryer control. (*Courtesy Mason-Neilan*)

Needless to say, effective dryer control by any method is dependent on a good condensate return system.

Control by temperature is usually done by measuring condensate temperature. In this case, a top middle dryer is used as the pilot dryer and the sensing bulb inserted in the condensate discharge pipe. Care must be taken not to restrict the proper flow of condensate. Figure 15.43 illustrates such an installation. The use of the temperature transmitter (TT) is modern practice to allow the recorder controllers to be centrally located. The use of miniature instruments reduces the space required for complex installations.

Figure 15.44 shows a method that may be used where individual dryer temperature control is required. Such a system is particularly applicable on a dryer section following an "on the machine coater." Steam pressure is held constant by the pressure recorder-controller (PRC). Each dryer is controlled by a non-indicating remote bulb temperature controller (TC). The set point of each controller can be independently

adjusted to give the desired temperature gradient throughout the section. Speed is recorded and a moisture recorder is incorporated as an aid to proper operation.

Where the wet end dryers must be operated at temperatures whose corresponding

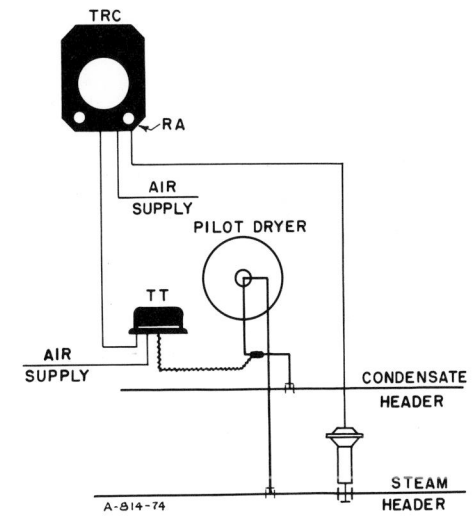

Fig. 15.43. Dryer temperature control. (*Courtesy Taylor Instrument Co.*)

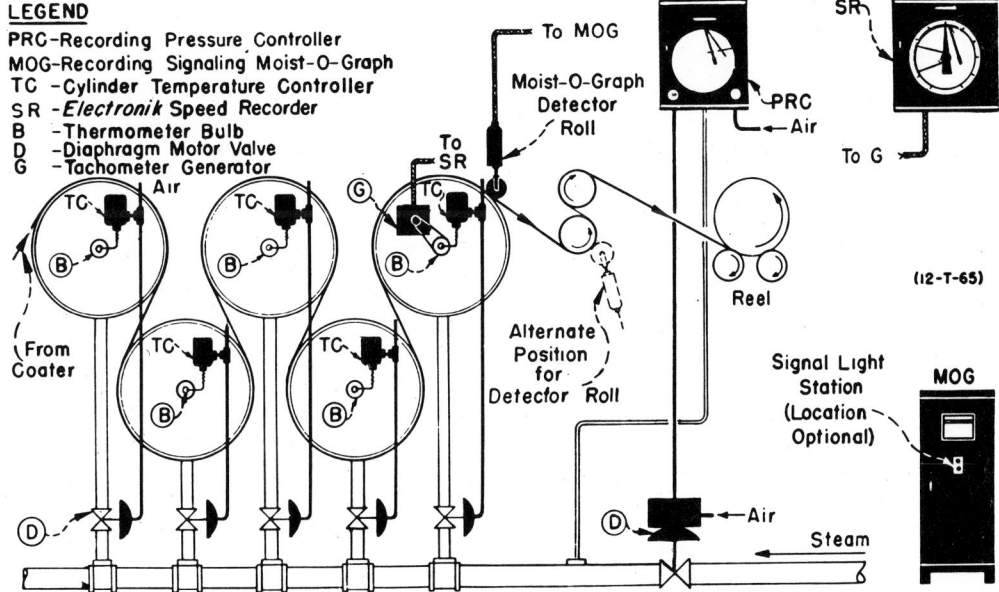

Fig. 15.44. Individual dryer temperature control. (*Courtesy Minneapolis-Honeywell*)

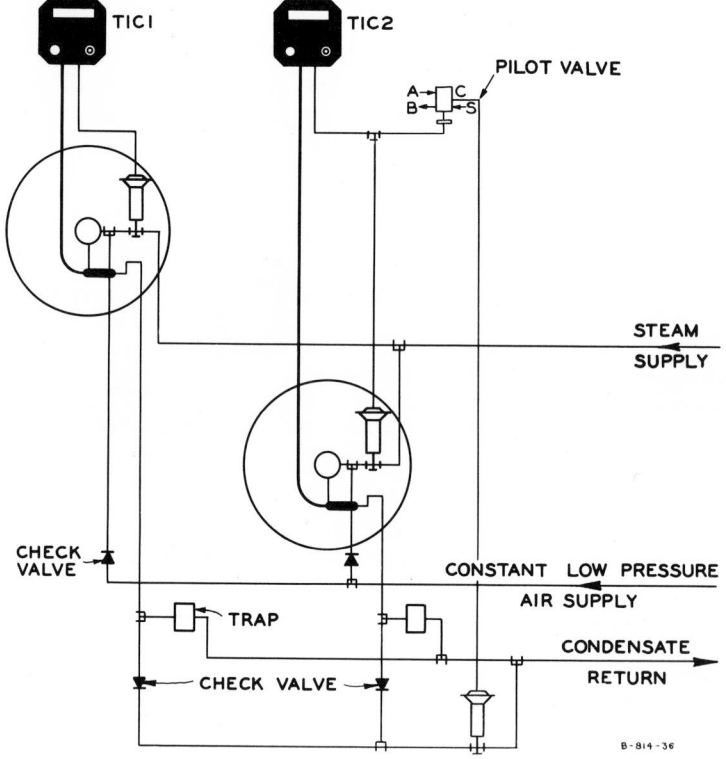

Fig. 15.45. Wet end dryer temperature control. (*Courtesy Taylor Instrument Co.*)

steam pressure is lower than that in the condensate return line, Figure 15.45 shows a system of control. Low pressure air (approximately 5 psi) is supplied to the dryer. This pressure is high enough to force out the condensate in the dryer. When the steam pressure required to maintain the required temperature is greater than the air pressure, the check valve closes and shuts off the air. For all temperatures corresponding to a saturation pressure lower than that of the air pressure, air will flow into the dryer and mix with the steam. Thus, the internal pressure will never fall below that of the air supply and the temperature of the mixture will be that of the corresponding partial pressure of the water vapor.

Basis Weight

Continuous measurement and control of *basis weight* is a large factor toward a quality sheet. There are several types of systems available for this purpose, employing either fixed or cross web scanning or multiple point measurement.

A fixed scanning system, beta-ray (β) type, is shown in Figure 15.46. The measuring head is suspended on a monorail track and so positioned that the sheet passes through a gap between a β-Ray emission source and a ray detector (ionization chamber). As the weight of the sheet increases, fewer rays reach the detector, and conversely, a decrease in sheet weight allows more rays to be detected. The detected rays are automatically compared with rays from a reference source which has been preset for the weight desired. The difference between the two rays is measured by an electronic recorder-controller with a zero center chart. Deviations above or below zero indicate a heavy or light sheet. Automatic correction of weight can be attained by tying the controller into a stock flow valve, gate position-

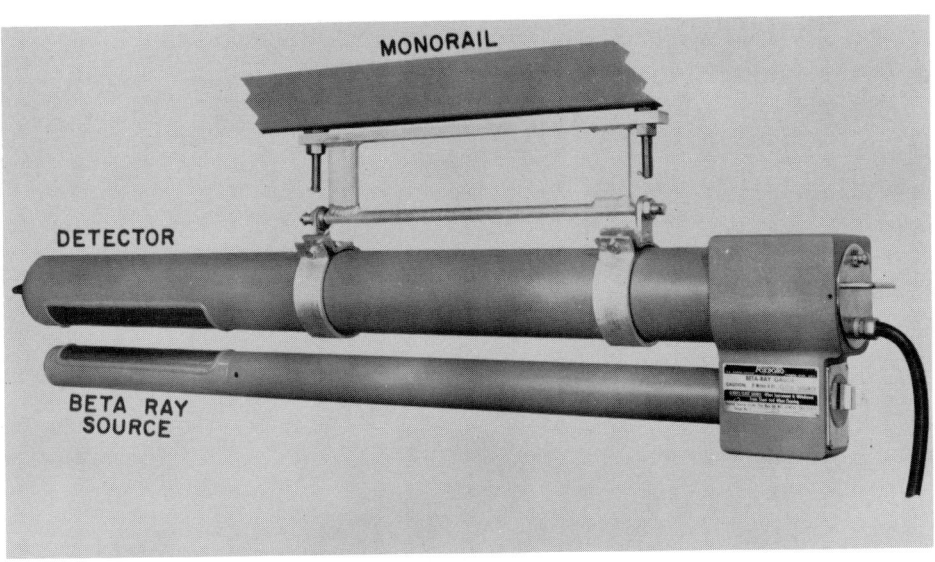

Fig. 15.46. Beta-ray basis weight control. (*Courtesy The Foxboro Co.*)

ers or consistency regulators. A lock-out feature is incorporated to prevent waste of stock and off-weight paper during a break. Both the radioactive source and detector are fourteen inches in width, affording a good "look" at the sheet. The head assembly can be positioned at any point across the web. An automatic retracting mechanism is available which withdraws the head in the event of a paper break.

A caliper and basis weight control system in current use is shown in Figure 15.47. Small rollers (2½-inch diameter x 5-inch length) with gauging transformers inside, measure the distance to a machine roll—a spacing controlled by the thickness of the sheet. A slight amount of wrap is required to prevent errors caused by wrinkles. Standard gauges have a range of .000 to .150 inch and spans of .001-0-.001 inch up to .015-0-.015 inch. Each has a zero setter and a strip chart recorder, as well as an amplifier and tolerance relays. Variations in type of stock, freeness, moisture content or room conditions have no effect on measurement.

The gauges are located after calenders continuously measure and record final sheet thicknesses. Calender pressures can be set properly, and slices can be adjusted to produce level sheets; in addition, the process is

monitored so that off-caliper paper or board can be detected.

Control of weight and caliper is developed by installing the gauges between the presses and the dryers and regulating stock flow to the machine to produce uniform wet end calipers. Gauges are usually located at the front and back edges and one on the middle of the sheet. Deviations of the middle gauge initiate corrective action to stock flow. Stock flow to the machine can be regulated by conventional head box gates. In closed systems, a pneumatic 3 to 15 psi signal can be supplied for loop pressure control or individual vat valve control.

Deviations of edge gauges relative to the middle, indicate off-level conditions which can be manually corrected by wing adjustments, or by automatic control of wings in 2 or 3 vats. The latter controls weights in-the-machine direction and also across the sheet.

Moisture Control

There are a number of "on machine" moisture control systems available, most of which employ a method of measuring related variables since it is difficult to measure moisture directly. Some of the related variables include sheet tension, conductivity,

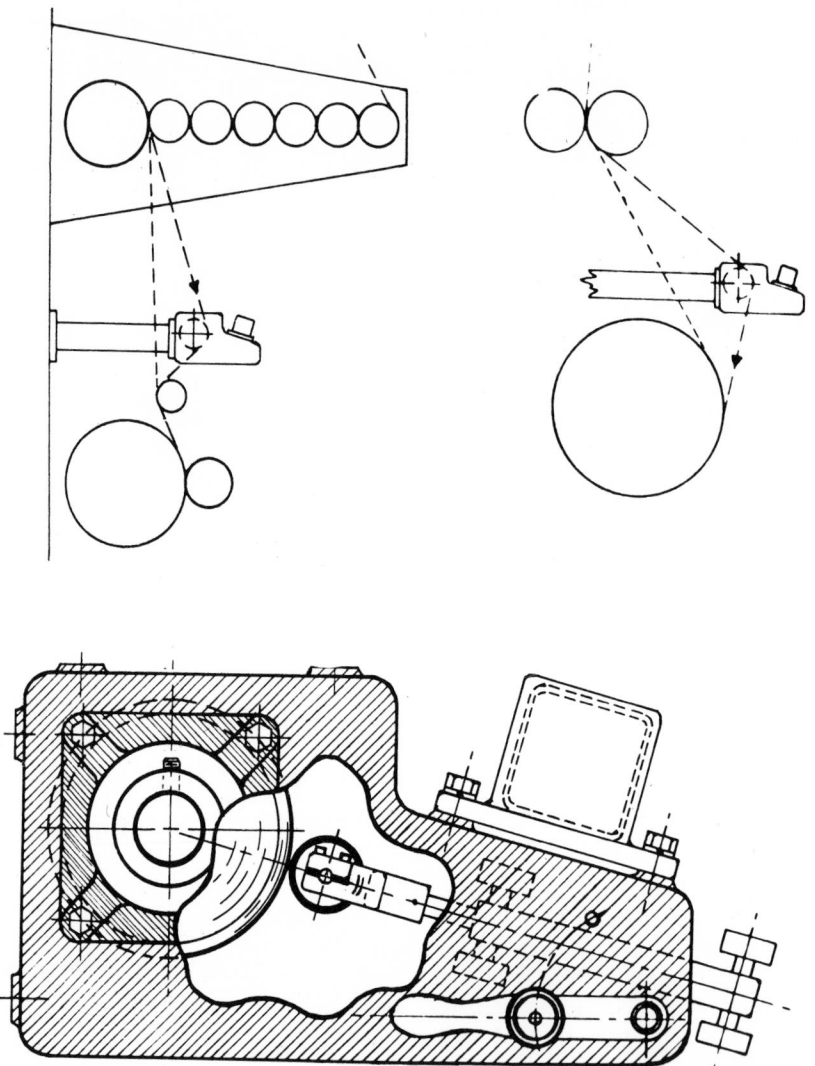

Fig. 15.47. Caliper and basis weight control. (*Courtesy Hurletron, Inc.*)

pilot dryer heat absorption, dielectric properties, absorption of radioactivity, temperature difference between a dryer and the leaving sheet, and measurement of the moisture film above the sheet. The success of any moisture control device depends largely on a properly engineered drying system.

Perhaps the oldest method of sensing a change in moisture, and one that is still used by many mills, is the tension roll method. The roll rides against the sheet in such a manner that its position changes due to contraction and expansion of the sheet. This movement is used to operate a pneumatic controller which in turn positions a valve in the dryer steam header.

The conductivity method is also in wide use and two types are available, one using direct current, the other alternating current. The d.c. method actually utilizes an ohmmeter, measuring the resistance of the sheet. A moisture change causes the resistance or conductivity of the sheet to vary and this signal is fed into an electronic controller which in turn positions the steam valve.

In the pilot dryer method of moisture control, the dryer chosen as the pilot is one which is located near the dry end of the machine and is supplied independently with constant pressure steam. The sheet, in passing over the pilot dryer, absorbs a varying amount of heat depending on the sheet moisture. The damper the sheet, the greater the steam consumption (steam flow) of the pilot dryer and vice versa. A valve-orifice in the constant pressure steam line is so positioned that the pressure differential across it is sufficient to measure changes in the steam flow. This measured change, due to sheet moisture, is used to reset the steam controller which supplies the dryer section. A pressure controller regulates a primary pressure reducing valve ahead of a capacity tank upstream of the orifice, and another pressure controller operates a valve downstream of the orifice to maintain constant pressure to the pilot dryer.

Another popular method of moisture control utilizes the dielectric properties of paper. Changes in moisture of the sheet change its dielectric constant. Since electrical capacitance is directly proportional to the dielectric constant of the material in the field of a capacitor, the sheet itself is used as the dielectric. The measuring head constitutes the plates of a condenser. This system uses an electronic recorder-controller which resets the dryer pressure or temperature controller to correct the deviation.

The temperature measurement type is shown in Figure 15.48. Temperature of paper and paperboard at a distance of 2½ feet from a reference dryer is dependent upon the moisture content of the sheet. As the percentage of water weight in a sheet increases, the rate of vaporization rises, and the sheet temperature drops further from the boiling point (attained while on the reference dryer). A sheet with 6% moisture content is 9°F cooler than it would be with moisture content of 5%. Variations in type of stock, freeness, weights, speeds, tension, and room conditions have negligible effect on this method of measurement. Ther-

mocouple heads measure the reference dryer and paper sheet with a temperature difference type circuit connected directly to standard emf type instruments.

Several gauges are positioned across the sheet at 18 to 24-inch increments. (If high velocity air dryers are installed, the gauges should align with the compartments.) All gauges are connected to a multipoint re-

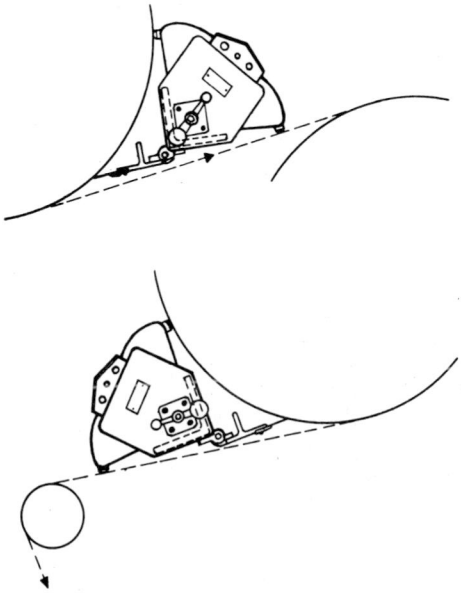

Fig. 15.48. Temperature measurement type of moisture control. (*Courtesy Hurletron, Inc.*)

corder for readout of moisture profiles and deviations. A pneumatic controller automatically regulates steam flow to control the drying process and maintain a set moisture content in the sheet.

Size and Coating Preparation

The proper preparation of size and coatings requires the use of instrumentation. Close temperature control is essential, and in many cases, coating preparation requires the use of time-temperature pattern control.

Figure 15.49 shows a typical size preparation system wherein the temperature of the cook is controlled and the levels of the mix tank and storage tanks are recorded. Electrical contact may be incorporated in the

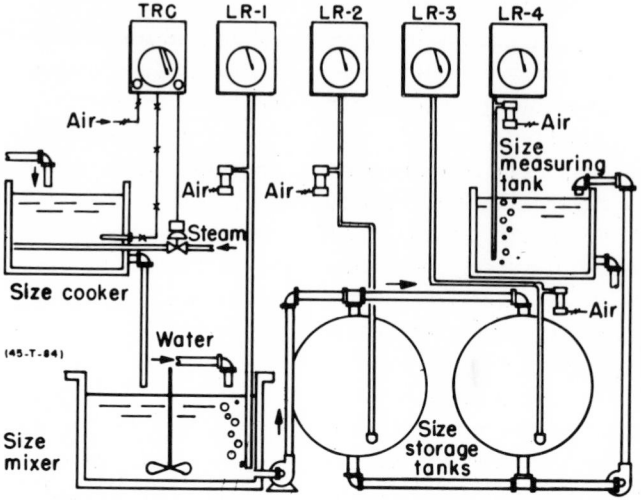

Fig. 15.49. Controls for size preparation. (*Courtesy Minnea-polis-Honeywell*)

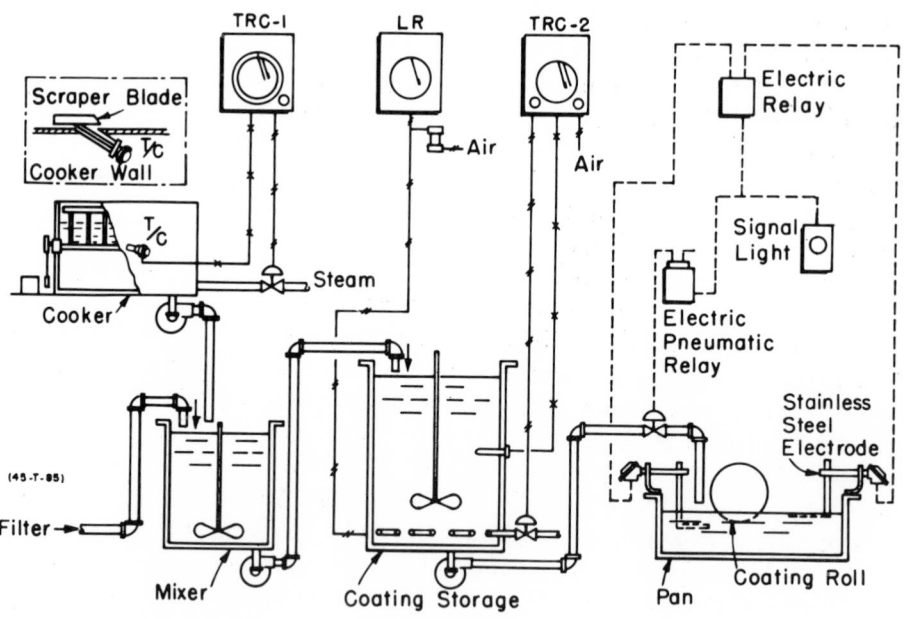

Fig. 15.50. Controls for coating preparation system. (*Courtesy Minneapolis-Honeywell*)

level instruments to sound an alarm or to control the pumps as needed.

In Figure 15.50 the coating preparation system is operated on a time-temperature basis. The operator needs only to start the cooking cycle. The rate of temperature rise and the time of the holding temperature are controlled positively and accurately. Each subsequent cook is exactly reproduced. Any

desired program or pattern can be obtained by using a properly shaped cam in the time pattern instrument.

BIBLIOGRAPHY

Canadian Pulp and Paper Assoc., *Tech. Sect. Phys. and Chem. Stds. Committee*. Bibliography of instrumentation. Pulp Paper Mag. Can. 61, No. 4:T242 (April, 1960); A.B.I.P.C. 31:311. 32 ref.

Index

The paper used in this book was manufactured by the S. D. Warren Company in Cumberland Mills, Maine. It is known in the trade as "Silkote Offset." The basis weight is 25 × 38—60 pounds. Test properties are shown in Table 14.5 on page 476.

The blank sheets provided herewith are intended to serve for tests which can be made by the user of the book at any time if he wishes to determine the effects of aging on paper by comparing his results with those given in Table 14.5.